GALVANOMAGNETIC EFFECTS
IN SEMICONDUCTORS

SOLID STATE PHYSICS

Advances in Research and Applications

Editors

FREDERICK SEITZ

Department of Physics
University of Illinois
Urbana, Illinois

DAVID TURNBULL

Division of Engineering
and Applied Physics
Harvard University
Cambridge, Massachusetts

The following monographs are published within the framework of the series:

1. T. P. DAS AND E. L. HAHN
Nuclear Quadrupole Resonance Spectroscopy, 1958

2. WILLIAM LOW
Paramagnetic Resonance in Solids, 1960

3. A. A. MARADUDIN, E. W. MONTROLL, G. H. WEISS
Theory of Lattice Dynamics in the Harmonic Approximation, 1963

4. ALBERT C. BEER
Galvanomagnetic Effects in Semiconductors, 1963

5. ROBERT S. KNOX
Theory of Excitons, 1963

6. S. AMELINCKX
The Direct Observation of Dislocations, *in preparation*

ACADEMIC PRESS • New York and London • 1963

GALVANOMAGNETIC EFFECTS IN SEMICONDUCTORS

ALBERT C. BEER

Battelle Memorial Institute
Columbus, Ohio

ACADEMIC PRESS • New York and London • 1963

ACADEMIC PRESS INC.
111 FIFTH AVENUE
NEW YORK 3, N. Y.

United Kingdom Edition

Published by
ACADEMIC PRESS INC. (LONDON) LTD.
BERKELEY SQUARE HOUSE, LONDON W. 1

Library of Congress Catalog Card Number: 63-23339

PRINTED IN THE UNITED STATES OF AMERICA

Preface

Galvanomagnetic phenomena in solids have received attention since before the turn of the century, with a significant event being the discovery of the Hall effect in 1879 by E. H. Hall. Subsequent contributions due to Drude and to Lorentz came in the early part of the present century. By the third decade, after significant work of men such as Pauli, Bloch, and Sommerfeld, the basic foundations for electrical transport phenomena in solids were well established, and detailed accounts can be found in such treatises as those by Sommerfeld and Bethe (1933 "Handbuch"), Mott and Jones (1936), Seitz (1940), and Wilson (1953).

The past decade has witnessed greatly expanded activity, mostly in the nature of refinements of the basic theory and application to specific examples, with particular attention to special cases of band structure and charge carrier interactions. The impetus for the accelerated activity has probably been the rapid growth in semiconductor research, an increased availability of good single crystals for measurements, and the development of a number of powerful tools (e.g., the cyclotron resonance) for establishing band structure and scattering mechanisms. As a result of the extensive activity, this monograph contains more than 1000 references published within the last decade.

The purposes in writing this volume are severalfold. The first and foremost objective is to provide a reasonably complete account of recent developments in the field. In this case the book is primarily directed to those readers who are active in solid state physics. It is especially to be hoped that the work will stimulate further research in various areas. A second group of readers are those physicists, chemists, metallurgists, and electronics engineers who may have occasion to interpret the results of galvanomagnetic measurements. For this group the author has tried to emphasize the limitations of the simple formulas, and to point out that unless the experimenter is familiar with the band structure of the material under study, the actual facts may be far from what a naive use of the simple relations for Hall effect or magneto-resistance might suggest. It is for these readers that substantial coverage is given to the effects of complex band structure and unusual scattering mechanisms. Finally, it is felt that the literature available to graduate students in solid state science lacks a treatise which has the completeness necessary for the student to gain adequate advantage of recent developments in transport theory. Therefore, for the volume to be of effective use to students, and to scientists and engineers specializing in other fields, the author has included the development of basic equations, specialized for the simple cases but with apparent applicability for the more complex examples.

In a field where publications are forthcoming at a rapid pace, it is a problem to keep a treatise up to date. The reader will note the large number of 1962 references and the various 1963 references inserted at the proof stage. It was felt that the appropriateness of these published works was such as to justify the inconvenience of the large number of letter suffixes — in one case extending into the second alphabet — and, in the case of the latest insertions, the space-dictated omission of some of the obvious English translations. Because of the volume of pertinent literature, it was not feasible to achieve complete coverage of all the areas encompassed in this monograph. For this reason, the author asks understanding from anyone whose contributions were inadvertently omitted.

In order that the book may be of greatest use to readers encompassing the three categories outlined above, the author has attempted to carry through a continuous and coherent development of the pertinent equations for transport phenomena, ranging from the simple cases of spherical energy surfaces and the relaxation-time approximation to the more complex examples involving various crystal symmetries, many-valley band structures, degenerate bands, anisotropic relaxation times, etc. Included also are discussions of such effects as strong electric- and magnetic-field phenomena, inhomogeneities, complex scattering processes, inapplicability of the relaxation-time concept, literature dealing with non-Boltzmann approaches to transport theory, and numerous other items. Many references are made to thermomagnetic phenomena, since data of these kinds often provide a useful supplement to galvanomagnetic measurements in furthering our understanding of the processes responsible for the observed transport behavior in a semiconductor. In a number of cases it has also been desirable to include information on conduction phenomena in metals, especially where the immediate concern has been scattering, magnetoresistance, or other investigations delineating the Fermi-surface topology.

There are many persons whose assistance and encouragement are responsible for making possible the writing of this volume. Besides those whose scientific contributions are acknowledged at the conclusion of the text, the writer wishes to express his indebtedness to the Battelle Memorial Institute for providing the facilities and the environment which made it possible to pursue the task. Thanks are also due the Air Force Office of Scientific Research for their support of research which has resulted in the contribution of a number of sections to this volume. Special words of praise are warranted for the library staff at Battelle for their patient untiring efforts and for the author's secretary for her careful checking of the proofs. Finally, the author wishes to mention his wife and his uncle, Jesse Beer, whose varied contributions were equally necessary to the achievement of this work.

ALBERT C. BEER

Battelle Memorial Institute
Columbus, Ohio
October, 1963

Contents

Tables

Figures

GALVANOMAGNETIC EFFECTS
IN SEMICONDUCTORS

I.
Introduction

Studies of galvanomagnetic effects have been very helpful in furthering our knowledge of conduction phenomena in semiconductors. Examples of the use of the Hall effect to determine charge-carrier densities and of transverse magnetoresistance to calculate mobilities are so well known as to require no emphasis here. Advantages occurring from measurements of the magnetic-field dependence of the galvanomagnetic effects, on the other hand, are not so obvious. Yet such investigations can yield a variety of information in the case of high-mobility semiconductors. This follows from the fact that in the weak-field region, conductivity phenomena are strongly influenced by the interactions of charge carriers and the lattice, for example, by the nature of the scattering process and by the dependence of the electron wave number on energy. In the region of strong magnetic fields, on the other hand, certain of the transport processes become indicative of the charge-carrier characteristics per se, such as their density and Fermi energy. The magnetic-field variation of the galvanomagnetic effects is expressed in terms of a dimensionless parameter involving the product of the mobility and the magnetic field strength. As a result the strong-field region can be achieved in high-mobility materials with normal laboratory magnets.

For intrinsic semiconductors, magneto-experiments on a single specimen can, in certain cases, give us information about both the conduction and the valence bands. This is possible when electrons and holes have widely differing mobilities. Examples of such materials are indium antimonide and indium arsenide, where the mobility due to lattice scattering is over 80 times as large for electrons as for holes. At weak magnetic fields, the galvanomagnetic and thermomagnetic characteristics are predominantly representative of the conduction band. As the field is increased, the electronic contributions to transport processes may saturate or decrease monotonically so that, at high fields, the controlling effects are due to the holes.

1

It is the intent of the author to devote most of the space in this book to contributions coming in the last 15 years. The principal concern will be with considerations occasioned by band structure and scattering mechanisms exemplified by a number of the well-known semiconductors. Nevertheless, the transport equations will be outlined quite generally, to serve as a starting point for more specialized derivations. The basic relationships are of course applicable to metals as well as semiconductors; and for a thorough presentation of this phase, the reader is referred to the article by Jan in Volume V of this series.[1]

Thermomagnetic phenomena — which would require the space of a parallel article — are not considered in detail except in those cases where they cause significant differences for isothermal and for adiabatic conditions. In order that the magnitude of such differences can be assessed for a given semiconductor, the temperature gradient terms will be included in the basic transport equations.

---

[1] J. P. Jan, *Solid State Phys.* 5, 1 (1957).

II.
Transport Equations

1. Phenomenological Equations for General Case of Anisotropic Solids

The density of the electric current **J** and that of the heat current **q** may be written in terms of the gradients of the electrochemical potential and the temperature as follows:[2]

$$J_i = \sigma_{ij}(\mathbf{H})E_j{}^* + \mathcal{M}_{ij}(\mathbf{H}) \frac{\partial T}{\partial x_j} \tag{1.1}$$

$$i = 1, 2, 3$$

$$q_i = \mathcal{N}_{ij}(\mathbf{H})E_j{}^* + \mathcal{L}_{ij}(\mathbf{H}) \frac{\partial T}{\partial x_j} \tag{1.2}$$

where the current and field vectors are represented by their components in a Cartesian coordinate system (x_1, x_2, x_3). The electrochemical fields $E_j{}^*$ are related to the electric fields E_j and to the electrochemical potential Λ of the electrons as follows:

$$E_j{}^* = E_j + \frac{1}{e} \frac{\partial \zeta}{\partial x_j} \equiv \frac{1}{e} \frac{\partial}{\partial x_j} (-e\varphi + \zeta) \equiv \frac{1}{e} \frac{\partial \Lambda}{\partial x_j}, \qquad e > 0 \text{ for electrons}$$

$$\tag{1.3}$$

where $-e$ is the charge on the electron, ζ is the chemical potential or Fermi energy, and φ is the electrostatic potential. The tensor transport coefficients σ, $\mathcal{M}$, $\mathcal{N}$, and $\mathcal{L}$ are functions of the magnetic field vector. Phenomenological relations such as Eqs. (1.1) and (1.2) are readily established by use of the thermodynamics of irreversible processes. For details, the reader may consult, for example, the *Handbuch* article of

---

[2] This standard convention implying summation over repeated indices is followed throughout this book.

Meixner and Reik,[2a] or other literature to be cited subsequently in this section.

A certain convenience is afforded by the inclusion of the spatial derivative of the Fermi energy in the force terms, and results are consistent with the interpretation of most standard measurements.[3] The case of a two-band semiconductor where the energy gap is a function of temperature has been discussed by Tauc,[3a] and the concept of an internal electric field was introduced. Such a consideration was useful also in the theory of photovoltaic effects when the band gap varied as a result of such factors as external pressure, as in the so-called photopiezoelectric effect.[3a] The case of strongly interacting particles in a strong magnetic field has been discussed by Kasuya[3b] and Nakajima.[3c] In such situations the electrical currents due to the external electric field and the gradient of the chemical potential are different in general, and the Einstein relation between electrical conductivity and charge-carrier diffusion coefficient is not in general applicable — being in general valid only for the symmetric part of the diffusion and electrical conductivity tensors.[3b,c]

Our heat current density $\mathbf{q}$ (identical with Jan's $\mathbf{w}^*$) is defined in terms of the entropy current density $\mathbf{J}_s$ by the thermodynamic relation[4]

$$\mathbf{q} = T\mathbf{J}_s. \tag{1.4}$$

Assuming transport by charge carriers of a single sign, the quantity $\mathbf{q}$ is related to the heat flow $\mathbf{J}_q$ as used by de Groot,[5] Fieschi,[6] and Domenicali,[7] and the heat current densities $\mathbf{J}_w$ of Kohler[8] and $\mathbf{w}$ of Wilson[9] as follows:

[2a] J. Meixner and H. G. Reik, *in* "Handbuch der Physik" (S. Flügge, ed.), Vol. III/2, p. 413. Springer, Berlin, 1959.

[3] See H. B. Callen, *Phys. Rev.* **85**, 16 (1952).

[3a] J. Tauc, *J. Phys. Soc. Japan* **14**, 1174 (1959).

[3b] T. Kasuya, *J. Phys. Soc. Japan* **14**, 410 (1959).

[3c] S. Nakajima, *Progr. Theoret. Phys. (Kyoto)* **20**, 948 (1958).

[4] H. B. Callen, *Phys. Rev.* **73**, 1349 (1948). Callen uses $\mathbf{Q}$ and $\mathbf{S}$, respectively, in his notation.

[5] S. R. de Groot, "Thermodynamics of Irreversible Processes," p. 152. Interscience, New York, 1951.

[6] See p. 12 of R. Fieschi, *Nuovo cimento Suppl.* [10] **1**, 1 (1955).

[7] C. A. Domenicali, *Revs. Modern Phys.* **26**, 237 (1954).

[8] M. Kohler, *Ann. Physik* **40**, 601 (1941).

[9] A. H. Wilson, "The Theory of Metals," 2nd ed. Cambridge Univ. Press, London and New York, 1953.

$$\mathbf{J}_q \equiv \mathbf{J}_w \equiv \mathbf{w} = \mathfrak{q} - \frac{1}{e} \zeta \mathbf{J}, \qquad e > 0 \text{ for electrons} \qquad (1.5)$$

where $- (1/e)\mathbf{J}$ is the particle flow density $\mathbf{J}_k$ as used by de Groot and Fieschi. Another quantity of interest, especially in connection with thermoelectric phenomena, is the total energy flux density $\mathbf{U}$, given by

$$\mathbf{U} = \mathfrak{q} - \frac{\Lambda}{e} \mathbf{J} = \mathbf{w} + \varphi \mathbf{J}. \qquad (1.6)$$

It is important to note that in Eqs. (1.1), (1.5), and (1.6) the electric current density $\mathbf{J}$ refers to transport by a single type of charged carrier. Furthermore, if additional types of carriers of different signs are present, the $\mathbf{J}$ in relations (1.5) and (1.6), in contrast to that in relation (1.1), cannot in general be expressed as an algebraic sum of the partial electric currents due to each type of carrier. In such cases, the individual particle currents $\mathbf{J}_i/(- e_i)$ must be summed. The $(-\zeta/e)\mathbf{J}$ term in (1.5) is thus replaced by[10] $\Sigma \zeta_k \mathbf{J}_k$ in de Groot's and Fieschi's notations where $\mathbf{J}_k$ is a particle current. The summation is done over the species of particles. As is discussed in the next paragraph, these considerations are important in the case of intrinsic semiconductors.

Laboratory measurements of certain quantities, e.g., thermal conductivity, are made under conditions that $\mathbf{J}$ be zero. In such cases, for *extrinsic* semiconductors (i.e., transport by charge carriers of a single sign), the distinction among the different heat currents discussed above ceases to exist.

When *intrinsic* conduction exists, however, both electrons and holes can drift down the temperature gradient to recombine in the cooler region. In such a process the total electric current vanishes when the individual electron and hole currents are equal and opposite. However, particle transport and energy transport are nonzero. This effect can be quite noticeable in intrinsic semiconductors.[11-15]

---

[10] See Eq. II.28 of reference 6.

[11] P. J. Price, *Phys. Rev.* **95**, 596 (1954); *Phil. Mag.* **46**, 1252 (1955).

[12] H. Fröhlich and C. Kittel, *Physica* **20**, 1086 (1954).

[13] J. M. Thuillier, *Compt. rend. acad. sci.* (*Paris*) **241**, 1121 (1955); **242**, 2633 (1956).

[14] A. F. Ioffe, "Semiconductor Thermoelements," translated edition, p. 46. Infosearch Limited, London, 1957.

[15] H. J. Goldsmid, *Proc. Phys. Soc.* (*London*) **B69**, 203 (1956).

Use of the heat current density $\mathbf{q}$ allows us to express relationships (1.1) and (1.2) in a convenient form for application of the thermodynamics of irreversible processes by the choice of grad Λ ($\equiv e\mathbf{E}^*$) and grad T as forces. Since $[1/(-e)]\mathbf{J}$ and $\mathbf{J}_s[\equiv (1/T)\mathbf{q}]$ are mass and entropy flows, respectively, Onsager's relations yield the following equalities[16,16a] between the transport coefficients in a magnetic field $\mathbf{H}$:

$$\sigma_{ij}(\mathbf{H}) = \sigma_{ji}(-\mathbf{H}),$$

$$\mathscr{L}_{ij}(\mathbf{H}) = \mathscr{L}_{ji}(-\mathbf{H}), \qquad (1.7)$$

$$\mathscr{N}_{ij}(\mathbf{H}) = -T\mathscr{M}_{ji}(-\mathbf{H}).$$

The relationship between the transport tensors used in Eqs. (1.1) and (1.2) and those of Kohler[8,17] are

$$\boldsymbol{\sigma} \equiv \mathbf{S}^{(1)}$$

$$\mathscr{M} \equiv -\frac{1}{T}\left[\mathbf{S}^{(2)} + \frac{\zeta}{e}\,\mathbf{S}^{(1)}\right]$$

$$\mathscr{N} \equiv \mathbf{S}^{(3)} + \frac{\zeta}{e}\,\mathbf{S}^{(1)} \qquad (1.8)$$

$$\mathscr{L} \equiv -\frac{1}{T}\left[\mathbf{S}^{(4)} + \frac{\zeta}{e}\,(\mathbf{S}^{(3)} + \mathbf{S}^{(2)}) + \left(\frac{\zeta}{e}\right)^2\mathbf{S}^{(1)}\right]. \qquad e > 0 \text{ for electrons}$$

By applying the Kohler symmetry relations, namely,

$$S_{kl}^{(m)}(\mathbf{H}) = S_{lk}^{(m)}(-\mathbf{H}) \qquad m = 1, 4$$

$$S_{kl}^{(2)}(\mathbf{H}) = S_{lk}^{(3)}(-\mathbf{H})$$

one also obtains Eqs. (1.7).

[16] Reference 6, p. 29. Note that Fieschi's J_e is a particle flow. See also, R. Fieschi, S. R. de Groot, and P. Mazur, *Physica* **20**, 67 (1954); S. R. de Groot and P. Mazur, *Phys. Rev.* **94**, 218 (1954).

[16a] For a more general theory of irreversible processes of which Onsager's relations are a special case, consult R. Zwanzig, *Phys. Rev.* **124**, 983 (1961).

[17] Similar results are given by Wilson[9] (p. 194) except that negative signs were apparently inadvertently omitted from the terms involving the tensors $\mathbf{S}^{(2)}$ and $\mathbf{S}^{(4)}$ in Eqs. (8.1.9) and (8.1.10).

An obvious consequence of the Kohler-Onsager relations is that in the absence of a magnetic field the conductivity tensor $\boldsymbol{\sigma}$ and the thermal flow tensor $\mathscr{L}$ be symmetric. When a field is present, it follows that all the diagonal matrix components of these tensors are even functions of the field; that is,

$$\sigma_{ll}(\mathbf{H}) = \sigma_{ll}(-\mathbf{H}), \qquad (1.9)$$

$$\mathscr{L}_{ll}(\mathbf{H}) = \mathscr{L}_{ll}(-\mathbf{H}).$$

Corresponding statements about the cross-effect tensors $\mathscr{M}$ and $\mathscr{N}$, which are related to the thermoelectric processes, cannot apparently be made without placing requirements on the symmetry of the crystal.[18-21]

2. Inversion of Fundamental Transport Equations

The basic transport relationships in the previous section present the currents in terms of electric and thermal gradients. This approach is very common in the literature. From a formalistic point of view, it has advantages in that the transport tensors in such a representation are more simply expressed in terms of material parameters such as Fermi energies, charge-carrier densities and mobilities, and band structure considerations. On the other hand, most measurements are carried out under conditions such that the electric current is the independent variable. For this reason, there is a practical advantage in inverting the basic transport relations so that the electrochemical potential gradients are no longer independent variables. This is done by multiplying Eq. (1.1) by components of the resistivity tensor ρ_{li} and summing over i. Since $\boldsymbol{\rho}$ and $\boldsymbol{\sigma}$ are reciprocal, one obtains

$$\rho_{li} J_i = \delta_{lj} E_j{}^* + \rho_{li} \mathscr{M}_{ik} (\partial T / \partial x_k), \qquad \begin{array}{l} \delta_{ij} = 1 \ \text{for} \ i = j \\ \delta_{ij} = 0 \ \text{for} \ i \neq j \end{array}$$

or

$$E_j{}^* = \rho_{jk} J_k - \rho_{ji} \mathscr{M}_{ik} (\partial T / \partial x_k). \qquad (2.1)$$

---

[18] E. A. Uehling, *Phys. Rev.* **39**, 821 (1932).
[19] M. Kohler, *Ann. Physik* **27**, 201 (1936).
[20] J. Meixner, *Ann. Physik* **40**, 165 (1941).
[21] See also comments on p. 14 of reference 1. Note, however, reference 432a.

Hence

$$q_i = \mathcal{N}_{ij}\,\rho_{jk}\,J_k - (\mathcal{N}_{ij}\,\rho_{jl}\,\mathcal{M}_{lk} - \mathcal{L}_{ik})\,(\partial T/\partial x_k);$$

that is,

$$E_i{}^* = \rho_{ik}\,J_k - \rho_{ij}\,\mathcal{M}_{jk}\,(\partial T/\partial x_k) \tag{2.2}$$

$$q_i = \mathcal{N}_{ij}\,\rho_{jk}\,J_k - (\mathcal{N}_{ij}\,\rho_{jl}\,\mathcal{M}_{lk} - \mathcal{L}_{ik})\,(\partial T/\partial x_k). \tag{2.3}$$

We choose to write these relations in terms of tensors of resistivity $\boldsymbol{\rho}$, absolute thermoelectric power $\boldsymbol{\alpha}$, absolute Peltier coefficient $\boldsymbol{\pi}$, and thermal conductivity $\boldsymbol{\kappa}$, as follows:

$$E_i{}^* = \rho_{ik}(\mathbf{H})J_k + \alpha_{ik}(\mathbf{H})\,\frac{\partial T}{\partial x_k} \tag{2.4}$$

$$i = 1, 2, 3.$$

$$q_i = \pi_{ik}(\mathbf{H})J_k - \kappa_{ik}(\mathbf{H})\,\frac{\partial T}{\partial x_k} \tag{2.5}$$

The relationship between the coefficients in the two representations is as follows:

$$\rho_{ij}\,\sigma_{jk} = \delta_{ik}, \tag{2.6}$$

$$\alpha_{ik} = -\,\rho_{ij}\,\mathcal{M}_{jk}, \tag{2.7}$$

$$\pi_{ik} = \mathcal{N}_{ij}\,\rho_{jk}, \tag{2.8}$$

$$\kappa_{ik} = \mathcal{N}_{ij}\,\rho_{jl}\,\mathcal{M}_{lk} - \mathcal{L}_{ik}. \tag{2.9}$$

Application of the Kohler-Onsager relations (1.7) yields the following reciprocal relations:

$$\rho_{ik}(\mathbf{H}) = \rho_{ki}(-\mathbf{H}), \tag{2.10}$$

$$\kappa_{ik}(\mathbf{H}) = \kappa_{ki}(-\mathbf{H}), \tag{2.11}$$

$$\pi_{ik}(\mathbf{H}) = T\alpha_{ki}(-\mathbf{H}). \tag{2.12}$$

The last equation is the form of the Kelvin second relation for applied magnetic fields.[21a]

[21a] The designation Kelvin *second* relation follows the practice employed by de Groot, Fieschi, and others. Some authors, however, refer to the expression as the *first* relation.

The fundamental transport equations (1.1) and (1.2) are sometimes expressed in terms of the measureable quantities α, π, and κ, namely,

$$J_i = \sigma_{ij}(\mathbf{H})E_j{}^* - \sigma_{il}(\mathbf{H})\alpha_{lj}(\mathbf{H})\frac{\partial T}{\partial x_j}, \qquad (2.13)$$

$$q_i = \pi_{il}(\mathbf{H})\sigma_{lj}(\mathbf{H})E_j{}^* - [\pi_{il}(\mathbf{H})\sigma_{lm}(\mathbf{H})\alpha_{mj}(\mathbf{H}) + \kappa_{ij}(\mathbf{H})]\frac{\partial T}{\partial x_j}. \qquad (2.14)$$

The sign convention adopted in Eqs. (2.4) and (2.5) is the same as that used by Kohler,[8] Wilson,[22] Price,[23] Samoilowitsch and Korenblit,[24] and others. The absolute thermoelectric power is positive for transport by holes, negative for transport by electrons. The difference in absolute Peltier coefficients for metals A and B, namely, $\pi_A - \pi_B$,[25] is defined as the heat *emitted* per second at the junction when a unit current is directed from conductor A to conductor B. The π_{AB} used by Callen,[4] by Fieschi,[26] and by de Groot[5] is defined as the heat *absorbed* when current passes from conductor A to conductor B. However, this relative coefficient is equivalent to $\pi_B - \pi_A$ and, therefore, the sign convention is identical with ours. A similar convention is used in Blatt's article.[27] The relative thermoelectric power used by de Groot, namely, $\Delta\varphi/\Delta T$, is apparently defined in terms of the absolute quantities as $\alpha_A - \alpha_B$, leading to the negative sign in some of his relations as applied to couples.

On the other hand, the sign convention for Domenicali's absolute Peltier coefficient is opposite from ours,[7] inasmuch as he defines $\pi_{XR} \equiv \pi_X^{abs} - \pi_R^{abs}$. This leads to a negative sign in his expression for the Kelvin second relation, since his thermoelectric power S^{abs} is defined similarly to our α.

The absolute thermoelectric coefficients are simply related to the entropy of transfer or transport, S^*, which is the entropy carried by a unit flow of particles at the isothermal state. The relation is

$$\pi_{ik} = -(T/e)S_{ik}{}^*, \qquad e > 0 \text{ for electrons.} \qquad (2.15)$$

[22] Reference 9, p. 202.
[23] P. J. Price, *Phys. Rev.* **104**, 1223 (1956).
[24] A. G. Samoilowitsch and L. L. Korenblit, *Fortschr. Physik* **1**, 487 (1954).
[25] Written as π_{AB} in Wilson's notation; as $\pi_B{}^A$ in Price's.
[26] Reference 6, p. 45.
[27] F. J. Blatt, *Solid State Phys.* **4**, 228 (1959).

Our thermoelectric tensor α_{ik} is equivalent to $-1/e\ \mathfrak{S}_{ik}$ of Wilson,[9] and to the negative of Meixner's ε_{ik}.[20,28,29] It is also seen that our π is the negative transpose of Meixner's π.[20,28] This definition is consistent with his expression of the Kelvin second relation as $T\varepsilon_{ik}(\mathbf{H}) = \pi_{ik}(-\ \mathbf{H})$.[20]

3. APPLICATION TO ISOTROPIC SOLIDS

Consider an isotropic medium[30] with the magnetic field vector along the z-coordinate direction. Isotropy then requires that

$$\sigma_{xx}(\mathbf{H}) = \sigma_{yy}(\mathbf{H}), \qquad \sigma_{xy}(\mathbf{H}) = -\ \sigma_{yx}(\mathbf{H}) \tag{3.1}$$

$$\mathbf{H} \equiv (0, 0, H_z)$$

$$\sigma_{xz}(\mathbf{H}) = \sigma_{zx}(\mathbf{H}) = \sigma_{yz}(\mathbf{H}) = \sigma_{zy}(\mathbf{H}) = 0 \tag{3.2}$$

with similar expressions for $\mathcal{M}, \mathcal{N}$, and $\mathcal{L}$.

The $\sigma_{zz}(\mathbf{H})$ will, in general, be different from the other two diagonal elements of the conductivity tensor except in the trivial case when $H_z = 0$. In the latter case, all off-diagonal elements will of course vanish in this isotropic example.

The symmetry considerations also require that the diagonal elements of the transport tensors be even functions of magnetic field; the off-diagonal elements, odd. Thus

$$\sigma_{ii}(\mathbf{H}) = \sigma_{ii}(-\ \mathbf{H}), \qquad \sigma_{ij}(\mathbf{H}) = -\ \sigma_{ij}(-\ \mathbf{H}) \qquad \mathbf{H} = (0, 0, H_z)$$

$$i = x, y \tag{3.3}$$

$$\sigma_{zz}(\mathbf{H}) = \sigma_{zz}(-\ \mathbf{H}) \qquad\qquad j = x, y.$$

with similar expressions for $\mathcal{M}, \mathcal{N}$, and $\mathcal{L}$.

The Kohler-Onsager relations, Eqs. (1.7) in conjunction with (3.1) and (3.2), also yield the same relations. In addition, they supply the further condition

[28] J. Meixner, *Ann. Physik* **35**, 701 (1939).
[29] See reference 1.   Jan also defines an absolute thermoelectric power S as the negative of Meixner's (see p. 62 of reference 1).
[30] Actually, less restrictive conditions are sufficient if certain crystallographic symmetry exists. See comment by H. B. Callen[4] (p. 1356).

$$\mathcal{N}_{ij}(\mathbf{H}) = -T\mathcal{M}_{ij}(\mathbf{H}) \qquad \mathbf{H} = (0, 0, H_z)$$

$$i = x, y \qquad (3.4)$$

$$\mathcal{N}_{zz}(\mathbf{H}) = -T\mathcal{M}_{zz}(\mathbf{H}) \qquad j = x, y.$$

Thus the use of the Kohler-Onsager relations and the isotropy of the medium has reduced the large number of coefficients in Eqs. (1.1) and (1.2) to nine independent quantities, as seen below:

$$J_x = \sigma_{xx}(\mathbf{H})E_x{}^* + \sigma_{xy}(\mathbf{H})E_y{}^* + \mathcal{M}_{xx}(\mathbf{H})\frac{\partial T}{\partial x} + \mathcal{M}_{xy}(\mathbf{H})\frac{\partial T}{\partial y}$$

$$\mathbf{H} = (0, 0, H_z)$$

$$J_y = -\sigma_{xy}(\mathbf{H})E_x{}^* + \sigma_{xx}(\mathbf{H})E_y{}^* - \mathcal{M}_{xy}(\mathbf{H})\frac{\partial T}{\partial x} + \mathcal{M}_{xx}(\mathbf{H})\frac{\partial T}{\partial y}$$

$$q_x = -T\mathcal{M}_{xx}(\mathbf{H})E_x{}^* - T\mathcal{M}_{xy}(\mathbf{H})E_y{}^* + \mathcal{L}_{xx}(\mathbf{H})\frac{\partial T}{\partial x} + \mathcal{L}_{xy}(\mathbf{H})\frac{\partial T}{\partial y}$$

$$q_y = T\mathcal{M}_{xy}(\mathbf{H})E_x{}^* - T\mathcal{M}_{xx}(\mathbf{H})E_y{}^* - \mathcal{L}_{xy}(\mathbf{H})\frac{\partial T}{\partial x} + \mathcal{L}_{xx}(\mathbf{H})\frac{\partial T}{\partial y} \qquad (3.5)$$

and for the longitudinal effects, we have

$$J_z = \sigma_{zz}(\mathbf{H})E_z{}^* + \mathcal{M}_{zz}(\mathbf{H})\frac{\partial T}{\partial z}$$

$$\mathbf{H} = (0, 0, H_z).$$

$$q_z = -T\mathcal{M}_{zz}(\mathbf{H})E_z{}^* + \mathcal{L}_{zz}(\mathbf{H})\frac{\partial T}{\partial z} \qquad (3.6)$$

The inverted form, Eqs. (2.4) and (2.5), for the isotropic case is as follows:

$$E_x{}^* = \rho_{xx}(\mathbf{H})J_x + \rho_{xy}(\mathbf{H})J_y + \alpha_{xx}(\mathbf{H})\frac{\partial T}{\partial x} + \alpha_{xy}(\mathbf{H})\frac{\partial T}{\partial y}$$

$$\mathbf{H} = (0, 0, H_z)$$

$$E_y{}^* = -\rho_{xy}(\mathbf{H})J_x + \rho_{xx}(\mathbf{H})J_y - \alpha_{xy}(\mathbf{H})\frac{\partial T}{\partial x} + \alpha_{xx}(\mathbf{H})\frac{\partial T}{\partial y}$$

$$q_x = \pi_{xx}(\mathbf{H})J_x + \pi_{xy}(\mathbf{H})J_y - \kappa_{xx}(\mathbf{H})\frac{\partial T}{\partial x} - \kappa_{xy}(\mathbf{H})\frac{\partial T}{\partial y} \qquad (3.7)$$

$$q_y = -\pi_{xy}(\mathbf{H})J_x + \pi_{xx}(\mathbf{H})J_y + \kappa_{xy}(\mathbf{H})\frac{\partial T}{\partial x} - \kappa_{xx}(\mathbf{H})\frac{\partial T}{\partial y}$$

$$E_z^* = \rho_{zz}(\mathbf{H})J_z + \alpha_{zz}(\mathbf{H})\frac{\partial T}{\partial z}$$

$$q_z = \pi_{zz}(\mathbf{H})J_z - \kappa_{zz}(\mathbf{H})\frac{\partial T}{\partial z}$$

where

$$\pi_{ij}(\mathbf{H}) = T\alpha_{ij}(\mathbf{H}) \qquad \mathbf{H} = (0, 0, H_z)$$
$$i = x, y \qquad (3.8)$$
$$\pi_{zz}(\mathbf{H}) = T\alpha_{zz}(\mathbf{H}) \qquad j = x, y.$$

In this example, with the transverse magnetic field, the existence of relations (3.2) yields a simple relation between the conductivity and resistivity tensors. In particular, relation (2.6) reduces to

$$\sigma_{xx} = \frac{\rho_{yy}}{\rho_{xx}\rho_{yy} - \rho_{xy}\rho_{yx}}, \qquad \sigma_{xy} = \frac{-\rho_{xy}}{\rho_{xx}\rho_{yy} - \rho_{xy}\rho_{yx}} \qquad \mathbf{H} \equiv (0, 0, H_z).$$
$$(3.9)$$

Due to isotropy in the xy-plane, i.e., applicability of relations (3.1), the following well-known expressions are obtained:

$$\sigma_{xx} = \frac{\rho_{xx}}{\rho_{xx}^2 + \rho_{xy}^2}, \qquad \sigma_{xy} = \frac{-\rho_{xy}}{\rho_{xx}^2 + \rho_{xy}^2}, \qquad \mathbf{H} = (0, 0, H_z). \quad (3.10)$$

4. Physical Significance of Transport Coefficients

The purpose of this section is to discuss the physical interpretation of the transport coefficients in the fundamental equations when simple boundary conditions are applied.

a. One-Dimensional Case, Absence of Magnetic Field

Transport equations (3.7) reduce to

$$E_x{}^* = \rho_{xx} J_x + \alpha_{xx} \frac{\partial T}{\partial x},\tag{4.1}$$

$$q_x = \pi_{xx} J_x - \kappa_{xx} \frac{\partial T}{\partial x}.\tag{4.2}$$

Consider the system of Fig. 1, where element A is a p-type semiconductor with ends at temperatures $T_2 > T_1$, and connecting leads of material B going to contacts 0,3 at temperature T_0.

The charge carriers — in this case positive holes — drift down the temperature gradient to produce an excess of positive charge at the lower temperature end. If the potentials, under open circuit conditions, at the respective contacts are φ_0 and φ_3, then, for the sign convention used by Price,[23] the thermoelectric power of the couple at temperature T is defined as

$$(TEP)_{\text{couple}} \equiv \lim_{\substack{T_2 \to T \\ T_1 \to T}} \left\{ \frac{\varphi_0 - \varphi_3}{T_1 - T_2} \right\} \equiv \alpha_{AB} \equiv \alpha_B - \alpha_A.\tag{4.3}$$

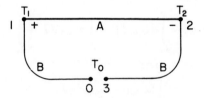

FIG. 1. Thermoelectric circuit with p-type semiconductor as element A.
$T_2 = T + \Delta T/2;$ $\qquad T_1 = T - \Delta T/2.$

It therefore follows that to obtain the thermoelectric power of semiconductor A at temperature T, one must determine

$$\lim_{\Delta T \to 0} \frac{\varphi_0 - \varphi_3}{\Delta T} \equiv \alpha_{BA} \equiv \alpha_A - \alpha_B\tag{4.4}$$

where element B is chosen so that α_B is known precisely or else is negligibly small.

We shall now show that (4.4) does yield the α_{xx} in Eq. (4.1). By summing potential drops in each section of the circuit of Fig. 1, one obtains

$$\varphi_0 - \varphi_3 = \tag{4.5}$$

$$= (\varphi_0 - \varphi_1)_B + (\varphi_B - \varphi_A)_{T_1} + (\varphi_1 - \varphi_2)_A + (\varphi_A - \varphi_B)_{T_2} + (\varphi_2 - \varphi_3)_B.$$

At each junction, with no electric current, the electrochemical potential $\Lambda \ (\equiv \zeta - e\varphi)$ must be continuous. Thus, with the additional use of Eq. (1.3), one obtains

$$\varphi_0 - \varphi_3 = \int_{(1)}^{(0)}\left[-E^* + \frac{1}{e}\frac{\partial\zeta}{\partial x}\right]_B dx + \frac{1}{e}(\zeta_B - \zeta_A)_{T_1} + \tag{4.6}$$

$$+ \int_{(2)}^{(1)}\left[-E^* + \frac{1}{e}\frac{\partial\zeta}{\partial x}\right]_A dx + \frac{1}{e}(\zeta_A - \zeta_B)_{T_2} + \int_{(3)}^{(2)}\left[-E^* + \frac{1}{e}\frac{\partial\zeta}{\partial x}\right]_B dx,$$

$$\varphi_0 - \varphi_3 = \frac{1}{e}(\zeta_{B,0} - \zeta_{B,3}) + \int_{(0)}^{(1)}E_B{}^* dx + \int_{(1)}^{(2)}E_A{}^* dx + \int_{(2)}^{(3)}E_B{}^* dx . \tag{4.7}$$

Since points 0 and 3 are at the same temperature, the first term vanishes, and use of (4.1) gives

$$\varphi_0 - \varphi_3 = \int_{T_0}^{T_1}\alpha_{xx,B}\, dT + \int_{T_1}^{T_2}\alpha_{xx,A}\, dT + \int_{T_2}^{T_0}\alpha_{xx,B}\, dT \tag{4.8}$$

$$= \int_{T - \Delta T/2}^{T + \Delta T/2}(\alpha_{xx,A} - \alpha_{xx,B})\, dT. \tag{4.9}$$

Thus

$$\lim_{\Delta T \to 0}\frac{\varphi_0 - \varphi_3}{\Delta T} = \alpha_{xx,A} - \alpha_{xx,B} \qquad \text{Q.E.D.} \tag{4.10}$$

In order to examine the Peltier effect, terminals 0,3 are joined by a resistance. For this power generation arrangement, heat is absorbed at T_2 and discharged at T_1. If the coordinate system is chosen so that $(\partial T/\partial x)_A > 0$, then $J_{x,A} < 0$ and $q_{x,A}$ at each junction is negative. Also, according to our sign convention, given in Section 2, it follows that

$\pi_A - \pi_B > 0$ at either junction. Thus, since π_B of the contacting metal is small, it follows that $\pi_A > 0$. This is in agreement with the sign of $\pi_{xx,A}$ as given by (4.2).

If external power is applied to terminals 0,3 so that $J_{x,A} > 0$, then heat is absorbed at T_1 and discharged at T_2, such process being commonly referred to as Peltier cooling. Inasmuch as both $q_{x,A}$ and $J_{x,A}$ have changed signs, $\pi_{xx,A}$ is still positive, as it should be, since it is representative of material A.

b. Isotropic Case, Transverse Magnetic Field, Absence of Thermal Gradients

The transport equations (3.5) assume the form

$$J_x = \sigma_{xx}(\mathbf{H})E_x{}^* + \sigma_{xy}(\mathbf{H})E_y{}^*$$

$$\mathbf{H} = (0, 0, H_z). \qquad (4.11)$$

$$J_y = -\sigma_{xy}(\mathbf{H})E_x{}^* + \sigma_{xx}(\mathbf{H})E_y{}^*$$

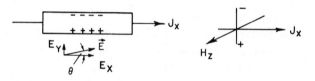

FIG. 2. Hall field due to action of magnetic field on positive charge carriers (holes). (Letters in the figures with overhead arrows are equivalent to boldface letters in the text.)

Galvanomagnetic measurements are commonly carried out under the conditions that J_y be zero. It is customary to define a Hall angle, θ, by the relation

$$\tan \theta \equiv E_y{}^*/E_x{}^* = E_y/E_x. \qquad (4.12)$$

The equality of $\mathbf{E}$ and $\mathbf{E}^*$ follows from the fact that the specimen is isothermal and homogeneous.

From (4.11) it is seen that

$$\tan \theta = \sigma_{xy}(\mathbf{H})/\sigma_{xx}(\mathbf{H}), \qquad J_y = 0. \qquad (4.13)$$

The Hall angle is simply illustrated by the free-particle example shown in Fig. 2.

Consider the motion of positive charges having velocities in the positive direction due to the impressed electric field E_x. In the absence of any transverse electric field, the Lorentz force due to the positive magnetic field vector H_z (out of the page, in Fig. 2) would produce a deflection in the negative y-direction. Therefore, to satisfy the boundary condition that J_y vanish, a transverse electric field must exist. This *Hall field* assumes such a value that the force on a charge carrier having a certain "average" velocity is zero in the crossed electric and magnetic fields. If all the charge carriers had the same velocity, then the Hall field force would exactly cancel the force due to the magnetic field on each moving charge. Hence no charge carriers would be deflected, and there would be no magnetoresistance. This is approximately the situation in an isotropic degenerate metal.[31] Here only those electrons of energy near ζ, where ζ is the Fermi energy, contribute to the conduction. In this case, as is shown in Section 14, the transverse magnetoresistance coefficient is proportional to $(d\tau/d\varepsilon)^2_{\varepsilon=\xi}$, where τ is the relaxation time and ε the energy of the charge carriers. Thus the one-band model yields a very low magnetoresistance for isotropic metals. This point has been discussed by Coldwell-Horsfall and ter Haar.[31a]

In semiconductors, however, a distribution of velocities exists. The carriers with velocities larger or smaller than the "average" referred to above may be regarded pictorially as traversing longer paths, thus increasing the resistance of the conductor. It also follows that any mechanism which tends to short out the Hall field — for example, shorting contacts, inhomogeneities in the material, etc. — will increase the magnetoresistance. More will be said of this point later.

Continuing a step further with our pictorial representation, the equality of transverse electric and magnetic forces on the charge carriers for the case of constant velocity, yields the result that

$$E_y = v_x H_z/c. \tag{4.14}$$

Gaussian units are implied, with c the velocity of light.

Since, under the same restrictions,

$$J_x = nqv_x = \sigma_{xx} E_x \tag{4.15}$$

---

[31] A. Sommerfeld and N. H. Frank, *Revs. Modern Phys.* **3**, 1 (1931).

[31a] R. Coldwell-Horsfall and D. ter Haar, *Phil. Mag.* **46**, 1149 (1955). There is a misprint in Eq. (2); the factor $\frac{1}{2}$ should be a 2.

where q is the charge on the carrier and n the concentration, it follows that

$$E_y/E_x = \sigma_{xx} H/nqc, \qquad H \equiv H_z, \tag{4.16}$$

$$\sigma_{xy} = (\sigma_{xx}^2/nqc)H. \tag{4.17}$$

Also, since the Hall constant R is defined by the relation

$$E_y = R J_x H \tag{4.18}$$

it is apparent that

$$R = 1/nqc. \tag{4.19}$$

Although the above relations were established here using an extremely restricted model, they can be shown rather simply to hold for the more general case of isotropic scattering of the charge carriers characterized by a relaxation time independent of the velocity of the carriers.[32, 33]

It is apparent from Fig. 2, as well as from Eq. (4.17), for a magnetic field vector in the positive z-direction in isotropic media that[34]

$$\sigma_{xy}(\mathbf{H}) > 0 \qquad \text{for holes,}$$

$$\sigma_{xy}(\mathbf{H}) < 0 \qquad \text{for electrons.} \tag{4.20}$$

It is also clear that $\sigma_{xx}(\mathbf{H}) > 0$ for either type of conduction.

---

[32] William Shockley, "Electrons and Holes in Semiconductors," p. 208. Van Nostrand, New York, 1950.

[33] Harvey Brooks, Advances in Electronics and Electron Phys. 7, 128 (1955).

[34] The relations may not necessarily hold if anisotropy is present in the energy surfaces (surfaces of constant energy in momentum space). Re-entrant energy surfaces will reverse the signs in (4.20). See p. 340 of reference 32.

III.
Expressions for Charge-Carrier
Transport Coefficients

5. GENERAL THEORY — THE BOLTZMANN EQUATION

The classical approach, as set forth by Lorentz and Sommerfeld, involves the determination of the distribution of the charge carriers among the different states in the presence of applied electric, magnetic, and thermal fields. If the states are expressed by the wave vectors $\mathbf{k}$, then the number of charge carriers in volume element d^3r ($\equiv dx\,dy\,dz$) characterized by their wave vectors $\mathbf{k}$ in the element d^3k ($\equiv dk_x\,dk_y\,dk_z$) is given by

$$\frac{1}{4\pi^3}\, f(\mathbf{k}, \mathbf{r})\, d^3k\, d^3r \qquad (5.0)$$

where $f(\mathbf{k}, \mathbf{r})$ is the distribution function for the charge carriers — that is, the probability that a carrier exists in the state designated by wave vector $\mathbf{k}$ and at position $\mathbf{r}$. The above expression leads to a density of states term, given by

$$n(\varepsilon)\Delta\varepsilon = \frac{2}{(2\pi)^3}\int d^3k. \qquad (5.0a)$$

The term on the left is the number of energy levels per unit volume of configuration space lying in the range ε, $\varepsilon + \Delta\varepsilon$. The integral is taken over the volume in k-space lying between the surfaces of constant energy ε and $\varepsilon + \Delta\varepsilon$. The factor of 2 is included because of spin, and the $(2\pi)^{-3}$ enters as a result of the use of the wave vector $\mathbf{k}$, to designate the quantum mechanical states.[34a, b]

[34a] See pp. 15 and 43 of Wilson's book.[9]
[34b] See pp. 55–57 *in* N. F. Mott and H. Jones, "The Theory of the Properties of Metals and Alloys," Oxford Univ. Press, London and New York, 1936.

In the classical limit (free electrons represented by plane waves) the momentum is related to the wave vector by the expression $\mathbf{p} = \hbar\mathbf{k}$, and it is seen that Eq. (5.0a) is equivalent to saying that two quantum states (including each direction of electron spin) exist in each volume h^3 in phase space,[34c] i.e.,

$$n(\varepsilon)\varDelta\varepsilon = \frac{2}{h^3}\int d^3p.$$

Once $f(\mathbf{k}, \mathbf{r})$ is known, the electrical and thermal currents due to the charge carriers are given by

$$\mathbf{J} = \left(-\frac{e}{4\pi^3}\right)\int \mathbf{v}f \, d^3k \qquad (5.1)$$

$$e > 0 \text{ for electrons}$$

$$\mathbf{q}_{el} = \left(\frac{1}{4\pi^3}\right)\int \mathbf{v}(\varepsilon - \zeta)f \, d^3k \qquad (5.2)$$

where $\mathbf{v}$ is the velocity of the charge carrier, and $\varepsilon - \zeta$ is its energy above the Fermi energy.

In the absence of fields, the function $f(\mathbf{k}, \mathbf{r})$ becomes the Fermi-Dirac distribution $f_0(\varepsilon)$, namely,

$$f_0(\varepsilon) = \frac{1}{e^{(\varepsilon - \zeta)/kT} + 1}. \qquad (5.3)$$

When fields exist, the usual procedure is to determine f by obtaining a solution of the Boltzmann equation. An alternative procedure, which has been employed in special cases, is a pictorial kinetic method based on calculations of the average drift velocity in the direction of the applied electric field. Certain difficulties which can arise in such an approach are discussed by Dingle.[34d] To overcome these, he introduces a *transport distribution function* defined, for a drift velocity in the z-direction, by

$$f_t = -v_z \, \partial f_0/\partial v_z. \qquad (5.3a)$$

[34c] See, for example, p. 335 of the article by A. Sommerfeld and H. Bethe *in* "Handbuch der Physik" (H. Geiger and Karl Scheel, eds.), Vol. 24, Part 2, p. 333. Springer, Berlin, 1933.

[34d] R. B. Dingle, *Physica* **22**, 671 (1956).

The use of this transport distribution function in obtaining results valid for semiconductors ($\zeta/kT \ll 0$, where ζ is positive when measured upward from the bottom of the conduction band), from relationships derived for metals ($\zeta/kT \gg 1$)[34e] is illustrated.

The Boltzmann equation referred to in the preceding paragraph is an expression of the fact that at steady state df/dt must vanish. The total rate of change of f is expressed as the sum of a term due to the applied fields and one due to collisions of the charge carriers with other particles, imperfections, or lattice vibrations:

$$(\partial f/\partial t)_{\text{fields}} + (\partial f/\partial t)_{\text{coll}} = 0. \tag{5.4}$$

The first factor is commonly expressed in terms of applied fields and the gradients of f as indicated below:

$$-\frac{e}{\hbar}\left(\mathbf{E} + \frac{1}{c}\mathbf{v} \times \mathbf{H}\right) \cdot \text{grad}_{\mathbf{k}}\, f + \mathbf{v} \cdot \text{grad}_{\mathbf{r}}\, f = \left(\frac{\partial f}{\partial t}\right)_{\text{coll}}, \tag{5.5}$$

$$e > 0 \text{ for electrons.}$$

The second term in the above equation is concerned with spatial variation in f, and in homogeneous materials it enters because of temperature gradients.

In the case of perfectly free electrons, the representation of $(\partial f/\partial t)_{\text{fields}}$ in terms of the electric and magnetic field vectors is precisely given by the first term of (5.5). The more realistic case of electrons moving in a periodic potential was studied by Jones and Zener.[35, 36] More recently, Adams and Argyres[37] have also considered certain aspects of the problem. These investigations have established for the periodic lattice, that starting with (5.4), the expression (5.5) is valid to first order in $\mathbf{E}$ and for values of $\mathbf{H}$ and times sufficiently short, so that $eHt/m^* c \ll 1$. The quantity m^*, which is the "effective mass" of the electron in the periodic potential of the solid, is discussed in more detail in Section 6a. Another consideration

---

[34e] The symbol "k" in the terms kT here, as well as in (5.3) is of course the Boltzmann constant, not the magnitude of the wave vector.

[35] H. Jones and C. Zener, *Proc. Roy. Soc.* **A144**, 101 (1934).

[36] Reference 9, p. 45 ff.

[37] E. N. Adams and P. N. Argyres, *Phys. Rev.* **102**, 605 (1956).

which also requires that the accelerations be not too large is that interband mixing of states does not occur.[37]

The condition obtained from Jones and Zener's derivation, namely, that $eHt/m^* c \ll 1$, appears to be more restrictive than is necessary. In fact, as will be seen later in discussing measurements of the Hall effect as a function of magnetic field in germanium and in indium antimonide, conductivity coefficients based on the Boltzmann equation seem to be reliable for values of $eHt/m^* c$ of 10^2 or 10^3, where t here is interpreted as the relaxation time. The principal restriction in the case of these high-field measurements is that the energy separation between quantized magnetic levels be significantly less than the Fermi energy, or than kT in the case of nondegenerate carriers, that is,

$$\hbar\omega \ll \zeta \quad \text{(degenerate charge carriers), or} \quad (5.6)$$

$$\hbar\omega \ll kT \quad \text{(classical statistics).}$$

In the above, k is the Boltzmann constant, T the absolute temperature, and $\omega \ (\equiv eH/m^* c)$ is the cycltron frequency. If condition (5.6) does not hold, then orbit quantization of the charge carriers becomes important. These strong-field effects are discussed briefly in Section 28. For further comments on the Jones-Zener conditions, the reader is referred to a discussion by Chambers.[38] Several articles by Kohn deal with the theory of Bloch electrons in a magnetic field.[38a] Pertinent comments also appear in the treatise by Ziman.[38b] See also Section 28a, namely footnote 498d.

The Boltzmann transport equation is, of course, a classical equation. Recently, Van Hove,[39] Kohn and Luttinger,[40] and others have presented quantum theories of transport. Special treatments, also taking into account quantum effects, have been developed by a number of investigators for the strong-magnetic-field limit. These cases will be discussed in more detail later (Section 28).

Kohn and Luttinger[40] pointed out a number of weaknesses in a conductivity theory based on relationships such as Eq. (5.4). These include

[38] R. G. Chambers, *Proc. Roy. Soc.* **A238**, 344 (1957).
[38a] W. Kohn, *Proc. Phys. Soc. (London)* **72**, 1147 (1958); *Phys. Rev.* **115**, 1460 (1959).
[38b] J. M. Ziman, "Electrons and Phonons." Oxford Univ. (Clarendon) Press, London and New York, 1960. In particular pp. 96 and 512.
[39] Leon Van Hove, *Physica* **21**, 517 (1955).
[40] W. Kohn and J. M. Luttinger, *Phys. Rev.* **108**, 590 (1957).

the random-phase assumption discussed by Van Hove[39] in his investigations of the approach to equilibrium of a quantum many-body system,[40a, b] and the fact that in the usual form of (5.4) the collision interaction is treated by the lowest order of perturbation theory.

Also, in the usual Boltzmann equation, the rate of change of the distribution function f at a given time depends only on the value of f at that time. In the more general case, the rate of change of f depends on all previous values up to the time in question. A number of papers dealing with the Boltzmann equation and with the transport of energy and matter in nonequilibrium systems were presented at the Conference on Transport Processes in Statistical Mechanics in 1956 in Brussels.[40c]

In Kohn and Luttinger's quantum mechanical development,[40] a density matrix[40d] formulation of the problem is used. Expansions are obtained in ascending powers of the strength of the scattering potential of "random" rigid impurity centers. In the limiting case of very weak interactions causing collisions, results reduce to the standard Boltzmann equation. In a subsequent treatment, the same investigators[41] develop the transport equation in powers of the density of scattering centers, without restriction to weak scattering potentials. Again, the first-order terms yield the Boltzmann equation. The density matrix approach has also been used by Lifshitz[42] in his development of a quantum theory of the electrical conductivity in metals in magnetic fields. Expressions are given for the asymptotic behavior of the conductivity tensor in strong magnetic fields — i.e., $\omega\tau \gg 1$ — a region where results could be deduced without special assumptions about the collision integral. These results are given as series in the variable $1/\omega t_0$, where t_0 is a relaxation time. Comparisons are made between the quantum and the classical expressions. Although the treatment by Lifshitz includes oscillatory effects, the region of the "quantum limit" effects in semiconductors (see Section 28) is excluded in that the theory involves the assumption $\hbar\omega \ll \zeta$.

[40a] Leon Van Hove, *Physica* **25**, 268 (1959).

[40b] L. Van Hove and E. Verboven, *Physica* **27**, 418 (1961).

[40c] Proceedings of the International Symposium on "Transport Processes in Statistical Mechanics" (I. Prigogine, ed.). Interscience, New York, 1958.

[40d] See, for example, D. ter Haar, "Elements of Statistical Mechanics," p. 147. Rinehart, New York, 1954.

[41] J. M. Luttinger and W. Kohn, *Phys. Rev.* **109**, 1892 (1958).

[42] I. M. Lifshitz, *Phys. and Chem. Solids* **4**, 11 (1958).

Since the solution of the Boltzmann equation is discussed rather extensively in Wilson[9] and also by Fan[43] and Blatt,[44] only a short discussion is given here. The general treatment involves putting

$$f = f_0 - \phi(\mathbf{k})\,(\partial f_0/\partial \varepsilon). \tag{5.7}$$

To first order in ϕ, the collision term is given by

$$\left(\frac{\partial f}{\partial t}\right)_{\text{coll}} = -\frac{1}{kT}\int V(\mathbf{k},\mathbf{k}')\,\{\phi(\mathbf{k}) - \phi(\mathbf{k}')\}\,d^3k' \tag{5.8}$$

where

$$V(\mathbf{k},\mathbf{k}') \equiv \mathscr{W}(\mathbf{k},\mathbf{k}')f_0(\mathbf{k})\{1 - f_0(\mathbf{k}')\} = V(\mathbf{k}',\mathbf{k}) \tag{5.9}$$

and $\mathscr{W}(\mathbf{k},\mathbf{k}')$ is the probability per unit time that an electron makes a transition from state $\mathbf{k}$ to state $\mathbf{k}'$.

The solution of (5.5) with (5.8) is somewhat involved and is usually accomplished by variational methods (see Section 25). The problem is greatly simplified when a relaxation time can be introduced such that

$$(\partial f/\partial t)_{\text{coll}} = -(f - f_0)/\tau. \tag{5.10}$$

We shall discuss this case in the next section, returning later (Section 25) to the more general approach.

6. Use of a Relaxation Time in the Boltzmann Equation

When the approach of the distribution function f to equilibrium, after the external fields are removed, can be expressed by

$$(f - f_0)_t = (f - f_0)_{t=0}\,e^{-t/\tau}, \tag{6.1}$$

then the integral equation (5.8) reduces to the simple relationship (5.10). With this simplification, the Boltzmann equation can quite readily be solved for a number of conditions of interest. In most cases, the relaxation time τ is considered as a function of the energy only of the charge carriers,

[43] H. Y. Fan, *Solid State Phys.* **1**, 283 (1955).
[44] F. J. Blatt, *Solid State Phys.* **4**, 199 (1957).

that is, it is isotropic on a surface of constant energy. If the energy surfaces have spherical symmetry, then τ is a function only of $|\mathbf{k}|$. In certain anisotropic solids, directional effects may be so important that it is desirable to take into account $\tau(\mathbf{k})$.

The use of a relaxation time appears quite justified for elemental semiconductors such as germanium and silicon, except perhaps at very low temperatures. An important condition, pointed out by Howarth and Sondheimer,[45] is that the energy emitted or absorbed by a charge carrier at collision must be small compared with its initial energy (see also Section 25b).

With a relaxation time, the expressions for f, to a first order, are relatively simple. It is convenient to distinguish two cases.

a. Quadratic Energy Surfaces

When the energy of the charge carriers is a quadratic function of their wave number it is possible to obtain an exact solution of the Boltzmann equation and to determine the distribution function f to first order in ϕ [see Eq. (5.7)] for small electric and thermal gradients.

A general quadratic expression, representing an expansion of the energy to second degree terms in $\mathbf{k}$ about an energy minimum at $\mathbf{k_0}$ may be written

$$\mathscr{E}(\mathbf{k}) = \mathscr{E}(\mathbf{k_0}) + (\hbar^2/2)(\mathsf{M}^{-1})_{ij}(k_i - k_{0i})(k_j - k_{0j}). \tag{6.1a}$$

Such an expansion is possible if the energy bands are not degenerate at the minima.[45a] Also there must be no combination of spin-orbit splitting and lack of inversion symmetry in the solid so that energy terms linear in k can occur.[45b, c] In cases involving such energy surfaces, the concept of effective mass does not exist in the usual sense, as is considered below.

The tensor M^{-1} in (6.1a) is commonly termed the inverse mass tensor or reciprocal mass tensor, and its components are

$$(\mathsf{M}^{-1})_{ij} = (1/\hbar^2)\,\partial^2\mathscr{E}(k)/\partial k_i\,\partial k_j. \tag{6.1b}$$

[45] D. J. Howarth and E. H. Sondheimer, Proc. Roy. Soc. A219, 53 (1953).

[45a] See, for example, the discussion on pp. 148 and 177 in the treatise, G. H. Wannier, "Elements of Solid State Theory," Cambridge Univ. Press, London and New York, 1959.

[45b] R. H. Parmenter, Phys. Rev. 100, 573 (1955).

[45c] G. Dresselhaus, Phys. Rev. 100, 580 (1955).

For spherical energy surfaces with the energy minimum at $\mathbf{k} = 0$, the reciprocal mass tensor reduces to a scalar, commonly known as the "effective mass," m*:

$$(\mathbf{M}^{-1})_{ij} = (1/m^*)\,\delta_{ij}. \tag{6.1c}$$

The effective mass differs from the free mass of the charge carrier because of the potential energy in the crystal.[45d] If this were constant, then m^* would be identical with the free electron mass m_0. When one considers the relation between acceleration and force on an electron in a periodic potential, it turns out that an electron in an energy band behaves in first approximation as though it had an effective mass $\mathbf{m}^*$ represented by the tensor

$$(\mathbf{m}^*)^{-1} = (1/\hbar^2)\,\mathrm{grad_k}\,\mathrm{grad_k}\,\mathscr{E}(\mathbf{k}), \tag{6.1d}$$

an expression which is analogous to (6.1b). An equivalent way of expressing the difference between m_0 and m^*, as pointed out by Kittel[45e], is to note that the latter takes into account the interaction of the electron and the crystal lattice. For example, in the case of negative m^*, the momentum transfer to the lattice is opposite to and larger than that transferred to the electron. That is, the Bragg reflections result in an actual decrease in the momentum of the electron.

Where possible, one usually chooses a coordinate system such that the inverse mass tensor is reduced to principal axes, thus[45f]

$$(\mathbf{M}^{-1})_{ij} = (1/m_i^*)\,\delta_{ij}, \tag{6.1e}$$

where we have followed the customary policy of abbreviating m_{ii}^* by m_i^*, it being implied that these are the components of the diagonalized mass tensor. For this specialized coordinate system, the quadratic relationship between energy and wave number becomes

$$\mathscr{E}(\mathbf{k}) = \mathscr{E}(\mathbf{k}_0) + (\hbar^2/2)\,(1/m_i^*)\,(k_i - k_{0i})^2. \tag{6.1f}$$

[45d] See pp. 141 and 317 in the treatise by F. Seitz.[209]
[45e] C. Kittel, *Am. J. Phys.* **22**, 250 (1954).
[45f] It is obvious that in an equation where indices are repeated on both sides, the convention of summation over such indices does not apply.

Finally, if the energy zero is at the minimum and if this point is taken as the origin of the coordinate system, i.e., $k_0 = 0$, then (6.1f) assumes a form which is frequently found in the literature, namely,

$$\varepsilon(k) = \tfrac{1}{2}\hbar^2 [k_1{}^2/m_1{}^* + k_2{}^2/m_2{}^* + k_3{}^2/m_3{}^*]. \tag{6.2}$$

The expression which is commonly quoted for the distribution function in the general case of quadratic energy surfaces is due to Bronstein[46] or to Blochinzev and Nordheim[47]. It was also developed by Jones[48] for application to bismuth. The expression for $\phi(\mathbf{k})$ when τ is a function of energy only is given in a number of review articles such as those by Fan[43] and Blatt[44], and may be written in the form

$$\phi(k) = - \frac{e\tau}{\hbar} \{\mathrm{grad_k}\, \varepsilon\} \cdot \left\{ \frac{\mathbf{F} - (e\tau/c)\mathbf{M}^{-1}\mathbf{F} \times \mathbf{H} + (e\tau/c)^2(\mathbf{F} \cdot \mathbf{HMH}/\|\mathbf{M}\|}{1 + (e\tau/c)^2(\mathbf{MH} \cdot \mathbf{H}/\|\mathbf{M}\|)} \right\}. \tag{6.2a}$$

The quantity $\mathbf{M}$ is the effective mass tensor and $\|\mathbf{M}\|$ is its determinant. For the case of spherical energy surfaces, the mass tensor reduces to a scalar, m^*, and (6.2a) becomes

$$\phi(\mathbf{k}) = - \frac{e\tau}{\hbar} \{\mathrm{grad_k}\, \varepsilon\} \cdot \left\{ \frac{\mathbf{F} - (e\tau/m^* c)\mathbf{F} \times \mathbf{H} + (e\tau/m^* c)^2\, \mathbf{F} \cdot \mathbf{HH}}{1 + (e\tau/m^* c)^2\, H^2} \right\} \tag{6.3}$$

where our sign convention is such that $e > 0$ for electrons, and where $\mathbf{F}$, the applied electrothermal field, is related to the $\mathbf{P}$ of Wilson[49] as follows:

$$\mathbf{P} \equiv - e\mathbf{F} \equiv - e\mathbf{E} + T\, \mathrm{grad_r}\, [(\varepsilon - \zeta)/T]. \tag{6.4}$$

In terms of the gradients used in Chapter II, the expression becomes

$$\mathbf{F} \equiv \mathbf{E}^* + \frac{1}{eT}\, (\varepsilon - \zeta)\, \mathrm{grad_r}\, T. \tag{6.5}$$

The electrical and thermal current densities due to the charge carriers can be written in terms of ϕ as follows:

[46] M. Bronstein, *Physik. Z. Sowjetunion* **2**, 28 (1932).
[47] D. Blochinzev and L. Nordheim, *Z. Physik* **84**, 168 (1933).
[48] H. Jones, *Proc. Roy. Soc.* **A155**, 653 (1936).
[49] Reference 9, p. 224.

$$\mathbf{J} = \frac{e}{4\pi^3} \int \mathbf{v}\phi \frac{\partial f_0}{\partial \varepsilon} d^3k = \frac{e}{4\pi^3 \hbar} \int \mathrm{grad}_\mathbf{k}\, \varepsilon\, \phi \frac{\partial f_0}{\partial \varepsilon} d^3k \qquad e > 0 \text{ for electrons,}$$

$$(6.6)$$

$$\mathbf{q}^{\mathrm{el}} = \frac{-1}{4\pi^3} \int \mathbf{v}(\varepsilon - \zeta)\phi \frac{\partial f_0}{\partial \varepsilon} d^3k = \frac{-1}{4\pi^3 \hbar} \int \mathrm{grad}_\mathbf{k}\, \varepsilon\, (\varepsilon - \zeta)\, \phi \frac{\partial f_0}{\partial \varepsilon} d^3k. \quad (6.7)$$

These results follow from (5.1) and (5.2) with the use of (5.7). Use is also made of the relation

$$\hbar \mathbf{v} = \mathrm{grad}_\mathbf{k}\, \varepsilon \qquad\qquad (6.8)$$

The case of ellipsoidal energy surfaces can also be treated from transport coefficients based on (6.3), since one can make a linear transformation in **k**-space which transforms the ellipsoids to spheres.[50,51] This approach may at times be preferable to the direct use of the expression for f for quadratic energy surfaces.

b. Nonquadratic Energy Surfaces

In the preceding case, an exact solution of the Boltzmann equation was possible, so that results were valid for arbitrary values of H — subject, of course, to the restrictions on (5.5), which were discussed. When, however, the energy of the charge carriers is not a quadratic function of their wave numbers, then it is necessary to resort to series solutions of the Boltzmann equation. Such a solution was obtained for the isothermal case by Jones and Zener[52] in ascending powers of H.[49] The results can also be expressed in terms of the electrothermal field vector, **F**, Eq. (6.5). The procedure is to write the Boltzmann equation in terms of an operator $\mathbf{\Omega}$, to be discussed later, as follows:

$$\frac{1}{\tau}\phi + \frac{e}{\hbar}\mathbf{F} \cdot \mathrm{grad}_\mathbf{k}\, \varepsilon + \frac{e}{\hbar^2 c}\mathbf{H} \cdot \mathbf{\Omega}\phi = 0. \qquad (6.9)$$

---

[50] Reference 44, p. 285.
[51] E. H. Sondheimer, *Proc. Roy. Soc.* **A224**, 260 (1954).
[52] H. Jones and C. Zener, *Proc. Roy. Soc.* **A145**, 268 (1934).

This expression follows from (5.5) with the use of (5.7), (5.10), (6.5), and (6.8) with neglect of terms involving products of $\mathbf{F}$ and ϕ. Equation (6.9) is now solved by an iterative method to yield

$$\phi = \frac{-e\tau}{\hbar}\left\{\mathbf{F}\cdot\text{grad}_\mathbf{k}\,\varepsilon - \left(\frac{e}{\hbar^2 c}\right)\mathbf{H}\cdot\mathbf{\Omega}(\tau\mathbf{F}\cdot\text{grad}_\mathbf{k}\,\varepsilon) +$$

$$+ \left(\frac{e}{\hbar^2 c}\right)^2 \mathbf{H}\cdot\mathbf{\Omega}\,[\tau\mathbf{H}\cdot\mathbf{\Omega}(\tau\mathbf{F}\cdot\text{grad}_\mathbf{k}\,\varepsilon)] + \ldots\right\}. \tag{6.10}$$

This expansion is valid when

$$e\tau H/m^* c \equiv \omega\tau < 1. \tag{6.10a}$$

The $\mathbf{\Omega}$ is an operator, usually written as

$$\mathbf{\Omega} \equiv \text{grad}_\mathbf{k}\,\varepsilon \times \text{grad}_\mathbf{k} \tag{6.11}$$

or in tensor notation

$$\Omega_i \equiv \varepsilon_{ijl}\,\frac{\partial\varepsilon}{\partial k_j}\,\frac{\partial}{\partial k_l}. \tag{6.12}$$

Summation over repeated indices is implied, and the permutation tensor ε_{ijl} — not to be confused with the energy ε — is defined in the usual manner,

$$\varepsilon_{123} = \varepsilon_{231} = \varepsilon_{312} = 1, \qquad \varepsilon_{213} = \varepsilon_{132} = \varepsilon_{321} = -1 \tag{6.13}$$

with all other components being zero.

In evaluating (6.9), it is helpful to note that $\mathbf{\Omega}$ commutes with any parameter which is a function of energy only; that is if $F(\varepsilon)$ is an arbitrary function of $\varepsilon(\mathbf{k})$, then

$$\mathbf{\Omega}F = F\mathbf{\Omega}. \tag{6.14}$$

This is easily established by operating on the function $F(\varepsilon)G(\mathbf{k})$ with Ω_i. Thus,

$$\Omega_i F(\varepsilon)G(\mathbf{k}) = \varepsilon_{ijl}\frac{\partial\varepsilon}{\partial k_j}\left[G(\mathbf{k})\,\frac{\partial F}{\partial\varepsilon}\,\frac{\partial\varepsilon}{\partial k_l} + F\,\frac{\partial}{\partial k_l}\,G(\mathbf{k})\right]$$

$$= F\varepsilon_{ijl}\frac{\partial\varepsilon}{\partial k_j}\,\frac{\partial}{\partial k_l}\,G = F\Omega_i G,$$

since it is readily apparent that

$$\varepsilon_{ijl} \frac{\partial \varepsilon}{\partial k_j} \frac{\partial \varepsilon}{\partial k_l} \equiv 0,$$

or in vector form,

$$(\text{grad}_\mathbf{k}\, \varepsilon \times \text{grad}_\mathbf{k}\, \varepsilon)_i \equiv 0.$$

Expressions for the conductivity coefficients in ascending powers of H are adequate for studying weak-magnetic-field phenomena but are not very useful when it is desired to investigate the magnetic field dependence of galvanomagnetic phenomena. Approximately at the point where the experimental results become interesting, the power series in H converges extremely slowly, or even begins to diverge. In such cases it may be advantageous to use a method discussed by Shockley[53] and developed in more detail by Chambers[38] and by McClure.[54]

In McClure's development, the components of the conductivity tensor are expressed as Fourier series expansions in harmonics of the frequency of the charge carrier around the hodograph in the magnetic field. This hodograph is the curve in k-space formed by the intersection of a surface of constant energy with a plane perpendicular to the magnetic field. In particular with $\mathbf{H}$ along the k_z-direction, the hodograph lies in the $k_x k_y$-plane, i.e., where k_z is constant. The third term of the Boltzmann equation, (6.9), expressed in terms of the velocity of the charge carrier, $\mathbf{v} = \hbar^{-1}\, \text{grad}_\mathbf{k}\, \varepsilon$, is

$$(e/\hbar c)\mathbf{H} \times \mathbf{v} \cdot \text{grad}_\mathbf{k}\, \phi. \tag{6.15}$$

This may be written as

$$\left(\frac{e}{\hbar c}\right) H v_\perp \frac{\partial \phi}{\partial k_s} \tag{6.16}$$

where $v_\perp$ is the magnitude of the velocity component perpendicular to $\mathbf{H}$, and $d\mathbf{k}_s$ is the component of the differential wave vector along the direction $\mathbf{v} \times \mathbf{H}$. Thus dk_s is an element of arc along the hodograph. Let us

[53] W. Shockley, *Phys. Rev.* **79**, 191 (1950).
[54] J. W. McClure, *Phys. Rev.* **101**, 1642 (1956).

denote by $t_s(\mathbf{k})$ the time at which an electron, precessing around the hodograph, in the absence of the electric field, is at point $\mathbf{k}$. Then the classical equation of motion on the hodograph yields

$$\frac{\partial(\hbar k_s)}{\partial t_s} = \left(\frac{e}{c}\right) H v_\perp \qquad (6.17)$$

where magnitude of the momentum on the hodograph has been expressed as $\hbar k_s$. Thus the term (6.15) is simply $\partial\phi/\partial t_s$, and the Boltzmann equation takes the form

$$\partial\phi/\partial t_s + \phi/\tau + e\mathbf{E}\cdot\mathbf{v} = 0. \qquad (6.18)$$

Although here we have included only the electric field, results are readily carried through for the electrothermal field vector $\mathbf{F}$. Solution of the above first-order differential equation is straightforward. The constant of integration is determined by the condition that ϕ be a single-valued function of $\mathbf{k}$, i.e., it must be periodic in t_s with a period equal to T, the time for the charge carrier to go around the hodograph. Then, as can be seen from (6.18), it follows that $\mathbf{v}$ and τ are also periodic functions of t_s with the same period. The expression for T, and the cyclotron frequency ω, is

$$T \equiv \frac{2\pi}{\omega} = \frac{\hbar c}{e H} \oint dk_s/v_\perp. \qquad (6.19)$$

The cyclotron frequency ω is related to a mass parameter m_H, namely,

$$\omega = eH/m_H c. \qquad (6.19a)$$

In the case of spherical energy surfaces, m_H is identical with the effective mass m^*. In the general case, however, it will involve the components of the effective mass tensor and will depend on the orientation of the magnetic field relative to the energy surfaces[54a, b]

Because of the periodicity of $\mathbf{v}$, it can be written as a Fourier series,

$$\mathbf{v} = \sum_{m=-\infty}^{\infty} \mathbf{v}(m) e^{im\omega t_s}. \qquad (6.20)$$

[54a] See, for example, p. 199 of the text by Wannier.[45a]
[54b] See, p. 514 of the text by Ziman.[38b]

Using (6.20), and the assumption that τ is constant on the hodograph, McClure is able to write the solution of (6.18) as follows:

$$\phi = -e\tau \mathbf{E} \cdot \sum_{m=-\infty}^{\infty} \frac{\mathbf{v}(m)e^{im\omega t_s}}{1 + im\omega\tau}. \tag{6.21}$$

In determining the current density, the quantity $\phi\mathbf{v}(\mathbf{k})$ is first averaged over the hodograph which passes through the point $\mathbf{k}$,

$$\langle \phi\mathbf{v} \rangle_s = \frac{1}{T} \oint_0^T \phi\mathbf{v} \, dt_s \tag{6.22}$$

$$= -\frac{e\tau}{T} \mathbf{E} \cdot \oint_0^T \sum_{m=-\infty}^{\infty} \frac{\mathbf{v}(m)e^{im\omega t_s}}{1 + im\omega\tau} \sum_{n=-\infty}^{\infty} \mathbf{v}(n)e^{in\omega t_s} \, dt_s.$$

Because of the orthogonality of the exponentials, the above reduces to

$$\langle \phi\mathbf{v} \rangle_s = -e\tau\mathbf{E} \cdot \sum_{m=-\infty}^{\infty} \frac{\mathbf{v}(m)\mathbf{v}(-m)}{1 + im\omega\tau}. \tag{6.23}$$

Here the magnetic field enters through the frequency ω, which follows from (6.19) once the shape of the energy surfaces is known. The Fourier components are determined from the appropriate gradients of the energy. Hence in principle, if $\varepsilon(\mathbf{k})$ is known, the problem is solved. There is, of course, the requirement that the relaxation time be a function of energy only, a restriction which was assumed in the derivation of (6.23).

Since for complex energy surfaces, analytical determinations of the Fourier components of the velocity can be very tedious, most evaluations have involved specialized cases. Of course, where the surfaces are spheres, the sequence of components terminates with $m = \pm 1$. Also, when the surfaces can be approximated by a cube, exact calculations are readily possible.[55] Where the band is a warped sphere, in particular the heavy mass valence band in germanium, Beer and Willardson[56] have obtained

[55] C. Goldberg, E. Adams, and R. Davis, *Phys. Rev.* 105, 865 (1957).
[56] A. C. Beer and R. K. Willardson, *Phys. Rev.* 110, 1286 (1958).

good agreement with experiment by considering only two harmonics in addition to the $m = \pm 1$ terms. Because of the cubic symmetry, only terms with m odd occur. These two special cases are discussed in detail later (Section 21).

The question of closed and open orbits in k-space formed by the intersection of a surface of constant energy, namely, the Fermi surface, with a plane normal to the direction of the magnetic field has been discussed by a number of authors[38, 54b, 57] in investigations of the galvanomagnetic effects in metals (see also Section 26). Ziman[58] has considered cylindrical Fermi surfaces — another example which can be treated exactly — with axes in certain principal directions. In order to compare results with some existing experimental data taken on polycrystalline specimens, the conductivity tensor is averaged over all orientations of the crystal axes relative to the magnetic field.

7. Expressions for Transport Coefficients in Isotropic Solids

a. Conductivity Coefficients

As a result of the isotropy, the transport tensors simplify greatly as was seen in Section 3. Concise expressions can be obtained for the diagonal elements, which are even functions of H. The same is true for the off-diagonal elements, which are odd in H, and therefore vanish when the magnetic field is zero.

In order to develop the explicit expressions we shall rewrite (6.6) and (6.7) using the tensor notation implying summations over repeated indices through the three coordinate directions:

$$J_i = \frac{e}{4\pi^3 \hbar} \int \frac{\partial \varepsilon}{\partial k_i} \phi \frac{\partial f_0}{\partial \varepsilon} \, d^3k \qquad e > 0 \text{ for electrons} \qquad (7.1)$$

$$q_i^{(el)} = -\frac{1}{4\pi^3 \hbar} \int \phi(\varepsilon - \zeta) \frac{\partial \varepsilon}{\partial k_i} \frac{\partial f_0}{\partial \varepsilon} \, d^3k \qquad (7.2)$$

[57] I. M. Lifshitz, M. Ia. Azbel', and M. I. Kaganov, *J. Exptl. Theoret. Phys.* (*USSR*) **31**, 63 (1956) [translation: *Soviet Phys.–JETP* **4**, 41 (1957)].
[58] J. M. Ziman, *Phil. Mag.* [8] **3**, 1117 (1958).

where the superscript on the heat current denotes that contribution due to the mobile charge carriers. This distinction is made since it is necessary to consider the heat transfer by other processes, for example by the lattice phonons, to obtain the total thermal current.

Making use of the permutation tensor ε_{ijl}, one can write Eq. (6.3) as follows:

$$\phi(\mathbf{k}) = -\frac{e\tau}{\hbar}\frac{1}{1+(e\tau/m^* c)^2 H^2} \cdot \tag{7.3}$$

$$\left\{\left[\frac{\partial\varepsilon}{\partial k_j} - \frac{e\tau}{m^* c}\varepsilon_{ljm}\frac{\partial\varepsilon}{\partial k_l}H_m + \left(\frac{e\tau}{m^* c}\right)^2\frac{\partial\varepsilon}{\partial k_l}H_j H_l\right]F_j\right\}$$

where

$$\mathbf{F} \equiv \mathbf{E}^* + \frac{1}{eT}(\varepsilon - \zeta)\,\mathrm{grad}_\mathbf{r}\,T. \tag{7.4}$$

Hence

$$J_i = -\frac{e^2}{4\pi^3\hbar^2}\int\tau\frac{\partial\varepsilon}{\partial k_i}\left\{\frac{\partial\varepsilon}{\partial k_j} - \frac{e\tau}{m^* c}\varepsilon_{ljm}\frac{\partial\varepsilon}{\partial k_l}H_m + \left(\frac{e\tau}{m^* c}\right)^2\frac{\partial\varepsilon}{\partial k_l}H_j H_l\right\} \cdot \tag{7.5}$$

$$F_j\left[1+\left(\frac{e\tau}{m^* c}\right)^2 H^2\right]^{-1}\frac{\partial f_0}{\partial\varepsilon}\,d^3k.$$

The conductivity tensor, as defined in Eq. (1.1), is then given by

$$\sigma_{ij}(H) = -\frac{e^2}{4\pi^3\hbar^2}\int\frac{\partial\varepsilon}{\partial k_i}\tau\left[1+\left(\frac{e\tau}{m^* c}\right)^2 H^2\right]^{-1} \cdot \tag{7.6}$$

$$\left\{\frac{\partial\varepsilon}{\partial k_j} - \frac{e\tau}{m^* c}\varepsilon_{ljm}\frac{\partial\varepsilon}{\partial k_l}H_m + \left(\frac{e\tau}{m^* c}\right)^2\frac{\partial\varepsilon}{\partial k_l}H_l H_j\right\}\frac{\partial f_0}{\partial\varepsilon}\,d^3k.$$

For a Cartesian coordinate system with $\mathbf{H}$ along the z-axis, we obtain

$$\sigma_{xx}(\mathbf{H}) = -\frac{e^2}{4\pi^3\hbar^2}\int\tau\left(\frac{\partial\varepsilon}{\partial k_x}\right)^2\left[1+\left(\frac{e\tau}{m^* c}\right)^2 H^2\right]^{-1}\frac{\partial f_0}{\partial\varepsilon}\,d^3k, \tag{7.7}$$

$$\sigma_{xy}(\mathbf{H}) = \frac{e^2}{4\pi^3\hbar^2}\int\tau\frac{e\tau H}{m^* c}\left(\frac{\partial\varepsilon}{\partial k_x}\right)^2\left[1+\left(\frac{e\tau}{m^* c}\right)^2 H^2\right]^{-1}\frac{\partial f_0}{\partial\varepsilon}\,d^3k, \tag{7.8}$$

$$\sigma_{xz}(\mathbf{H}) = 0, \tag{7.9}$$

$$\sigma_{zz}(\mathbf{H}) = -\frac{e^2}{4\pi^3\,\hbar^2}\int \tau\left(\frac{\partial\varepsilon}{\partial k_z}\right)^2\frac{\partial f_0}{\partial\varepsilon}\,d^3k. \tag{7.10}$$

Part of the simplification of (7.6) has resulted from the fact that terms in the first power of $\partial\varepsilon/\partial k_i$ vanish when integrated over k-space.

It is to be noted that

$$\sigma_{zz}(\mathbf{H}) = \sigma_{zz}(0) = \sigma_{xx}(0), \qquad H = H_z. \tag{7.11}$$

This shows that the longitudinal magnetoresistance in an isotropic solid is zero.

The relationship between energy and wave number is given by

$$\varepsilon(\mathbf{k}) = (\hbar^2/2m^*)\,[k_x{}^2 + k_y{}^2 + k_z{}^2] = \hbar^2\,k^2/2m^*. \tag{7.12}$$

All terms in $k_i{}^2$ in the integrands are replaced by $k^2/3$, and the volume element is $4\pi k^2\,dk$. Thus the integrals in (7.7) to (7.10) can be replaced by integrals over energy, and the results written as follows:

$$\sigma_{xx}(\mathbf{H}) = \mathscr{C}_1, \qquad \sigma_{xy}(\mathbf{H}) = -\,\mathscr{D}_1, \tag{7.13}$$

$$\sigma_{xz}(\mathbf{H}) = 0, \qquad \sigma_{zz}(\mathbf{H}) = \sigma_{xx}(0) \tag{7.14}$$

for which $\mathbf{H} \equiv (0, 0, H)$ and where

$$\mathscr{C}_n \equiv -\frac{2e^2(2m^*)^{1/2}}{3\pi^2\,\hbar^3}\int_0^\infty \frac{\tau}{1+(\omega\tau)^2}\,\varepsilon^{n+1/2}\frac{\partial f_0}{\partial\varepsilon}\,d\varepsilon \tag{7.15}$$

$$\mathscr{D}_n \equiv -\frac{2e^2(2m^*)^{1/2}}{3\pi^2\,\hbar^3}\int_0^\infty \frac{\omega\tau^2}{1+(\omega\tau)^2}\,\varepsilon^{n+1/2}\frac{\partial f_0}{\partial\varepsilon}\,d\varepsilon. \tag{7.16}$$

The cyclotron frequency is given by $\omega = eH/m^*\,c$, and $e > 0$ for electrons.

With the use of (1.1) and (7.1)—(7.4), the electronic contributions to the other transport coefficients can be written down by inspection. They are

$$\mathscr{M}_{xx}^{(el)} = \frac{1}{eT}\,[\mathscr{C}_2 - \zeta\mathscr{C}_1], \qquad \mathscr{M}_{xy}^{(el)} = -\frac{1}{eT}\,[\mathscr{D}_2 - \zeta\mathscr{D}_1], \tag{7.17}$$

$$\mathscr{N}_{xx}^{(el)} = -\frac{1}{e}\,[\mathscr{C}_2 - \zeta\mathscr{C}_1], \qquad \mathscr{N}_{xy}^{(el)} = \frac{1}{e}\,[\mathscr{D}_2 - \zeta\mathscr{D}_1], \tag{7.18}$$

$$\mathscr{L}_{xx}^{(el)} = -\frac{1}{e^2 T} [\mathscr{C}_3 - 2\zeta\mathscr{C}_2 + \zeta^2\mathscr{C}_1], \tag{7.19}$$

$$\mathscr{L}_{xy}^{(el)} = \frac{1}{e^2 T} [\mathscr{D}_3 - 2\zeta\mathscr{D}_2 + \zeta^2 \mathscr{D}_1]. \tag{7.20}$$

The superscripts are used to draw particular attention to the fact that the above formulae yield only the electronic contributions, that is, those due to the charge carriers. It is well known that in materials other than the high conductivity metals, a significant thermal transport occurs through the lattice. This phonon transport can contribute appreciably to the thermal conductivity of the material. It can also affect the thermoelectric quantities through the phonon-drag effect, resulting from electron-phonon coupling (see Section 29). A detailed discussion of these phenomena is beyond the scope of this work. For orientation, the reader may consult the literature — in particular, articles by Sondheimer,[59] ter Haar and Neaves,[60] and Herring et al.[61]

b. Phenomenological Expression for Current Density Vector

In many instances it is customary to express the current density vector in terms of components along $\mathbf{E}$, $\mathbf{H}$, and $\mathbf{E} \times \mathbf{H}$. An expression of this sort follows directly from (7.5):

$$J_i = -\frac{e^2}{4\pi^3 \hbar^2} \int \tau \left(\frac{\partial \varepsilon}{\partial k_i}\right)^2 \cdot \tag{7.21}$$

$$\left\{F_i - \left(\frac{e\tau}{m^* c}\right) (\mathbf{F} \times \mathbf{H})_i + \left(\frac{e\tau}{m^* c}\right)^2 \mathbf{F} \cdot \mathbf{H} H_i\right\} \left[1 + \left(\frac{e\tau}{m^* c}\right)^2 H^2\right]^{-1} \frac{\partial f_0}{\partial \varepsilon} d^3 k.$$

In the above expression, the subscript i, although repeated, is not a summation index, but rather a component in the Cartesian coordinate system. It thus follows that for the isothermal case of our isotropic solid, we may write

$$\mathbf{J} = \sigma_H \mathbf{E^*} + \alpha_H \mathbf{E^*} \times \mathbf{H} + \gamma_H \mathbf{E^*} \cdot \mathbf{HH} \tag{7.22}$$

[59] E. H. Sondheimer, Proc. Roy. Soc. A234, 391 (1956).
[60] D. ter Haar and A. Neaves, Advances in Phys. 5, 241 (1956).
[61] C. Herring, T. Geballe, and J. Kunzler, Phys. Rev. 111, 36 (1958).

where

$$\sigma_H \equiv -\frac{e^2}{4\pi^3 \hbar^2} \int \tau \left(\frac{\partial \varepsilon}{\partial k_i}\right)^2 \left[1 + \left(\frac{e\tau}{m^* c}\right)^2 H^2\right]^{-1} \frac{\partial f_0}{\partial \varepsilon} d^3 k, \qquad (7.23)$$

$$\alpha_H \equiv \frac{e^2}{4\pi^3 \hbar^2} \int \tau \left(\frac{\partial \varepsilon}{\partial k_i}\right)^2 \left(\frac{e\tau}{m^* c}\right) \left[1 + \left(\frac{e\tau}{m^* c}\right)^2 H^2\right]^{-1} \frac{\partial f_0}{\partial \varepsilon} d^3 k, \qquad (7.24)$$

$$\gamma_H \equiv -\frac{e^2}{4\pi^3 \hbar^2} \int \tau \left(\frac{\partial \varepsilon}{\partial k_i}\right)^2 \left(\frac{e\tau}{m^* c}\right)^2 \left[1 + \left(\frac{e\tau}{m^* c}\right)^2 H^2\right]^{-1} \frac{\partial f_0}{\partial \varepsilon} d^3 k \qquad (7.25)$$

where $i \equiv x, y,$ or z. Also,

$$\left(\frac{\partial \varepsilon}{\partial k_x}\right)^2 = \left(\frac{\partial \varepsilon}{\partial k_y}\right)^2 = \left(\frac{\partial \varepsilon}{\partial k_z}\right)^2 = \frac{\hbar^4}{m^{*2}}.$$

The factor α_H is related to the Hall coefficient, and γ_H is one of the magnetoresistance constants.

A relationship of the form (7.22) was established by Seitz.[62] His coefficients are given through second order terms in H, the development being sufficiently general so that they can be applied to solids of cubic symmetry.

To first terms in H or H^2 in (7.22), our coefficients α_H and γ_H become identical with those of Seitz, and our σ_H is related to his σ_0 and β by

$$\sigma_H = \sigma_0 + \beta H^2. \qquad (7.26)$$

8. Transport Coefficients in Anisotropic Isothermal Solids

a. Conductivity Tensors

The usual procedure in the case of anisotropic solids is to express the transport coefficients in power series of the magnetic field intensity. In this connection we note the fact that a second rank tensor is always divisible into symmetric and antisymmetric parts. From the Kohler-Onsager relation,

$$\sigma_{ij}(\mathbf{H}) = \sigma_{ji}(-\mathbf{H}), \qquad (8.1)$$

---

[62] F. Seitz, *Phys. Rev.* **79**, 372 (1950). For arbitrary H, consult García-Moliner.[428]

it follows that the symmetric tensor must contain only even powers of the magnetic field, and the antisymmetric tensor only odd powers.[63,64] One may therefore write

$$\sigma_{ij}(\mathbf{H}) = \sigma_{ij}{}^0 + \alpha_{ijl} H_l + \beta_{ijlm} H_l H_m + \gamma_{ijlmn} H_l H_m H_n + \tag{8.2}$$

$$\zeta_{ijlmnp} H_l H_m H_n H_p + \ldots$$

where

$$\alpha_{ijl} = \left(\frac{\partial \sigma_{ij}(\mathbf{H})}{\partial H_l}\right)_{H=0}, \tag{8.3a}$$

$$\beta_{ijlm} = \frac{1}{2!}\left(\frac{\partial^2 \sigma_{ij}(\mathbf{H})}{\partial H_l \, \partial H_m}\right)_{H=0}, \tag{8.3b}$$

$$\gamma_{ijlmn} = \frac{1}{3!}\left(\frac{\partial^3 \sigma_{ij}(\mathbf{H})}{\partial H_l \, \partial H_m \, \partial H_n}\right)_{H=0}, \tag{8.4a}$$

$$\zeta_{ijlmnp} = \frac{1}{4!}\left(\frac{\partial^4 \sigma_{ij}(\mathbf{H})}{\partial H_l \, \partial H_m \, \partial H_n \, \partial H_p}\right)_{H=0}. \tag{8.4b}$$

The validity of the expansion is the same as for Eq. (6.10), namely, that $e\tau H/m^* c \equiv \omega\tau < 1$. In Eq. (8.2), $\sigma_{ij}{}^0$ is the zero-magnetic-field conductivity; the third and fifth rank tensors are associated with the Hall conductivity, and the fourth and sixth rank tensors are associated with the magnetoconductivity.

It is often customary to use the notation in which all the above tensors are designated by σ, their galvanomagnetic association being apparent from the rank. Thus, the electric current density is written as

$$J_i = \sigma_{ij}^0 E_j + \sigma_{ijl}^0 E_j H_l + \sigma_{ijlm}^0 E_j H_l H_m + \sigma_{ijlmn}^0 E_j H_l H_m H_n + \ldots, \tag{8.5}$$

$$\omega\tau < 1.$$

We choose to use the superscript to differentiate these field-independent tensors from the general transport coefficients $\sigma_{ij}(\mathbf{H})$ which appear throughout this volume. It will be seen later that in cubic solids the

---

[63] See p. 12 of reference 1.
[64] W. Mason, W. Hewitt, and R. Wick, *J. Appl. Phys.* **24**, 166 (1953).

σ^0_{ijl} are associated with the nondirectional Hall effect. The σ^0_{ijlmn} terms give directional contributions to the Hall effect. From the use of (6.10), (6.12), and (7.1), it is readily established that the tensors in (8.5) are given by the following expressions:

$$\sigma^0_{ij} = -\frac{e^2}{4\pi^3\,\hbar^2}\int \tau\,\frac{\partial f_0}{\partial \varepsilon}\,\frac{\partial \varepsilon}{\partial k_i}\,\frac{\partial \varepsilon}{\partial k_j}\,d^3k, \tag{8.6}$$

$$\sigma^0_{ijl} = \frac{e^3}{4\pi^3\,\hbar^4\,c}\int \tau\,\frac{\partial f_0}{\partial \varepsilon}\,\frac{\partial \varepsilon}{\partial k_i}\,\frac{\partial \varepsilon}{\partial k_p}\,\frac{\partial}{\partial k_q}\left(\tau\,\frac{\partial \varepsilon}{\partial k_j}\right)\varepsilon_{lpq}\,d^3k, \tag{8.7}$$

$$\sigma^0_{ijlm} = -\frac{e^4}{4\pi^3\,\hbar^6\,c^2}\int \tau\,\frac{\partial f_0}{\partial \varepsilon}\,\frac{\partial \varepsilon}{\partial k_i}\,\frac{\partial \varepsilon}{\partial k_r}\,\frac{\partial}{\partial k_s}\left[\tau\,\frac{\partial \varepsilon}{\partial k_p}\,\frac{\partial}{\partial k_q}\left(\tau\,\frac{\partial \varepsilon}{\partial k_j}\right)\right]\mathscr{E}_{lrs,mpq}\,d^3k$$

$$e > 0 \quad \text{for electrons.} \tag{8.8}$$

In the last expression, the double permutation tensor is commonly given as the product of two standard permutation tensors, namely,

$$\mathscr{E}_{lrs,mpq} = \varepsilon_{lrs}\,\varepsilon_{mpq}. \tag{8.8a}$$

It may, however, equally well be written as

$$\mathscr{E}_{lrs,mpq} = \varepsilon_{mrs}\,\varepsilon_{lpq}. \tag{8.8b}$$

The important point is that (8.8a) and (8.8b) yield different results when (8.8) is evaluated for the expansion coefficient σ^0_{ijlm}. This is readily established by choosing a very simple case, namely, σ^0_{xyxy} and spherical energy surfaces.

The above situation does not cause errors in practice inasmuch as the summation over indices l and m causes (8.8a) and (8.8b) always to occur in pairs. Nevertheless, from a formalistic standpoint, it appears preferable to use coefficients in (8.5) which are symmetric in the indices lm. That is,

$$\sigma^0_{ijlm} = \sigma^0_{ijml}. \tag{8.9}$$

That such an arrangement is logically the most satisfactory follows from direct inspection of such relations as (6.10), (8.3b), or (8.5). A number of authors,[65, 66] for example, have discussed the symmetry of the mag-

[65] C. Herring, *Bell System Tech. J.* **34**, 237 (1955).
[66] M. Kohler, *Ann. Physik* **20**, 891 (1934).

netoconductivity and magnetoresistivity tensors in the indices representing the components of the magnetic field, and have introduced the
symmetry condition explicitly in the expression for σ^0_{ijlm}.[65] This is readily
accomplished in (8.8) by expressing the double permutation tensor as
follows[67]:

$$\mathscr{E}_{lrs,mpq} = \tfrac{1}{2}\left[\varepsilon_{lrs}\,\varepsilon_{mpq} + \varepsilon_{mrs}\,\varepsilon_{lpq}\right]. \tag{8.10}$$

Symmetric and antisymmetric relationships with interchange of the
indices representing components of current and electric field also occur
as a result of the Kohler-Onsager reciprocity relations. For example, if
(8.1) is applied to (8.2), it is apparent from the required equality of
terms that

$$\sigma^0_{ij} = \sigma^0_{ji}, \qquad \sigma^0_{ijl} = -\,\sigma^0_{jil}, \qquad \sigma^0_{ijl} = 0 \qquad \text{if} \qquad i = j,$$

$$\sigma^0_{ijlm} = \sigma^0_{jilm}, \quad \text{if the coefficients are symmetric in } l \text{ and } m. \tag{8.11}$$

If symmetry in l and m does not exist in the magnetoconductivity coefficients — that is, if (8.8a) or (8.8b) is used instead of (8.10) — then the
latter expression in (8.11) must be replaced by

$$\sigma^0_{ijlm} = \sigma^0_{jiml}. \tag{8.11a}$$

This latter relation follows directly from Eq. (8.8), and is shown by
Jones[67a] through a transformation of the integral. It also follows that
σ^0_{iiii} and σ^0_{iijj} are always negative.

Much space in the literature is devoted to magnetoconductivity in
crystals possessing cubic symmetry. For cubic group O_h (point group
$m3m$) the different nonvanishing conductivity components through the
fourth rank tensors are given by[64]

$$\sigma^0_{ij}:\ \sigma^0_{11},$$

$$\sigma^0_{ijl}:\ \sigma^0_{123}, \tag{8.12}$$

$$\sigma^0_{ijlm}:\ \sigma^0_{1111},\,\sigma^0_{1122},\,\sigma^0_{1212}.$$

[67] J. R. Drabble and R. Wolfe, *Proc. Phys. Soc. (London)* **B69**, 1101 (1956).
[67a] H. Jones, *in* "Handbuch der Physik" (S. Flügge, ed.), Vol. 19, p. 300. Springer,
Berlin, 1956.

All other components of these tensors are related as follows:

$$\sigma^0_{33} = \sigma^0_{22} = \sigma^0_{11}, \qquad \sigma^0_{ij} = 0 \qquad \text{if} \qquad i \neq j,$$

$$\sigma^0_{ijl} = \varepsilon_{ijl}\, \sigma^0_{123}. \tag{8.12a}$$

Because of the symmetry in indices ij and lm, the fourth rank magnetoconductivity tensor can be displayed as a 6×6 matrix. Thus, the values of all the elements are expressed in the following matrix[64]:

$$\sigma^0_{ijlm} \equiv \sigma^0_{(ij),(lm)} = \begin{bmatrix} \sigma^0_{1,1} & \sigma^0_{1,2} & \sigma^0_{1,2} & 0 & 0 & 0 \\ \sigma^0_{1,2} & \sigma^0_{1,1} & \sigma^0_{1,2} & 0 & 0 & 0 \\ \sigma^0_{1,2} & \sigma^0_{1,2} & \sigma^0_{1,1} & 0 & 0 & 0 \\ 0 & 0 & 0 & \sigma^0_{6,6} & 0 & 0 \\ 0 & 0 & 0 & 0 & \sigma^0_{6,6} & 0 \\ 0 & 0 & 0 & 0 & 0 & \sigma^0_{6,6} \end{bmatrix} \tag{8.12b}$$

where

$$(11) = 1; \qquad (22) = 2; \qquad (33) = 3; \tag{8.12c}$$

$$(23) = (32) = 4; \qquad (13) = (31) = 5; \qquad (12) = (21) = 6.$$

In addition to cubic group O_h (point group $m3m$) the above representation also applies to cubic systems O and T_d (point groups 432 and $\bar{4}3m$, respectively). In the case of cubic groups T and T_h (23 and $m3$, respectively), there is an additional nonvanishing coefficient, namely, $\sigma^0_{1,3}$,[67b,c] which is different from the three independent coefficients listed above.

An equation including second-order terms in magnetic field strength often used in analyzing magnetoconductivity in cubic solids is due to Seitz[62] and can be written as follows:

$$\mathbf{J} = \sigma_0\,\mathbf{E} + \alpha(\mathbf{E} \times \mathbf{H}) + \beta H^2\,\mathbf{E} + \gamma(\mathbf{E}\cdot\mathbf{H})\mathbf{H} + \delta\mathsf{T}\mathbf{E}, \qquad \omega\tau \ll 1 \tag{8.13}$$

where the coordinate axes are coincident with the crystal axes, and where T is a diagonal tensor with the elements H_1^2, H_2^2, H_3^2. In tensor notation, and taking account of the symmetry in l and m, this may be written

---

[67b] See, for example, Table VIII, in C. S. Smith, in *Solid State Phys.* **6**, 175 (1958).
[67c] L. P. Kao and E. Katz, *Phys. and Chem. Solids* **6**, 223 (1958).

$$J_i = \sigma_0 \, \delta_{ij} E_j + \varepsilon_{ijl} \, \alpha \, E_j \, H_l + \beta \delta_{ij} \, \delta_{lm} \, H_l \, H_m + \tag{8.14}$$

$$\tfrac{1}{2} \gamma \left[\delta_{im} \, \delta_{lj} + \delta_{il} \, \delta_{mj} \right] E_j \, H_l \, H_m + \delta \delta_{ij} \, \delta_{il} \, \delta_{im} \, E_j \, H_l \, H_m$$

where summation is over all indices except i, and where the coefficient δ is not to be confused with the Kronecker deltas.

A comparison of (8.5) and (8.13) reveals that

$$\sigma_{ij}^0 = \sigma_0 \, \delta_{ij}, \qquad \sigma_{ijl}^0 = \varepsilon_{ijl} \, \alpha, \tag{8.15}$$

$$\tfrac{1}{2} \left[\sigma_{ijlm}^0 + \sigma_{ijml}^0 \right] = \beta \delta_{ij} \, \delta_{lm} + \tfrac{1}{2} \gamma \left[\delta_{im} \, \delta_{lj} + \delta_{il} \, \delta_{mj} \right] + \delta \delta_{ij} \, \delta_{il} \, \delta_{im}. \tag{8.16}$$

The form of the expressions in brackets is chosen so that the symmetry in the indices l and m is explicitly expressed.

By using appropriate values for the indices in (8.16) one obtains the following set of relations:

$$\sigma_{1111}^0 = \beta + \gamma + \delta, \qquad \sigma_{1122}^0 = \beta, \qquad \sigma_{1212}^0 = \gamma/2. \tag{8.17}$$

If (8.15) and (8.16) are evaluated for all sets of indices, one obtains again all the information presented in (8.12a) and (8.12b).

From (8.17) we see that the Seitz coefficients are related to the basic conductivity components of (8.12) as follows:

$$\sigma_0 = \sigma_{11}^0, \qquad \alpha = \sigma_{123}^0, \qquad \beta = \sigma_{1122}^0,$$

$$\gamma = 2\sigma_{1212}^0, \qquad \delta = \sigma_{1111}^0 - \sigma_{1122}^0 - 2\sigma_{1212}^0. \tag{8.18}$$

In the case of isotropic materials,

$$\delta = 0, \qquad \beta + \gamma = 0. \tag{8.18a}$$

b. Resistivity Tensors

In many galvanomagnetic measurements, the current density is maintained constant, and the electric field, which is permitted to adjust itself, is determined from measurements of potential differences.

In such cases, it is desirable to express electrical transport effects in terms of the resistivity tensor $\rho(\mathbf{H})$, as is done in (2.4). For the isothermal case,[68]

---

[68] For homogeneous materials with zero temperature gradients, it is to be noted that $\mathbf{E}^* = \mathbf{E}$. Since many of the sections to follow are concerned with such cases, the quantity $\mathbf{E}$ will appear in most equations.

$$E_i = \rho_{ik}(\mathbf{H}) J_k. \tag{8.19}$$

The above expression is often written in a way analogous to (8.5), namely,

$$E_i = \rho_{ik}^0 J_k + \rho_{ikl}^0 J_k H_l + \rho_{iklm}^0 J_k H_l H_m + \tag{8.20}$$

$$\rho_{iklmn}^0 J_k H_l H_m H_n + \ldots, \qquad \omega\tau < 1.$$

The higher rank tensors ρ_{ikl}^0, ρ_{iklm}^0, ... are commonly known as galvanomagnetic coefficients. They can be expressed explicitly in terms of the conductivity coefficients of (8.5) through the use of relation (2.6), namely, $\rho_{ij}(\mathbf{H})\sigma_{jk}(\mathbf{H}) = \delta_{ik}$.

Another form of (8.19), given by Casimer,[69,70] can be written as follows:

$$E_i = \rho_{ik}^s(\mathbf{H}) J_k + [\mathbf{R}(\mathbf{H}) \times \mathbf{J}]_i. \tag{8.21}$$

The sign convention used above is such that the first term in the $\mathbf{R}(\mathbf{H})$ expansion for the isotropic case is $R\mathbf{H}$, where R is precisely the ordinary Hall coefficient. In (8.21) the resistivity tensor has been split into a symmetrical part $\rho_{ik}^s(\mathbf{H})$, which is an even function of the magnetic field, and an antisymmetrical part $\rho_{ik}^a(\mathbf{H})$ expressed in terms of a *Hall vector*[71] $\mathbf{R}(\mathbf{H})$. The Hall vector is an odd function of $\mathbf{H}$, with components

$$R_1(\mathbf{H}) = \rho_{32}^a(\mathbf{H}), \qquad R_2(\mathbf{H}) = \rho_{13}^a(\mathbf{H}), \qquad R_3(\mathbf{H}) = \rho_{21}^a(\mathbf{H}). \tag{8.23}$$

In tensor notation, (8.23) and (8.21) may be written

$$R_s(\mathbf{H}) = \tfrac{1}{2} \varepsilon_{sut} \rho_{tu}^a(H), \tag{8.24}$$

$$E_i = \rho_{ik}^s(\mathbf{H}) J_k + \varepsilon_{isk} R_s(\mathbf{H}) J_k. \tag{8.25}$$

[69] H. B. G. Casimer and A. N. Gerritsen, *Physica* 8, 1107 (1941).

[70] H. B. G. Casimer, *Revs. Modern Phys.* 17, 343 (1945).

[71] With $\mathbf{R}(\mathbf{H})$ defined as a Hall vector and the last term of (8.21) therefore representing the Hall field, it follows that the Hall effect thus defined is an odd function of magnetic field. This definition, although frequently adhered to, is not universally followed. Some authors adopt a more general definition, which permits the occurrence of even powers of H in the Hall terms. These considerations are discussed in Chapter IV.

Since $R_s(\mathbf{H})$ is odd in H, its general expansion is of the form

$$R_s(\mathbf{H}) = R^0_{sl} H_l + R^0_{slmn} H_l H_m H_n + \ldots, \qquad \omega\tau < 1. \qquad (8.26)$$

It is thus apparent that (8.25) and (8.26) are equivalent to (8.20) provided that

$$R^0_{sl} = \tfrac{1}{2}\varepsilon_{sut}\,\rho^0_{tul}, \qquad R^0_{slmn} = \tfrac{1}{2}\,\varepsilon_{sut}\,\rho^0_{tulmn} \qquad (8.27)$$

or that

$$\varepsilon_{isk}\,R^0_{sl} = \rho^0_{ikl}, \qquad \varepsilon_{isk}\,R^0_{slmn} = \rho^0_{iklmn}. \qquad (8.28)$$

There is also the obvious relation that

$$\rho^s_{ik}(\mathbf{H}) = \rho^0_{ik} + \rho^0_{iklm} H_l H_m + \ldots, \qquad \omega\tau < 1.$$

The factor of $\tfrac{1}{2}$ appears in expressions (8.27) because the summations there are over the two indices in which the tensors are antisymmetric.

c. Application of Phenomenological Relations to Various Crystal Systems

(1) General systems. The number of nonvanishing independent components of a given order galvanomagnetic coefficient is determined by physical requirements such as expressed in (8.9) and (8.11) and by the symmetry of the material. The application of group theory and direct inspection procedures has been applied by a number of investigators[67b,c,72–78c] to establish these independent components and to determine the other components of the tensors. Results are available for all of the crystallographic groups. Terms as high as the sixth order have been considered.

---

[72] M. Kohler, *Ann. Physik* **20**, 878, 891 (1934).
[73] D. Shoenberg, *Proc. Cambridge Phil. Soc.* **31**, 265 (1935).
[74] H. J. Juretschke, *Acta Cryst.* **5**, 148 (1952).
[75] F. G. Fumi, *Acta Cryst.* **5**, 44, 691 (1952).
[76] F. G. Fumi, *Nuovo cimento* **9**, 739 (1952).
[77] R. Fieschi and F. G. Fumi, *Nuovo cimento* **10**, 865 (1953).
[78] H. B. Huntington, *Solid State Phys.* **7**, 213 (1958).
[78a] H. Bross, *Z. Naturforsch.* **15a**, 859 (1960).
[78b] G. F. Koster, *Solid State Phys.* **5**, 173 (1957).
[78c] A. V. Sokolov and V. P. Shirokovskii, *Uspekhi Fiz. Nauk* **71**, 485 (1960) [translation: *Soviet Phys.-Uspekhi* **3**, 551 (1961)].

(2) *Cubic groups O_h, O, or T_d (systems of point group symmetry m3m, 432, 43m).* The five different nonvanishing conductivity components through the terms involving second powers of the magnetic field, and their relation to the constants in the equation of Seitz, have been given in Subsection *a*. These conductivity coefficients may be transformed to the galvanomagnetic coefficients in Eq. (8.20) by use of the reciprocal relation

$$\rho_{ij}(\mathbf{H})\sigma_{jp}(\mathbf{H}) = \delta_{ip}. \tag{8.29}$$

In using this relation, care must be taken to take the interchangeability of the magnetic field indices into account. This is readily done by writing a symmetric form whenever two or more such indices occur. This procedure is outlined by the several steps below:

$$\rho_{ij}(H) = \rho_{ij}^0 + \rho_{ijl}^0 H_l + \tfrac{1}{2}(\rho_{ijlm}^0 + \rho_{ijml}^0) H_l H_m + \cdots,$$

$$\sigma_{jp}(H) = \sigma_{jp}^0 + \sigma_{jpm}^0 H_m + \tfrac{1}{2}(\sigma_{jplm}^0 + \sigma_{jpml}^0) H_l H_m + \cdots. \tag{8.29a}$$

Carrying out summations over j yields, for the product (8.29),

H^0 terms:
$$\rho_{i1}^0 \sigma_{1p}^0 + \rho_{i2}^0 \sigma_{2p}^0 + \rho_{i3}^0 \sigma_{3p}^0 = \delta_{ip},$$

H terms:
$(m = l)$
$$\rho_{i1}^0 \sigma_{1pl}^0 + \rho_{i2}^0 \sigma_{2pl}^0 + \rho_{i3}^0 \sigma_{3pl}^0 + \sigma_{1p}^0 \rho_{i1l}^0 + \sigma_{2p}^0 \rho_{i2l}^0 + \sigma_{3p}^0 \rho_{i3l}^0 = 0,$$

H^2 terms:
$$\tfrac{1}{2}(\rho_{i1l}^0 \sigma_{1pm}^0 + \rho_{i1m}^0 \sigma_{1pl}^0) + \tfrac{1}{2}(\rho_{i2l}^0 \sigma_{2pm}^0 +$$
$$\rho_{i2m}^0 \sigma_{2pl}^0) + \tfrac{1}{2}(\rho_{i3l}^0 \sigma_{3pm}^0 + \rho_{i3m}^0 \sigma_{3pl}^0) + \tfrac{1}{2}\rho_{i1}(\sigma_{1plm}^0 + \sigma_{1pml}^0) +$$
$$\tfrac{1}{2}\rho_{i2}(\sigma_{2plm}^0 + \sigma_{2pml}^0) + \tfrac{1}{2}\rho_{i3}(\sigma_{3plm}^0 + \sigma_{3pml}^0) + \tfrac{1}{2}\sigma_{1p}^0(\rho_{i1lm}^0 + \rho_{i1ml}^0) +$$
$$\tfrac{1}{2}\sigma_{2p}^0(\rho_{i2lm}^0 + \rho_{i2ml}^0) + \tfrac{1}{2}\sigma_{3p}^0(\rho_{i3lm}^0 + \rho_{i3ml}^0) = 0. \tag{8.29b}$$

The above relationships are completely general. For the basic components of the cubic system, given in (8.12) they yield

$$\sigma_{11}^0 = 1/\rho_{11}^0, \qquad \sigma_{123}^0 = -\rho_{123}^0/\rho_{11}^{0\,2}, \qquad \sigma_{1111}^0 = -\rho_{1111}^0/\rho_{11}^{0\,2},$$

$$\sigma_{1122}^0 = -\rho_{1122}^0/\rho_{11}^{0\,2} - \rho_{123}^{0\,2}/\rho_{11}^{0\,3}, \qquad \sigma_{1212}^0 = -\rho_{1212}^0/\rho_{11}^{0\,2} + \tfrac{1}{2}\rho_{123}^{0\,2}/\rho_{11}^{0\,3}. \tag{8.29c}$$

An inverted form of (8.13), again to second order in H, due to Pearson and Suhl[79] may be written

$$\mathbf{E} = \rho_0[\mathbf{J} + a\mathbf{J} \times \mathbf{H} + bH^2 \mathbf{J} + c(\mathbf{J} \cdot \mathbf{H})\mathbf{H} + d\mathsf{T} \mathbf{J}], \qquad \omega\tau < 1. \qquad (8.30)$$

The constants in the above expression are related, to within H^2 terms, to those in (8.13) as follows:

$$\rho_0 = 1/\sigma_0 \qquad\qquad c = -(\gamma - \alpha^2/\sigma_0)\sigma_0$$
$$a = -\alpha/\sigma_0 \qquad\qquad d = -\delta/\sigma_0. \qquad (8.31)$$
$$b = -(\beta + \alpha^2/\sigma_0)/\sigma_0$$

Some authors write the weak-field Hall coefficient, in place of the factor $a\rho_0$, although others are inclined to interpret the Hall effect in a more general manner.[71] In our notation this would give

$$a\rho_0 = -R. \qquad (8.31a)$$

The relationships between the constants in (8.30) and the galvano-magnetic coefficients are similar to those given in (8.18), namely,

$$\rho_0 = \rho_{11}^0, \qquad a = \rho_{123}^0/\rho_0, \qquad b = \rho_{1122}^0/\rho_0, \qquad (8.31b)$$
$$c = 2\rho_{1212}^0/\rho_0, \qquad d = [\rho_{1111}^0 - \rho_{1122}^0 - 2\rho_{1212}^0]/\rho_0.$$

In the case of isotropic materials,

$$d = 0, \qquad b + c = 0. \qquad (8.31c)$$

Higher order terms in H, for Hall effect and for magnetoresistance, have been taken into account by Mason et al.[64] The effect of these terms can be appreciable when the magnetic field is not along a crystallographic axis of symmetry. It turns out that there are two independent constants necessary to describe the second-order terms of the Hall effect (i.e., the terms of the third power in H); and that six constants are required for a complete description of the fourth power terms in H.

Considerable data on the determination of the galvanomagnetic coefficients of germanium and silicon, including contributions by the authors quoted in this section, are available. These will be discussed in the sections dealing specifically with those semiconductors.

---

[79] G. L. Pearson and H. Suhl, *Phys. Rev.* **83**, 768 (1951).

(3) System of point group symmetry $3m$ *or* $\bar{3}m$ *(trigonal system* C_{3v} *or* D_{3d}*).* In this case there are a total of 12 different nonzero components of the tensors ρ_{ik}^0, ρ_{ikl}^0, ρ_{iklm}^0, each tensor requiring respectively 2, 2, and 8 different constants. A detailed study of the coefficients including those for terms up to the fourth power in H has been presented by Juretschke.[80] The third-power terms involve 6 constants, while those of the fourth power in H require 18 constants for their specification. The 12 independent lower order terms and their relation to the corresponding conductivity coefficients are shown below for a Cartesian coordinate system with direction 3 parallel to the threefold axis of the crystal and with the (2,3) plane as one of the three equivalent planes of reflection, i.e., coordinate direction 1 is along one of the three twofold (binary) axes in the case of $\bar{3}m$ systems[81]:

$$\rho_{11}^0 = 1/\sigma_{11}^0, \qquad \rho_{33}^0 = 1/\sigma_{33}^0; \qquad \rho_{123}^0 = -\sigma_{123}^0/\sigma_{11}^{0\,2}, \qquad \rho_{231}^0 = -\sigma_{231}^0/\sigma_{11}^0\,\sigma_{33}^0, \tag{8.32}$$

$$\rho_{1111}^0 = -\sigma_{1111}^0/\sigma_{11}^{0\,2}; \qquad \rho_{1122}^0 = -\sigma_{1122}^0/\sigma_{11}^{0\,2} - \sigma_{231}^{0\,2}/\sigma_{11}^{0\,2}\,\sigma_{33}^0$$

$$\rho_{3333}^0 = -\sigma_{3333}^0/\sigma_{33}^{0\,2}; \qquad \sigma_{1133}^0 = -\sigma_{1133}^0/\sigma_{11}^{0\,2} - \sigma_{123}^{0\,2}/\sigma_{11}^{0\,3}, \tag{8.33}$$

$$\rho_{1123}^0 = -\sigma_{1123}^0/\sigma_{11}^{0\,2}; \qquad \rho_{3311}^0 = -\sigma_{3311}^0/\sigma_{33}^{0\,2} - \sigma_{231}^{0\,2}/\sigma_{11}^0\,\sigma_{33}^{0\,2},$$

$$\rho_{2311}^0 = -\sigma_{2311}^0/\sigma_{11}^0\,\sigma_{33}^0; \qquad \rho_{2323} = -\sigma_{2323}^0/\sigma_{11}^0\,\sigma_{33}^0 + \tfrac{1}{2}\sigma_{123}^0\,\sigma_{231}^0/\sigma_{11}^{0\,2}\,\sigma_{33}^0.$$

The above equalities hold if ρ^0 and σ^0 are interchanged throughout.

The other components of the resistivity and Hall effect tensors, not given in (8.32), are as follows:

$$\rho_{22}^0 = \rho_{11}^0, \qquad \rho_{ik}^0 = 0 \qquad \text{if} \qquad i \neq k, \tag{8.34}$$

$$\rho_{312}^0 = \rho_{231}^0, \qquad \rho_{ikl}^0 = 0 \qquad \text{if} \quad i = k \text{ or } k = l \text{ or } l = i. \tag{8.35}$$

All the components of the magnetoresistance tensor are displayed in the matrix below:

[80] H. J. Juretschke, *Acta Cryst.* 8, 716 (1955).

[81] The statement in Juretschke's[80] article that the plane of (x, z) is one of the three equivalent planes of reflection should be corrected to read the plane of (y, z) [Juretschke, private communication]. The expressions applicable when the (x, z) coordinate plane is a plane of reflection have been derived by Drabble, Groves, and Wolfe. See p. 442 in reference 87.

$$\rho^0_{(ik),(lm)} = \begin{bmatrix} \rho^0_{1,1} & \rho^0_{1,2} & \rho^0_{1,3} & \rho^0_{1,4} & 0 & 0 \\ \rho^0_{1,2} & \rho^0_{1,1} & \rho^0_{1,3} & -\rho^0_{1,4} & 0 & 0 \\ \rho^0_{3,1} & \rho^0_{3,1} & \rho^0_{3,3} & 0 & 0 & 0 \\ \rho^0_{4,1} & -\rho^0_{4,1} & 0 & \rho^0_{4,4} & 0 & 0 \\ 0 & 0 & 0 & 0 & \rho^0_{4,4} & \rho^0_{4,1} \\ 0 & 0 & 0 & 0 & \rho^0_{1,4} & \tfrac{1}{2}(\rho^0_{1,1} - \rho^0_{1,2}) \end{bmatrix} \qquad (8.36)$$

where, as in (8.12c),

$$(11) = 1; \qquad (22) = 2; \qquad (33) = 3;$$
$$(23) = (32) = 4; \qquad (13) = (31) = 5; \qquad (12) = (21) = 6.$$

The above relations have been used by Freedman and Juretschke[82] in an investigation of antimony. All 12 independent components of the resistivity tensor through second power terms in H were measured. A theoretical treatment was then carried out using three-valleyed bands for both valence and conduction bands and energy-independent isotropic relaxation times. The theory contains 9 parameters: three principal mobilities for electrons and three for holes, an angle of tilt of one of the principal axes of the electron energy ellipsoid out of the base plane, a corresponding angle for holes, and the carrier density. The best values of these parameters to fit the experimental data were obtained with the aid of an IBM 650 computer.

The preceding relationships have also been applied to investigations of the galvanomagnetic coefficients of bismuth and of bismuth telluride. Substantial experimental data on bismuth are presented by Okada.[83,84] Theoretical calculations were made by Abeles and Meiboom[85] by approximating the band structure by a many-valley model in which the energy surfaces are approximated by ellipsoids. These are arranged in momentum

---

[82] S. J. Freedman and H. J. Juretschke, Tech. Rept. No. 6, Contract NONR 839(06) (April 15, 1959). Subject report forms part of a Ph.D. thesis presented by S. J. Freedman in the Physics Department of the Polytechnic Institute of Brooklyn. Most of the work has subsequently appeared in print: S. J. Freedman and H. M. Juretschke, *Phys. Rev.* **124**, 1379 (1961).

[83] T. Okada, *J. Phys. Soc. Japan* **11**, 89 (1956).

[84] T. Okada, *J. Phys. Soc. Japan* **12**, 1327 (1957).

[85] B. Abeles and S. Meiboom, *Phys. Rev.* **101**, 544 (1956).

space in configurations appropriate for the symmetry of the crystal. A constant relaxation time is assumed. Low-temperature galvanomagnetic data at intermediate field strengths are also available in a number of publications.[85a, b]

A similar model was used by Coldwell-Horsfall and ter Haar.[86] They, however, choose a relaxation time proportional to $\varepsilon^{-1/2}$, i.e., a constant mean free path. These authors are careful to use the three-dimensional transport equations in calculating the Hall effect. The point is made that, although in the isotropic case with **J** normal to **H** it follows that there is no component of **E** along **H**, the statement is not generally true in the case of anisotropy. For bismuth, with **H** along the binary axis, it is calculated that E in the direction of **H** might amount to the order of 0.1% $|E|$, and should be measurable.

A similar procedure to that used for bismuth was adopted by Drabble and Wolfe for bismuth telluride.[67] Both the conduction[87] and valence[87a] bands are considered, and these authors modify Eqs. (8.32) – (8.36) to provide expressions which are applicable when one of the three equivalent reflection planes of the crystal is coincident with the (x, z) coordinate plane.[81]

Further information on the many-valley model and its application to a number of semiconductors, including a discussion of the results for bismuth telluride, is given in Chapter VIII.

(4) Orthorhombic system (group D_{2h}). For this system, the number of independent components of the resistivity tensors are 3 for the zero-magnetic-field resistivity, 3 for the first power Hall term, 12 for the magnetoresistance terms, and 9 for the H^3 Hall term.[67c]

The lower order galvanomagnetic coefficients are discussed in Kohler's article.[72] However, the number of independent relations for the linear Hall term — namely, 6 as determined from the crystal symmetry — is

---

[85a] R. A. Connell and J. A. Marcus, *Phys. Rev.* **107**, 940 (1957).

[85b] S. Mase and S. Tanuma, *Sci. Repts. Research Insts. Tohoku Univ.* **12**, 35 (1960).

[86] R. Coldwell-Horsfall and D. ter Haar, *Physica* **24**, 848 (1958).

[87] J. R. Drabble, R. D. Groves and R. Wolfe, *Proc. Phys. Soc. (London)* **71**, 430 (1958).

[87a] J. R. Drabble, *Proc. Phys. Soc. (London)* **72**, 380 (1958).

IV.
Experimental Determination of Transport Coefficients in Isothermal Media

MEASUREMENTS ON ISOTROPIC MATERIALS

When the anisotropy of the crystal can be neglected, the transport coefficients are specified if we know the conductivity (or resistivity) and the Hall coefficient as functions of magnetic field. The resistivity is determined with the magnetic field normal to the current — leading to transverse magnetoresistance — and also with **H** parallel to **J** — leading to longitudinal magnetoresistance. Actually, the longitudinal magnetoresistance should vanish if complete isotropy occurs. Thus, the relative smallness of this quantity is an indication as to how well the idealized conditions are realized.

In order to illustrate the contributions of the coefficients discussed above, we shall derive a vector equation for **J(E)**. Let us consider a specimen which may deviate only slightly from isotropy, so that there is a small but nonzero longitudinal magnetoresistance yet the theory for isotropic systems can be used. The procedure is to express the conductivity coefficients of (7.22) in terms of $\sigma_\perp(H)$, the conductivity in a transverse magnetic field and $\sigma_\parallel(H)$, the conductivity in a longitudinal magnetic field.

Thus,

$$\sigma_\perp(H) = (J/E)_{\mathbf{E} \perp \mathbf{H}} = \sigma_H, \qquad (9.1)$$

$$\sigma_\parallel(H) = (J/E)_{\mathbf{E} \parallel \mathbf{H}} = \sigma_H + \gamma_H H^2,$$

and Eq. (7.22) assumes the form

$$\mathbf{J} = \sigma_\perp(H)\mathbf{E} + \alpha_H \, \mathbf{E} \times \mathbf{H} + \frac{\sigma_\parallel(H) - \sigma_\perp(H)}{H^2} \, \mathbf{E} \cdot \mathbf{H}\mathbf{H}. \qquad (9.1a)$$

50

halved as a result of the antisymmetry in electric fie
The Kohler-Onsager relations (2.10) had not yet be
when the article in question was written.

Extensive data on a number of gallium crysta
measurements by Yahia and Marcus[88] at several ten
and at $77\,°K$, the galvanomagnetic properties are
by the phenomenological coefficients discussed.
results indicate an apparent reduction in the crysta
a larger number of independent components are nec
resistivity tensor, $\rho(\mathbf{H})$. It is suggested that this migh
structure of the Fermi surface existing at low temp
where high mobilities are encountered at low tempera
by Jain that additional components in the resistivity
noticeable as a result of the weak-magnetic-field limit

9.

co
the
de
tra
to
re
sr
cc

a
s
a
is
c
r
t

[88] J. Yahia and J. A. Marcus, *Phys. Rev.* **113**, 137 (1959).
[88a] A. L. Jain, *Phys. Rev.* **114**, 1518 (1959).

halved as a result of the antisymmetry in electric field and current indices. The Kohler-Onsager relations (2.10) had not yet been established in 1934 when the article in question was written.

Extensive data on a number of gallium crystals are available from measurements by Yahia and Marcus[88] at several temperatures. At 290°K and at 77°K, the galvanomagnetic properties are adequately described by the phenomenological coefficients discussed. At 4°K, however, results indicate an apparent reduction in the crystal symmetry, so that a larger number of independent components are necessary to specify the resistivity tensor, $\rho(\mathbf{H})$. It is suggested that this might result from a sharp structure of the Fermi surface existing at low temperatures. In cases where high mobilities are encountered at low temperatures, it was noted by Jain that additional components in the resistivity tensor can become noticeable as a result of the weak-magnetic-field limit being exceeded.[88a]

[88] J. Yahia and J. A. Marcus, *Phys. Rev.* **113**, 137 (1959).
[88a] A. L. Jain, *Phys. Rev.* **114**, 1518 (1959).

IV.
Experimental Determination of Transport Coefficients in Isothermal Media

9. MEASUREMENTS ON ISOTROPIC MATERIALS

When the anisotropy of the crystal can be neglected, the transport coefficients are specified if we know the conductivity (or resistivity) and the Hall coefficient as functions of magnetic field. The resistivity is determined with the magnetic field normal to the current — leading to transverse magnetoresistance — and also with $\mathbf{H}$ parallel to $\mathbf{J}$ — leading to longitudinal magnetoresistance. Actually, the longitudinal magneto-resistance should vanish if complete isotropy occurs. Thus, the relative smallness of this quantity is an indication as to how well the idealized conditions are realized.

In order to illustrate the contributions of the coefficients discussed above, we shall derive a vector equation for $\mathbf{J(E)}$. Let us consider a specimen which may deviate only slightly from isotropy, so that there is a small but nonzero longitudinal magnetoresistance yet the theory for isotropic systems can be used. The procedure is to express the conductivity coefficients of (7.22) in terms of $\sigma_\perp(H)$, the conductivity in a transverse magnetic field and $\sigma_\parallel(H)$, the conductivity in a longitudinal magnetic field.

Thus,

$$\sigma_\perp(H) = (J/E)_{\mathbf{E}\perp\mathbf{H}} = \sigma_H, \tag{9.1}$$

$$\sigma_\parallel(H) = (J/E)_{\mathbf{E}\parallel\mathbf{H}} = \sigma_H + \gamma_H H^2,$$

and Eq. (7.22) assumes the form

$$\mathbf{J} = \sigma_\perp(H)\mathbf{E} + \alpha_H\,\mathbf{E}\times\mathbf{H} + \frac{\sigma_\parallel(H) - \sigma_\perp(H)}{H^2}\,\mathbf{E}\cdot\mathbf{HH}. \tag{9.1a}$$

The coefficient $\alpha_H H$ is sometimes referred to as the Hall conductivity, i.e.,

$$\alpha_H H \equiv \sigma^H(H), \tag{9.1b}$$

and with the customary choice of coordinate system

$$\sigma^H(H) \equiv \sigma_{xy}(H). \tag{9.1c}$$

In the case of exact isotropy, $\sigma_\parallel(H) = \sigma_\parallel(0) = \sigma_0$.

The inverted form of (7.22) can be written as follows [cf. (8.30)]:

$$\mathbf{E} = \rho_H \mathbf{J} - R(H)\mathbf{J} \times \mathbf{H} + C(H)\mathbf{J} \cdot \mathbf{HH}. \tag{9.1d}$$

In terms of resistivities in transverse and longitudinal magnetic fields, one has

$$\mathbf{E} = \rho_\perp(H)\mathbf{J} + R(H)\mathbf{H} \times \mathbf{J} + \frac{\rho_\parallel - \rho_\perp}{H^2}\mathbf{J} \cdot \mathbf{HH}. \tag{9.1e}$$

The term $R(H)$ is the Hall coefficient, and $R(H)H$ is the Hall resistivity;

$$R(H)H = \rho^H(H),$$

$$= \rho_{yx}(H) \quad \text{if} \quad \mathbf{H} \equiv (0, 0, H). \tag{9.1f}$$

The latter equality applies for the customary choice of coordinate axes.

The above equations are similar to those given by Jan.[88b] They are mathematically exact in H, and are not expressions derived from expansions valid to certain powers in H.

The relations between the conductivities and resistivities are as follows:

$$\sigma_\perp(H) = \frac{\rho_\perp(H)}{\rho_\perp{}^2(H) + [R(H)H]^2}, \quad \sigma_\parallel(H) = \frac{1}{\rho_\parallel(H)}, \tag{9.1g}$$

$$\alpha_H = \frac{R(H)}{\rho_\perp{}^2(H) + [R(H)H]^2}.$$

The transverse relations include contributions from the Hall effect. In determining the Hall coefficient, the common procedure is for $\mathbf{J}$ and $\mathbf{H}$

[88b] See pp. 15–17 of reference 1. The meaning of our $\sigma_\perp$ is identical with that of Jan's $\gamma_\perp$.

to be normal to each other, and the Hall field is then measured in a direction perpendicular to each. Variations of these phenomena, which include magnetoconductivity, Corbino magnetoresistance, and planar Hall effect, will be discussed later.

a. Discussion of Transverse Magnetoresistance and Hall Effects

Consider $\mathbf{H} = (0, 0, H)$ and the current $\mathbf{J}$ to exist in the x-direction in the isothermal solid. Then relations (1.1) and (2.4) become

$$J_x = \sigma_{xx}(H)E_x + \sigma_{xy}(H)E_y + \sigma_{xz}(H)E_z, \qquad (9.2)$$

$$0 = \sigma_{yx}(H)E_x + \sigma_{yy}(H)E_y + \sigma_{yz}(H)E_z, \qquad H \equiv H_z, \qquad (9.3)$$

$$0 = \sigma_{zx}(H)E_x + \sigma_{zy}(H)E_y + \sigma_{zz}(H)E_z \qquad (9.4)$$

and

$$E_x = \rho_{xx}(H)J_x, \qquad E_y = \rho_{yx}(H)J_x, \qquad E_z = \rho_{zx}(H)J_x. \qquad (9.4a)$$

For the isotropic case, relation (3.2) requires that E_z vanish.[89] Hence, using the symmetry expressed by (3.1), we may write

$$J_x = \sigma_{xx}(H)E_x + \sigma_{xy}(H)E_y,$$

$$0 = -\sigma_{xy}(H)E_x + \sigma_{xx}(H)E_y, \qquad J \equiv J_x \qquad (9.5)$$

and

$$E_x = \rho_{xx}(H)J_x, \qquad E_y = \rho_{yx}(H)J_x. \qquad (9.6)$$

In terms of the fields and current shown above, the Hall coefficient, the conductivity, and the magnetoresistance are given by

$$R_H = E_y/J_x H, \qquad (9.7)$$

$$\sigma(H) = J_x/E_x, \qquad (9.8)$$

$$\Delta\rho/\rho_0 = [\rho(H) - \rho(0)]/\rho_0 = [E_x(H)/E_x(0)] - 1, \qquad J_x = \text{const.} \qquad (9.9)$$

---

[89] It is important to note that according to (9.2)–(9.4), E_z will vanish if and only if $\sigma_{yx}(H)\sigma_{zy}(H) - \sigma_{zx}(H)\sigma_{yy}(H) = 0$. Therefore the condition $J_y = J_z = 0$ is not sufficient to allow use of the two-dimensional relations (9.5) in the case of anisotropic media. This point, which has led to difficulties in the literature, is emphasized by Coldwell-Horsfall and ter Haar.[86]

In all of the above definitions, the boundary conditions are

$$J_y = \partial T/\partial x = \partial T/\partial y = 0, \qquad \mathbf{H} = (0, 0, H) \qquad (9.10)$$

along with the obvious fact, alluded to in connection with (9.5), that

$$E_z = J_z = \partial T/\partial z = 0. \qquad (9.11)$$

The requirement that $\partial T/\partial y$ vanish is imposed by our consideration of isothermal phenomena. It is possible, of course, to define adiabatic phenomena.[90] These are discussed briefly in Section 29. Then the condition that $\partial T/\partial y$ vanish is usually replaced by the requirement that the transverse heat current q_y be zero. A great simplification results in the transport equations, however, whenever the isothermal approximation can

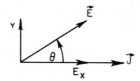

FIG. 3.   Illustration of Hall angle.

be used. As will be shown later, such a treatment is fairly good for a number of semiconductors, even when measurements are taken under conditions which are favorable to the adiabatic situation.

From (9.5) and (9.6) it follows that for isotropic systems with $\mathbf{H} = (0, 0, H)$

$$R_H = \frac{\rho_{yx}(H)}{H} = \frac{\sigma_{xy}(H)}{H[\sigma_{xx}{}^2(H) + \sigma_{xy}{}^2(H)]}, \qquad (9.12)$$

$$\sigma(H) = \frac{1}{\rho_{xx}(H)} = \frac{\sigma_{xx}{}^2(H) + \sigma_{xy}{}^2(H)}{\sigma_{xx}(H)}, \qquad (9.13)$$

$$\Delta\rho/\rho_0 = \left[\frac{\rho_{xx}(H)}{\rho_{xx}(0)}\right] - 1 = \frac{\sigma_{xx}(H)\sigma_{xx}(0)}{\sigma_{xx}{}^2(H) + \sigma_{xy}{}^2(H)} - 1. \qquad (9.14)$$

---

[90] See p. 6 of reference 1.

Since the Hall phenomenon is essentially a rotation of the electric field vector by the magnetic field, many authors have introduced a Hall angle[91] (Fig. 3), defined as

$$\tan \theta = E_y/E_x, \qquad \mathbf{H} = (0, 0, H). \tag{9.15}$$

Although the Hall angle is most frequently employed in the weak-magnetic-field region, we shall present general equations below, which are valid for arbitrary values of H. These relations are

$$\tan \theta = \rho_{yx}(H)/\rho_{xx}(H) = \sigma_{xy}(H)/\sigma_{xx}(H), \qquad \mathbf{H} = (0, 0, H). \tag{9.16}$$

From (9.12) and (9.13) we see that

$$\tan \theta = R_H \sigma(H) H. \tag{9.17}$$

Further relations involving the Hall angle are discussed in Section 12d.

b. Experimental Determinations of Hall Coefficient and Magnetoresistance

We shall omit a discussion of measurement techniques used in the laboratory. Details can be found in a number of textbooks and articles, several of which are referenced here.[79,92−95] The specimens are usually cut in the form of rectangular parallelepipeds or in the bridge shape.[94,96] The latter design has the advantage of providing large contact areas with a reasonably small disturbance of the electric fields to be measured.

When, however, magnetoresistance is to be determined in high-mobility materials (that is, where the Hall angle is relatively large), the bridge samples with lateral arms may not be satisfactory. Even such a small amount of disturbance of the Hall field cannot be tolerated. In

[91] See, for example, p. 209 of reference 32; p. 16 of reference 1.
[92] I. Estermann and A. Foner, *Phys. Rev.* **79**, 365 (1950).
[93] E. H. Putley, "The Hall Effect and Related Phenomena," Butterworths, London, 1960.
[93a] Reference 1, pp. 17–25.
[94] W. C. Dunlap, "An Introduction to Semiconductors," pp. 178–194. Wiley, New York, 1957.
[95] O. Lindberg, *Proc. I. R. E.* **40**, 1414 (1952).
[96] P. P. Debye and E. M. Conwell, *Phys. Rev.* **93**, 693 (1954).

those cases it is desirable to use only carefully fashioned point contacts for the potential probes. This problem is discussed in more detail later.

In order to take advantage of the simplifications of rectangular geometry it is essential that the current lines be parallel and that the electric field which is being measured to determine the Hall effect be normal to these lines. Misalignment in the Hall potential probes will add an "IR drop" to the transverse voltage. Since this spurious voltage at weak magnetic fields is independent of H but proportional to J_x, it is usually eliminated by averaging data for opposite directions of current and of magnetic field. Many problems are associated with satisfying the boundary conditions (9.10). These are discussed in subsequent paragraphs in this section.

It is also possible to determine certain galvanomagnetic coefficients on samples of various other shapes, for example, those of circular symmetry,[93a] of infinite planes,[97] and of other shapes,[97a] including arbitrary two-dimensional geometry.[98,99] By use of a "clover-shaped" sample, the influence of the contacts can be reduced considerably.[99] Such a design has several advantages over the bridge shape, such as improved heat dissipation and mechanical strength. By cutting discs with planes normal to the appropriate directions in the crystal, one can determine the directional resistivities of anisotropic conductors, as was shown by Hornstra and van der Pauw.[99a] The disk technique has subsequently been extended by van der Pauw[99b] to provide means for determining all the components of the zero-magnetic-field resistivity tensor and also those of the weak-field Hall tensor in an anisotropic solid.[99b] In the most general case, where the solid has no elements of symmetry, the six independent resistivity constants are obtained from the sheet resistivites, at zero magnetic field, of six plane-parallel samples through six linear equations. The nine constants associated with the Hall effect are established through measurements on three samples, combined with three different orienta-

[97] J. La Plume, *L'Onde Elec.* **35**, 113 (1955); M. Wintenberger, *Compt. rend. acad. sci. (Paris)* **246**, 2366 (1958).

[97a] R. Jaggi and R. Sommerhalder, *Helv. Phys. Acta* **32**, 167 (1959).

[98] R. M. Broudy, *J. Appl. Phys.* **29**, 853 (1958).

[99] L. J. van der Pauw, *Philips Research Repts.* **13**, 1 (1958).

[99a] J. Hornstra and L. J. van der Pauw, *J. Electronics and Control* **7**, 169 (1959).

[99b] L. J. van der Pauw, *Philips Research Repts.* **16**, 187 (1961).

tions of the magnetic field. The measurement of weak-field magneto-resistance coefficients of cubic materials, using two flat samples of arbitrary shape, is discussed by Matthews and Doherty.[99c]

For determining resistivities alone, the four-point probe techniques, discussed by Valdes[99d] and by Uhlir,[99e] are sometimes employed. Application to anisotropic media has been discussed by Airapetyants and Bresler.[99f]

(1) Effect of transverse current on Hall voltage. It is apparent that a shorting of the Hall field by any means such as area contacts, inhomogeneous sections in the material, or external circuitry will reduce the Hall voltage. When area contacts are used at the ends, the length of the specimen must be substantial compared to the width (the magnetic field vector being along the *thickness* of the parallelepiped) so that the measured Hall voltage is not reduced because of the shorting at the ends. Another possibility would be to use point contacts at the ends. Such an arrangement however will produce nonparallel current lines near the ends, and the specimen will still need to be long in order to assume parallel current lines in the neighborhood of the Hall probes. The effects of end-contact shorting where the Hall angle is small have been studied by Isenberg *et. al.,*[100] Volger,[101] and others. The relative decrease in the measured Hall voltage is shown in Fig. 4.

Volger also uses his results to examine aspects of certain macroscopic inhomogeneities in the specimens. Analysis of geometries other than rectangular was made by Frank[102] who also examined the effects of pin contacts for current electrodes. The case of a nonuniform magnetic field was included in the investigations of Flanagan *et al.*[103] It is interesting to note that for a flat-topped bell-shaped magnetic field variation in the

---

[99c] H. Matthews and W. R. Doherty, *J. Electronics and Control* **10**, 273 (1961).
[99d] L. B. Valdes, *Proc. I. R. E.* **42**, 420 (1954).
[99e] A. Uhlir, *Bell System Tech. J.* **34**, 105 (1955).
[99f] S. V. Airapetyants and M. S. Bresler, *Fiz. Tverd. Tela* **1**, 152 (1959) [translation: *Soviet Phys. — Solid State* **1**, 134 (1959)].
[100] I. Isenberg, B. R. Russel, and R. F. Greene, *Rev. Sci. Instr.* **19**, 685 (1948).
[101] J. Volger, *Phys. Rev.* **79**, 1023 (1950).
[102] V. Frank, *Appl. Sci. Research* **B3**, 129 (1953).
[103] W. F. Flanagan, P. A. Flinn, and B. L. Averbach, *Rev. Sci. Instr.* **25**, 593 (1954); **26**, 233 (1955).

x-direction, with H reduced to approximately 20% at the contacted ends of the specimen, the V_m/V_H was found to be 0.74 for a specimen with $L/W = 1.5$, as compared to 0.85 when the magnetic field is uniform.

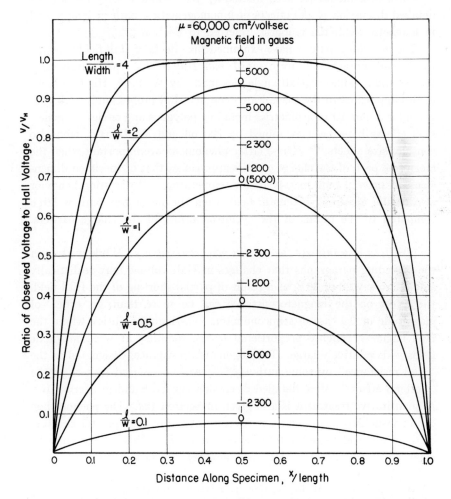

FIG. 4. Effect on Hall voltage, as a function of position along specimen, of transverse currents caused by electrode shorting at ends. Curves are drawn for the case of small Hall angles $(H \sim 0)$ for various length-width ratios. At larger Hall angles (increased magnetic fields) the reduction in Hall voltage is less (larger V/V_H), as is evidenced by the points calculated for these cases when probes are located at
$$x/l = 0.5.$$

Further information on the effects of inhomogeneous magnetic fields is available in the article by Koppe and Bryan.[104] These authors also discuss the effects of macroscopic inhomogeneities in the samples. The special case of porous media has been treated by Juretschke *et al.*[105] For a more detailed discussion of the effects of inhomogeneities, both in sample and in magnetic field, the reader is referred to Section 27.

The preceding articles have examined the effects of Hall field shorting by the end contacts only for cases of *small Hall angles*. An analysis valid for arbitrary values of Hall angle was made by Wick.[106] His treatment is also applicable to the case of area-contact Hall probes, and results are given for a number of geometries including polygons and circles. Geometrical effects have been examined by Barron and MacDonald, who also consider size effects.[106a] These latter phenomena are important when the mean free path of the charge carriers approaches that of specimen dimensions, as in very pure metals at low temperatures. Interesting behavior also results at strong magnetic field when the mean free path is large compared to the radius of the cyclotron orbits of the charge carriers.

(2) Effect of transverse currents on magnetoresistance. While we saw in the preceding paragraphs that changes in Hall voltage may realistically amount to say 20 or 30% as a result of partial shorting of the Hall field, the effect on the magnetoresistance can be more than an order of magnitude in the case of semiconductors with high mobilities, where the Hall angle — roughly proportional to the mobility at weak magnetic fields — is relatively large. The augmented resistance, designated as the "Hall resistance" by some authors,[106,107] will be referred to here as the "Corbino effect." More detailed discussion can be found in Section 10b. A quantitative treatment is also given in Section 12d. The phenomenon can be visualized qualitatively in several ways. For example, the shorting of the Hall field causes a transverse current J_y. This current may be regarded as producing a Hall field along J_x in such a direction as to

---

[104] H. Koppe and J. M. Bryan, *Can. J. Phys.* **29**, 274 (1951).

[105] H. J. Juretschke, R. Landauer, and J. A. Swanson, *J. App. Phys.* **27**, 839 (1956); E. Goldin and H. J. Juretschke, *Trans. AIME* **212**, 357 (1958).

[106] R. F. Wick, *J. Appl. Phys.* **25**, 741 (1954).

[106a] T. H. K. Barron and D. K. C. MacDonald, *Physica* **24** (Kamerlingh Onnes Conference, Leiden), S102 (1958).

[107] J. R. Drabble and R. Wolfe, *J. Electronics and Control* **3**, 259 (1957).

decrease J_x — or increase E_x, depending whether the driving power is of constant voltage or of constant current — and therefore being reflected as an increase in resistance. On the other hand, the result may be regarded as a more general magnetoresistance, where the boundary condition $J_y = 0$ is relaxed and the general form of (9.5) is applied. It will be seen later that in the limiting case where E_y is zero, the "magnetoresistance" in first approximation increases proportional to H^2 and does not saturate. This behavior can be anticipated from the simple physical picture presented in Section 4b. Without a Hall field to cancel the Lorentz force, the charge carriers will be deflected at angles increasing with H, leading to a monotonic increase in resistance with magnetic field.

A mathematical treatment of the effect of shorting at the end contacts on magnetoresistance is presented by Drabble and Wolfe, and results are given for length/width ratios greater than two.[107] The results illustrate quite vividly the problem that arises when the Hall angle becomes appreciable. Experimental findings are given by Broom for GaAs and InSb.[108] Frederikse and Hosler discuss the "geometry effect" in InSb, and also point out the seriousness of having inhomogeneities in the material.[109]

The measurements show that when measuring magnetoresistance in a high-mobility semiconductor, all lateral contacts should be extremely minute. Welded platinum wires of 3-mil diameter appeared permissible. On the other hand, soldered probes of 0.25-mm diameter, or bridge-type arms were not satisfactory.

(3) *Nongeometrical causes of transverse currents.* An important consideration here is the effect of inhomogeneities in impurity concentrations. This matter is examined in considerable detail in Section 27. It is seen that large influences on the galvanomagnetic effects can result from spatial variations in carrier density. Either random fluctuations or monotonic gradients can seriously affect the field dependence of the magnetoresistance. A contributing factor which occurs for most nonuniformities is a variation in current distribution in the specimen with magnetic field. This rearrangement of the flow lines results from the boundary conditions

[108] R. F. Broom, *Proc. Phys. Soc.* (*London*) **71**, 500 (1958).
[109] H. P. R. Frederikse and W. R. Hosler, *Phys. Rev.* **108**, 1136 (1957).

and the fact that **E** and **J** are, respectively, lamellar and solenoidal vector point functions.

In view of the complications that occur, it behooves the investigator to check carefully the homogeneity of the specimens by measuring potentials between various contacting points. Other techniques such as resistivity probing, thermoelectric probing[94] and photoconductive measurements with a traveling light spot are often employed. The latter method is often used to measure diffusion lengths of nonequilibrium charge carriers.[110–112] An unnatural variation of the photovoltage with position of the light spot could be indicative of nonuniformity in the specimens.[112a]

Analyses of *bulk* photovoltaic phenomena (changes in impurity concentration occur over distances large compared with nonequilibrium charge carrier diffusion lengths) and of *barrier-layer* photovoltaic phenomena (abrupt changes in impurity density) have been made by Tauc.[113] He also outlines a compensation method, due to Frank,[114] for measuring the bulk photovoltage, which provides a highly sensitive method for detection of inhomogeneities in a semiconductor. Additional investigations of bulk photoeffects in inhomogeneous semiconductors, including phenomena at an illuminated *p-n* junction, were done by Cox.[114a] Experimental data, taken on germanium filaments, are also supplied.

Thus far, we have dealt principally with transport by a single charge carrier, choosing to introduce multiband contributions later. At this point, however, it is important to consider the simultaneous presence of electrons and holes — as, for example, in intrinsic semiconductors. The boundary condition that J_y vanish does not imply that the electron and hole currents are individually zero, but rather that

$$j_y^e + j_y^h = 0. \qquad (9.18)$$

In the magnetic field, both holes and electrons are directed to the same side of the specimen, producing concentration gradients and diffusion

[110] F. S. Goucher, *Phys. Rev.* **81**, 475 (1951).

[111] L. B. Valdes, *Proc. I. R. E.* **40**, 1420 (1952).

[112] T. S. Moss, *Proc. Phys. Soc. (London)* **B66**, 993 (1953).

[112a] J. Arthur, W. Bardsley, A. Gibson, and C. Hogarth, *Proc. Phys. Soc. (London)* **B68**, 121 (1955).

[113] Jan Tauc, *Revs. Modern Phys.* **29**, 308 (1957).

[114] H. Frank, *Czechoslov. J. Phys.* **6**, 433 (1956).

[114a] C. D. Cox, *Can. J. Phys.* **38**, 1328 (1960).

currents. The generation and recombination of carriers in the bulk may often be neglected and one can consider hole-electron pairs to be continuously generated at one surface and continuously recombined at the other. A treatment of galvanomagnetic properties must therefore include a description of these diffusion processes. Additional parameters of interest are diffusion constants, sample width, lifetime of excess carriers in the bulk, and surface recombination velocities.

An investigation of these phenomena was begun by Welker[115] after he noticed a frequency effect in ac Hall measurements[116] on mixed (i.e., both electrons and holes are present) semiconductors. This behavior comes about as a result of the hole-electron accumulations no longer being able to follow the oscillations of the applied field.

When the lifetime of the excess carriers is very low, their concentrations are everywhere near equilibrium and therefore concentration gradients and diffusion currents are not significant. The effect is largest in the case of infinite lifetimes. This example has been considered by Fowler.[117]

Further analyses of the problem have been given by Landauer and Swanson[118] and by Banbury et al.[119] Explicit results are available for the magnitudes of the corrections to the Hall fields for most cases of interest. Another complication is the fact that the measured transverse potentials can be affected by the nature of the probes. In many cases rectifying barriers will exist at the contacts and floating potentials[120] will be measured along with the other contributions to the Hall voltage.

The prominence of the effects discussed above is decreased when the departures of the charge carrier concentrations from equilibrium are reduced, as can be accomplished by increasing surface recombination rates. Thus the surfaces of the specimens should be abraded rather than etched. Attempts should also be made to make ohmic contacts at the voltage and current probes. This usually requires a specific treatment

115 H. Welker, *Z. Naturforsch.* **6a**, 184 (1951).

116 H. Welker, *L'Onde Elec.* **30**, 309 (1950).

117 R. H. Fowler, "Statistical Mechanics," p. 428, Cambridge Univ. Press, Cambridge, 1936.

118 R. Landauer and J. Swanson, *Phys. Rev.* **91**, 555 (1953).

119 P. C. Banbury, H. K. Kenisch, and A. Many, *Proc. Phys. Soc. (London)* **A66**, 753 (1953).

120 J. Bardeen, *Bell System Tech. J.* **29**, 469 (1950).

for each type semiconductor. Certain general procedures have been described by Waltz[121] and the characteristics of certain metal contacts on germanium have been given by Bocciarelli.[122] Thermocompression bonding techniques have been described by Anderson et al.[123] In many cases useful information is given in the sections on "Experimental Details" in articles dealing with measurements of electrical properties of given semiconductors.[124–126a]

The careful investigator will usually repeat the galvanomagnetic measurements for several different surface conditions, including the extremes of sand blasting and etching.[126] Checks between symmetrical pairs of contacts are also desirable. If all of these operations reveal negligible differences, then it is likely that the effects that have just been discussed are not significant.

Another important phenomenon which can usually be detected when measurements are taken under different surface conditions is that of surface conduction. The existence of such processes can lead to serious errors in the determination of galvanomagnetic coefficients.[94,127]

When measuring high-lifetime materials, it is desirable to take precautions to ensure that errors are not introduced through occurrence of minority carrier injection at the current contacts. If possible, all voltage probes should be located well over a diffusion length from these contacts.

---

[121] M. C. Waltz, *Bell Lab. Record* **33**, 260 (1955).

[122] C. V. Bocciarelli, *Physica* **20**, 1020 (1954).

[123] O. Anderson, H. Christensen, and P. Andreatch, *J. Appl. Phys.* **28**, 923 (1957).

[124] For germanium, see for example: J. R. Haynes and W. Shockley, *Phys. Rev.* **81**, 835 (1951); F. J. Morin and J. P. Maita, *ibid.* **94**, 1525 (1954); W. C. Dunlap, Jr., *ibid.* **96**, 40, (1954); C. Herring, T. Geballe, and J. Kunzler, *ibid.* **111**, 36 (1958).

[125] For silicon, see, for example: F. J. Morin and J. P. Maita, *Phys. Rev.* **96**, 28 (1954); G. W. Ludwig and R. L. Watters, *ibid.* **101**, 1699 (1956); Donald Long, *ibid.* **107**, 672 (1957); A. Gorodetskii, V. Mel'nik, and I. Mel'nik, *Fiz. Tverd. Tela* **1**, 173 (1959) [translation: *Soviet Phys.-Solid State* **1**, 153 (1959)].

[126] E. H. Putley and W. H. Mitchell, *Proc. Phys. Soc.* (*London*) **72**, 193 (1958).

[126a] For certain III–V compounds, see, for example: (InP) W. Reynolds, M. Lilburne, and R. Dell, *Proc. Phys. Soc.* (*London*) **71**, 416 (1958); (GaAs) J. M. Whelan and G. H. Wheatley, *Phys. and Chem. Solids* **6**, 169 (1958); R. K. Willardson, *J. Appl. Phys.* **30**, 1158(1959); (AlSb) H.-J. Henkel, *Z. Metallk.* **50**, 51 (1959).

[127] See, for example, the results of Frederikse et al.: H. P. R. Frederikse, W. R. Hosler, and D. E. Roberts, *Phys. Rev.* **103**, 67 (1956).

Another precaution is to maintain low current densities at the contacts. As a matter of fact, the careful experimentalist will determine galvanomagnetic voltages as a function of specimen current, generally over ranges of 1 or 2 decades. If the voltages are not linear with the currents, then the reason must be ascertained. Noticeable heating of the specimen must of course be avoided. In addition, the electric field must not be so high that the specimen becomes non-ohmic. This happens when the charge carrier receives more power from the field than it can dissipate readily by the usual interaction with the lattice. Such a situation is referred to as the "hot-carrier case." Another non-ohmic phenomenon is charge carrier multiplication through avalanche or breakdown processes. These effects are discussed briefly in Section 32. In most semiconductors they are not encountered at electric fields low enough to preclude heating, except at temperatures of liquid helium.

Hunter et al.[127a] have discussed a scheme for determining charge-carrier lifetimes from the changes in Hall coefficient produced by deviations in carrier concentration from equilibrium. It was suggested that the method may be of especial advantage in measuring very short lifetimes, i.e., those of the order of 0.1 μ sec.

One may expect that the influence of transverse diffusion currents will be especially great on the magnetoresistance effect. This premise has been verified by the experiments done on the "magnetic barrier layer" phenomena. In these experiments, dissymmetry is created by using different surface treatments on the two sides of the specimen normal to the Hall field.[128] The roughened surface (Fig. 5) has a high recombination velocity s, while the other surface is etched to produce low s. Thus, for a preferred direction of current, recombination is facilitated. With germanium, resistance ratios of the order of 10 were readily observed for magnetic fields of 10 kgauss.

The effects of nonequilibrium carrier concentrations on galvanomagnetic and thermomagnetic effects in semiconductors have been studied

---

[127a] L. Hunter, E. Huibregtse, and R. Anderson, Phys. Rev. 91, 1315 (1953).

[128] See E. Weisshaar and H. Welker, Z. Naturforsch. 8a, 681 (1953); 9a, 184 (1954); O. Madelung, Naturwissenschaften 42, 406 (1955); O. Madelung, L. Tewordt, and H. Welker, Z. Naturforsch. 10a, 476 (1955); E. Weisshaar, Z. Naturforsch. 10a, 488 (1955); T. S. Moss in "Semiconductors and Phosphors" (M. Schön and H. Welker, eds.), p. 109. Interscience, New York, 1958.

quite generally by Pikus. Both the cases of weak magnetic fields[129] and strong magnetic fields[129a] are included. The expression for weak-field

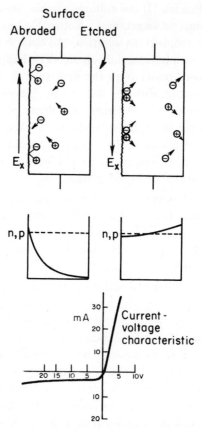

FIG. 5. Principle of the magnetic barrier layer. The abraded surface has a high recombination velocity, facilitating recombination of electrons and holes. Thus, for a current direction such that the charge carriers are deflected toward the abraded surface, the carrier concentration is impoverished and the current is reduced (after Madelung[128]).

[129] G. E. Pikus, *J. Tech. Phys. U.S.S.R.* **26**, 22 (1956) [translation: *Soviet Phys.-Tech. Phys.* **1**, 17 (1956)].

[129a] G. E. Pikus, *J. Tech. Phys. U.S.S.R.* **26**, 36 (1956) [translation: *Soviet Phys.-Tech. Phys.* **1**, 32 (1956)].

magnetoresistance includes linear terms in H if the surface recombination effects are different on the two surfaces normal to the Hall field. If the width of the sample is small compared to a diffusion length, the linear term may become relatively large at weak magnetic fields.

The influence of nonequilibrium charge carrier distributions on thermoelectric and thermomagnetic effects is also considered by Pikus. The effects include electrical resistance in a temperature gradient, the Ettingshausen effect, and thermal conduction by electrons and by phonons. A discussion is also given of the measurement of thermoelectric power by point probes and how the results can depend on the radius of the tip of the probe due to a buildup of excess charge carriers at the point contact due to a large temperature gradient. This problem has been investigated both theoretically and experimentally by Tauc and Trousil.[129b] Additional discussion of nonisothermal effects is given in Section 29.

The large effects on magnetoresistance resulting from assymmetry in surface recombination rates in intrinsic semiconductors has been examined by several investigators[129c] as a means for measuring surface recombination velocities and bulk lifetimes. Under certain conditions, quantitative agreement with results of other measurement techniques was obtained.

Another method for obtaining magnetoresistance data under the conditions of zero Hall field is to measure a mixed semiconductor (i.e., both electrons and holes are present) at the Hall effect null. In many p-type materials it is possible to choose a temperature and a magnetic field H_1 such that in Eq. (9.5) the absolute values of

$$\overset{\text{electrons}}{\sigma_{xy}(H_1)} = \overset{\text{holes}}{\sigma_{xy}(H_1)}. \tag{9.18}$$

Under these conditions E_y vanishes, and if $\sigma_\infty{}^e = \sigma_\infty{}^h$, the magnetoresistance will fail to saturate. For the more general case where $\sigma_\infty{}^e \neq \sigma_\infty{}^h$, consult the equations given in Section 16.

129b J. Tauc and Z. Trousil, *Czechoslov. J. Phys.* **3**, 120 (1953). See also Section 7 of reference 113 and literature cited therein; J. Tauc, *Izvest. Akad. Nauk S.S.S.R.* **20**, 1479 (1956) [translated by Columbia Technical Translations: Ia. Tauts, *Bull. Acad. Sci. U.S.S.R. (Phys. Ser.)* **20**, No. 12b, 1357 (1956)].

129c See, for example: S. A. Poltinnikov and L. S. Stil'bans, *J. Tech. Phys. U.S.S.R.* **27**, 30 (1957) [translation: *Soviet Phys. — Tech. Phys.* **2**, 23 (1957)]. O. V. Sorokin, *J. Tech. Phys. U.S.S.R.* **27**, 2774 (1957) [translation: *Soviet Phys. — Tech. Phys.* **2**, 2572 (1957)]. A Rzhanov, I. Arkhipova, and V. Bidulia, *J. Tech. Phys. U.S.S.R.* **28**, 1051 (1958) [translation: *Soviet Phys. — Tech. Phys.* **3**, 978 (1958)].

(4) *Temperature gradients.* The interpretation of galvanomagnetic data in terms of fundamental parameters of the semiconductor is greatly simplified if isothermal conditions are assumed. However, this state of affairs will, for ordinary measurement techniques, exist precisely only for materials with very special characteristics — as can be seen from Eqs. (3.5). The other possibility of achieving isothermal environment is an experimental setup involving complicated equipment for adding or removing heat from various faces of the specimen so as to reduce the temperature gradients. For these reasons, many investigators have resorted to the use of ac measurements. These usually involve expensive instrumentation equipment. A promising alternative is the Dauphinee-Mooser scheme in which square wave currents of alternating polarity are produced by a special chopper.[130] This arrangement combines the desirable features of both the dc and the ac techniques.

In dc measurements, nonisothermal contributions can arise from thermoelectric and thermomagnetic effects. These are sometimes considered separately as follows:

(i) *Peltier effect:* This phenomen is associated with heat transport across a junction, and it therefore causes a temperature gradient to exist along the sample in which there is an electric current. The Peltier effect occurs because of a nonzero differential thermoelectric power between the sample and the metal contacts.

(ii) *Nernst effect* (transverse): A longitudinal temperature gradient or heat current gives rise to a transverse electric field in a crossed magnetic field. Designation of this phenomenon by *Nernst* effect is used by a number of authors,[3, 31, 46, 61, 131 − 134] although others prefer the term *Ettingshausen-Nernst.*[90, 135, 135a] The situation is complicated by the fact that a longitudinal temperature gradient due to a longitudinal current in a transverse magnetic field is also known as the Nernst effect.

[130] T. M. Dauphinee and E. Mooser, *Rev. Sci. Instr.* **26**, 660 (1955).

[131] R. Fieschi, S. de Groot, and P. Mazur, *Physica* **20**, 259 (1954). These authors use the term *Ettingshausen-Nernst* to designate the thermoelectric power in a magnetic field.

[132] See p. 60 of the article by O. Madelung in "Handbuch der Physik" (S. Flügge, ed.), Vol. 20, p. 1. Springer, Berlin, 1957.

[133] See p. 230 of the article by Blatt.[44]

[134] P. J. Price, *Phys. Rev.* **102**, 1245 (1956).

[135] R. G. Chambers, *Proc. Phys. Soc. (London)* **A65**, 903 (1952).

[135a] Reference 9, p. 209.

(iii) *Righi-Leduc effect:* This designation refers to the transverse temperature gradient resulting from a longitudinal temperature gradient, or heat current, in a crossed magnetic field.

(iv) *Ettingshausen effect:* In this case, a longitudinal electric current produces a transverse temperature gradient in a crossed magnetic field.

Both (iii) and (iv) will produce spurious Hall voltages because of the differential thermoelectric power of the specimen against the Hall probe materials. This contribution could be minimized by making the Hall leads of the same material as the specimen; but such a procedure is hardly feasible in the case of semiconductors.

In general, measurements are taken for both directions of magnetic field and of sample current. In this way, some of the spurious effects can be reduced.[95] A point of caution should be injected, however, inasmuch as there is a tendency among some experimenters to assume that since the Nernst and the Righi-Leduc phenomena depend on temperature gradients, they will remain unchanged with reversal of the electric current. This is the state of affairs if the source of the thermal gradients is, for example, nonelectrical, or results from nonuniform joule heating either in the specimen or at the end contacts. Any contribution from the *Peltier* effect, or related irreversible phenomena, will, on the other hand, change sign upon reversal of the electric current.

Other safeguards involve the use of isothermal baths for the specimen and of observing whether there are discernible time lags in the approach to the steady state voltage as the current is reversed. These would be evidence of a reversal in thermal gradients. The magnetic field is usually reversed by switching the polarity of the dc into the electromagnet. It has been found, however, that unless demagnetization procedures were used, differences in $|\mathbf{H}|$ of about 2% existed after such a reversal in a 12-inch magnet.[136] Hence for precise measurements, the magnitude of $\mathbf{H}$ is continuously monitored by a nuclear magnetic resonance gaussmeter. Upon reversal of the magnet current, an adjustment is made to maintain $|\mathbf{H}|$ unchanged.

An important question is when are differences between isothermal and adiabatic galvanomagnetic coefficients significant? This matter is discussed in Section 29, where it is seen that an important consideration

---

[136] R. T. Bate, Unpublished findings at the Battelle Memorial Institute.

is the "thermoelectric figure of merit" Z^*, defined in terms of thermo-electric power, temperature, thermal conductivity, and electrical resistivity as follows:

$$Z^* \equiv \alpha^2 \, T / \kappa \rho. \tag{9.19}$$

This point was recognized by Chambers[135] who showed that expressions for adiabatic effects simplified considerably when the square of the thermoelectric power was much smaller than the Lorenz number.

In view of (9.19) it appears likely that in materials with the diamond lattice or zincblende structure, where the lattice contribution to κ is relatively large, the corrections to the isothermal equations for specimens measured under adiabatic conditions may be relatively small, at least in the weak-magnetic-field region. This was found to be the case for the Hall coefficient according to calculations by Stil'bans[137] and by Johnson and Shipley.[138] In the latter article, the results for materials such as silicon and germanium showed differences well under 1% for a wide variation of temperatures and carrier concentrations.

The problem is much more complicated when the weak magnetic field approximation is not applicable, for then expansions utilizing powers up to H^2 are no longer adequate. The transport integrals must be evaluated exactly. In addition, various product terms occur which cannot be neglected. For this reason, certain investigators have carried out experiments on high-mobility semiconductors under the conditions that E_y and $\partial T / \partial y$ vanish, as is achieved with the Corbino disk, rather than for conditions such that J_y and q_y vanish.[139]

10. Other "Hall" and Magnetoresistance Phenomena

a. Various Hall Phenomena

(1) Quadratic "Hall" effect. Discussions of quadratic contributions to the Hall effect can be found in early articles by Kohler[140] and by

---

[137] L. S. Stil'bans, *J. Tech. Phys. USSR* **22**, 77 (1952).

[138] V. A. Johnson and F. M. Shipley, *Phys. Rev.* **90**, 523 (1953).

[139] A. C. Beer, J. A. Armstrong, and I. N. Greenberg, *Phys. Rev.* **107**, 1506 (1957)

[140] M. Kohler, *Ann. Physik* **20**, 891 (1934).

Shoenberg.[141]   Some of the equations need to be modified as a result
of the Kohler-Onsager relations — which at that time had not been
established. However, Shoenberg does present equations for a quadratic
"Hall" effect which results from a component of **E** being perpendicular
to **J** in a crossed magnetic field, because of anisotropy of the medium.
Such a situation can occur, for example, if the galvanomagnetic tensor
component ρ^0_{3211} does not vanish. This is true in a crystal such as bismuth
[see Eq. (8.36)], but is not the case for the higher symmetry of the cubic
system [see Eq. (8.12b)] when the coordinate axes are along the axes
of cubic symmetry.

(2) *Less conventional "Hall" phenomena.* In the preceding paragraph,
we abandoned the requirement that the Hall field be an odd function
of H,[71] maintaining only the condition that $\mathbf{E}_{\text{Hall}}$, **J**, and **H** be mutually
orthogonal. We saw that in anisotropic media, terms involving even
powers of H could contribute to E_{Hall} via the galvanomagnetic tensor ρ^0_{ijkk}.
If one goes a step further, and requires only that $\mathbf{E}_{\text{Hall}}$ be normal to **J**,
then quadratic Hall terms can occur even in *isotropic* media. This general
definition is adopted by Kao and Katz.[67c] If $\mathbf{E}_{\text{meas}}$ is normal to **J**, they
call the dependence E_{meas} (**J**, **H**) a Hall effect; if $\mathbf{E}_{\text{meas}}$ is parallel to **J**,
then E_{meas} (**J**, **H**) is called the magnetoresistance. This extension in definition is illustrated by the "planar Hall effect," which was investigated by
Goldberg and Davis.[142] It has also been referred to as the "pseudo-
Hall-effect."[143]

Consider an isotropic solid, or a cubic crystal with axes along the
coordinate axes, with **J** along the x_1-direction and **H** in the $x_1 x_2$-plane
at an angle φ with **J** (Fig. 6).

It is apparent that

$$E_2 = (\rho^0_{2112} + \rho^0_{2121})JH_1 H_2 = 2\rho^0_{2121} JH^2 \sin\varphi \cos\varphi, \qquad (10.1)$$

$$E_2 = \rho^0_{2121} JH^2 \sin 2\varphi. \qquad (10.2)$$

---

[141] D. Shoenberg, *Proc. Cambridge Phil. Soc.* **31**, 271 (1935).
[142] C. Goldberg and R. E. Davis, *Phys. Rev.* **94**, 1121 (1954).
[143] K. M. Koch, *Z. Naturforsch.* **10a**, 496 (1955).

The ρ^0_{2121} can be expressed in terms of the constants in (8.30) by use of relations (8.31b) to give

$$E_2 = (c\rho_0/2)JH^2 \sin 2\varphi. \tag{10.3}$$

This is the expression given by Goldberg and Davis. They also show another orientation of the cubic system which can be chosen so as to

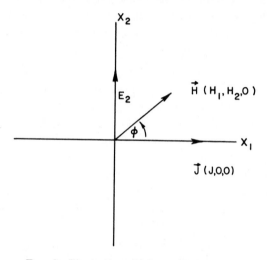

Fig. 6. Illustration of planar Hall effect.

yield the constant d, in the form of the coefficient $(c + d)\rho_0/2$. Since d, which vanishes in an isotropic crystal, is small in most cubic systems, it is not very accurately determined by means of the above coefficient. To obtain improved accuracy, the authors suggest a procedure which involves determination of the coefficient of the quadratic term in the Hall coefficient discussed in Subsection (1) above for a special orientation of crystallographic and coordinate axes.

It is important to note that the simple form of Eqs. (10.1) – (10.3) applies only if there is sufficient symmetry — as is true, for example, in the cubic system and the trigonal system which were considered previously — so that coefficients such as ρ^0_{21}, ρ^0_{211}, ρ^0_{2111}, ρ^0_{2122}, vanish.

(3) Concerning the definitions of the Hall effect. It is apparent that various definitions of the Hall effect found in the literature can lead to

different results, depending upon the contributions entering through the tensors ρ^0_{iklm}. When the results of the measurements are interpreted in terms of fundamental characteristics of the semiconductors, the fields resulting from the different resistivity tensor components will need to be separated. The experimenter must therefore isolate the effects which are even in H from those which are odd. In view of this, there would appear to be advantages in defining the Hall effect as the antisymmetrical part of the resistivity tensor $\rho_{ik}(\mathbf{H})$, as is done by Jan.[144, 144a] As a result of the Kohler-Onsager relations, the antisymmetrical part is that part which changes its sign upon reversal of $\mathbf{H}$. The Hall effect thus defined is represented by the Hall vector $\mathbf{R}(\mathbf{H})$ in Eq. (8.21). It is approximated to first order in H by the ρ^0_{ikl} tensors.

The *magnetoresistance* effects are then defined as those contributions arising from the *symmetric* part of $\rho_{ik}(\mathbf{H})$. It thus follows that magnetoresistance is an even function of $\mathbf{H}$ — as is assumed in Section 11b.

Regardless of the definition adopted for the Hall effect, it is necessary for the person analyzing the data to recognize what basic effects are included in each measurement. In isotropic media where $\mathbf{E}_{meas}$, $\mathbf{J}$, and $\mathbf{H}$ are mutually orthogonal, there is no ambiguity. This, as we have seen, is not true when anisotropy exists.

In view of the problems discussed above, there is a growing tendency to avoid use of the terms Hall effect and magnetoresistance when dealing with weak-magnetic-field measurements in anisotropic crystals. Instead, the basic galvanomagnetic coefficients are determined. In those cases where stronger magnetic fields are used, however, expansions of the components of $\boldsymbol{\rho}(\mathbf{H})$ in power series of H are not possible (see Section 6b). Then the galvanomagnetic coefficients as defined in Eq. (8.20) do not exist. [For additional discussion of Hall phenomena, see Section 11b (2).]

b. Corbino Magnetoresistance, Magnetoconductivity

We have seen that the ordinary magnetoresistance is measured under the boundary condition that the transverse current be zero [Eq. (9.10)]. It is possible, however, to arrange a shorting of the Hall voltage, so that

---

[144] See reference 1, p. 13.

[144a] Such a point of view was adopted by Logan and Marcus. See J. K. Logan and J. A. Marcus, *Phys. Rev.* **88**, 1234 (1952).

the transverse electric field is zero. Then, for isotropic media and isothermal conditions, the following form of Eq. (9.5) applies:

$$J_x = \sigma_{xx}(H)E_x \tag{10.4}$$

$$H \equiv H_z, \quad E_y = 0.$$

$$J_y = -\sigma_{xy}(H)E_x \tag{10.5}$$

It is seen from the first equation that a measurement of the ratio of J_x
and E_x yields directly the conductivity tensor component $\sigma_{xx}(H)$, since
the nondiagonal component $\sigma_{xy}(H)$ enters only via the shorting current J_y.

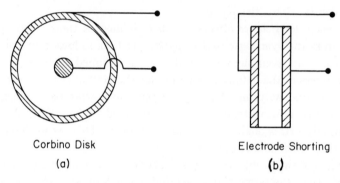

Corbino Disk

(a)

Electrode Shorting

(b)

FIG. 7. Mechanisms to produce shorting of the Hall voltage.

In effect, then, we are determining directly the *magnetoconductivity* of the
specimen when we measure the ratio of currents appearing in the equation
below:

$$\frac{\sigma(H) - \sigma(0)}{\sigma(0)} = \frac{J_x}{(J_x)_{H=0}} - 1 = \frac{\sigma_{xx}(H)}{\sigma_{xx}(0)} - 1, \qquad \begin{array}{l} E_y = 0 \\ E_x = \text{const.} \end{array} \tag{10.6}$$

The above relation follows at once from (9.8) and (10.4).

The most effective arrangement for shorting the Hall field, so that
(10.4) and (10.5) apply, is by use of the Corbino disk geometry,[145] having
highly conducting metal contacts at the center and along the periphery
(Fig. 7a).

---

[145] After O. M. Corbino who investigated the circulating secondary currents in a
bismuth disk carrying a primary radial electric current in a magnetic field.[146]

Originally, much interest centered around the circulating current, called the Corbino effect. It has been determined by measuring the current induced in a coil of wire placed parallel to the disk when the radial current was reversed about 20 cps.[147] Further determinations of the Corbino effect have been done by measuring the torque exerted on the current carrying disk by the magnetic field. Adams[146,147] established the relationship between the Corbino effect and the Hall effect.

With the use of Eq. (9.12) for weak magnetic fields, (10.5) may be put in the form

$$J_y = - R_0 \sigma_0 H J_x, \qquad \omega\tau \ll 1 \tag{10.7}$$

where R_0 and σ_0 are the zero magnetic field Hall coefficient and conductivity, respectively. The total currents per unit thickness, circulating and radial, are given in terms of the current densities as follows:

$$I_c = \int_{r_1}^{r_2} J_y(r)\, dr, \qquad I = \int_0^{2\pi} J_x(r)\, r\, d\theta \tag{10.8}$$

where r_1 and r_2 are the inner and outer radii of the disk, and where we have associated subscripts x and y with the radial and angular components, respectively, of $\mathbf{J}$.

Expression (10.7) thus becomes

$$I_c = - \frac{R_0 \sigma_0}{2\pi} HI \log \frac{r_2}{r_1}, \tag{10.9}$$

an expression identical with that of Adams. The results given by Adams for the Corbino magnetoresistance are

$$(\Delta\rho/\rho_0)_{E_y = 0} = (R_0 \sigma_0 H)^2. \tag{10.10}$$

We shall see in Section 12 [Eq. (12.36)] that this result — derived before 1915 — applies precisely for the case of constant relaxation time, under

[146] L. L. Campbell, "Galvanomagnetic and Thermomagnetic Effects: The Hall and Allied Phenomena," p. 125. Longmans, Green, New York and London, 1923.
[147] E. P. Adams, *Proc. Am. Phil. Soc.* **54**, 47 (1915).

which condition the Hall coefficient and resistivity are independent of H.

Because of the fact that Corbino disk measurements yield directly the value of $\sigma_{xx}(H)$ and that the Corbino magnetoresistance does not saturate at higher fields, it is a useful technique for studying the high-mobility semiconducting materials such as those of the III–V compounds.[139,148]

Another means for shorting the Hall field is the use of area end contacts with small length-width ratios of the specimen (Fig. 7b). It was found by Welker that the Corbino magnetoresistance in n-type InSb at room temperature could be approximated very closely up to 3500 gauss by measurements on a specimen of such a rectangular geometry.[148] Experimental data on a number of length-width ratios for high purity InSb are also presented by Beer.[149] Shorting effects can also be produced in a long specimen by depositing thin metallic strips, or "shorting bars," across the surface.[150] This avoids the very low resistance which results from small length-width ratios. The width-length ratio necessary to approach the limiting case of the disk within a given percentage can of course be calculated by the theory of Wick[106] for an arbitrary Hall angle (magnetic field intensity).

We have seen that with $E_y = 0$, a "magnetoresistance" measurement yields the magnetoconductivity of the specimen. The distinction is that in magnetoresistance measurements the direction of the current $\mathbf{J}$ is fixed, independent of $\mathbf{H}$, while the direction of $\mathbf{E}(H)$ is given by

$$E_y/E_x = \sigma_{xy}(H)/\sigma_{xx}(H) = \tan \theta$$

in the two-dimensional case. The quantity θ is the Hall angle. In magnetoconductance measurements, the direction of the electric field $\mathbf{E}$ is fixed, independent of $\mathbf{H}$, and the direction of $\mathbf{J}(H)$ is given by

$$J_y/J_x = -\sigma_{xy}(H)/\sigma_{xx}(H) = -\tan \theta \qquad (10.12)$$

in the two-dimensional case. Thus, in the Corbino disk, where the equipotential curves are circles, the current lines spiral at the angles $-\theta$ with the normals to the equipotentials.[150]

---

[148] H. Weiss and H. Welker, Z. Physik **138**, 322 (1954).
   O. Madelung, Naturwissenschaften **42**, 406 (1955).
[149] A. C. Beer, J. Electrochem. Soc. **105**, 743 (1958).
[150] H. Welker and H. Weiss, Solid State Phys. **3**, 1 (1956); see especially pp. 38–39.

Use of the Corbino disk for magnetoconductivity determinations is feasible only for materials isotropic in the plane of the disk. Somewhat greater flexibility is possible with the large-area-contact specimens. Such a method has been used by Goldberg in studies on n-type germanium.[151,152] A serious experimental difficulty is the necessity for effective low-resistance contacts, and the importance of ascertaining that such conditions have been realized. The problem of contact resistance can be alleviated, however, by using an array of four closely spaced contacts at the center of an "infinite" sheet. Two of the contacts are for current connections and two are potential probes, permitting a measurement of potential difference with no voltage drop due to contact resistance. In addition, there are no shorting electrodes which might introduce other resistive losses. As long as the distance between the contacts is small compared to the distances to the boundaries, a measurement of the ratio $V(0)/V(H)$ at constant current, where V is the voltage difference between the potential probes, yields $\sigma_{xx}(H)/\sigma_{xx}(0)$. For purposes of subsequent identification we shall call this arrangement a "Corbino sheet."[152a] A conductivity measurement yields directly the magnetoconductivity inasmuch as the equipotential curves are unaffected — and therefore so is the direction of $\mathbf{E}$ — by the magnetic field. This is a result of the fact that the boundary condition which involves the Hall angle, and therefore the magnetic field, has been removed to infinity. The potential distribution is established simply by the solution of Laplace's equation subject to the boundary condition specifying fixed potentials at the two current contacts. The solution for the potential does not therefore involve the magnetic field, and the equipotential curves are unchanged as the field varies. A similar situation was encountered by Baker and Martyn in studies of electric currents in the ionosphere when circumstances were such that the Hall current built up no polarization.[152b] It has been pointed out by Barron and MacDonald that Corbino effects can occur when measuring very low resistivity metals (for example, very pure sodium at

---

[151] C. Goldberg, *Bull. Am. Phys. Soc.* **2**, 65 (1957).

[152] C. Goldberg, *Phys. Rev.* **109**, 331 (1958).

[152a] The similarity between the Corbino sheet and the Corbino disk was first pointed out to the author by Dr. S. W. Kurnick ca. 1956. Salient features in the argument that $\sigma = \sigma_{xx}$ are due to Dr. F. J. Milford.

[152b] W. G. Baker and D. F. Martyn, *Phil. Trans. Roy. Soc. London* **A246**, 281 (1953); W. G. Baker, *ibid.* **A246**, 295 (1953).

liquid helium temperatures) where the contacting electrodes have higher resistivities than do the samples.[106a]

In spite of the experimental problems, Corbino measurements possess a number of attractive features as tools for studying high-mobility semiconductors — either through measurements of galvanomagnetic or thermomagnetic properties.[139]

11. Measurements on Anisotropic Materials

In anisotropic solids the transport properties are, in general, directional. Therefore it is necessary to specify the crystallographic directions of the currents and the applied magnetic fields. For example, magnetoresistance may be designated by $M_{[\mathbf{J}]}^{[\mathbf{H}]}$, which is defined phenomenologically as follows:

$$M_{[\mathbf{J}]}^{[\mathbf{H}]} = \left(\frac{\Delta\rho}{\rho_0}\right)_{[\mathbf{J}]}^{[\mathbf{H}]} = \frac{[\mathbf{E}(\mathbf{H}) - \mathbf{E}(0)] \cdot \mathbf{J}}{\mathbf{E}(0) \cdot \mathbf{J}}. \tag{11.1}$$

The subscript gives the direction of the current and the superscript that of the magnetic field. In general, measurements are taken for both directions of magnetic field so that $\mathbf{E}(\mathbf{H})$ is even in H. This point is discussed in more detail in Section 11b, to follow. It is convenient to define directional magnetoresistance *coefficients* for the crystallographic directions of the current and the magnetic field as follows:

$$\Upsilon_{hkl}^{mnp}(H) \equiv \frac{M_{hkl}^{mnp}(H)}{H^2} = \left(\frac{\rho(H) - \rho(0)}{\rho(0)H^2}\right)_{\mathbf{J}[hkl]}^{\mathbf{H}[mnp]} \tag{11.2}$$

For longitudinal magnetoresistance, where both sets of indices are identical, it is customary to write only the lower set. In the transverse magnetoresistance, $\mathbf{H}$ is of course normal to $\mathbf{J}$. In both cases

$$\mathbf{E}_{\text{meas}} \parallel \mathbf{J}. \tag{11.2a}$$

In a following section (Subsection b) we shall discuss other galvanomagnetic effects which are even in H, but where $\mathbf{E}_{meas}$ is normal to $\mathbf{J}$. These phenomena lead to quadratic "Hall" voltages.

a. Weak-Magnetic-Field Region

When $\omega\tau$ — or $\mu H/c$, where μ is the mobility of the charge carrier in the semiconductor — is less than unity, the transport coefficients can be expanded in a power series in H, as was seen in Section 8. Thus the electrical transport properties can be specified by the zero-magnetic-field resistivity and by the galvanomagnetic coefficients, as is seen in Eq. (8.20). This approach is preferable to that of classifying the experimental data in the categories of Hall coefficients and magnetoresistance, inasmuch as it avoids problems discussed in Section 10, which can arise as a result of joint contributions to transverse electric fields from Hall and magneto-resistance effects. The number of independent measurements necessary to determine the galvanomagnetic characteristics is dependent on the crystal symmetry, as was illustrated in Section 8.

In the weak-field region, the magnetoresistance varies as H^2. Using the notation of Eq. (11.2), we may therefore define weak-magnetic-field directional magnetoresistance coefficients as follows:

$$\Upsilon_{hkl}^{mnp} \equiv \frac{M_{hkl}^{mnp}}{H^2} = \lim_{H \to 0} \left[\frac{M_{hkl}^{mnp}(H)}{H^2} \right] = \lim_{H \to 0} [\Upsilon_{hkl}^{mnp}(H)]. \qquad (11.3)$$

These quantities appear frequently in the literature dealing with meas-urements on cubic systems.

(1) *Diamond cubic symmetry.* In cubic systems the zero-magnetic-field resistivity and the weak-field Hall coefficient are isotropic. The customary procedure is to determine the phenomenological weak-field magneto-resistance coefficients of Eq. (8.30). From this relation and (11.1), together with the requirement that $\mathbf{E}(\mathbf{H})$ be even in $\mathbf{H}$, one obtains

$$\frac{\Delta\rho}{\rho_0} \cong bH^2 + c\frac{(\mathbf{J} \cdot \mathbf{H})^2}{J^2} + d\frac{J_1^2 H_1^2 + J_2^2 H_2^2 + J_3^2 H_3^2}{J^2}, \qquad \omega\tau \ll 1.$$

$$(11.3a)$$

Let us designate the direction cosines of $\mathbf{J}$ and $\mathbf{H}$ by ι_j and η_j ($j = 1, 2, 3$), respectively. Then $\iota_1\, \iota_2\, \iota_3$ are related to hkl by an ordinary normalization factor, as also are $\eta_1 \, \eta_2 \, \eta_3$ and mnp. The weak-field directional magneto-resistance coefficient can then be written

$$\Upsilon_{hkl}^{mnp} = b + c(\iota_j \eta_j)^2 + d(\iota_j{}^2 \eta_j{}^2) \tag{11.4}$$

where the summation is from $j = 1$ to $j = 3$.

The above form was given by Pearson and Suhl,[79] who present data on n- and p-type germanium for the following directional coefficients:

$$\Upsilon_{100} = b + c + d \qquad \Upsilon_{100}^{010} = b$$

$$\Upsilon_{110} = b + c + \tfrac{1}{2}d$$

$$\Upsilon_{110}^{001} = b. \tag{11.5}$$

$$\Upsilon_{110}^{1\bar{1}0} = b + \tfrac{1}{2}d$$

The absence of the upper indices indicates that $\mathbf{H}$ has the same direction as $\mathbf{J}$.

In studies of materials with the many-valley type band structure, it is of interest to know the ratio c/b reasonably accurately. For the model usually used for n-type germanium, where the energy surfaces are approximated by ellipsoids of revolution oriented along the [111] directions in k-space, the ratio should be -1. In order to determine this quantity from (11.5), three coefficients must be measured. The values of the weak-field plateaus of $\Delta\rho/\rho_0 \, H^2$ are required, necessitating measurements at small $\Delta\rho$ and at small values of magnetic field, which enters as the square. Usually extrapolations to $H = 0$ can amount to uncertainties of the order of several per cent. Thus substantial experimental problems are involved in obtaining c/b with good accuracy. Several useful techniques are described by Goldberg and Howard,[153] which have enabled them to secure improved results. Their findings give values of c/b within 3% of the theoretical figure for n-type germanium of 6×10^{15} carriers cm^{-3} and lower. Other measurements which have been used to provide information on magnetoresistance or magnetoconductance coefficients are the planar "Hall" effect (Section 10a) and magnetoconductivity (Section 10b). In the case of n-germanium, the planar "Hall" effect does not appear to yield the accuracy of the more direct methods.[153] The magnetoconductivity

---

[153] C. Goldberg and W. E. Howard, *Phys. Rev.* **110**, 1035 (1958).

technique is not capable of providing results on the off-diagonal components of the conductivity tensor $\sigma(\mathbf{H})$.

Higher order galvanomagnetic coefficients for n-type germanium have been evaluated by Mason et al.[64] Using Pearson and Suhl's data, they have determined four of the six coefficients of the H^4 terms. To determine the higher order terms in the Hall effect, they did measurements on two cylindrical specimens, one with its axis along the [100] direction and the other with the axis along a [110] direction. Hall coefficients were determined as a function of magnetic field up to 22 kgauss, using the following equation derived for the case of cylindrical geometry of diameter d:

$$ R_H = \frac{V_H/d}{JH} = \frac{\pi}{4} \frac{V_H d}{IH} \tag{11.6} $$

where V_H is the measured Hall voltage, J the current density, and I the total current. The authors illustrate the orientations necessary to ensure a zero cross magnetoresistance effect on the Hall voltage for the cubic crystal. Using data obtained for such orientations, they determine the two coefficients for the first order correction to R_H [i.e., the coefficients of H^3 terms in the expression for $\rho(\mathbf{H})$] and three coefficients[153a] for the second-order correction (i.e., coefficients of the H^5 terms). From the results, it is seen that the correction terms on R_H are least if $\mathbf{H}$ is inclined only slightly from the appropriate cubic axis. Since several errors exist in the indices printed on Figs. 9 and 10 in the article, the text should be consulted.

(2) *Other crystal systems.* In the crystal systems of lower symmetry, many investigators prefer to carry out straightforward determinations of the galvanomagnetic coefficients rather than to use the conventional classifications, which can be ambiguous due to intermixing of voltages from Hall effect and magnetoresistance. Experimental arrangements which enable one to obtain the two resistivities and the 16 galvanomagnetic coefficients (through H^3 terms) in a crystal such as antimony have been outlined by Juretschke[80, 82] and by Okada.[84] There are three sets of such measurements, defined by the orientations of $\mathbf{J}$ and $\mathbf{H}$ with

---

[153a] According to the results obtained by Kao and Katz,[67c] four independent constants are necessary to specify these terms in the general case.

respect to the principal crystallographic axis c, usually directed along the z-coordinate axis. In each case the orientation of $\mathbf{J}$ with respect to the crystallographic axes is fixed by the cut of the specimen.

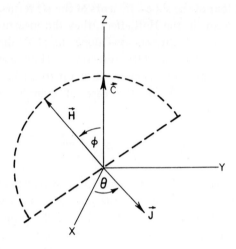

FIG. 8.   Illustration of arrangement where $\mathbf{J} \perp c$ and $\mathbf{H} \perp \mathbf{J}$.

As an illustration, consider the schemes discussed by Juretschke[80] and outlined below.

Arrangement I. — $\mathbf{J} \perp c$, $\mathbf{H} \perp \mathbf{J}$: If we designate by φ the angle between $\mathbf{H}$ and c, and by θ the angle between $\mathbf{J}$ and Ox — usually Ox or Oy is chosen coincident with one of the binary axes of the crystal — the relationship of the vectors is shown in Fig. 8. We may phrase the preceding clause more generally to include systems such as $3m$, which do not possess binary axes, by stating that the (y, z) or the (x, z) coordinate plane is made coincident with one of the three equivalent planes of reflection of the crystal. The angle θ, although arbitrary, is fixed by the cut of the specimen, and the angle φ is varied during measurements. The fields, which are measured in the directions indicated by the subscripts, are $E_{\mathbf{J}}$, E_c, and $E_{c \times \mathbf{J}}$. By a choice of θ appropriate for the particular coefficients desired, 12 of the 16 galvanomagnetic coefficients (including through the third order in the magnetic-field index) can be determined from this arrangement. Separation is accomplished by means of the φ-dependence. This takes account of the parity in H if φ is varied between zero and 2π.

Arrangement II. — $\mathbf{J} \parallel \mathbf{c}$, $\mathbf{H} \perp \mathbf{J}$: A measurement of $E_\mathbf{J}$ yields a value of $\rho_{3,1}^0$, in the notation of Eq. (8.36). Although measurements of $E_\mathbf{H}$ and $E_{\mathbf{J}\times\mathbf{H}}$ yield nothing which was not obtained in I, they are of interest as checks. The variable angle is that between $\mathbf{H}$ and Ox.

Arrangement III. — $\mathbf{J} \parallel \mathbf{H}$: An arbitrary angle with respect to $\mathbf{c}$ is necessary to include the determination of $\rho_{4,4}^0$. Both θ and φ are fixed, and the only degree of freedom is the reversal of $\mathbf{H}$. Relations connecting the unknown coefficients $\rho_{1,1}^0$, $\rho_{3,3}^0$, and $\rho_{4,4}^0$ through the angle φ with other coefficients are obtained for $E_\mathbf{J}$ and $E_{\mathbf{J}\times(\mathbf{c}\times\mathbf{J})}$. A measurement of $E_{\mathbf{c}\times\mathbf{J}}$ confirms preceding results. To separate the $\rho_{1,1}^0$, $\rho_{3,3}^0$, and $\rho_{4,4}^0$ it is desirable to have data for $\varphi = \pi/2$, $\varphi = 0$, and φ arbitrary (approximately $\pi/4$). Only one specimen needs to be fabricated for this arrangement, however, since the first two values of φ are obtained from the specimens used in arrangements I and II.

The specimen geometries are usually long thin cylindrical rods, or parallelepipeds of square cross section. Since the current direction must be *along* the length of the specimen, so as to avoid shorting effects discussed in Section 9b, each orientation of $\mathbf{J}$ with respect to the crystallographic directions requires a uniquely cut specimen. Thus three different specimens are necessary to determine the galvanomagnetic coefficients with the scheme outlined above. There is redundancy in the set of measurements, however, so that a number of cross checks between the different specimens are obtained.

A variation of the above scheme was used by Drabble[87a] in determining the 10 galvanomagnetic coefficients through H^2 terms. This procedure, in which the direction of $\mathbf{H}$ with respect to $\mathbf{J}$ was allowed to vary, has the advantage that only two specimens are required in the three arrangements. The system, again with the principal axis $\mathbf{c}$ in the coordinate direction Oz, is as follows:

Arrangement I ("$\perp$ *specimen*") — $\mathbf{J} \perp \mathbf{c}$, $\mathbf{H} \perp \mathbf{c}$: The current $\mathbf{J}$ is fixed at an arbitrary angle θ with respect to the x-axis, where the orientation is such that the (x, z) plane is coincident with one of the three equivalent planes of reflection of the crystal. The specimen is rotated about the c axis, which is equivalent to varying $0 \leqslant \varphi \leqslant 2\pi$, where φ is the angle between $\mathbf{H}$ and $\mathbf{J}$. Measurements of $E_{\mathbf{J}}$, E_c allow determination of ρ_{11}^0 and four galvanomagnetic coefficients; and $E_{c \times \mathbf{J}}$ gives a connecting relation.

Arrangement II ("$\perp$ *specimen*") $- \mathbf{J} \perp c$, $\mathbf{H} \perp (c \times \mathbf{J})$: Here the crystal is rotated about the $c \times \mathbf{J}$ direction and therefore $\mathbf{H}$ is rotated throughout the $c\mathbf{J}$-plane. Measurements of $E_{\mathbf{J}}$, E_c, and $E_{c \times \mathbf{J}}$ provide four additional galvanomagnetic coefficients.

Arrangement III ("$\parallel$ *specimen*") $- \mathbf{J} \parallel c$: The crystal is rotated about an axis normal to c, and $\mathbf{H}$ is of course perpendicular to this rotation axis. Measurement of $E_{\mathbf{J}}$ in this experiment allows determination of ρ_{33}^0, ρ_{3333}^0, and ρ_{3311}^0. Connecting relations are obtained if E is measured parallel to the rotation axis. The reader will note that the term *rotation axis* is used here to denote the axis about which the specimen is rotated during measurements in the magnetic field. This is in contrast to the specification of Drabble, [87a] who uses the term to denote the trigonal axis of the crystal.

In the case of n-type bismuth telluride, measurements with $\mathbf{J}$ along c were considered unreliable by Drabble *et al.*[87] since their specimens were highly subject to cracks in directions parallel to the cleavage planes. Therefore arrangement III was not used. This allowed determination of nine of the 12 coefficients, and only one specimen was required.

b. Magnetic Fields of Arbitrary Intensity

(1) General discussion of parameters of interest. In the cases where the condition $e\tau H/m^* c < 1$ is not fulfilled, expansion of the transport tensors in powers of H is not possible. Therefore the directional properties cannot be specified by a certain number of galvanomagnetic coefficients, and the problem is more complicated.

Experimentally, one commonly determines directional magneto-resistance coefficients $\Upsilon_{kkl}^{mnp}(H)$, operationally defined in (11.2). There are also directional Hall coefficients written as $R_{kkl}^{mnp}(H)$. It is now especially important to pay attention to the intermixing of contributions to E_{meas}

from the Hall field and from the magnetoresistance voltage. To illustrate, we shall write the general form of the resistivity tensor, making use only of the Kohler-Onsager reciprocal relations. We begin by writing the second rank tensor as a sum of symmetric and antisymmetric parts

$$\rho_{ik}(\mathbf{H}) = \rho_{ik}^s(\mathbf{H}) + \rho_{ik}^a(\mathbf{H}), \tag{11.7}$$

$$\rho_{ik}^s(\mathbf{H}) = \rho_{ki}^s(\mathbf{H}) = \tfrac{1}{2}\,[\rho_{ik}^s(\mathbf{H}) + \rho_{ki}^s(\mathbf{H})], \tag{11.8}$$

$$\rho_{ik}^a(\mathbf{H}) = -\,\rho_{ki}^a(\mathbf{H}) = \tfrac{1}{2}\,[\rho_{ik}^a(\mathbf{H}) - \rho_{ki}^a(\mathbf{H})].$$

Use of the Kohler-Onsager relations with (11.8) yields

$$\rho_{ik}^s(\mathbf{H}) = \rho_{ik}^s(-\,\mathbf{H}), \tag{11.9}$$

$$\rho_{ik}^a(\mathbf{H}) = -\,\rho_{ik}^a(-\,\mathbf{H}).$$

According to the last relation of (11.8), it is apparent that

$$\rho_{ik}^a(\mathbf{H}) = 0, \qquad i = k. \tag{11.10}$$

As a result of the preceding, it follows that there are six independent components in the resistivity tensor $\boldsymbol{\rho}(\mathbf{H})$; namely,

$$\boldsymbol{\rho}(\mathbf{H}) = \begin{pmatrix} \rho_{11}^s(\mathbf{H}) & \rho_{12}^s(\mathbf{H}) + \rho_{12}^a(\mathbf{H}) & \rho_{13}^s(\mathbf{H}) + \rho_{13}^a(\mathbf{H}) \\ \rho_{12}^s(\mathbf{H}) - \rho_{12}^a(\mathbf{H}) & \rho_{22}^s(\mathbf{H}) & \rho_{23}^s(\mathbf{H}) + \rho_{23}^a(\mathbf{H}) \\ \rho_{13}^s(\mathbf{H}) - \rho_{13}^a(\mathbf{H}) & \rho_{23}^s(\mathbf{H}) - \rho_{23}^a(\mathbf{H}) & \rho_{33}^s(\mathbf{H}) \end{pmatrix}. \tag{11.11}$$

Although the diagonal elements are even in H, the off-diagonal terms can include phenomena having both even and odd dependencies on H. Thus, unless highly symmetrical directions are chosen for $\mathbf{H}$, $\mathbf{J}$, and $\mathbf{E}$, one may expect complications from these cross effects. The simplification of doing experiments which avoid the off-diagonal components is not useful, since standard measurements yield directly the elements of the *resistivity* tensor. To compare with theory, it is desirable to obtain the *conductivity*, or inverse tensor; and the inversion process requires a knowledge of all the components.

Because of the cross effects, it seems desirable to adopt the definitions of Hall and magnetoresistance coefficients suggested in Section 10a(3), namely, that the Hall phenomena are represented by the $\rho_{ik}^a(H)$ and the magnetoresistance phenomena by the $\rho_{ik}^s(H)$ of (11.11).[153b] The Hall and magnetoresistance fields are then given by

$$E^a(\mathbf{H}) = \tfrac{1}{2}[\mathbf{E}(\mathbf{H}) - \mathbf{E}(-\mathbf{H})], \tag{11.12}$$

$$E^s(\mathbf{H}) = \tfrac{1}{2}[\mathbf{E}(\mathbf{H}) + \mathbf{E}(-\mathbf{H})], \tag{11.13}$$

where $\mathbf{E}(\mathbf{H})$ is the electric field in the crystal when magnetic field $\mathbf{H}$ exists.

(2) *Hall phenomena.* The general Hall vector, $\mathbf{R}(\mathbf{H})$ of Eq. (8.21), is defined by

$$\mathbf{E}^a(\mathbf{H}) = \mathbf{R}(\mathbf{H}) \times \mathbf{J}. \tag{11.14}$$

The general Hall field is therefore perpendicular to $\mathbf{J}$, but not necessarily to $\mathbf{H}$,[63] and it is odd in $\mathbf{H}$.

(i) *Conventional Hall effect:* Many authors adopt the convention that the Hall field by definition is that field in the direction $\mathbf{H} \times \mathbf{J}$. We shall designate the quantity so defined by $\mathbf{E}_H$. It is sometimes known as the *transverse* Hall field, in distinction to the *longitudinal* Hall field, which will be discussed subsequently. The expression for the conventional Hall field may therefore be written

$$\mathbf{E}_H = \mathbf{E}^a(\mathbf{H}) \cdot \frac{\mathbf{H} \times \mathbf{J}}{|\mathbf{H} \times \mathbf{J}|} \frac{\mathbf{H} \times \mathbf{J}}{|\mathbf{H} \times \mathbf{J}|} = \frac{\mathbf{E}^a(\mathbf{H}) \cdot \mathbf{H} \times \mathbf{J}}{(\mathbf{H} \times \mathbf{J})^2} \mathbf{H} \times \mathbf{J}. \tag{11.15}$$

In this convention, the Hall field is expressed in terms of a Hall coefficient R_H as follows[153b,c]

$$\mathbf{E}_H = R_H \mathbf{H} \times \mathbf{J} \tag{11.16}$$

where the subscript H indicates a function of magnetic field. The weak-field limit is written as R_0, where

$$R_0 = \lim_{H \to 0} R_H. \tag{11.17}$$

[153b] This is the convention adhered to by Jan[63] and by Herring.[65]

[153c] Examples of the adoption of this convention in anisotropic solids for arbitrary magnetic field strengths are found in references 154–156.

[154] M. Shibuya, *Phys. Rev.* **95**, 1385 (1954).

From (11.12), (11.15), and (11.16) it follows that

$$R_{hkl}^{mnp}(H) = R_H = \tfrac{1}{2}\,[\mathbf{E}(\mathbf{H}) \cdot \mathbf{H} \times \mathbf{J} - \mathbf{E}(-\mathbf{H}) \cdot \mathbf{H} \times \mathbf{J}]/(\mathbf{H} \times \mathbf{J})^2. \qquad (11.18)$$

To avoid duplication of subscripts, we are writing the directional Hall coefficient R_H as $R_{hkl}^{mnp}(H)$. Since it is not a vector, there should be no confusion with $\mathbf{R}(\mathbf{H})$ in (11.14). The expression (11.18) above is identical with that given by Gold and Roth.[155]

(ii) *Longitudinal Hall effect:* The general relation (11.14) can, of course, specify a Hall field which is not collinear with $\mathbf{H} \times \mathbf{J}$. In particular, we may consider the direction $\mathbf{J} \times (\mathbf{H} \times \mathbf{J})$. This direction is parallel to $\mathbf{H}$ when $\mathbf{H}$ and $\mathbf{J}$ are perpendicular. The Hall field in question has been called the longitudinal Hall field by Grabner.[156a] Its magnitude is given by the relation

$$E_{\mathbf{J} \times (\mathbf{H} \times \mathbf{J})} = \frac{\mathbf{E}^a(\mathbf{H}) \cdot \mathbf{J} \times (\mathbf{H} \times \mathbf{J})}{|\mathbf{J} \times (\mathbf{H} \times \mathbf{J})|}. \qquad (11.18a)$$

The longitudinal Hall effect has been investigated both theoretically and experimentally for n-type germanium by Grabner.[156a] It vanishes for spherical energy surfaces or when the magnetic field is parallel to an axis of rotation of the crystal. It also approaches zero in the limit of infinitely strong magnetic fields.

(iii) *Longitudinal magnetic field Hall phenomena:* The Hall field expression, Eq. (11.14), can formally yield a nonzero field when $\mathbf{H}$ is parallel to $\mathbf{J}$, although such a situation is precluded for the conventional Hall field defined by Eq. (11.16). In most measurements the existence of a Hall voltage of this type is ruled out by considerations of symmetry. It has been pointed out, however, that such an effect, of third order in H or higher, can occur even in a cubic crystal if $\mathbf{J}$ is not along a direction of symmetry.[156b]

---

[155] L. Gold and L. Roth, *Phys. Rev.* **107**, 358 (1957).
[156] W. M. Bullis, *Phys. Rev.* **109**, 292 (1958).
[156a] L. Grabner, *Phys. Rev.* **117**, 689 (1960).
[156b] See p. 84 of the article by García-Moliner.[428]

(3) *Magnetoresistance phenomena.* All galvanomagnetic effects which are even in the magnetic field can be accounted for symbolically by the following generalized magnetoresistivities:

$$_{[E]}\rho_{[J]}^{[H]}(H) \tag{11.19}$$

where only even powers of H are involved and where the crystallographic directions of $\mathbf{E}$, $\mathbf{J}$, and $\mathbf{H}$ are indicated. When $\mathbf{E} \parallel \mathbf{J}$, the above quantity represents the ordinary magnetoresistivity, designated as $\rho(H)$ in Eq. (11.2), and the advance subscript is omitted. For transverse directions of $\mathbf{E}$, (11.19) will encompass resistivities leading to even-power "Hall" terms [Section 10a(1)] and to planar "Hall" phenomena [Section 10a(2)]. Thus

$$_{[\mathbf{H} \times \mathbf{J}]}\rho_{[J]}^{[H]}(H), \quad \text{responsible for even-power "Hall" terms, } \mathbf{E} \text{ normal}$$
$$\text{to } \mathbf{J} \text{ and to } \mathbf{H}, \tag{11.20}$$

$$_{[(\mathbf{J} \times \mathbf{H}) \times \mathbf{J}]}\rho_{[J]}^{[H]}(H), \quad \text{responsible for even-power terms via planar "Hall"}$$
$$\text{effect, } \mathbf{E} \text{ normal to } \mathbf{J} \text{ and coplanar with } \mathbf{J} \text{ and } \mathbf{H}.$$
$$\tag{11.21}$$

The resistivities in (11.19) are even in H and are given in the usual way by the double dot product of the symmetric part of the resistivity tensor with unit vectors in the specified directions. Thus

$$_{[E]}\rho_{[J]}^{[H]}(H) = \hat{\mathbf{E}} \cdot \boldsymbol{\rho}^s(\mathbf{H})\hat{\mathbf{J}} \tag{11.22}$$

where $\hat{\mathbf{E}}$ and $\hat{\mathbf{J}}$ are unit vectors in the direction of $\mathbf{E}$ and $\mathbf{J}$, respectively. Hence, for the even-power "Hall" phenomena, we have

$$_{[\mathbf{H} \times \mathbf{J}]}\rho_{[J]}^{[H]}(H) = \frac{(\mathbf{H} \times \mathbf{J}) \cdot \boldsymbol{\rho}^s(\mathbf{H})\mathbf{J}}{|\mathbf{H} \times \mathbf{J}| \, |\mathbf{J}|} = \frac{\mathbf{H} \times \mathbf{J} \cdot \mathbf{E}^s(\mathbf{H})}{|\mathbf{H} \times \mathbf{J}| \, |\mathbf{J}|}, \tag{11.23}$$

$$_{[(\mathbf{J} \times \mathbf{H}) \times \mathbf{J}]}\rho_{[J]}^{[H]}(H) = \frac{(\mathbf{J} \times \mathbf{H}) \times \mathbf{J} \cdot \boldsymbol{\rho}^s(\mathbf{H})\mathbf{J}}{|(\mathbf{J} \times \mathbf{H}) \times \mathbf{J}| \, |\mathbf{J}|} = \frac{(\mathbf{J} \times \mathbf{H}) \times \mathbf{J} \cdot \mathbf{E}^s(\mathbf{H})}{|\mathbf{J} \times \mathbf{H}| \, J^2}$$
$$\tag{11.24}$$

where the $\mathbf{E}^s(\mathbf{H})$ are given by (11.13).

The fields for these even-power "Hall" effects are given by

$$\mathbf{E}_H^s = \frac{[\mathbf{E}^s(\mathbf{H}) \cdot \mathbf{H} \times \mathbf{J}]\mathbf{H} \times \mathbf{J}}{(\mathbf{H} \times \mathbf{J})^2}, \qquad (11.25)$$

$$\mathbf{E}_H^p = \frac{[\mathbf{E}^s(\mathbf{H}) \cdot (\mathbf{J} \times \mathbf{H}) \times \mathbf{J}]\,[(\mathbf{J} \times \mathbf{H}) \times \mathbf{J}]}{(\mathbf{J} \times \mathbf{H})^2\, J^2} \qquad (11.26)$$

The voltage $\mathbf{E}_H^p$ is sometimes expressed in terms of a planar Hall coefficient, which we shall write as $\mathscr{R}_H^p$. Such a representation is possible if the system has sufficient symmetry so that the contributions to $\mathbf{E}_H^p$ from $\mathbf{J}$ arise from a single type of galvanomagnetic coefficient [Section 10a(2)]. This is true, for example, in a cubic crystal when $\mathbf{E}$ and $\mathbf{J}$ are along cube axes, or in a trigonal system when the plane of $\mathbf{E}$, $\mathbf{J}$, and $\mathbf{H}$ is normal to the threefold axis. In such cases, we have from Eq. (10.1), to first order in H^2,

$$E_2 = 2\rho_{2121}^0\, JH^2 \sin\varphi \cos\varphi = \mathscr{R}_0^p\, JH^2 \sin\varphi \cos\varphi. \qquad (11.27)$$

Thus, for systems of appropriate symmetry, we may write

$$\mathbf{E}_H^p = \mathscr{R}_H^p\, [(\mathbf{J} \cdot \mathbf{H})/J^2]\, [(\mathbf{J} \times \mathbf{H}) \times \mathbf{J}]. \qquad (11.28)$$

From (11.26) to (11.28) it follows that

$$\mathscr{R}_H^p = [\mathbf{E}^s(\mathbf{H}) \cdot (\mathbf{J} \times \mathbf{H}) \times \mathbf{J}]/(\mathbf{J} \times \mathbf{H})^2\, (\mathbf{J} \cdot \mathbf{H}). \qquad (11.29)$$

This expression for the planar "Hall" coefficient is similar to that given by Bullis,[156] except that our definition explicitly excludes any contributions from $\mathbf{E}^a(\mathbf{H})$.

If the vectors $\mathbf{E}$, $\mathbf{J}$, and $\mathbf{H}$ are designated relative to an orthogonal coordinate system, then all of the coefficients discussed in this section can be written in terms of components of the resistivity tensor (11.11). The expressions can be quite complex if the fields and the current are not in directions of high symmetry, as will be noted from the explicit results presented in a number of the references cited. In general, $\rho_{xy}(H) \neq -\rho_{yx}(H)$ because of nonzero symmetric parts in the off-diagonal elements. Also, even if the measurement directions are chosen so as that the observed effects can be described by a two-dimensional $\rho_{ik}(H)$, the transformation to $\sigma_{ik}(H)$ whose components are desired for a comparison with theory, requires a knowledge of the other components of the $\rho_{ik}(H)$ tensor. Thus the simple results obtained in the isotropic case — e.g., Eqs. (9.12) and (9.14) — represent a tremendous simplification from what may be encountered in an anisotropic system.

(4) *Illustrative examples.* By measuring a number of parameters from among those given in (11.14) or (11.18), (11.19) — or in some cases, (11.29) — it is possible to determine the components of the resistivity tensor $\rho(H)$ for specified directions of H. Through inversion of the resistivity tensor the components of $\sigma(H)$ can be obtained for comparison with theory.

Most of the effort in this direction has been applied to cubic crystals, in particular, the conduction bands of silicon and germanium, where the many-valley approximation to the band structure is applicable. Since mathematically exact evaluations of the transport coefficients for arbitrary values of H are possible only for quadratic energy surfaces, treatment of anisotropy by the ellipsoid model (discussed in detail in Section 23) has an important advantage.

The method, using ellipsoids of revolution to express $\varepsilon(k)$, was applied by Abeles and Meiboom[157] and by Shibuya[154] to germanium and silicon. Explicit expressions are given for Hall and magnetoresistance coefficients, in terms of the effective mass ratios which characterize the ellipsoids, for several crystallographic directions of J and H. A relaxation time proportional to $\varepsilon^{-1/2}$ was used, corresponding to scattering by acoustic phonons. The expressions are easily evaluated in the weak and in the strong magnetic field limits.

For intermediate field strengths, the formulae for the $\varepsilon^{-1/2}$ dependence of ρ, although tractable, are rather laborious to evaluate. Results are greatly simplified in the constant-τ treatment, which has been carried out by Gold and Roth.[155,158] Then the magnetic-field dependence enters directly through the term $\omega\tau$, rather than via more complicated functions of $\omega\tau$. It is of particular interest to note the large changes in the Hall coefficients R_H for the model representative of n-type germanium at intermediate field strengths as J and H are moved off the cube axes.

The experimental arrangements necessary to determine the components of $\rho(H)$ for an arbitrary direction of H are discussed by Broudy and

[157] B. Abeles and S. Meiboom, *Phys. Rev.* **95**, 31 (1954).
[158] L. Gold and L. Roth, *Phys. Rev.* **103**, 61 (1956).

Venables.[159] The authors point out the necessity for redundancy as a check on the homogeneity of the sample. In the stronger magnetic field regions, the effects from inhomogeneities can be pronounced. General expressions are worked out, using spheroidal models representative of the conduction bands of germanium and silicon, for the components of the conductivity tensor.

Experimental data on Hall coefficient and magnetoresistance at room temperature in n- and p-type germanium as a function of magnetic field are given by Della Pergola and Sette.[160] Results on the Hall coefficient in n-type germanium at 77 °K have been presented by Bullis and Krag.[161] These authors define a theoretical R_H^{th} in terms of $\mathbf{E} \cdot \mathbf{J} \times \mathbf{H}$, where $\mathbf{E}$ is the total electric field in the crystal, rather than the antisymmetric field used in (11.18). Contributions to the R_H^{th} defined above from the symmetrical parts of the resistivity tensor are subsequently removed. The magnitude of the cross effects at intermediate magnetic field strengths can be substantial for the less highly symmetric directions, as is seen in Fig. 9.

Much more extensive data are available in subsequent articles by Bullis[162] on n-type germanium and by Krag[163] on n-type silicon. Magneto-resistance, Hall coefficients, and planar "Hall" coefficients were measured at 77° and at 300 °K for a number of magnitudes and orientations of $\mathbf{H}$. A detailed investigation of the anisotropy of the Hall coefficient in germanium containing 5×10^{14} donors/cm^3 was done by Miyazawa and Maeda.[163a] A number of orientations were studied, and data were taken over a range of temperatures and magnetic field strengths.

In the valence bands of germanium and silicon, the anisotropy is much less pronounced than in the conduction bands. Experimental data on the directional properties of the galvanomagnetic effects as a function of magnetic field for p-type germanium and silicon are meager in the

[159] R. M. Broudy and J. D. Venables, *Phys. Rev.* **105**, 1757 (1957); **103**, 1129 (1956).

[160] G. C. Della Pergola and D. Sette, *Nuovo cimento* **5**, 1670 (1957).

[161] W. M. Bullis and W. E. Krag, *Phys. Rev.* **101**, 580 (1956).

[162] W. M. Bullis, *Phys. Rev.* **109**, 292 (1958).

[163] W. E. Krag, *Phys. Rev.* **118**, 435 (1960).

[163a] H. Miyazawa and H. Maeda, *J. Phys. Soc. Japan* **15**, 1924 (1960); "Proc. of the Intern. Conf. on Semiconductor Physics, Prague, 1960," p. 169, Publishing House Czech. Acad. Sci., Prague, 1961.

literature. The orientations used by Della Pergola and Sette in germanium show a negligible effect at room temperature.[160] Results of investigations by Beer and Willardson[56, 164] reveal fine structure in the Hall coefficient

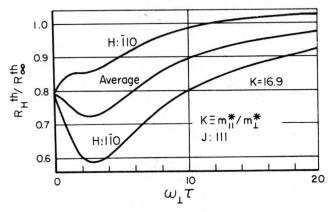

FIG. 9. Relative "theoretical" Hall coefficient (see text) as a function of $\omega_\perp \tau \, (\equiv eH\tau/m_\perp{}^* c)$ for **J** in the [111] direction (after Bullis and Krag[161]). The quantity $m_\parallel{}^*$ is the longitudinal mass (that associated with the axis of revolution of the energy spheroid), and $m_\perp{}^*$ is the transverse mass.

of p-type germanium and silicon at 77 °K. Data on germanium for **H**[100] and **H**[1$\bar{1}$1] suggest an enhancement of the structure in the latter case. This enhancement of structure for $R_{\mathbf{H}}^{[111]}$ was also observed by Miyazawa[164a] in his studies of the anisotropy of the Hall effect in p-type germanium, using specimens containing acceptor densities ranging from 2×10^{12} to 1×10^{16} cm^{-3}. Magnetoresistance studies on p-type silicon carried out by Long,[125] show the coefficient $\Upsilon_{110}^{1\bar{1}0}$ to be several per cent higher than Υ_{110}^{001} at 77 °K; at room temperature, however, the difference is over 30%. Considerable augmentation also occurs in the ratio of longitudinal and transverse coefficients at the higher temperature. These results suggest an anisotropy becoming more pronounced with increase in temperature. At the higher temperature, however, transport may be complicated by contributions from the split-off band (see Section 17b).

164 A. C. Beer, *Phys. and Chem. Solids* 8, 507 (1959).
164a H. Miyazawa, *in* "Proc. of the Conf. on the Physics of Semiconductors, Exeter, July, 1962," p. 636. The Institute of Physics and the Physical Society, London, 1962.

The band structure for p-type germanium and silicon cannot, of course, be approximated by the ellipsoidal model since the band edge is at $\mathbf{k} = 0$. Instead, one must deal with degenerate bands, where one or more is described as a "warped sphere" (Chapter VII).

V.
Transport Coefficients for Isothermal Solids Assuming a Single Parabolic Energy Band and the Relaxation Time Approximation

This section is devoted to transport by a single band having spherical energy surfaces: first for exact quantum (Fermi-Dirac) statistics, and second for the classical (Maxwell-Boltzmann) approximation. In the latter case, especially, results are obtained for a number of different dependencies of the relaxation time on energy, including a mixed scattering process. The limiting cases of weak and strong magnetic fields are considered in some detail; and for certain scattering mechanisms, solutions are given for arbitrary values of magnetic field strength.

12. GENERAL CONSIDERATIONS — EXACT STATISTICS

a. Expressions for Conductivity Coefficients

It is instructive to express the conductivity coefficients in terms of the charge carrier density n. This parameter is given by an integration over energy of the product of the density of states by the Fermi-Dirac distribution function, which expresses the probability of occupation of a given state of energy, designated by ε. Thus, using (5.0a) we may write

$$n = \int_0^\infty n(\varepsilon) f_0(\varepsilon)\, d\varepsilon = \frac{1}{4\pi^3} \int_{\varepsilon=0}^{\varepsilon=\infty} f_0(\varepsilon)\, d^3 k(\varepsilon). \tag{12.1}$$

The Fermi-Dirac distribution function is given by

$$f_0(\varepsilon) = \frac{1}{e^{x-\eta} + 1} \tag{12.2}$$

where x is the reduced energy of the charge carrier and η is the reduced Fermi energy[165]:

$$x \equiv \varepsilon/kT; \qquad \eta \equiv \zeta/kT. \qquad (12.3)$$

For spherical energy surfaces

$$d^3k = 4\pi k^2\, dk \qquad (12.4)$$

and

$$\varepsilon(k) = [\hbar^2/2m^*]\,[k_x{}^2 + k_y{}^2 + k_z{}^2] = \hbar^2\, k^2/2m^*. \qquad (12.5)$$

The expression for the carrier density can therefore be put in the form

$$n = \frac{1}{2\pi^2}\left(\frac{2m^*\, kT}{\hbar^2}\right)^{3/2} F_{1/2}(\eta). \qquad (12.6)$$

The quantity $F_{1/2}(\eta)$ is the Fermi-Dirac function of order $1/2$, defined generally as

$$F_k(\eta) \equiv \int\limits_0^\infty \frac{x^k}{e^{x-\eta} + 1}\, dx. \qquad (12.7)$$

The characteristics of the Fermi-Dirac functions have been investigated by McDougall and Stoner[166] and values are tabulated for $k = -1/2$, $1/2$, and $3/2$. Results were extended by Beer et al.[167] to include $k = 5/2$, $7/2$, $9/2$, and $11/2$. The behavior of the functions for even indices was studied by Rhodes[168] and he presents values for $k = 1, 2, 3$, and 4. Relationships of the Fermi-Dirac integrals to other functions have been investigated by Dingle[169] and a number of expansions were developed.

---

[165] For sake of custom, it is desirable to use the same symbol for the Boltzmann constant in (12.3) as is used for the magnitude of the wave vector. It will be apparent from the formulae which designation is meant. Furthermore, the Boltzmann constant usually occurs in conjunction with T. The exceptions will be noted.

[166] J. McDougall and E. C. Stoner, *Phil. Trans. Roy. Soc. London* **A237**, 67 (1938).

[167] A. C. Beer, M. N. Chase, and P. F. Choquard, *Helv. Phys. Acta* **28**, 529 (1955).

[168] P. Rhodes, *Proc. Roy. Soc.* **A204**, 396 (1950).

[169] R. B. Dingle, *Appl. Sci. Research* **B6**, 225 (1957).

These are sufficiently complete so that integrals of all orders can be calculated without recourse to numerical integration. In his development, Dingle introduces the function $\mathscr{F}_k(\eta)$, where $\mathscr{F}_k(\eta)$ is defined as

$$\mathscr{F}_k(\eta) = F_k(\eta)/k!. \tag{12.8}$$

This representation has a number of mathematical advantages in connection with interpolation, classical limit as $\eta \ll 0$, etc. Also, unlike $F_k(\eta)$, the function $\mathscr{F}_k(\eta)$ exists even for negative integer indices. Tabulated values of $\mathscr{F}_k(\eta)$ are given by Dingle for integer indices from -1 to 4. A further tabulation of $F_k(\eta)$ by Madelung[170] goes through $F_7(\eta)$.

With use of relation (12.6), the expression (7.15) for the conductivity coefficient $\sigma_{xx}(H)$ can be put in the form

$$\sigma_{xx}(H) = \frac{ne^2}{m^*}\left[-\frac{2}{3}\frac{1}{F_{1/2}(\eta)}\int_0^\infty \frac{\tau}{1+\omega^2\tau^2} x^{3/2}\frac{\partial f_0}{\partial x}\,dx \right], \qquad H \equiv H_z. \tag{12.9}$$

To gain an insight into meaning of the expression in brackets, we evaluate $\sigma_{xx}'(H)$ for the case of constant τ, i.e., τ independent of ε. After an integration by parts, one obtains

$$\sigma_{xx}(H) = \frac{n\,e^2}{m^*}\left[\frac{\tau}{1+\omega^2\tau^2} \right], \qquad \tau = \text{const.} \tag{12.10}$$

In the general case, we may regard the bracketed factor in (12.9) as an average of $\tau/(1+\omega^2\tau^2)$ over the Fermi-Dirac distribution. Thus, for a general function of energy, $q(\varepsilon/kT)$, we define

$$\langle q \rangle_{\text{F-D}} \equiv -\frac{2}{3}\frac{1}{F_{1/2}(\eta)}\int_0^\infty q(x)x^{3/2}\frac{\partial f_0}{\partial x}\,dx. \tag{12.11}$$

The concept of the average is also brought out by the observation that

$$F_{1/2}(\eta) = -\frac{2}{3}\int_0^\infty x^{3/2}\frac{\partial f_0}{\partial x}\,dx. \tag{12.11a}$$

The conductivity coefficients can now be written

$$\sigma_{xx}(H) = \frac{ne^2}{m^*}\left\langle \frac{\tau}{1+\omega^2\tau^2} \right\rangle_{\text{F-D}}, \qquad H \equiv H_z, \tag{12.12}$$

---

[170] O. Madelung, pp. 53–62 of the 1957 "Handbuch."[132]

$$\sigma_{xy}(H) = - \frac{ne^2 \omega}{m^*} \left\langle \frac{\tau^2}{1 + \omega^2 \tau^2} \right\rangle_{F-D}, \qquad (12.13)$$

$\omega = eH/m^* c$, and $e > 0$ for electrons.

In principle, $\sigma_{xx}(H)$ and $\sigma_{xy}(H)$ can be evaluated for arbitrary values of H if $\tau(\varepsilon)$ is known. However, numerical integrations are necessary in most cases, and calculations are laborious even for simple energy dependencies such as $\tau \sim \varepsilon^n$. The problem is greatly simplified if one is interested only in the behavior in the limiting cases of weak and strong magnetic fields.

In dealing with transport problems, several investigators have found it advantageous to introduce *complex* gradients.[171,172] In fact, it is shown by Dingle that it is possible to introduce simultaneously two complex operators, one of spatial rotation around the z-axis to account for the two orthogonal components of the electrical and thermal gradients in the xy-plane, and another as a measure of phase lag for treating effects in high-frequency electric fields. This technique has been used by Moore[173] to present in a concise manner general formulae describing both electrical and thermal transport for the gradient vectors in the xy-plane with **H** along the z-axis. Results are also given for the two-band model, i.e., where both electrons and holes contribute to the transport process. Explicit expressions are provided for most of the electrical and thermal effects with and without magnetic fields.

b. Limiting Cases of Weak and of Strong Magnetic Fields

For weak fields the denominators in (12.12) and (12.13) are usually expanded in powers of ω.[174] The results, up to powers of H^2, are

---

[171] E. H. Sondheimer, *Phys. Rev.* **80**, 401 (1950).

[172] R. B. Dingle, *Physica* **22**, 701 (1956).

[173] E. J. Moore, *Australian J. Phys.* **11**, 235 (1958).

[174] Although such expansions are made to render evaluation of the integrals less laborious, certain mathematical difficulties can arise because of the fact that τ and powers thereof are averaged over energy from $\varepsilon = 0$ to $\varepsilon = \infty$. Thus if τ is approximated by an ε^λ dependence and $\lambda < 0$, it is apparent that in the neighborhood of $\varepsilon = 0$, the term $\omega\tau$ can actually become very large for any nonzero value of ω, however small. The expansion is thus invalid in this region. If λ is sufficiently negative the contributions to the integrand from this region can actually cause the integral to diverge. From a physical standpoint, infinite relaxation times are not realistic; additional scattering processes come in for the low-energy electrons.[178]

$$\sigma_{xx}(H) \cong \frac{ne^2}{m^*}\{\langle\tau\rangle_{F-D} - \langle\tau^3\rangle_{F-D}\,\omega^2\}, \qquad \omega\tau \ll 1, \qquad (12.14)$$

$$\sigma_{xy}(H) \cong -\frac{ne^2}{m^*}\langle\tau^2\rangle_{F-D}\,\omega. \qquad\qquad (12.15)$$

For strong fields, the denominator reduces to $\omega^2\tau^2$, and the result is

$$\sigma_{xx}(H) \approx \frac{ne^2}{m^*}\left\langle\frac{1}{\tau}\right\rangle_{F-D}\frac{1}{\omega^2}, \qquad \omega\tau \gg 1 \qquad (12.16)$$

$$\sigma_{xy}(H) \approx -\frac{ne^2}{m^*}\frac{1}{\omega} \approx -\frac{nec}{H}. \qquad\qquad (12.17)$$

In connection with the factor $\langle 1/\tau\rangle_{F-D}$, mathematical difficulties can arise for $\tau \sim \varepsilon^\lambda$, where λ is positive.[175]

It is seen from the preceding development that at weak fields σ_{xx} dominates σ_{xy}, but at high fields the reverse occurs.

An especially interesting point is that the asymptotic form of $\sigma_{xy}(H)$ is *independent of the relaxation time.* Although this fact is shown here specifically for spherical energy surfaces, it is readily established for a general quadratic relation, $\varepsilon(k)$, that $\sigma_{xy}^a(H)$ — the part of $\sigma_{xy}(H)$ which is odd in H — behaves as does (12.17).[65] This independence of $\sigma_{xy}^a(H)$ in the high-magnetic-field limit on the nature of the scattering mechanism has in fact been shown to hold quite generally[176] — for all scattering processes represented by the general collision integral, Eq. (5.8), with no restriction on the shape of the energy surfaces other than that the hodograph in the magnetic field (see Section 6b) be a closed curve.[177] A similar result is obtained by Lifshitz from his quantum-mechanical treatment of conductivity in a magnetic field.[42]

---

[175] The argument is similar to that advanced for the weak-field case[174] except that here the divergences arise for sufficiently large positive values of λ.

[176] J. A. Swanson, *Phys. Rev.* **99**, 1799 (1955).

[177] I. Lifshitz, M. Azbel' and M. Kaganov, *J. Exptl. Theoret. Phys. U.S.S.R.* **30**, 220 (1956) [translation: *Soviet Phys.-JETP* **3**, 143 (1956)].

For certain applications, the relaxation time can be approximated by the simple power-law dependence on energy[178]:

$$\tau = a\varepsilon^\lambda = \tau_0\, x^\lambda. \qquad (12.18)$$

In such cases the averages in (12.14) to (12.16) can be expressed in terms of the Fermi-Dirac functions by means of an integration by parts to yield

$$\sigma_{xx}(H) \cong \frac{2ne^2}{3m^*\,F_{1/2}(\eta)}\,\{\tau_0(\lambda + \tfrac{3}{2})\,F_{\lambda+(1/2)}(\eta) - \omega^2\,\tau_0^3(3\lambda + \tfrac{3}{2})\,F_{3\lambda+(1/2)}(\eta)\},$$

$$\omega\tau \ll 1, \qquad (12.19)$$

$$\sigma_{xy}(H) \cong -\frac{2}{3}\frac{ne^2}{m^*\,F_{1/2}(\eta)}\,\omega\tau_0^2(2\lambda + \tfrac{3}{2})F_{2\lambda+1/2}(\eta), \qquad (12.20)$$

$$\sigma_{xx}(H) \approx \frac{2}{3}\frac{ne^2}{m^*\,F_{1/2}(\eta)}\frac{1}{\omega^2}\frac{1}{\tau_0}\,(\tfrac{3}{2} - \lambda)F_{(1/2)-\lambda}(\eta), \qquad \omega\tau \gg 1. \quad (12.21)$$

---

[178] This approximation, while helpful in certain cases, must be used with caution. Negative values of λ, which are representative of many high-purity semiconductors, yield values of τ which increase rapidly as ε approaches zero. If low-energy charge carriers contribute too strongly to the integrals of the type $\langle \tau^r \rangle_{F-D}$, not only will unrealistic contributions result, but the integrals may actually diverge. This situation has been pointed out by a number of authors,[179] and is discussed in detail by Brooks.[180] Two aspects are involved in the divergence of the integrals: (1) The inadequacy of (12.18) to represent τ satisfactorily over the range of integration $0 \leqslant \varepsilon < \infty$ and (2) the failure of the mathematical expansion of $[1 + \omega^2 \tau^2]^{-1}$ over part of this region. In regard to (1), the relaxation time for low-energy carriers is actually limited by other scattering processes such as those from neutral impurities, dislocations, and ionized impurities. In semiconductors, the latter process, with $\tau \underset{\sim}{a} \varepsilon^{3/2}$, is usually the important one. The difficulty introduced as a result of (1) can be corrected by taking account of composite or mixed scattering — this precludes use of the simple expression (12.18) — or by applying a suitable cutoff to the low energy limit of the integral involving (12.18).[180]

    The difficulty in item (2) can, of course, be overcome by avoiding the expansion and obtaining numerical evaluations. Where classical statistics are applicable, the integrals can sometimes be evaluated in terms of tabulated functions (see Section 15).

    Brooks points out that the factor determining which situation predominates is whether $\omega^2 \tau^2$ is smaller or larger than unity at that energy for which τ reaches its maximum when the scattering process effective at low energies is taken into account.

[179] See, for example, p. 253 of reference 44.

[180] See pp. 130–133 of reference 33; and, in particular, the article by Benedek et al.[329]

For the case of scattering in semiconductors by thermal lattice vibrations through acoustic modes ($\lambda = -\frac{1}{2}$), and scattering by ionized impurities ($\lambda = \frac{3}{2}$), the weak-field expressions reduce to those given by Madelung.[170] For $\lambda = -\frac{1}{2}$, the product $(3\lambda + \frac{3}{2})F_{3\lambda+1/2}(\eta)$ becomes indeterminate. It can be shown that the limit is given by Dingle's function $\mathscr{F}_{-1}(\eta)$, which is identical with $(1 + e^{-\eta})^{-1}$. One can, of course, insert the specific value of λ in (12.18) and evaluate directly the second term of (12.14) by means of (12.11). Since the integrand contains no powers of x, there is no partial integration and one obtains directly $\int_0^\infty df_0(\varepsilon)$. For a scattering process approximated by (12.18) with $\lambda < -\frac{3}{2}$, difficulties can arise with expansions (12.19) and (12.20).[174,178] A similar situation is apparent with (12.21) for $\lambda > \frac{3}{2}$.[175]

Madelung also gives the form of the integrals when mixed scattering by thermal lattice vibrations and ionized impurities is considered. For this case the relaxation time is approximated by

$$1/\tau = 1/\tau_L + 1/\tau_I = (\tau_L{}^0)^{-1} x^{1/2} + (\tau_I{}^0)^{-1} x^{-3/2}. \qquad (12.22)$$

In the present case of exact statistics, the integrals must be evaluated numerically.

c. Conductivity Mobility

We shall define a general conductivity mobility, μ, by the relation[180a]

$$\sigma(H) = -ne\mu(\eta), \qquad e > 0 \text{ for electrons.} \qquad (12.23)$$

The quantity defined above is a function of the reduced Fermi energy η (measured from the bottom of the conduction band for electrons) and of the magnetic field intensity H. The quantity η is often referred to as the degeneracy parameter. The value of the conductivity mobility for

---

[180a] The mobility, which is the charge carrier velocity (suitably averaged) per unit electric field, should strictly carry a negative sign for electrons and a positive sign for holes. This is the convention adopted in (12.23). There is considerable tendency in the literature, however, to regard μ as a positive quantity and to take care of the polarity of the charge carriers explicitly by means of the algebraic signs preceding each term. This latter convention will be adopted here whenever μ is supplied with a subscript to denote a particular band, especially the electron or hole band.

vanishing magnetic fields is denoted by $\mu_0(\eta)$. In the limit of classical statistics, $\eta \ll 0$, the mobility becomes independent of η, and is written as μ and μ_0, respectively.

By using (9.13), (12.12), and (12.13) we find that

$$\mu(\eta) = -\frac{e}{m^*}\left\{\left\langle\frac{\tau}{1+\omega^2\tau^2}\right\rangle_{\mathrm{F-D}} + \omega^2\left\langle\frac{\tau^2}{1+\omega^2\tau^2}\right\rangle^2_{\mathrm{F-D}}\bigg/\left\langle\frac{\tau}{1+\omega^2\tau^2}\right\rangle_{\mathrm{F-D}}\right\}.$$

(12.24)

Unless specified otherwise, it is the zero-magnetic-field mobility which is usually quoted in the literature. Thus (12.24) simplifies greatly to give

$$\mu_0(\eta) = -(e/m^*)\langle\tau\rangle_{\mathrm{F-D}}, \qquad e > 0 \text{ for electrons.} \qquad (12.25)$$

d. Hall Coefficient, Hall Mobility, and Magnetoresistance

The expressions for the Hall coefficient, conductivity, and Hall angle in isotropic media with $\mathbf{H}$ $(0, 0, H)$ and the boundary conditions $J_y = \partial T/\partial x = \partial T/\partial y = 0$ and $E_z = J_z = \partial T/\partial z = 0$ were given in (9.12) to (9.17), namely,

$$R_H = \rho_{yx}(H)/H = \sigma_{xy}(H)/H\,[\sigma_{xx}{}^2(H) + \sigma_{xy}{}^2(H)], \qquad (12.26)$$

$$\sigma(H) = 1/\rho_{xx}(H) = [\sigma_{xx}{}^2(H) + \sigma_{xy}{}^2(H)]/\sigma_{xx}(H), \qquad (12.27)$$

$$E_y/E_x \equiv \tan\theta = \sigma_{xy}(H)/\sigma_{xx}(H) = R_H\,\sigma(H)H. \qquad (12.28)$$

It is not necessary to indicate antisymmetric parts of the ρ_{yx} and the ρ_{xy} (see Section 11b) since in isotropic media there are no symmetric contributions to the off-diagonal elements.

It is customary, especially in the weak-magnetic-field case, to introduce a *Hall mobility*,[181] defined by means of (12.28). Thus

$$\mu^H H/c = \tan\theta, \qquad (12.29)$$

$$\cong \theta, \qquad \theta \ll 1. \qquad (12.29a)$$

---

[181] See, for example, p. 209 of reference 32.

We shall define this mobility parameter in a general manner for arbitrary magnetic fields and degree of degeneracy[182]:

$$\mu^H(\eta) \equiv R_H \sigma(H)c. \tag{12.30}$$

A useful relationship follows from (12.28) and (12.29), namely,

$$\sigma_{xy}(H) = \sigma_{xx}(H)\tan\theta = (\mu^H H/c)\sigma_{xx}(H) \tag{12.30a}$$

$$= R_H \sigma(H)H\sigma_{xx}(H) \qquad (\text{Gaussian units, } H \equiv H_z).$$

The Hall mobility in the limit of vanishing magnetic field is designated by

$$\mu_0^H(\eta) \equiv R_0 \sigma_0 c. \tag{12.31}$$

In the case of classical statistics, the notation is μ^H and μ_0^H, respectively.

The transverse magnetoresistance, Eq. (9.14), in an isotropic system is given by

$$\frac{\Delta\rho}{\rho_0} \equiv \frac{\rho(H)}{\rho_0} - 1 = \frac{\sigma_0}{\sigma(H)} - 1 = \frac{\sigma_{xx}(H)\sigma_{xx}(0) - \sigma_{xx}^2(H) - \sigma_{xy}^2(H)}{\sigma_{xx}^2(H) + \sigma_{xy}^2(H)}. \tag{12.32}$$

The Corbino magnetoresistance (see Section 10b) is measured under the conditions that the transverse electric field, rather than the transverse electric current, be zero. Accordingly, we have

$$(\Delta\rho/\rho_0)_{E_y = 0} = \frac{\sigma_{xx}(0)}{\sigma_{xx}(H)} - 1. \tag{12.33}$$

By means of relations (12.28), the Corbino magnetoresistance can be written in terms of the ordinary transverse magnetoresistance and the Hall angle, thus

---

[182] It is important to keep in mind that the Hall mobility — certainly, as the term is commonly used — is indicative of the electronic processes in a given band. If multiband contributions to the transport occur, then there is associated with *each* band a Hall mobility — as there is also a conductivity mobility. If R is the *measured* Hall coefficient of the material, then (12.30) and (12.31) cannot be used unless single band conduction occurs. To use these expressions for multiband transport, requires that we determine R_H or R_0 *for the band in question.* This situation has caused considerable confusion in the literature. In particular, formulae such as (12.31) have been used in cases where intrinsic conduction is significant (both electrons and holes present) and where there are degenerate valence bands (several types of holes having different effective masses and mobilities).

$$(\Delta\rho/\rho_0)_{E_y=0} = (1 + \tan^2\theta)(\Delta\rho/\rho_0) + \tan^2\theta \qquad (12.34)$$

$$= \Delta\rho/\rho_0 + [\rho(H)/\rho_0]\tan^2\theta \qquad (12.35)$$

$$= \Delta\rho/\rho_0 + R_H^2\,\sigma(H)\sigma(0)H^2 \qquad (12.36)$$

$$= \Delta\rho/\rho_0 + \frac{\mu_0(\eta)}{\mu(\eta)}\left(\frac{\mu^H(\eta)H}{c}\right)^2. \qquad (12.37)$$

The relationship (12.34) has been given by Madelung.[148]

Although explicit expressions can be given for all of the above coefficients by means of (12.12) and (12.13), we shall discuss only the results in the limits of low and high magnetic field strengths. For weak magnetic fields, $\omega\tau \ll 1$, one obtains

$$R_0 = \lim_{H\to 0}\left[\frac{\sigma_{xy}(H)}{H}\right]\cdot\frac{1}{\sigma_{xx}^2(0)} = -\frac{1}{nec}\frac{\langle\tau^2\rangle_{F-D}}{\langle\tau\rangle_{F-D}^2}, \qquad e > 0 \text{ for electrons,} \qquad (12.38)$$

$$\mu_0^H(\eta) = -\frac{e}{m*}\frac{\langle\tau^2\rangle_{F-D}}{\langle\tau\rangle_{F-D}} \qquad (12.39)$$

$$\frac{\mu_0^H(\eta)}{\mu_0(\eta)} = \frac{\langle\tau^2\rangle_{F-D}}{\langle\tau\rangle_{F-D}^2}, \qquad (12.40)$$

$$\frac{\Delta\rho}{\rho_0} = \frac{\langle\tau^3\rangle_{F-D}\langle\tau\rangle_{F-D} - \langle\tau^2\rangle_{F-D}^2}{\langle\tau\rangle_{F-D}^2}\omega^2, \qquad \omega\tau \ll 1, \qquad (12.41)$$

$$\left(\frac{\Delta\rho}{\rho_0}\right)_{E_y=0} = \omega^2\frac{\langle\tau^3\rangle_{F-D}}{\langle\tau\rangle_{F-D}}, \qquad \omega\tau \ll 1. \qquad (12.41a)$$

Thus, in the weak-magnetic-field case,

$$(\Delta\rho/\rho_0)_{E_y=0} = \Delta\rho/\rho_0 + \omega^2\langle\tau^2\rangle_{F-D}^2/\langle\tau\rangle_{F-D}^2 \qquad (12.42)$$

$$= \Delta\rho/\rho_0 + (\mu_0^H H/c)^2. \qquad (12.43)$$

The above expression is obviously the weak-field version of (12.37). In view of (12.25), the condition $\omega\tau \ll 1$ is, for practical purposes, equivalent to

$$\mu_0 H/c \ll 1 \qquad (12.44)$$

where the Gaussian system of units is implied. If laboratory units are used where μ is in cm²/volt-sec and H in gauss, then the condition is

$$\mu_0 H/10^8 \ll 1. \tag{12.45}$$

A significant point, apparent from the preceding, is that the conductivity mobility μ_0 involves an average of τ, the Hall mobility μ_0^H includes averages of τ^2, and the transverse magnetoresistance coefficients include averages of τ^3.

It is also possible to define a magnetoresistance mobility, inasmuch as the dimensions of $\Delta\rho/\rho H^2$ are those of a mobility squared. However, the factor of proportionality is somewhat arbitrary. It is not possible to adopt the same convention as that used for μ_0^H, which in the constant-τ approximation reduces to μ_0. The reason is that the magnetoresistance vanishes for constant τ in our isotropic model. It is necessary, therefore, to base the definition on a model where τ is a simple function of energy — as, for example, the $\varepsilon^{-1/2}$ case representative of thermal scattering. Because of this complication, further discussion of magnetoresistance mobility will be deferred until later. It would be possible, of course, to consider a mobility based on the Corbino magnetoresistance in connection with the constant-τ model. However, it seems better to treat both types of magnetoresistance together (see Section 15b).

For the limiting values in strong magnetic fields, the following relationships develop:

$$R_\infty = \lim_{H \to \infty} [1/H\sigma_{xy}(H)] = -1/nec, \quad e > 0 \text{ for electrons.} \tag{12.46}$$

This particular relationship, (12.46), holds not only for spherical energy surfaces as derived here, but under quite general conditions (see discussion in Section 12b).

Where it is possible experimentally to reach the strong-magnetic-field plateau, Eq. (12.46) is an extremely useful relation. For example, we can obtain very simply the carrier concentration, without being specifically concerned about the scattering mechanism or the shape of the constant-energy surfaces. The *conductivity* mobility is obtained directly through use of (12.23), namely,

$$\mu(\eta) = R_\infty \sigma(H)c \tag{12.47}$$

and

$$\mu_0(\eta) = R_\infty \, \sigma_0 \, c. \tag{12.48}$$

The latter expression was used by Harman et al.[183] to obtain mobilities in p-type germanium.

Furthermore, by measuring both strong- and weak-field Hall plateaus, one has determined the ratio of Hall and conductivity mobilities for weak fields, that is,

$$\mu_0{}^H(\eta)/\mu_0(\eta) = R_0/R_\infty. \tag{12.49}$$

The relation between Hall coefficient and carrier density for a single band is often written as[183a]

$$R_0 = -r/nec, \qquad e > 0 \text{ for electrons} \tag{12.50}$$

where, in general, r depends on the scattering mechanism and on the nature of the energy surfaces. The above expression can be generalized to apply for arbitrary values of H and degeneracy, namely,

$$R_H = -r_H(\eta)/nec, \qquad e > 0 \text{ for electrons.} \tag{12.51}$$

The *Hall coefficient factor* $r_H(\eta)$ depends on H, on the reduced Fermi level η (except in the limit of classical statistics), and on the scattering mechanism. In the general case, it also depends on the band structure. Experimentally, however, it is determined by use of the relation

$$R_H/R_\infty = r_H(\eta). \tag{12.52}$$

For the ordinary transverse magnetoresistance we obtain in the strong-magnetic-field limit

$$\Delta\rho/\rho_0 \approx \langle 1/\tau \rangle_{\text{F}-\text{D}} \langle \tau \rangle_{\text{F}-\text{D}} - 1, \qquad \omega\tau \gg 1 \tag{12.53}$$

and for the Corbino effect,

$$(\Delta\rho/\rho_0)_{E_y=0} \approx \{\omega^2 \langle \tau \rangle_{\text{F}-\text{D}}/\langle 1/\tau \rangle_{\text{F}-\text{D}}\} - 1, \qquad \omega\tau \gg 1 \tag{12.54}$$

$$\approx \{\langle \tau \rangle_{\text{F}-\text{D}}/\langle 1/\tau \rangle_{\text{F}-\text{D}}\}\omega^2. \tag{12.55}$$

Thus, we see that the magnetoresistance becomes independent of ω, i.e., it *saturates* at high fields. The Corbino magnetoresistance, on the other hand, goes as H^2 at large fields. This is to be expected because of

---

[183] T. Harman, R. Willardson, and A. Beer, *Phys. Rev.* **94**, 1065 (1954).
[183a] See, for example, V. A. Johnson and K. Lark-Horovitz, *Phys. Rev.* **79**, 176 (1950).

the loss of the Hall field in the Corbino experiments. Actually, at extremely large values of $\omega\tau$, the Corbino effect is found to deviate from the H^2 curve. Possible causes are influence of minority carriers (Section 17a), inhomogeneities in specimen or magnetic field (Section 27), or orbit quantization effects (Section 28).

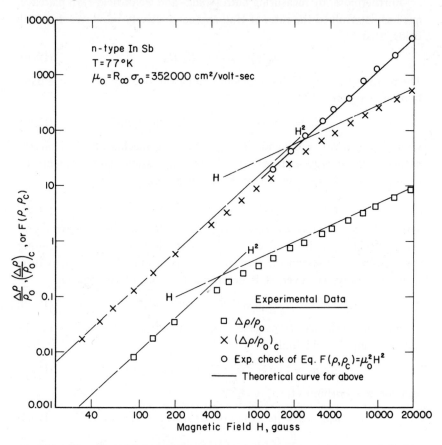

Fig. 10. Magnetic-field dependence of transverse magnetoresistance and Corbino magnetoresistance in InSb specimen. Data are also plotted to provide an experimental check of the theoretical relationship, valid when R_H saturates:

$$\frac{\rho}{\rho_0}\left[\left(\frac{\rho}{\rho_0}\right)_C - \left(\frac{\rho}{\rho_0}\right)\right] \equiv F(\rho, \rho_C) = (\mu_0 H/10^8)^2.$$

The ordinary magnetoresistance was measured on a parallelepiped fabricated from the Corbino disk (after Beer[184]).

One can show quite generally that a deviation in the Corbino magneto-resistance from the H^2 dependence at strong magnetic fields results from a nonsaturation of the ordinary transverse magnetoresistance. This can be seen from the general relation given in Eq. (12.36) which, in the region where the Hall coefficient saturates, can be put in the form

$$\left[\left(\frac{\rho_H}{\rho_0} \right)_{E_y=0} - \left(\frac{\rho_H}{\rho_0} \right) \right] \frac{\rho_H}{\rho_0} = \left(\frac{\mu_0 H}{c} \right)^2, \qquad \frac{\mu_0 H}{c} \gg 1 \qquad (12.55a)$$

where the conductivity mobility is given by Eq. (12.48). If laboratory units (μ in cm²/volt-sec and H in gauss) are used, then the factor c is replaced by 10^8.

An experimental check on relation (12.55a) is available from some unpublished measurements of Bate.[184] The procedure was to measure first the Corbino effect at 77 °K as a function of magnetic field on a disk with soldered annular electrodes. Since the disk was 12.9 mm in diameter and 2.28 mm thick, with a hole 3.35 mm in diameter at the center, it was subsequently possible to cut a sample in the shape of a rectangular parallelepiped, and then to measure directly the Hall effect, resistivity, and transverse magnetoresistance as functions of field at 77 °K. A determination of the resistance of the contacts and connecting leads of the original Corbino disk was then made by subtracting from its measured resistance that resistance calculated using its dimensions and the resistivity measured on the parallelepiped. The total resistance of the contacts and leads was about 35% of the disk resistance at zero field. The Corbino data were then corrected for contact effects by subtracting the contact resistance (assumed independent of magnetic field) from the resistance of the disk in the field. The resulting data, along with those of the transverse magnetoresistance, are shown in Fig. 10. The fairly good coincidence of the circles and the theoretical line indicates a satisfying verification of the relation between Corbino effect, transverse magnetoresistance, and conductivity mobility.

e. Arbitrary Magnetic Field Strengths

When H is arbitrary, expansions are not possible and the fractional functions of the relaxation times shown in (12.12) and (12.13) must be

---

[184] See A. C. Beer, *J. Appl. Phys.* **32**, 2107 (1961).

used. The expression for the conductivity coefficient $\sigma_{xx}(H)$ assumes the following form for the simple power dependence of τ, namely, $\tau = \tau_0\, x^\lambda$:

$$\sigma_{xx}(H) = -\frac{2}{3}\frac{ne^2}{m^*}\frac{\tau_0}{F_{1/2}(\eta)}\int_0^\infty \frac{x^{\lambda+3/2}}{1+\gamma_\lambda x^{2\lambda}}\frac{\partial f_0}{\partial x}dx, \qquad H \equiv H_z \qquad (12.56)$$

where

$$\gamma_\lambda = \omega^2\,\tau_0^2. \qquad (12.57)$$

It is to be noted that $\partial f_0/\partial x$ is a negative quantity.

It is convenient to express τ_0 in terms of the zero-magnetic-field conductivity mobility $\mu_0(\eta)$, where $\sigma_0 = -\, ne\mu_0(\eta)$ [cf. Eq. (12.23)]:

$$\mu_0(\eta) = -\frac{2}{3}\frac{e}{m^*}\frac{(\lambda+\tfrac{3}{2})}{F_{1/2}(\eta)}F_{\lambda+1/2}(\eta)\tau_0, \qquad e > 0 \text{ for electrons.} \qquad (12.58)$$

Thus

$$\sigma_{xx}(H) = ne\mu_0(\eta)[(\lambda+\tfrac{3}{2})F_{\lambda+1/2}(\eta)]^{-1}\int_0^\infty \frac{x^{\lambda+3/2}}{1+\gamma_\lambda x^{2\lambda}}\frac{\partial f_0}{\partial x}dx \qquad (12.59)$$

and

$$\gamma_\lambda = \left[\frac{3F_{1/2}(\eta)}{2(\lambda+\tfrac{3}{2})F_{\lambda+1/2}(\eta)}\right]^2\left[\frac{\mu_0(\eta)H}{c}\right]^2. \qquad (12.60)$$

Similarly, for $\sigma_{xy}(H)$, we obtain[184a]

$$\sigma_{xy}(H) = -\, ne\mu_0(\eta)\gamma_\lambda^{1/2}[(\lambda+\tfrac{3}{2})F_{\lambda+1/2}(\eta)]^{-1}\int_0^\infty \frac{x^{2\lambda+3/2}}{1+\gamma_\lambda x^{2\lambda}}\frac{\partial f_0}{\partial x}dx,$$

$$H \equiv H_z. \qquad (12.61)$$

[184a] In these expressions the sign conventions are: For electrons: e, $\gamma_\lambda^{1/2}$, and $\omega > 0$; $\mu_0 < 0$. For positive carriers e, $\gamma_\lambda^{1/2}$, and $\omega < 0$; $\mu_0 > 0$.

13. COMMONLY ENCOUNTERED SCATTERING MECHANISMS — EXACT STATISTICS

Appropriate descriptions of the scattering of charge carriers in solids, even in the cases considered here where the processes can be represented by relaxation times (Section 6), are complicated, and the transport integrals have been evaluated principally for certain specialized cases. We shall consider the effects of several of the more representative scattering mechanisms on the galvanomagnetic effects.

An analysis of the scattering process itself will not be presented. For information on these aspects, the reader is referred to the review articles by Brooks[185] and by Blatt,[186] to Wilson's book,[187] and to literature to be cited later (e.g., Sections 25, 30, and 31). The case of conduction in thin wires and films of metals is included in an article by Sondheimer.[188] We shall discuss the energy dependence of the relaxation time characteristic of the scattering mechanisms, and shall present explicit evaluations of the transport parameters for each $\tau(\varepsilon)$.

a. Scattering by Thermal Lattice Vibrations

At this point, it is desirable to restrict our scope to semimetals and semiconductors. Most of the preceding developments have been sufficiently general and would apply to metals, with $\eta \gg 1$. The interaction between the charge carriers and the lattice vibrations, however, is very complex. It therefore seems desirable to take advantage of the simplifications which result from the lower concentration of charge carriers.

One of the simplest kinds of interactions between carriers and lattice is the scattering by the longitudinal acoustic modes of the lattice vibrations, i.e., by the emission or absorption of an acoustical phonon. In such a case, the relaxation time is given by[188a]

$$\tau_L = \tau_L{}^0 \, x^{-1/2}. \tag{13.1}$$

---

[185] See p. 144 ff. of reference 33.
[186] See p. 287 ff. of reference 44.
[187] See p. 251 ff. of reference 9.
[188] E. H. Sondheimer, *Advances in Phys.* 1, 1 (1952).
[188a] The designations τ_0 and τ^0 will be used interchangeably in this article to indicate the energy-independent factor in the relaxation time, depending on the particular combinations of subscripts or superscripts.

It will subsequently be shown that the above relation leads to a $T^{-3/2}$ temperature dependence for the conductivity mobility.

Calculations based on (13.1) have been very useful in studying the properties of semiconductors where the temperature and degree of purity were high enough so that the scattering by ionized impurities was not appreciable.[189-191] When fairly good quantitative agreement between theory and experiment is desired, however, it is usually necessary to consider additional mechanisms of interaction between the carriers and the lattice for a number of semiconductors.[186,192] For example, in p-type germanium the influence of the optical modes is significant; in semiconductors with band structure described by the many-valley model, the effect of intervalley scattering may be important. Finally, if there are two unlike atoms in a unit cell so that optical vibrations can produce an electric polarization (polar solids), then further complications occur. These more sophisticated considerations will be discussed later in connection with the individual semiconductor, or class of semiconductors, requiring such treatment.

The form of $\tau_L{}^0$ in (13.1) for acoustical mode scattering has been presented by a number of authors.[187,193,194] The particular result we shall quote here arises most directly from calculations based on the concept of a *deformation potential*.[195,196] This scheme is applicable when strains vary slowly with interatomic distances so that the solid can be treated as a continuum, and local deformations produced by the lattice waves are similar to those in homogeneously deformed crystals. The mobilities of the carriers are related to shifts of the band edges associated with dilatations due to the longitudinal waves. The technique has been extended by Hunter and Nabarro[197] to include inhomogeneously deformed lattices and also the changes in effective masses of the electrons with strain.

---

[189] See, for example, the results given in Shockley's book.[32]
[190] G. L. Pearson and J. Bardeen, *Phys. Rev.* **75**, 865 (1949).
[191] P. P. Debye and E. M. Conwell, *Phys. Rev.* **93**, 693 (1954).
[192] E. M. Conwell, *Proc. I.R.E.* **46**, 1281 (1958).
[193] See p. 560 in the article by Sommerfeld and Bethe.[34c]
[194] F. Seitz, *Phys. Rev.* **73**, 549 (1948).
[195] W. Shockley and J. Bardeen, *Phys. Rev.* **77**, 407 (1950).
[196] J. Bardeen and W. Shockley, *Phys. Rev.* **80**, 72 (1950).
[197] S. C. Hunter and F. R. N. Nabarro, *Proc. Roy. Soc.* **A220**, 542 (1953).

The theory is used to analyze effects of edge and screw dislocations in metals, with specifical calculations for copper and sodium.

The deformation potential calculation gives the following result:

$$\tau_L = \tau_L{}^0 \, x^{-1/2} \tag{13.2}$$

where

$$\tau_L{}^0 = \frac{\pi \hbar^4 \, \rho u_l{}^2}{\sqrt{2} \, E_1{}^2 \, m^{*3/2} (kT)^{3/2}}. \tag{13.3}$$

The parameter ρ is the density of the solid, u_l is the velocity of the longitudinal sound waves, and E_1 is the change in band edge energy per unit dilation. The energy E_1 is related by a numerical factor to the interaction constant C appearing in the earlier theories of lattice mobility.[187, 193, 194] It can be estimated from independent measurements such as changes in energy gap with pressure and with temperature.[186] Since E_1 is essentially constant with temperature, it is seen that $\tau_L{}^0$ varies as $T^{-3/2}$.

When (13.2) is used to evaluate the coefficients defined in the preceding section, one obtains for the conductivity mobility in the zero-magnetic-field limit,

$$\mu_0{}^L(\eta) = -\frac{2}{3} \frac{e \tau_L{}^0}{m^*} \frac{F_0(\eta)}{F_{1/2}(\eta)} = -\frac{\sqrt{2} \, \pi e \hbar^4 \, \rho u_l{}^2 \, F_0(\eta)}{3 E_1{}^2 \, m^{*5/2} (kT)^{3/2} F_{1/2}(\eta)}, \tag{13.4}$$

and for the corresponding Hall mobility

$$\mu_0{}^{H,L}(\eta) = -\frac{1}{2} \frac{e \tau_L{}^0}{m^*} \frac{F_{-1/2}(\eta)}{F_0(\eta)}, \qquad e > 0 \text{ for electrons.} \tag{13.5}$$

Thus, the mobilities have mass and temperature dependencies of $m^{*-5/2}$ and $T^{-3/2}$, respectively, for scattering by acoustic mode lattice vibrations.

The other quantities in the zero-magnetic-field limit are

$$r_0{}^L(\eta) = \frac{\mu_0{}^{H,L}(\eta)}{\mu_0{}^L(\eta)} = \frac{3}{4} \frac{F_{-1/2}(\eta) F_{1/2}(\eta)}{[F_0(\eta)]^2} \tag{13.6}$$

$$\left(\frac{\Delta\rho}{\rho_0}\right)^L \cong (\omega \tau_L{}^0)^2 \left\{ \frac{\mathscr{F}_{-1}(\eta)}{F_0(\eta)} - \frac{1}{4} \left[\frac{F_{-1/2}(\eta)}{F_0(\eta)}\right]^2 \right\}, \qquad \omega \tau_L{}^0 \ll 1 \tag{13.7}$$

where $\mathscr{F}_{-1}(\eta)$ is Dingle's function, Eq. (12.8):

$$\mathscr{F}_{-1}(\eta) = (e^{-\eta} + 1)^{-1}. \qquad (13.8)$$

The Corbino magnetoresistance is given by

$$(\Delta\rho/\rho_0)^L_{E_y=0} \cong (\omega\tau_L^0)^2 \, \mathscr{F}_{-1}(\eta)/F_0(\eta), \qquad \omega\tau_L^0 \ll 1. \qquad (13.9)$$

Both (13.7) and (13.9) can be expressed in terms of the conductivity mobility, since with the use of (13.4) one obtains[184a]

$$\omega\tau_L^0 = -\frac{3}{2}\frac{F_{1/2}(\eta)}{F_0(\eta)}\frac{\mu_0^L H}{c}. \qquad (13.10)$$

In the limit of strong magnetic fields, the corresponding expressions are

$$(\Delta\rho/\rho_0)^L \approx (8/9)\{F_0(\eta)F_1(\eta)/[F_{1/2}(\eta)]^2\} - 1, \qquad \omega\tau_L \gg 1, \qquad (13.10a)$$

$$(\Delta\rho/\rho_0)^L_{E_y=0} \approx \omega^2\tau_L^{02} F_0(\eta)/2F_1(\eta), \qquad \omega\tau_L \gg 1 \qquad (13.11)$$

$$\approx \frac{9}{8}\frac{F_{1/2}^2(\eta)}{F_0(\eta)F_1(\eta)}\left(\frac{\mu_0^L H}{c}\right)^2, \qquad \omega\tau_L \gg 1. \qquad (13.11a)$$

For the case of arbitrary magnetic field strengths, the expressions (12.59 – 12.61) must be utilized. With $\lambda = -\frac{1}{2}$ for lattice scattering, we obtain

$$\sigma_{xx}^L(H) = ne\mu_0^L(\eta)\frac{1}{F_0(\eta)}\int_0^\infty \frac{x^2}{\gamma^L + x}\frac{\partial f_0}{\partial x}\,dx, \qquad e > 0 \text{ for electrons}, \qquad (13.12)$$

$$\sigma_{xy}^L(H) = -ne\mu_0^L(\eta)\frac{(\gamma^L)^{1/2}}{F_0(\eta)}\int_0^\infty \frac{x^{3/2}}{\gamma^L + x}\frac{\partial f_0}{\partial x}\,dx \qquad (13.12a)$$

where

$$\gamma^L = \left[\frac{3F_{1/2}(\eta)}{2F_0(\eta)}\right]^2\left[\frac{\mu_0^L(\eta)H}{c}\right]^2. \qquad (13.12b)$$

It is to be noted that in the present sign convention $\mu_0^L(\eta)$ is negative for transport by electrons.[184a]

b. Scattering by Ionized Impurities

The usual treatments of the scattering of carriers by an array of ionized centers lead to a relaxation time given by an expression of the following type:[198]

$$\tau_I = \frac{K^2(2m^*)^{1/2}(kT)^{3/2}}{\pi e^4 N_I} \frac{x^{3/2}}{g(n^*, T, x)} = \tau_I{}^0 \frac{x^{3/2}}{g(n^*, T, x)} \qquad (13.13)$$

where x is the reduced energy ($\varepsilon \equiv xkT$), $g(n^*, T, x)$ is a slowly varying function, K is the dielectric constant, N_I is the total density of ionized impurities, and n^* depends in general on both N_I and the carrier concentration, i.e., on the degree of compensation.

The problem was originally treated by Conwell and Weisskopf,[199] who considered the Rutherford scattering of each ion independently. The divergence arising from the increasing contributions at small angle scattering was removed by arbitrarily cutting off the scattering cross sections at an angle corresponding to a closest approach of half the average distance between impurities. The Conwell-Weisskopf theory gives the following result for $g(n^*, T, x)$:

$$g(n^*, T, x) = \ln\,[1 + (KkT/e^2 N_I{}^{1/3})^2\, x^2]. \qquad (13.14)$$

In subsequent work by Brooks and Herring[200] and by Dingle,[201] a screened Coulomb potential was used. This screening, which takes care of the divergence difficulty, arises from the fact that charge carriers distribute themselves around the impurity and cancel its field at large distances. Let us designate this screening distance, or Debye-Hückel length, by a, defined in terms of the screened scattering potential

$$|V(r)| = (e/Kr)e^{-r/a}. \qquad (13.15)$$

---

[198] A factor of 2 appears inadvertently to have entered the numerator of this equation given in the articles by Brooks[185] and by Blatt[186]. The result quoted here is in agreement with the results of other authors to be cited later. After averaging over energy, (13.13) yields the same $\mu_0{}^I$ as is quoted in all the literature examined.

[199] E. M. Conwell and V. F. Weisskopf, *Phys. Rev.* **77**, 388 (1950).

[200] See H. Brooks, *Phys. Rev.* **83**, 879 (1951); see also references 185 and 191.

[201] R. B. Dingle, *Phil. Mag.* [7] **46**, 831 (1955).

The slowly varying function g in Eq. (13.13) can then be written[201, 202]

$$g(n^*, T, x) = \ln(1 + z) - z/(1 + z), \qquad z \equiv (2ka)^2 \qquad (13.16)$$

where k is the magnitude of the wave vector of the charge carrier; and the screening distance "a" is a function of n^*, T, and x. It is important to point out that assumptions inherent in the classical derivation, that is, (13.14), require essentially that

$$ka \gg 1. \qquad (13.17)$$

The quantum-mechanical treatment, which leads to (13.16), is based on the Born approximation, and it is pertinent to note that in this range of validity, (13.17) is satisfied for representative values of the parameters.[186, 202] Hence we may state the range of validity of the treatments discussed thus far to be given by

$$z \gg 1. \qquad (13.18)$$

Other considerations pertinent to the range of applicability of conventional scattering theory are discussed in Section 31.

Consideration of the elastic displacements of the lattice as a result of polarization of atoms surrounding the impurity ion was done by Horie.[203] His results give an equation identical to (13.13) except that the slowly varying factor $g(n^*, T, x)$ is more complicated than is the function in (13.14) or (13.16).

When only impurities of one sign are present in the crystal, the screening distance is the same order as the mean distance between impurities and the Conwell-Weisskopf and Brooks-Herring, Dingle treatments give closely the same results. Where compensation occurs, however, and the charge-carrier density is less than the ionized impurity density, the latter formula can give a lower mobility for the same N_I, because of the reduction in screening for smaller n.[191]

By using the results obtained by Dingle, we can write an explicit expression for z, which for a single type of charge carrier can be put in the form

[202] N. Sclar, *Phys. Rev.* **104**, 1548 (1956).
[203] C. Horie, *Sci. Repts. Tôhoku Univ.* **34**, 29 (1950).

$$z = \frac{4Km^*(kT)^2}{\pi e^2 \hbar^2 n} \left[\frac{F_{1/2}(\eta)}{F_{-1/2}(\eta)} \right] x \qquad (13.19)$$

where n is the density of charge carriers in the conduction band, Eq. (12.6). Where both electrons and holes are present, the reference[201] should be consulted.

In the limit of classical statistics, $\eta \ll 0$, relation (13.19) yields the Brooks-Herring expression if n is replaced by n^*. The density n^* can differ slightly from the carrier density n when compensation occurs.[185, 186] The explicit expression will be given in the section dealing with classical statistics.

Evaluation of the transport coefficients presents somewhat of a problem since the integrals containing (13.13) cannot be evaluated analytically. However, in view of the requirement that $z \gg 1$, it is seen from (13.16) and (13.19) that $g(n^*, T, x)$ is a slowly varying function of x, so that fairly good approximations are possible. The procedure is to evaluate the function $g(n^*, T, x)$ at an appropriately chosen value of x, designated by $\bar{x}$, and thus to take it outside the integral. One thereby obtains

$$\langle \tau_I{}^s \rangle_{F-D} \cong -\frac{2}{3} \frac{1}{F_{1/2}(\eta)} \left[\frac{\tau_I{}^0}{g(n^*, T, \bar{x})} \right]^s \int_0^\infty x^{3(s+1)/2} \frac{\partial f_0}{\partial x} dx. \qquad (13.20)$$

The value of $\bar{x}$ is commonly determined by the condition that the integrand remaining after the removal of $g(n^*, T, \bar{x})$ be a maximum at $x = \bar{x}$. This technique was used in the original calculations by Conwell and Weisskopf. An alternative procedure, suggested by Dingle,[201] is to choose $\bar{x}$ as that value which, when used as an upper limit cutoff for the integral remaining after removal of $g(n^*, T, x)$, yields a median value. Since the first method of determining $\bar{x}$ appears most consistently in the literature, it will be considered further. It would, however, be interesting to have a quantitative comparison of the two techniques.

For determining transport coefficients in the limiting cases of weak and of strong magnetic fields — and because of the complicated integrals these are the only examples which will be considered in the case where an arbitrary degree of degeneracy exists — it is necessary to know averages of different powers of τ_I. These are given in (13.20), where $\bar{x}$ is determined by the condition

$$[x^{3(s+1)/2}(\partial f_0/\partial x)]_{x=\bar{x}} = \text{maximum.} \qquad (13.21)$$

From the above, one obtains

$$[\bar{x} - 3(s+1)/2] = [\bar{x} + 3(s+1)/2]\exp(\eta - \bar{x}). \qquad (13.22)$$

It is important to note that $\bar{x}$ depends on s and on η (except in the classical limit). The significance of this point has been brought out by Mansfield.[204, 205]

Carrying out the integration in (13.20) gives

$$\langle \tau_I{}^s \rangle_{\text{F}-\text{D}} \cong \frac{2}{3}\left[\frac{3s+3}{2}\right]\frac{F_{(3s+1)/2}(\eta)}{F_{1/2}(\eta)}\left[\frac{\tau_I{}^0}{g(\bar{x}_{s,\eta})}\right]^s \qquad (13.23)$$

where $g(n^*, T, \bar{x}_{s,\eta})$ is abbreviated by $g(\bar{x}_{s,\eta})$ with $\bar{x}_{s,\eta}$ given by the solution of (13.22) for the appropriate values of s and η. The quantity $\tau_I{}^0$ is defined in (13.13).

The mobilities and galvanomagnetic coefficients representative of ionized impurity scattering are then given by

$$\mu_0{}^I(\eta) = -\frac{2F_2(\eta)}{F_{1/2}(\eta)}\frac{e\tau_I{}^0}{m^* g(\bar{x}_{1,\eta})} = -\frac{2F_2(\eta)}{F_{1/2}(\eta)}\left\{\frac{2^{1/2}K^2(kT)^{3/2}}{\pi e^3 m^{*1/2}N_I g(\bar{x}_{1,\eta})}\right\}, \qquad (13.24)$$

$$\mu_0{}^{H,I}(\eta) = -\frac{3}{2}\frac{F_{7/2}(\eta)g^2(\bar{x}_{1,\eta})}{F_2(\eta)g^2(\bar{x}_{2,\eta})}\left\{\frac{2^{1/2}K^2(kT)^{3/2}}{\pi e^3 m^{*1/2}N_I g(\bar{x}_{1,\eta})}\right\}, \qquad (13.25)$$

$$r_0{}^I(\eta) = \frac{\mu_0{}^{H,I}(\eta)}{\mu_0{}^I(\eta)} = \frac{3}{4}\frac{F_{7/2}(\eta)F_{1/2}(\eta)g^2(\bar{x}_{1,\eta})}{F_2{}^2(\eta)g^2(\bar{x}_{2,\eta})}, \qquad (13.26)$$

$$\left(\frac{\Delta\rho}{\rho_0}\right)^I \cong \left\{\frac{2F_5(\eta)g^3(\bar{x}_{1,\eta})}{F_2(\eta)g^3(\bar{x}_{3,\eta})} - \left[\frac{3F_{7/2}(\eta)g^2(\bar{x}_{1,\eta})}{2F_2(\eta)g^2(\bar{x}_{2,\eta})}\right]^2\right\}\left[\frac{\omega\tau_I{}^0}{g(\bar{x}_{1,\eta})}\right]^2, \qquad \frac{\omega\tau_I{}^0}{g} \ll 1$$

$$(13.27)$$

$$\left(\frac{\Delta\rho}{\rho_0}\right)^I_{E_y=0} \cong \frac{2F_5(\eta)g^3(\bar{x}_{1,\eta})}{F_2(\eta)g^3(\bar{x}_{3,\eta})}\left[\frac{\omega\tau_I{}^0}{g(\bar{x}_{1,\eta})}\right]^2, \qquad \frac{\omega\tau_I{}^0}{g} \ll 1. \qquad (13.28)$$

[204] R. Mansfield, *Proc. Phys. Soc. (London)* **B69**, 76 (1956).
[205] R. Mansfield, *Proc. Phys. Soc. (London)* **B69**, 862 (1956).

In the limit of strong magnetic fields, one obtains

$$\left(\frac{\Delta\rho}{\rho_0}\right)^I \approx \frac{4\mathscr{F}_{-1}(\eta)F_2(\eta)g(x^*_{-1,\eta})}{3\,[F_{1/2}(\eta)]^2\,g(\bar{x}_{1,\eta})} - 1, \qquad \frac{\omega\tau_I{}^0}{g} \gg 1, \qquad (13.29)$$

$$\left(\frac{\Delta\rho}{\rho_0}\right)^I_{E_y=0} \approx \frac{3F_2(\eta)g(\bar{x}_{1,\eta})}{\mathscr{F}_{-1}(\eta)g(x^*_{-1,\eta})}\,[\omega\tau_I{}^0/g(\bar{x}_{1,\eta})]^2, \qquad \frac{\omega\tau_I{}^0}{g} \gg 1. \qquad (13.30)$$

The parameter x^*_{-1} is introduced inasmuch as the treatment culminating in Eq. (13.22) breaks down when $s = -1$, since in such cases the integrand with $g(x)$ constant no longer possess a maximum. The designation $\bar{x}_{-1}$, therefore, has no meaning. The x^*_{-1} can, however, be determined by the method of Dingle [see discussion following (13.20)], or the complete integrand including the $g(x)$ can be handled by numerical methods.

The factor $\omega\tau_I{}^0/g$ can be expressed in terms of the conductivity mobility at zero magnetic field by means of (13.24), thus

$$\frac{\omega\tau_I{}^0}{g(\bar{x}_{1,\eta})} = -\left[\frac{F_{1/2}(\eta)}{2F_2(\eta)}\right]\left[\frac{\mu_0{}^I(\eta)H}{c}\right], \qquad \mu_0{}^I(\eta) < 0 \text{ for electrons.} \quad (13.31)$$

Several investigators have made studies of the range of validity of the simplified treatment of the impurity scattering problem presented in this section. Inasmuch as explicit results were obtained only for the case of classical statistics, detailed discussion will be deferred until later. We shall point out here, however, that it is generally desirable to take account of the behavior of $g(n^*, T, \bar{x}_{s,\eta})$ when plotting the temperature dependence of $\mu_0{}^I(\eta)$ and $\mu_0{}^{H,I}(\eta)$. Also in calculating $r_0{}^I(\eta)$ for relating the Hall coefficient and carrier density, it is best to determine the values of $g(\bar{x}_2, \eta)$ and of $g(\bar{x}_1, \eta)$, rather than to replace their ratio by unity.[204, 205] In any case, it appears quite essential that the theory be applied only for those cases where $z \gg 1$, as specified in (13.18).

The general expressions (12.59) – (12.61) for the case of arbitrary magnetic field strengths, when used with the relaxation times given in this section, yield formally:

$$\sigma^I_{xx}(H) = ne\mu_0{}^I(\eta)\,\frac{g(\bar{x}_{1,\eta})}{3F_2(\eta)}\int_0^\infty \frac{x^3}{1 + [\omega\tau_I{}^0/g(x)]^2\,x^3}\,\frac{1}{g(x)}\,\frac{\partial f_0}{\partial x}\,dx, \quad (13.32)$$

$$\sigma^I_{xy}(H) = ne\mu_0{}^I(\eta) \frac{F_{1/2}(\eta)g^2(\bar{x}_{1,\eta})}{6F_2{}^2(\eta)} \frac{\mu_0{}^I H}{c} \int_0^\infty \frac{x^{9/2}}{1 + [\omega\tau_I{}^0/g(x)]^2 x^3} \frac{1}{g^2(x)} \frac{\partial f_0}{\partial x} dx$$

(13.33)

where $e > 0$ and $\mu_0{}^I(\eta) < 0$, for transport by electrons. The value of $\bar{x}_{1,\eta}$ is given from (13.22) with $s = 1$; the $g(x)$ is, of course, the function written as $g(n^*, T, x)$ in (13.13).

In the above equations, $g(x)$ now also occurs in the binomial denominator. Therefore, the method for obtaining an approximate value of the integral by replacing $g(x)$ by a constant $g(\bar{x})$, is not so simple as in the case of (13.20). The value of $\bar{x}$ — that is, the value of x which causes the integrand with the $g(x)$ replaced by $g(\bar{x})$ to be a maximum — is now a function of $\omega\tau_I{}^0/g(\bar{x})$ as well as of η. For arbitrary values of η, there is not an overwhelming advantage in using this procedure, inasmuch as a numerical integration is still necessary after the $g(x)$ is replaced by $g(\bar{x})$. Therefore, one might as well work directly with the integrand containing the $g(x)$. This is obviously true if results are required for only one value of n^* and of T [see Eq. (13.16) and following] so that the other parameters in $g(x)$ are constant. Of course, if a number of values of n^* and T are to be used, the $g(\bar{x})$ technique can save repeated numerical integrations. With classical statistics, on the other hand, the simpler integral can be evaluated in terms of tabulated functions, and numerical integrations are avoided.

The simplest approximation is to neglect the difference between $g(\bar{x}_{1,\eta,\omega})$ and $g(\bar{x}_{1,\eta})$. In such a case the g's drop out of (13.32) except for the magnetic field parameter, which is then given by (13.31). In (13.33), of course, the factor $[g(\bar{x}_{1,\eta})/g(\bar{x}_{2,\eta})]^2$ will enter. No information is available to the error introduced either by this approximation or by the procedure involving determination of the $\bar{x}$ appropriate to the particular value of $\omega\tau_I{}^0/g(\bar{x})$.

c. Mixed Scattering

A more realistic treatment of the relaxation process involves consideration of two or more scattering mechanisms, the effectiveness of each being dependent on the energy of the charge carrier.[178] This requirement becomes especially stringent when galvanomagnetic data are studied over a wide range of temperatures. For the two scattering mechanisms discussed in the preceding sections, it is seen that at high temperatures the relaxation time is limited principally by interaction of the charge carriers with the lattice vibrations; at low temperatures, by the interaction with ionized impurities. Inclusion of these particular processes in the transport integrals provides a composite scattering system which has been studied frequently in the literature.

Since $1/\tau_i$ is proportional to the probability of scattering by mechanism i, one obtains for the case of mixed scattering by lattice vibrations and ionized impurities

$$1/\tau = 1/\tau_L + 1/\tau_I. \tag{13.34}$$

This representation assumes, of course, that the two scattering processes can be regarded as independent of each other. For a further discussion of this point, consult Section 30b.

Hence, from (13.2) and (13.13),

$$\tau = \frac{\tau_L{}^0 \, x^{3/2}}{(\tau_L{}^0/\tau_I{}^0)g(x) + x^2} \tag{13.35}$$

where g is the slowly varying function of n, T, and x discussed previously.

Because of the complexity of the integrals, the application of (13.35) is usually restricted to the limiting cases of weak or strong magnetic fields or to where classical statistics are applicable. The transport coefficients in the former case will depend on averages of powers of τ, thus:

$$\langle \tau^s \rangle_{\text{F}-\text{D}} = -\frac{2}{3} \frac{(\tau_L{}^0)^s}{F_{1/2}(\eta)} \int_0^\infty \frac{x^{3(s+1)/2}}{[x^2 + (\tau_L{}^0/\tau_I{}^0)g(x)]^s} \frac{\partial f_0}{\partial x} \, dx. \tag{13.36}$$

To simplify the above integral by the $g(\bar{x})$ technique requires that $\bar{x}$ be chosen so that

$$\frac{x^{3(s+1)/2}}{(x^2 + \beta)^s} \frac{e^{x-\eta}}{(1 + e^{x-\eta})^2} = \text{maximum} \tag{13.37}$$

where

$$\beta \equiv (\tau_L{}^0/\tau_I{}^0)g(\bar{x}_{s,\eta,\beta}). \tag{13.38}$$

The solution for (13.37) is

$$\frac{(3-s)\bar{x}^2 + 3(s+1)\beta}{2(\bar{x}^3 + \beta\bar{x})} = \frac{e^{\bar{x}-\eta}-1}{e^{\bar{x}-\eta}+1} = \tanh\frac{\bar{x}-\eta}{2} \qquad (13.39)$$

where $\bar{x} \equiv \bar{x}_{s,\eta,\beta}$. A relation such as the above, for $s = 1$, has been given by Mansfield.[204]

It is seen that x is a function of s, η, and β. For $\beta \to \infty$, (13.39) reduces to (13.22) as it should, since then τ is determined by the ionized impurity scattering. For arbitrary values of η, if results are required only for a single value of n^* and T, it is probably expedient to do the numerical integration on (13.36) directly, as was suggested in connection with (13.32).

It is often convenient to express the "actual" mobility $\mu_0(\eta)$ when mixed scattering occurs in terms of the mobility $\mu_0^L(\eta)$, due to lattice scattering and the mobility $\mu_0^I(\eta)$ due to ionized impurities.

With the use of (12.25), (13.4), (13.24), (13.36), and (13.38) it is seen that

$$\mu_0(\eta) = \frac{\mu_0^L(\eta)}{F_0(\eta)} \int_0^\infty \frac{x^3}{x^2+\beta} \frac{e^{x-\eta}}{(1+e^{x-\eta})^2} \, dx \qquad (13.40)$$

where

$$\beta = 3 \frac{F_2(\eta)}{F_0(\eta)} \frac{\mu_0^L(\eta)}{\mu_0^I(\eta)} \frac{g(\bar{x}_{1,\eta,\beta})}{g(\bar{x}_{1,\eta,\infty})}. \qquad (13.41)$$

Numerical integrations were done on Eq. (13.40) for a sequence of values of η, and results are presented in Fig. 11.

In the classical case, $\eta < -4$, the integral can be evaluated exactly in terms of sine and cosine integrals, and the results have been plotted by Conwell.[206] In the case of extreme degeneracy, the integrand is large only for energies near the Fermi level, and hence the mobilities combine as do the relaxation times; that is,

$$1/\mu_0 = 1/\mu_0^L + 1/\mu_0^I, \qquad \eta \gg 0. \qquad (13.42)$$

It is seen from Fig. 11 that this relation is approximated quite closely when $\eta > 10$. It is also evident that the use of (13.42) for semiconductors,

[206] E. M. Conwell, *Proc. I.R.E.* **40**, 1327 (1952).

as was done in some of the early literature, can be a rather rough approximation when the two mobilities are nearly equal.

A numerical evaluation of (13.40) has also been carried out by Mansfield.[204] His results are presented in a slightly different form, which involves sums of partial resistivities. It is to be noted that Mansfield's

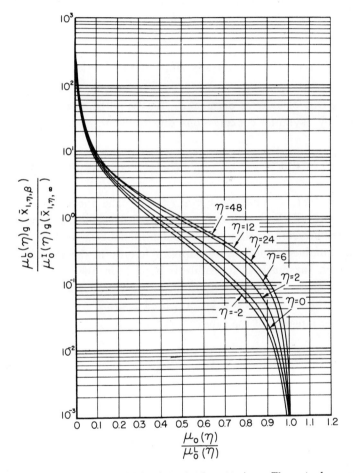

FIG. 11. Composition of mobilities for mixed scattering. The actual or resultant conductivity mobility, at weak-magnetic-field strengths, is denoted by $\mu_0(\eta)$. The mobility due to scattering by lattice vibrations is $\mu_0^L(\eta)$; that due to scattering by ionized impurities is $\mu_0^I(\eta)$. The slowly varying functions $g(\bar{x})$ are discussed in the text.

σ_I is equivalent to our $\sigma_0{}^I$ multiplied by the factor $g(\bar{x}_{1,\eta,\infty})/g(\bar{x}_{1,\eta,\beta})$. Solutions of (13.39), for $s = 1$, are also presented in graphical form so that $\bar{x}_{1,\eta,\beta}$ is readily determined.

Other conductivity coefficients can be expressed through the use of Eqs. (13.36)–(13.39) for higher values of s. The general form of the relationship will not be given here; instead, the results for classical statistics are presented in Section 15.

14. Conductivity Coefficients in the Limit of Extreme Degeneracy

In the case of extreme degeneracy, the Fermi-Dirac functions can be replaced by asymptotic expressions due to Sommerfeld and others[207]:

$$F_k(\eta) \approx \frac{\eta^{k+1}}{k+1} + \frac{\pi^2}{6} k\eta^{k-1} + \ldots, \qquad \eta \gg 1 \qquad (14.1)$$

where $\eta = \zeta/kT$, ζ being the Fermi energy. The above expansion can be used with all the coefficients which were developed in terms of the $F_k(\eta)$ in the preceding sections. The results will not be given here, however, since most of those equations were applicable only in the weak-magnetic-field region. Inasmuch as it readily is possible in the case of extreme degeneracy to develop relationships which are valid for arbitrary values of H, such development will be presented instead.

Consider integrals of the type

$$\int_0^\infty G(\varepsilon) \frac{\partial f_0}{\partial \varepsilon} \partial \varepsilon \qquad (14.2)$$

where $G(\varepsilon)$ is any well-behaved function of energy, and f_0 is the Fermi-Dirac distribution function, $[1 + e^{(\varepsilon-\zeta)/kT}]^{-1}$. It was pointed out by Sommerfeld and Bethe[208] that as the carriers become more degenerate — that is, at larger values of ζ/kT — the derivative $\partial f_0/\partial \varepsilon$ becomes

---

[207] See, for example, E. C. Stoner, *Phil. Mag.* [7] **21**, 145 (1936). The result is given in reference 166, except for a typographical error in the Eq. (5.3).

[208] See p. 344 of reference 34c.

increasingly larger and sharper in the neighborhood of $\varepsilon = \zeta$. In the limiting case of $T \to 0$, it approaches a δ-function. A good approximation to (14.2) is, therefore, obtained by expanding $G(\varepsilon)$ about $\varepsilon = \eta$. Details have been presented by Seitz[209] and more recently in other works.[210] The result to second-order terms, is

$$\int_0^\infty G(\varepsilon) \frac{\partial f_0}{\partial \varepsilon}\, d\varepsilon = -\, G(\zeta) - \frac{\pi^2}{6}\, (kT)^2 \left(\frac{d^2 G(\varepsilon)}{d\varepsilon^2} \right)_{\varepsilon\,=\,\zeta} - \; \ldots, \qquad \zeta/kT \gg 1$$

(14.3)

or, since $\varepsilon = x kT$ and $\zeta = \eta kT$, we have

$$\int_0^\infty G(x) \frac{\partial f_0}{\partial x}\, dx = -\, G(\eta) - \frac{\pi^2}{6} \left(\frac{d^2 G(x)}{dx^2} \right)_{x\,=\,\eta} - \; \ldots. \tag{14.4}$$

With the use of the *first* term in the above approximation, Eqs. (12.12) and (12.13) become

$$\sigma_{xx}(H) = \frac{ne^2}{m^*}\, \frac{\tau(\eta)}{1 + \omega^2\, \tau^2(\eta)}, \qquad \eta \gg 1, \quad H \equiv H_z, \tag{14.5}$$

$$\sigma_{xy}(H) = -\, \frac{ne^2\, \omega}{m^*}\, \frac{\tau^2(\eta)}{1 + \omega^2\, \tau^2(\eta)} \tag{14.6}$$

where the first term of (14.1) has been used to approximate $F_{1/2}(\eta)$. From these results it is readily found [using Eqs. (12.26), (12.27), and (12.51)] that

$$\lim_{\eta \to \infty}\, [r_H(\eta)] = 1, \tag{14.7}$$

$$\lim_{\eta \to \infty}\, \frac{\Delta\rho}{\rho_0} = 0. \tag{14.8}$$

Thus, for spherical energy surfaces and isotropic relaxation times, the Hall coefficient factor is unity and the magnetoresistance vanishes, in

[209] See p. 147 *in* F. Seitz, "The Modern Theory of Solids." McGraw-Hill, New York, 1940.

[210] See p. 13 of reference 9; p. 205 of reference 44.

the limit of extreme degeneracy, regardless of the magnetic field strength and of the dependence of τ on energy.

Actually, the relations (14.5)–(14.8) are obvious from physical considerations. In the degenerate limit, only those charge carriers having energies of the Fermi surface contribute to transport. Therefore, insofar as the integrals are concerned, the situation is one of constant τ, with $\tau = \tau(\zeta)$.

To obtain a nonzero magnetoresistance, we must consider higher order terms in (14.3), that is derivatives of τ with respect to energy. From (12.12), (12.13), and (12.27) it is readily shown that the transverse magnetoresistance can be written in the form

$$\Delta \rho / \rho_H \equiv 1 - \sigma_H / \sigma_0 = E\omega^2 \tag{14.9}$$

or

$$\Delta \rho / \rho_0 \equiv (\sigma_0 / \sigma_H) - 1 = E\omega^2 / [1 - E\omega^2] \tag{14.10}$$

where

$$E \equiv \frac{\langle \tau^3 [1 + \omega^2 \tau^2]^{-1} \rangle_{\text{F-D}} \langle \tau [1 + \omega^2 \tau^2]^{-1} \rangle_{\text{F-D}} - \langle \tau^2 [1 + \omega^2 \tau^2]^{-1} \rangle^2_{\text{F-D}}}{\langle \tau \rangle_{\text{F-D}} \langle \tau [1 + \omega^2 \tau^2]^{-1} \rangle_{\text{F-D}}}.$$

$$\tag{14.11}$$

In the above development, use was made of the identity

$$\langle \tau [1 + \omega^2 \tau^2]^{-1} \rangle_{\text{F-D}} \equiv \langle \tau \rangle_{\text{F-D}} - \omega^2 \langle \tau^3 [1 + \omega^2 \tau^2]^{-1} \rangle_{\text{F-D}}. \tag{14.12}$$

As we saw before, to obtain a nonvanishing E, we must include the second term of the approximation (14.4). The algebra, which is somewhat tedious, is simplified by a substitution such as

$$z = \tau x^{3/2} (1 + \omega^2 \tau^2)^{-1}. \tag{14.13}$$

Also from (12.11), (14.1), and (14.4) it is seen that

$$\langle q \rangle_{\text{F-D}} \cong q(\eta) + \frac{\pi^2}{6} \eta^{-3/2} \left[\frac{d^2(q x^{3/2})}{dx^2} \right]_{x=\eta} + \cdots, \qquad \eta \gg 1. \tag{14.14}$$

The expression for E, to terms in τ', is found to be

$$E = \frac{\pi^2}{3} \frac{\tau'^2}{1 + \omega^2 \tau^2}, \qquad \eta \gg 1 \tag{14.15}$$

where $\tau' \equiv d\tau/dx$. Hence

$$\frac{\Delta\rho}{\rho_H} = \frac{\pi^2}{3} \frac{(kT)^2 \omega^2}{1 + \omega^2 \tau^2} \left(\frac{d\tau}{d\varepsilon}\right)^2_{\varepsilon = \zeta}, \qquad \eta \gg 1, \tag{14.16}$$

$$\frac{\Delta\rho}{\rho_0} = \frac{\pi^2}{3} \frac{(kT)^2 \omega^2}{1 + \omega^2 \tau^2} \left(\frac{d\tau}{d\varepsilon}\right)^2_{\varepsilon = \zeta} \Bigg/ \left[1 - \frac{\pi^2}{3} \frac{(kT)^2 \omega^2}{1 + \omega^2 \tau^2} \left(\frac{d\tau}{d\varepsilon}\right)^2_{\varepsilon = \zeta}\right], \qquad \eta \gg 1. \tag{14.17}$$

It is sometimes customary to express results in terms of a mean free path $l(= v\tau)$, as has been done in discussions of (14.16).[31a]

15. Conductivity Coefficients in the Limit of Classical Statistics

When the temperature is relatively high and the charge-carrier density sufficiently low so that there are a number of unoccupied energy states at low energies, then Maxwell-Boltzmann or classical statistics are applicable. In such cases, $\partial f_0/\partial \varepsilon$ looses its sharpness at $\varepsilon = \zeta$,[211] and contributions to the transport integrals occur throughout a wide range of ε. In these cases, $\eta \ll 0$, so that

$$f_0 \simeq e^\eta e^{-x}, \qquad \partial f_0/\partial x \simeq -e^\eta e^{-x}, \qquad \eta \ll 0 \tag{15.1}$$

and it is readily established that[166]

$$F_k(\eta) \simeq k! \cdot e^\eta, \qquad \eta \ll 0. \tag{15.2}$$

It also follows from (12.6) that

$$n = \frac{1}{4\pi^3} \left(\frac{2\pi m^* kT}{\hbar^2}\right)^{3/2} e^\eta. \tag{15.3}$$

All of the relationships developed in Sections 12–14 are readily applied to the present case through the use of (15.2). However, because of the simpler form of $\partial f_0/\partial x$ for classical statistics, many of the developments have been carried further. These will be discussed subsequently. The average of a quantity over the classical distribution, cf. (12.11), is given by

$$\langle q \rangle \equiv \frac{4}{3\sqrt{\pi}} \int_0^\infty q(x) x^{3/2} e^{-x} dx. \tag{15.4}$$

---

[211] See for example, Fig. 2, p. 145 of reference 209.

a. Limiting Cases of Weak and of Strong Magnetic Fields

(1) *General power law scattering.* For the simple scattering law of (12.18), the conductivities assume the following form:

$$\sigma_{xx}(H) \simeq \frac{ne^2}{m^*} \frac{4}{3\sqrt{\pi}} \{\tau_0(\lambda + \tfrac{3}{2})! - \omega^2 \tau_0^3 (3\lambda + \tfrac{3}{2})!\}, \qquad H \equiv H_z, \quad \omega\tau \ll 1,$$

$$(15.5)$$

$$\sigma_{xy}(H) \simeq -\frac{ne^2}{m^*} \frac{4}{3\sqrt{\pi}} \omega\tau_0^2 (2\lambda + \tfrac{3}{2})!, \qquad \omega > 0, \text{ for electrons} \qquad (15.6)$$

$$\sigma_{xx}(H) \approx \frac{ne^2}{m^*} \frac{4}{3\sqrt{\pi}} \frac{1}{\omega^2} \frac{1}{\tau_0} (\tfrac{3}{2} - \lambda)!, \qquad H \equiv H_z, \quad \omega\tau \gg 1 \qquad (15.7)$$

and, of course,

$$\sigma_{xy}(H) \approx - nec/H, \qquad \omega\tau \gg 1, \quad e > 0 \text{ for electrons.} \qquad (15.8)$$

It thus follows that[184a]

$$\mu_0 = - [e\tau_0/m^*] [4(\lambda + \tfrac{3}{2})!/(3\sqrt{\pi})], \qquad (15.9)$$

$$r_0 \equiv \mu_0^H/\mu_0 = [3\sqrt{\pi}/4] [(2\lambda + \tfrac{3}{2})!] [(\lambda + \tfrac{3}{2})!]^{-2} \qquad (15.10)$$

$$\omega\tau_0 \text{ (or}^{188a} \omega\tau^0) = - [3\sqrt{\pi}/4(\lambda + \tfrac{3}{2})!] [\mu_0 H/c] \equiv \gamma_\lambda^{1/2}, \qquad (15.11)$$

$$\frac{\Delta\rho}{\rho_0} \simeq \left\{ \frac{(3\lambda + \tfrac{3}{2})!}{(\lambda + \tfrac{3}{2})!} - \frac{[(2\lambda + \tfrac{3}{2})!]^2}{[(\lambda + \tfrac{3}{2})!]^2} \right\} \gamma_\lambda, \qquad \gamma_\lambda \ll 1, \qquad (15.12)$$

$$(\Delta\rho/\rho_0)_{E_y = 0} \simeq \{(3\lambda + \tfrac{3}{2})!/(\lambda + \tfrac{3}{2})!\}\gamma_\lambda, \qquad \gamma_\lambda \ll 1, \qquad (15.13)$$

$$\Delta\rho/\rho_0 \approx \{(16/9\pi)(\lambda + \tfrac{3}{2})! \cdot (\tfrac{3}{2} - \lambda)!\} - 1, \qquad \gamma_\lambda \gg 1, \qquad (15.14)$$

$$(\Delta\rho/\rho_0)_{E_y = 0} \approx \{(\lambda + \tfrac{3}{2})!/(\tfrac{3}{2} - \lambda)!\}\gamma_\lambda, \qquad \gamma_\lambda \gg 1. \qquad (15.15)$$

(2) *Acoustic phonon scattering.* From (13.1) it is seen that $\lambda = - \tfrac{1}{2}$. The expressions in most common use are as follows:

$$\mu_0^L = - [e\tau_L^0/m^*][4/3\sqrt{\pi}], \qquad e > 0 \text{ for electrons,} \qquad (15.16)$$

$$r_0^L \equiv \mu_0^{H,L}/\mu_0^L = 3\pi/8, \qquad (15.17)$$

$$\omega \tau_L{}^0 = - [3 \sqrt{\pi}/4][\mu_0{}^L H/c] \equiv (\gamma^L)^{1/2}, \tag{15.18}$$

$$(\Delta \rho/\rho_0)^L \cong [1 - \pi/4]\gamma^L, \qquad \gamma^L \ll 1, \tag{15.19}$$

$$(\Delta \rho/\rho_0)^L_{E_y = 0} \cong \gamma^L, \qquad \gamma^L \ll 1, \tag{15.20}$$

$$(\Delta \rho/\rho_0)^L \approx (32/9\pi) - 1, \qquad \gamma^L \gg 1, \tag{15.21}$$

$$(\Delta \rho/\rho_0)^L_{E_y = 0} \approx \tfrac{1}{2}\gamma^L, \qquad \gamma^L \gg 1. \tag{15.22}$$

The temperature dependence of $\tau_L{}^0$ is given by (13.3), and $(\gamma^L)^{1/2}$ is positive for electrons; negative for holes.[184a]

(3) *Ionized impurity scattering.* From the results given in Section 13b, it is readily found that

$$\mu_0{}^I = - \frac{8}{\sqrt{\pi}} \frac{e\tau_I{}^0}{m^* g(\bar{x}_1)} = - \frac{8}{\sqrt{\pi}} \left\{ \frac{2^{1/2} K^2 (kT)^{3/2}}{\pi e^3 m^{*1/2} N_I g(\bar{x}_1)} \right\} \tag{15.23}$$

where N_I is the total ionized impurity concentration and where

$$g(x) \equiv g(n^*, T, x) = \ln(1 + z) - z/(1 + z) \tag{15.24}$$

in the Brooks-Herring treatment, with

$$z = \frac{2Km^*(kT)^2}{\pi e^2 \hbar^2 n^*} x. \tag{15.25}$$

The effective shielding ion density n^* is identical with the carrier concentration n for an extrinsic semiconductor with no compensation and when the impurity level is fully ionized. For the case where the impurity level of total density N_D is only partially ionized, Brooks' result is[185]

$$n^* = n(2 - n/N_D). \tag{15.26}$$

Where compensation occurs — that is, an acceptor level of density N_A exists — the expression for an n-type extrinsic semiconductor with N_A assumed fully ionized has the form[185, 186]

$$n^* = n + [n + N_A][1 - (n + N_A)/N_D]. \tag{15.27}$$

For p-type specimens, n is the concentration of carriers in the valence band, and N_A and N_D in (15.27) are to be interchanged.

The quantity $\bar{x}_s$ is given by (13.22) adapted to classical statistics, namely,

$$\bar{x}_s = 3(s+1)/2. \tag{15.28}$$

Other transport parameters, for scattering by ionized impurities are

$$r_0{}^I \equiv \mu_0{}^{H,I}/\mu_0{}^I = [315\pi/512][g^2(\bar{x}_1)/g^2(\bar{x}_2)], \tag{15.29}$$

$$\omega\tau_I{}^0/g(\bar{x}_1) = -[\sqrt{\pi}/8][\mu_0{}^I H/c] \equiv (\gamma^I)^{1/2}, \tag{15.30}$$

$$(\varDelta\rho/\rho_0)^I \cong [120g^3(\bar{x}_1)/g^3(\bar{x}_3) - \{[315\sqrt{\pi}/64][g^2(\bar{x}_1)/g^2(\bar{x}_2)]\}^2]\gamma^I, \qquad \gamma^I \ll 1, \tag{15.31}$$

$$(\varDelta\rho/\rho_0)^I_{E_y=0} \cong [120g^3(\bar{x}_1)/g^3(\bar{x}_3)]\gamma^I, \qquad \gamma^I \ll 1, \tag{15.32}$$

$$(\varDelta\rho/\rho_0)^I \approx [32/3\pi][g(x^*_{-1})/g(\bar{x}_1)] - 1, \qquad \gamma^I \gg 1, \tag{15.33}$$

$$(\varDelta\rho/\rho_0)^I_{E_y=0} \approx 6[g(\bar{x}_1)/g(x^*_{-1})]\gamma^I, \qquad \gamma^I \gg 1. \tag{15.33a}$$

The parameter $(\gamma^I)^{1/2}$ is positive for electrons, negative for holes.[184a] The quantity x^*_{-1} is used inasmuch as Eqs. (13.22) and (15.28) are no longer valid for $s = -1$, so that $\bar{x}_{-1}$ has no meaning. For the case where $s = -1$, the integral reduces to $\int g^{-1}(x)e^{-x}\,dx$, so that the integrand for $g(x)$ constant no longer possesses a maximum. Dingle's method can still be used [see discussion following (13.20)], and this procedure gives $x^*_{-1} = \ln 2$. It is also possible to evaluate the simplified integral in terms of tabulated functions.

Approximations involved in the development of the preceding equations for impurity scattering have been examined by several investigators. The errors inherent in the evaluation of the integrals by the use of the $g(\bar{x})$ method were determined by Mansfield for a number of cases by numerical integration of the complete integrand. His results for the Hall coefficient factor[205] are shown in Fig. 12.

Further calculations by Mansfield include the integrals for other weak-magnetic-field galvanomagnetic and thermomagnetic coefficients.[212]

---

[212] R. Mansfield, *Proc. Phys. Soc. (London)* **B70**, 240 (1957).

In all cases the errors become small when $z/x \geqslant 5$. To get an estimate of what this condition means, consider the case where $m^* = 0.3\,m_0$, $K = 15$, and $T = 300\,°K$. Then (15.25) yields

$$z/x = 1.7 \times 10^{19}/n^*. \tag{15.33b}$$

Thus, the condition is satisfied at room temperature for most non-degenerate semiconductors.

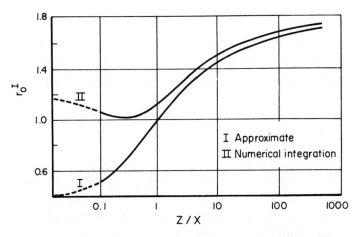

FIG. 12. Hall coefficient factors as approximated by Eq. (15.29) and from a numerical integration of the exact integrands (after Mansfield[205]).

The integrals which were evaluated numerically are those in the expression

$$r_0^I \equiv \frac{\mu_0^{H,I}}{\mu_0^I} = \frac{\langle \tau_I^2 \rangle}{\langle \tau_I \rangle^2} = \left[\frac{3\sqrt{\pi}}{4} \right] \int_0^\infty x^{9/2}\, g^{-2}(x) e^{-x}\, dx \Bigg/ \left[\int_0^\infty x^3\, g^{-1}(x) e^{-x}\, dx \right]^2 \tag{15.34}$$

which follows from (12.40), (13.13), and (15.4).

Inasmuch as $\bar{x}$ is the order of unity — being 3 for $\langle \tau \rangle$ and 4.5 for $\langle \tau^2 \rangle$ — it follows that $z \gg 1$ in the region of applicability of the impurity scattering formulae. Therefore, (15.24) is often written as

$$g(x) \cong \ln z - 1. \tag{15.35}$$

Hence, making rise of the fact that $\bar{x}_1 = 3$, $\bar{x}_2 = 4.5$, one obtains the commonly quoted results

$$\mu_0{}^I = -\frac{2^{7/2}\,K^2(kT)^{3/2}}{\pi^{3/2}\,e^3\,m^{*\,1/2}\,N_I}\left[\ln\frac{6Km^*(kT)^2}{\pi e^2\hbar^2\,n^*} - 1\right]^{-1}, \quad e > 0 \quad \text{for} \quad \text{electrons,}$$

(15.36)

$$r_0{}^I \equiv \frac{\mu_0{}^{H,\,I}}{\mu_0{}^I} = \frac{315\pi}{512}\left\{\frac{\ln\,[6Km^*(kT)^2/\pi e^2\,\hbar^2\,n^*] - 1}{\ln\,[9Km^*(kT)^2/\pi e^2\,\hbar^2\,n^*] - 1}\right\}^2. \quad (15.37)$$

In most cases the logarithmic term gives a noticeable contribution to the temperature dependence of $\mu_0{}^I$, and to the value of $r_0{}^I$.[186]

The applicabilities of the Conwell-Weisskopf ionized impurity scattering formula and of the Brooks-Herring treatment, which hinges on the validity of the Born approximation, were considered by several investigators who performed partial wave calculations. Sclar[202] used a square-well potential and Blatt[186, 213] carried out machine calculations with the screened Coulomb potential used by Brooks and Dingle, discussed in Section 13b. The Born approximation is found to yield quite closely the results of the Blatt's partial wave calculations as long as $z/x \gg 1$.[213] For smaller values of this parameter, the Born approximation considerably overestimates the scattering cross sections. Another interesting fact is that in this region the partial wave calculations reveal a significant difference between cross sections due to scattering from repulsive centers and from attractive centers. The attractive centers have the larger cross section and, therefore, minority impurities are not so effective in scattering charge carriers as are the majority centers, in this region where z/x may be the order of unity or less.

(4) Charge carrier interactions. In this category we consider electron-hole collisions and electron-electron (or hole-hole collisions). The first situation may commonly be encountered in low band-gap semiconductors where the intrinsic concentration of carriers is large. An example is indium antimonide, in which n_i is approximately 2×10^{16} cm^{-3} at room temperature. Here it seems quite well established that electron-hole

---

[213] F. J. Blatt, Phys. and Chem. Solids 1, 262 (1957).

scattering is significant.[214,215] This case is commonly treated as an ordinary ionized impurity scattering process — the holes, due to their heavier masses, being considered immobile.[215] A general analysis of transport phenomena in ionized gases has been given by Spitzer and co-workers,[216,217] and their results are applicable to semiconductors.

In the case of electron-electron scattering, there is no first-order effect since the mutual electronic interactions cannot alter the total electron momentum developed by the electric field.[216] However, they do affect the distribution of the total among the different energy groups. Therefore $\langle \tau \rangle$ is affected through the other scattering mechanisms — except, of course, in the case of scattering processes for which τ is independent of energy. The implications of these effects have been discussed by Debye and Conwell.[191]

The results of Spitzer and Härm were used by Sodha and collaborators to determine transport coefficients in weak- and strong-magnetic-field limits.[218,219] Numerical integrations were done, and the slowly varying logarithmic term in the expression for the relaxation time was taken as a constant in energy. The effect of the electron-electron collisions is manifested via the impurity scattering. Calculations show that for an extrinsic semiconductor where the only scattering mechanisms is that by ionized impurities and where each impurity has produced one electron, the effect of electron-electron interactions is to reduce the conductivity mobility by 0.58. For the same sample, the ratio of Hall and conductivity mobilities is 1.18. Calculations were also done for a special case of mixed scattering,[220] namely where the relaxation time is determined by the expression

$$1/\tau = 1/\tau_{e-I} + 1/\tau_L \qquad (15.38)$$

[214] See discussion concerning Fig. 4 in reference 139.
[215] H. Ehrenreich, *Phys. and Chem. Solids* **2**, 131 (1957).
[216] R. Cohen, L. Spitzer, and P. Routly, *Phys. Rev.* **80**, 230 (1950).
[217] L. Spitzer and R. Härm, *Phys. Rev.* **89**, 977 (1953).
[218] M. S. Sodha and Y. P. Varshni, *Phys. Rev.* **111**, 1203 (1958).
[219] M. S. Sodha and Y. P. Varshni, *Phys. Rev.* **114**, 717 (1959).
[220] M. S. Sodha and Y. P. Varshni, *Z. Physik* **153**, 555 (1959). This is an extended and corrected version of an earlier article, namely, M. S. Sodha and P. C. Eastman *Z. Physik* **150**, 242 (1958).

where τ_{e-I} expresses the relaxation time resulting from the joint mechanisms of electron-electron and electron-ion collisions operating under the conditions outlined above, and τ_L is that due to ordinary lattice scattering.

The effect of electron-electron scattering on the electrical and thermal transport phenomena in nonpolar semiconductors in the absence of a magnetic field has been investigated by Appel.[220a] A variational treatment was used (see Section 25) inasmuch as it is not possible to define a uniform relaxation time encompassing both charge and heat transport for electron-electron scattering processes. Results indicate generally that electron-electron scattering causes the electrical conductivity to be reduced less than the electronic thermal conductivity. Quantitative calculations are obtained for nondegenerate semiconductors, both for electron-phonon and electron-ion scattering as the primary mechanism. The influence of electron-electron scattering is found to be greater in the latter case, as would be expected from arguments advanced previously, since the relaxation time for electron-ion scattering has a greater energy dependence than does that for electron-phonon scattering.

(5) *Mixed scattering.* By mixed scattering we mean the simultaneous occurrence of two or more independent scattering processes. The mechanism considered most commonly is that by lattice acoustic phonons and by ionized impurities. General relationships applicable to this case were presented in Section 13c. In the limit of classical statistics, however, the integrals simplify, and treatments of a number of special cases appear in the literature. In particular, Eq. (13.40) for the actual mobility in the case of composite scattering by lattice acoustic phonons and ionized impurities reduces to

$$\mu_0 = \mu_0{}^L K(\beta) \tag{15.39}$$

where

$$K(\beta) \equiv \int_0^\infty \frac{x^3 e^{-x}}{x^2 + \beta} dx. \tag{15.40}$$

[220a] J. Appel, *Phys. Rev.* **122**, 1760 (1961).

The parameter β, expressing the degree of impurity scattering, is given by

$$\beta \equiv 6 \frac{\mu_0^L}{\mu_0^I} \frac{g(\bar{x}_{1,\beta})}{g(\bar{x}_{1,\infty})} \qquad (15.41)$$

where μ_0^L is the mobility which would exist if the scattering by ionized impurities were negligible (i.e., $\mu_0^I \to \infty$), and μ_0^I is the mobility value which would result if lattice vibrations had a negligible influence on the mobility (i.e., $\mu_0^L \to \infty$). The function $g(x)$ is given by (15.24), and $\bar{x}_{s,\beta}$ is given by the limiting form of (13.39) for classical statistics (i.e., $\eta \to -\infty$), namely,

$$2\bar{x}^3 - (3-s)\bar{x}^2 + 2\beta\bar{x} - 3(s+1)\beta = 0 \qquad (15.42)$$

where $\bar{x} \equiv \bar{x}_{s,\beta}$.

The integral (15.40) can be evaluated in terms of tabulated functions to yield

$$K(\beta) = 1 + \beta \left[\cos \sqrt{\beta}\, \mathrm{Ci}\, \sqrt{\beta} + \sin \sqrt{\beta} \left(\mathrm{Si}\, \sqrt{\beta} - \frac{\pi}{2} \right) \right], \qquad (15.43)$$

where

$$\mathrm{Ci}\, x \equiv - \int_x^\infty \frac{\cos t}{t}\, dt \qquad \text{and} \qquad \mathrm{Si}\, x \equiv \int_0^x \frac{\sin t}{t}\, dt. \qquad (15.44)$$

The function $K(\beta)$ has been plotted by Conwell.[206]

Equation (15.39) has been used by a number of investigators in analyzing germanium.[191,221] In these cases, the ratio of the slowly varying factors, namely, $g(\bar{x}_{1,\beta})/g(\bar{x}_{1,\infty})$ of Eq. (15.41), has been taken as unity.

The Hall mobility is conveniently approached through the ratio [cf. (12.40)]

$$\mu_0^H/\mu_0 = r_0 = \langle \tau^2 \rangle / \langle \tau \rangle^2. \qquad (15.45)$$

The averages over energy are defined by (15.4). The expression for τ in the case of mixed scattering is given by (13.35) with

$$\tau_L^0/\tau_I^0 = 6\mu_0^L / [\mu_0^I g(\bar{x}_{1,\infty})]. \qquad (15.46)$$

[221] V. A. Johnson and K. Lark-Horovitz, *Phys. Rev.* **82**, 977 (1951).

The Hall coefficient factor can be written in the form

$$\mu_0{}^H/\mu_0 = r_0 = (3\pi/8)L(\beta^H)/[K(\beta)]^2 \qquad (15.47)$$

where $K(\beta)$ is given by (15.40) and $L(\beta^H)$ is

$$L(\beta^H) = \frac{2}{\sqrt{\pi}} \int_0^\infty \frac{x^{9/2} e^{-x} dx}{(x^2 + \beta^H)^2}. \qquad (15.48)$$

The expression for β^H, when the slowly varying factor is taken account of by means of the procedure outlined in connection with Eq. (13.37), is

$$\beta^H = 6 \frac{\mu_0{}^L}{\mu_0{}^I} \frac{g(\bar{x}_2, \beta^H)}{g(\bar{x}_1, \infty)}. \qquad (15.49)$$

The $\bar{x}_{2, \beta^H}$ is given by (15.42) when $s = 2$, $\beta = \beta^H$.

The integral (15.48) can be evaluated in terms of tabulated functions, namely,

$$L(x) = 1 + x + 7\sqrt{\pi/2}\, x^{3/4} \{[C(\sqrt{x}) - \tfrac{1}{2}] \cos\sqrt{x} + [S(\sqrt{x}) - \tfrac{1}{2}] \sin\sqrt{x}\} +$$
$$\sqrt{2\pi}\, x^{5/4} \{[S(\sqrt{x}) - \tfrac{1}{2}] \cos\sqrt{x} - [C(\sqrt{x}) - \tfrac{1}{2}] \sin\sqrt{x}\} \qquad (15.50)$$

where the Fresnel integrals are defined by[222]

$$\begin{matrix} C(\alpha) \\ S(\alpha) \end{matrix} = \frac{1}{\sqrt{2\pi}} \int_0^\alpha \begin{matrix} \cos t \\ \sin t \end{matrix} \Big/ \sqrt{t}\, dt. \qquad (15.51)$$

The integrals $K(x)$ and $L(x)$ can also be obtained from the functions $\mathfrak{C}_p$ and $\mathfrak{D}_p$ tabulated by Dingle et al.[223] for respective values of p of 3 and 9/2.

Values of the Hall coefficient factor r_0 have been plotted by several authors for different degrees of impurity scattering, assuming the factor $g(\bar{x}_{2, \beta^H})/g(\bar{x}_{1, \infty})$ to be unity.[221,224] More recently, Mansfield[205] has taken

---

[222] See p. 545 of G. N. Watson, "Treatise on the Theory of Bessel Functions," 2nd ed. Cambridge Univ. Press and the Macmillan Co., London and New York, 1945. Tables of the integrals are given on p. 744. The entry for S(1.5) should apparently be 0.415483. Fresnel integrals are readily evaluated from series of spherical Bessel functions.

[223] R. Dingle, D. Arndt, and S. Roy, *Appl. Sci. Research* **B6**, 155 (1957).

[224] H. Jones, *Phys. Rev.* **81**, 149 (1951).

this factor into account, through the use of Eqs. (15.42) and (15.49). His results are reproduced in Fig. 13.

It is seen that for small or moderate amounts of impurity scattering the simple calculation is adequate, the difference being only about 5% when $\mu_0^I = \mu_0^L$. For larger contributions from ion scattering, it appears desirable to take into account the value of $g(\bar{x}_{2,\,\beta^H})/g(\bar{x}_{1,\,\infty})$.

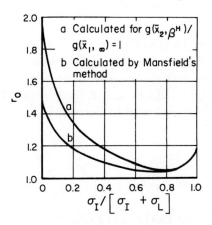

FIG. 13. Weak-magnetic-field Hall coefficient factor for different admixtures of impurity scattering and lattice scattering (after Mansfield[205]). The abscissa at 0 denotes existence of impurity scattering only, that at 1.0 denotes existence of lattice scattering only.

Plots of integrals given above, as well as those entering into the expressions for magnetoresistance and thermomagnetic effects, are given by Madelung.[170, 225]

The expression for transverse magnetoresistance is readily obtained by use of (12.41), (13.35), (15.4), and (15.46). It may be written in the form

$$\frac{\Delta\rho}{\rho_0} = \left[-\frac{K'(\beta^M,0)}{K(\beta)} - \frac{\pi}{4}\frac{L^2(\beta^H)}{K^2(\beta)} \right]\gamma^L, \qquad \gamma^L \ll 1 \qquad (15.52)$$

where

$$\gamma^L = \frac{9\pi}{16}\left(\frac{\mu_0^L H}{c}\right)^2, \qquad (15.53)$$

[225] O. Madelung, Z. Naturforsch. 9a, 667 (1954).

$$-K'(\beta^M, 0) = \int_0^\infty \frac{x^6 e^{-x} dx}{(x^2 + \beta^M)^3},$$

(15.54)

and

$$\beta^M \equiv 6 \frac{\mu_0{}^L}{\mu_0{}^I} \frac{g(\bar{x}_{3,\beta^M})}{g(\bar{x}_{1,\infty})}.$$

(15.55)

The $\bar{x}_{3,\beta^M}$ is given by (15.42) when $s = 3$, $\beta = \beta^M$. The other symbols have already been defined. The choice of notation for the integral (15.54) is occasioned by the fact that a general integral $K(\beta, \gamma)$ is introduced later, for which $K(\beta) = K(\beta, 0)$ and $K'(\beta, 0) = [\partial K(\beta, \gamma)/\partial \gamma]_{\gamma=0}$. The integral (15.54) can be evaluated in terms of the tabulated functions of (15.44), namely,

$K'(x, 0)$

$$= -\tfrac{1}{8}\{8 - x + [x^{3/2} - 15\sqrt{x}] [\sin\sqrt{x} \operatorname{Ci}\sqrt{x} + \cos\sqrt{x} (\tfrac{1}{2}\pi - \operatorname{Si}\sqrt{x})] -$$

$$9x [\cos\sqrt{x} \operatorname{Ci}\sqrt{x} - \sin\sqrt{x} (\tfrac{1}{2}\pi - \operatorname{Si}\sqrt{x})]\}.$$

(15.56)

For small values of β, reasonably accurate values of $K'(\beta, 0)$ can usually be obtained through use of the tabulations of the $K(\beta, \gamma)$ functions discussed in Section 15c. In the case of large values ($\beta \geqslant 1000$), asymptotic solutions of the integral (15.54) are satisfactory. For the intermediate range, it is probably necessary to evaluate formula (15.56). This was done, using 9-place tables, and results are presented in Table I.

The Corbino magnetoresistance is obviously given by

$$\left(\frac{\Delta\rho}{\rho_0}\right)_{E_y=0} = -\frac{K'(\beta^M, 0)}{K(\beta)} \gamma^L, \qquad \gamma^L \ll 1.$$

(15.57)

Expressions for the case of mixed scattering in the strong-magnetic-field region are readily worked out from basic equations in Sections 12, 13, and 15. Results are

$$\sigma_\infty = -ne\mu_\infty \approx \frac{ne^2}{m^*} \left\langle \frac{1}{\tau} \right\rangle^{-1},$$

(15.57a)

$$\mu_\infty \approx -\frac{e}{m^*}\left\langle\frac{1}{\tau}\right\rangle^{-1} \approx \frac{9\pi}{16}\mu_0{}^L\frac{1}{\beta_\infty+2}, \qquad \gamma^L \gg 1, \qquad (15.58)$$

$$\mu_\infty{}^H = \mu_\infty, \qquad (15.59)$$

$$\frac{\Delta\rho}{\rho_0} \approx \frac{16}{9\pi}(\beta_\infty+2)K(\beta)-1, \qquad \gamma^L \gg 1, \qquad (15.60)$$

$$\left(\frac{\Delta\rho}{\rho_0}\right)_{E_y=0} \approx \frac{9\pi}{16}\frac{K(\beta)}{(\beta_\infty+2)}\left(\frac{\mu_0{}^L H}{c}\right)^2 = \frac{K(\beta)}{\beta_\infty+2}\gamma^L \qquad (15.61)$$

where

$$\beta_\infty \equiv 6\frac{\mu_0{}^L}{\mu_0{}^I}\frac{g(x^*_{-1})}{g(\bar{x}_{1,\infty})}. \qquad (15.62)$$

The quantity x^*_{-1} has been discussed in connection with Eq. (15.33).

TABLE I. VALUES OF THE FUNCTION $K'(\beta, 0)$

β	$-K'(\beta, 0)$
0.01	0.7778
0.03	0.6636
0.10	0.5020
0.30	0.3374
1	0.1738
3	0.07107
10	0.01752
30	0.003057
100	0.0002581
300	0.0000170
1000	0.000000616[a]

[a] Calculated from the asymptotic expansion of the integral.

Since $K(\beta)$ decreases monotonically with increasing β, it is apparent that in the strong-magnetic-field region, it is the Corbino magneto-resistance, rather than the ordinary magnetoresistance, which is highly sensitive to the degree of impurity scattering. This is opposite to the behavior at weak magnetic fields.

In the limit of infinite μ_0^I, which is representative of lattice scattering, β and β_∞ vanish, and Eqs. (15.60) and (15.61) reduce to (15.21) and (15.22). For the case of simple impurity scattering, μ_0^L becomes infinite. Also, the asymptotic form of $K(\beta)$ can be shown to be

$$K(\beta) \approx 3!/\beta, \qquad \beta \gg 1. \tag{15.63}$$

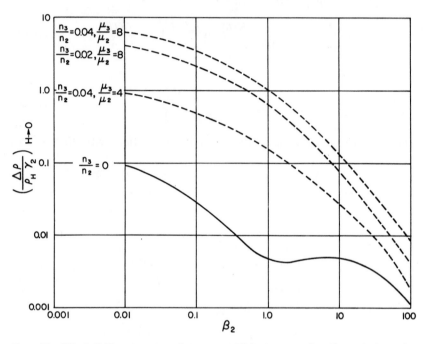

FIG. 14. Weak-field magnetoresistance coefficient as a function of impurity scattering parameter. The solid curve is for a single band, characterized by subscript 2. The dashed curves are for two-band conduction, with relative carrier densities and mobilities as indicated. The parameter γ_2 is the usual magnetic field parameter $(9\pi/16)(\mu_2^L H/c)^2$ if a Gaussian system of units is used, or $(9\pi/16)(\mu_2^L H/10^8)^2$ for μ in cm²/volt-sec and H in gauss (after Beer *et al.*[225a]).

Thus

$$\beta_\infty K(\beta) \approx 6g(x_{-1}^*)/g(\bar{x}_{1,\infty}), \qquad \mu_0^L \to \infty, \tag{15.64}$$

$$[K(\beta)/\beta_\infty](\mu_0^L)^2 \approx [g(\bar{x}_{1,\infty})/6g(x_{-1}^*)](\mu_0^I)^2, \qquad \mu_0^L \to \infty. \tag{15.65}$$

Thus it is apparent in the limit of negligible scattering by lattice vibrations that Eqs. (15.60) and (15.61) reduce to (15.33) and (15.33a).

It is interesting to note that at weak magnetic fields the magneto-resistance is degraded substantially by the presence of ionized impurity scattering, even for relatively small values of β. In the strong magnetic field limit, however, the behavior is quite different. After a slight decrease, the magnetoresistance rises rather sharply with increasing β and for the

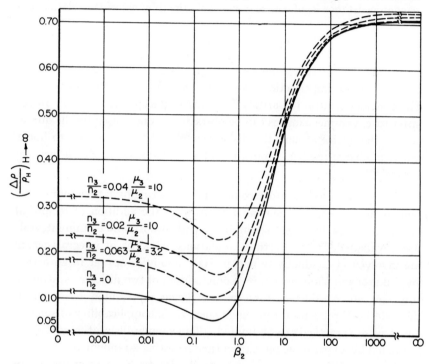

FIG. 15. Strong-field saturation magnetoresistance as a function of impurity scattering parameter. The solid curve is for a single band, characterized by subscript 2. The dashed curves are for two-band conduction, with relative carrier densities and mobilities as indicated (after Beer *et al.*[225a]).

limiting case of scattering only by ionized impurities is substantially larger than that for the case of pure acoustic phonon scattering. To illustrate this behavior, we present the results of some simplified calculations[225a] in which the ratios of the $g(\bar{x})$ factors were taken as unity, so

---

[225a] A. C. Beer, F. J. Reid, G. Kendall, and R. K. Willardson, Final Rept. AFOSR-TR-58-9, ASTIA AD 148 007 (unpublished). Available from Office of Technical Services, Rept. PB-133476, Investigation of the Effects of the Valence Band Degeneracy on the Conduction Processes in Germanium.

that in all integrals β was defined as $6\mu_0^{L}/\mu_0^{I}$. The calculations were carried out to include several examples of two-band conduction (see Section 17). The results for the single-band case, which is of primary interest here, are given by the solid curves in Figs. 14 and 15. It is to be noted that the ordinate for these graphs is $\Delta\rho/\rho_H$. The ordinary magnetoresistance is, of course, readily obtained by use of the relationship

$$\Delta\rho/\rho_0 = [1 - (\Delta\rho/\rho_H)]^{-1} - 1. \tag{15.65a}$$

In addition to that from ionized impurities, scattering from several other types of imperfections has been considered in the literature.[186] These include neutral impurities[226, 227] and edge-type dislocations. In the latter case, two mechanisms can be operative — one caused by the dilatation of the lattice around the dislocation[228] and the other due to linear arrays of charge resulting from the trapping of carriers at the dislocation sites.[229, 230]

Expressions, taking into account joint scattering by lattice vibrations, ionized impurities, and neutral impurities by the addition of reciprocal relaxation times, have been set up by several authors, and certain integrals were evaluated.[231, 232] Further tabulations of values of integrals which are involved in conductivity and in Hall mobilities appear in an article by Fukuroi and Yamanouchi.[233] Combinations of two different scattering processes are considered, each process being represented by a power dependence of relaxation time upon energy. The applicability of some of the results to practical cases is limited — for example, dislocation scattering is treated by an isotropic relaxation time requiring a random arrangement of edge-type dislocations operative via the Dexter-Seitz mechanism. In many cases, however, one can expect preferential arrangement of dislocations, and charge trapping effects, to be significant. Integrals which appear

[226] C. Erginsoy, *Phys. Rev.* **79**, 1013 (1950).

[227] N. Sclar, *Phys. Rev.* **104**, 1559 (1956).

[228] D. L. Dexter and F. Seitz, *Phys. Rev.* **86**, 964 (1952).

[229] W. Shockley, *Phys. Rev.* **91**, 228 (1953).

[230] W. T. Read, *Phil. Mag.* [7] **45**, 119, 775 (1954); **46**, 111 (1955).

[231] C. N. Klahr, *Phys. Rev.* **82**, 109 (1951).

[232] M. S. Sodha and P. C. Eastman, *Phys. Rev.* **108**, 1373 (1957); **112**, 44 (1958).

[233] T. Fukuroi and C. Yamanouchi, *Sci. Repts. Research Insts. Tôhoku Univ.* **A9**, 267 (1957).

in the expressions for thermoelectric power when energy-dependent relaxation times are involved have been calculated by Hashimoto.[233a]

The composite mechanism of scattering by lattice vibrations and by edge-type dislocations via the anisotropic process involving the Shockley-Read array of charge has been studied by Logan et al.[234] Since their experimental data were on n-type germanium, account was taken of the effect of the ellipsoidal structure of the conduction band on the lattice mobility. Their treatment is able to account fairly well for the behavior of plastically bent n-type germanium at temperatures above $50\,°K$. Other extensions of Read's theory were carried out by Kamada[234a] and applied to his data on n-type silicon; also by Duga for application to data on indium antimonide.[234b]

b. Conductivity, Hall, and Magnetoresistance Mobilities

Certain aspects concerned with the definition of mobilities were discussed in Section 12d. It is now appropriate to consider the situation more fully and to define a magnetoresistance mobility for the case where classical statistics apply.

From dimensional considerations, one can define zero-magnetic-field mobilities in terms of conductivity, Hall coefficient, and transverse magnetoresistance as follows:

$$\mu_0 = C_c\,\sigma/n|e|, \tag{15.66}$$

$$\mu_0 = C_H\,R_0\,\sigma_0, \tag{15.67}$$

$$\mu_0{}^2 = C_M\,\Delta\rho/\rho_0\,H^2. \tag{15.68}$$

If we choose laboratory units, then C_c is unity, being negative for electrons and positive for transport by positive charges. Note that here we have absorbed in C_c the sign of e, in contrast to previous procedure.[184a] In the case of spherical energy surfaces and constant relaxation time, C_H is unity for laboratory units and is equal to c, the speed of light, for the

[233a] K. Hashimoto, Mem. Fac. Sci. Kyusyu Univ. B2, 165 (1958).
[234] R. A. Logan, G. L. Pearson, and D. A. Kleinman, J. Appl. Phys. 30, 885 (1959).
[234a] K. Kamada, J. Phys. Soc. Japan 15, 998 (1960).
[234b] J. J. Duga, J. Appl. Phys. 33, 169 (1962).

Gaussian system of units. Under these conditions the *Hall mobility* is defined such that

$$\mu_0^H = \mu_0, \qquad \tau = \text{const., spherical energy surfaces, and classical statistics.}$$

$$(15.69)$$

Thus, in general, [cf. Eq. (12.31)], for Gaussian units,[235]

$$\mu_0^H = R_0 \sigma_0 c. \qquad (15.70)$$

A choice of C_M to give an analogous definition for a magnetoresistance mobility, μ_0^M is not possible since $\Delta\rho/\rho_0$ vanishes for constant τ and spherical energy surfaces. Therefore, it is customary to define the constant of proportionality for magnetoresistance mobility such that

$$\mu_0^{M,L} = \mu_0^L. \qquad (15.71)$$

That is, the normalization is chosen such that the equality exists for the case of simple scattering by lattice vibrations. It follows immediately from (15.18), (15.19), and (15.68) that, for the Gaussian system of units,[236]

$$\mu_0^M = \left\{ \left(\frac{\Delta\rho}{\rho_0\,H^2} \right) \frac{16c^2}{9\pi(1 - \pi/4)} \right\}^{1/2}, \qquad \frac{\mu_0\,H}{c} \ll 1. \qquad (15.72)$$

It is clear that it is possible also to define a Corbino mobility in a manner analogous to the preceding development. In this case, however, two choices are obvious. Inasmuch as the Corbino magnetoresistance does not vanish for the constant-τ case, one can determine the constant of proportionality by use of a condition analogous to (15.69), as was done for the Hall mobility. On the other hand, one may with equal logic use relation (15.71), to maintain parallelism with the case of ordinary magnetoresistance. We shall adopt the latter definition, thus

$$\mu_0^C = \left\{ \left(\frac{\Delta\rho}{\rho_0\,H^2} \right)_c \frac{16c^2}{9\pi} \right\}^{1/2}, \qquad \frac{\mu_0\,H}{c} \ll 1. \qquad (15.72a)$$

---

[235] In laboratory units where σ is in (ohm-cm)$^{-1}$, R in cm^3/coulomb, and μ in cm^2/volt-sec, the factor c is replaced by unity.

[236] In laboratory units where μ is in cm^2/volt-sec and H in gauss, the dimensionless factor $\mu H/c$ is replaced by $\mu H/10^8$.

The reader will readily verify that for spherical energy surfaces and classical statistics the constant-τ definition would lead to a Corbino mobility of magnitude $3\sqrt{\pi}/4$ times that of the quantity adopted here.

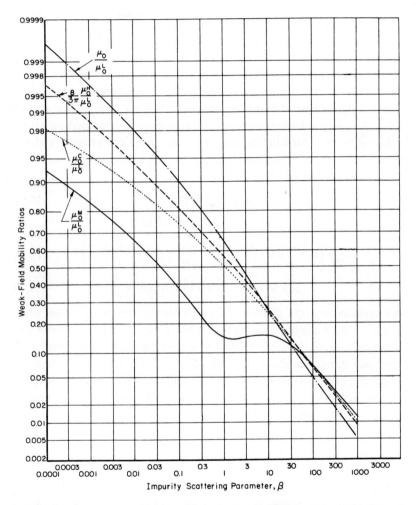

FIG. 16. Sensitivity of conductivity, Hall, Corbino-magnetoresistance, and magneto-resistance mobilities to degree of impurity scattering in the case of mixed scattering, under the assumption that $\beta^{M} = \beta^{H} = \beta$. The plots are made on logarithmic probability coordinates to expand the region where β is small. As β approaches zero, each of the four curves approaches unity.

In view of the above definitions, it is seen that for a semiconductor of simplest band structure and lattice scattering by acoustic phonons only, the mobility factors μ_0, $8\mu_0^H/3\pi$, μ_0^M, and μ_0^C are all expected to be equal, thus

$$\mu_0^L = (8/3\pi)\mu_0^{H,L} = \mu_0^{M,L} = \mu_0^{C,L}. \tag{15.73}$$

In the general case, the observed differences in the mobilities are useful in giving an indication of the departure from ideal conditions. The influence of anisotropy will be examined in subsequent sections. The sensitivity of the different mobilities to the scattering process can be illustrated by consideration of the case of mixed scattering. For a single band and spherical energy surfaces — the conditions imposed on all the developments presented in this section — the equations presented above, together with those in Section 15a(5), yield the following expressions for the different mobilities:

$$\mu_0 = \mu_0^L K(\beta), \tag{15.74}$$

$$(8/3\pi)\mu_0^H = \mu_0^L L(\beta^H)/K(\beta)$$

$$\mu_0^M = \mu_0^L \left\{ \frac{[-K'(\beta^M, 0)/K(\beta)] - [\pi/4][L(\beta^H)/K(\beta)]^2}{1 - \pi/4} \right\}^{1/2}, \tag{15.75}$$

$$\mu_0^C = \mu_0^L \{- K'(\beta^M, 0)/K(\beta)\}^{1/2}. \tag{15.76}$$

These relationships are plotted in Fig. 16 for the simplifying case where $\beta^M = \beta^H = \beta$. An interesting feature is the noticeable effect of even very small amounts of ionized impurity scattering upon the weak-field magnetoresistance mobility. In view of this sensitivity, the determination of magnetoresistance mobility has been found useful in studying the introduction of ionized centers by plastic deformation and by neutron bombardment of certain semiconductors.[237,238]

c. General Case of Arbitrary Magnetic Field Strengths

Because of the complexity of the transport integrals, only certain examples involving specialized scattering mechanisms have been considered in the literature.

[237] J. Duga, R. Willardson, and A. Beer, *J. Appl. Phys.* **30**, 1798 (1959).
[238] R. K. Willardson, *J. Appl. Phys.* **30**, 1158 (1959).

(1) Power-law scattering. Here we assume the energy dependence of the relaxation time to be given by

$$\tau = \tau_0 \, x^\lambda, \qquad x = \varepsilon/kT. \tag{15.77}$$

The expressions for the components of the conductivity tensor given in (12.59) and (12.61) reduce for classical statistics[238a] to

$$\sigma_{xx}(H) = n|e\mu_0| \, [(\lambda + \tfrac{3}{2})!]^{-1} \int_0^\infty \frac{x^{\lambda + 3/2} \, e^{-x}}{1 + \gamma_\lambda \, x^{2\lambda}} \, dx, \qquad H \equiv H_z, \tag{15.78}$$

$$\sigma_{xy}(H) = \mp \, n|e\mu_0 \gamma_\lambda^{1/2}| \, [(\lambda + \tfrac{3}{2})!]^{-1} \int_0^\infty \frac{x^{2\lambda + 3/2} \, e^{-x}}{1 + \gamma_\lambda \, x^{2\lambda}} \, dx,$$

$$- \text{ for electrons, } + \text{ for holes} \tag{15.79}$$

where

$$\gamma_\lambda \equiv \left[\frac{3\sqrt{\pi}}{4} \, \frac{1}{(\lambda + \tfrac{3}{2})!} \right]^2 \left[\frac{\mu_0 H}{c} \right]^2. \tag{15.80}$$

For certain values of λ, the integrals in (15.78) and (15.79) can be evaluated in terms of tabulated functions. Numerical results, covering a considerable latitude in λ, are also available from the work of Dingle and collaborators.[239]

The case which has received most attention is that of $\lambda = -\tfrac{1}{2}$, representative of scattering by lattice acoustic phonons. The conductivity components are commonly written as

$$\sigma_{xx}(H) = |ne\mu_0 \, K(\gamma)|, \tag{15.81}$$

$$\sigma_{xy}(H) = \mp \left| ne\mu_0 \gamma^{1/2} \frac{\sqrt{\pi}}{2} L(\gamma) \right|, \qquad - \text{ for electrons, } + \text{ for holes} \tag{15.82}$$

[238a] Here we have deviated from our previous convention[184a] and are considering e, μ, $\gamma^{1/2}$, ω to be always positive quantities, the signs appropriate to electron or hole conduction being placed in front of the expressions.

[239] R. Dingle, D. Arndt, and S. Roy, *Appl. Sci. Research* **B6**, 144, 155, 245 (1957).

where

$$K(\gamma) = \int_0^\infty \frac{x^2 e^{-x}}{x+\gamma} dx, \qquad L(\gamma) = \frac{2}{\sqrt{\pi}} \int_0^\infty \frac{x^{3/2} e^{-x}}{x+\gamma} dx, \qquad (15.83)$$

and

$$\gamma \equiv (9\pi/16)(\mu_0 H/c)^2, \qquad \text{in Gaussian units.}^{[236]} \qquad (15.84)$$

The above integrals may be expressed in terms of standard exponential integrals and error functions, as defined in Jahnke-Emde[240]:

$$K(\gamma) = 1 - \gamma - \gamma^2 e^\gamma Ei(-\gamma),$$

$$L(\gamma) = 1 - 2\gamma + 2\pi^{1/2}\gamma^{3/2} e^\gamma [1 - \Phi(\gamma^{1/2})]. \qquad (15.85)$$

The usual weak-field approximations neglect terms higher than the first degree in γ. For magnetoresistance calculations, which involve differences, good accuracy is realized in such an approximation only when $\gamma < 0.001$. It is, therefore, of limited practical validity if the mobility is high. A better approximation, involving Euler's constant, is

$$K(\gamma) \cong 1 - \gamma - \gamma^2(0.577 + \ln \gamma), \qquad \gamma < 0.025$$

$$L(\gamma) \cong 1 - 2\gamma + 2\pi^{1/2}\gamma^{3/2}, \qquad \gamma < 0.01. \qquad (15.86)$$

For strong magnetic fields, the following asymptotic expressions may be useful:

$$K(\gamma) \approx 2!/\gamma - 3!/\gamma^2 + \dots$$

$$(\gamma > 25). \qquad (15.87)$$

$$L(\gamma) \approx 1 \cdot 3/2\gamma - 1 \cdot 3 \cdot 5/2^2 \gamma^2 + \dots$$

The preceding relationships, (15.81)ff, were first presented by Harding,[241] who applied them to investigations of the Hall coefficient and magnetoresistance as a function of magnetic field in semiconductors. A similar development can be carried through for $\lambda = \frac{3}{2}$, which — except

---

[240] E. Jahnke and F. Emde, "Tables of Functions." Dover, New York, 1945.
[241] J. W. Harding, *Proc. Roy. Soc.* **A140**, 205 (1933).

for the slowly varying factor of $g(x)$ discussed in preceding sections — approximates the situation due to scattering from ionized impurities. This has been done by Johnson and Lark-Horovitz.[183a] Results are given for the magnetic-field dependence of the Hall coefficient factor $r(H)$.

Numerical values of the integrals (15.83) are available in the tables given by Dingle,[239] as well as from the special values of the general functions $K(\beta, \gamma)$ and $L(\beta, \gamma)$ — defined by Eqs. (15.92) and (15.93) — for $\beta = 0$. The functions $K(\gamma)$ and $L(\gamma)$ have also been tabulated by Gray[241a] for the interval $0.0001 \leqslant \gamma < 100$.

(2) *Mixed scattering.* The examples which appear in the literature are for the joint scattering mechanism of lattice acoustic phonons and ionized impurities for which the relaxation time is given by the simplified expression which follows from Eqs. (13.35), (15.16), and (15.46), namely,

$$\tau = -\frac{3\sqrt{\pi}}{4}\frac{m^*}{e}\mu_0^L \frac{x^{3/2}}{6\mu_0^L/\mu_0^I + x^2} \tag{15.88}$$

where the ratio μ_0^L/e is negative for both electron and hole conduction, and where $x \equiv \varepsilon/kT$. It is noted that in (15.88) the slowly varying function $g(x)$ has been replaced by the constant $g(\bar{x}_1)$, as defined by means of (15.24) and (15.28). This is occasioned by the fact a determination of a specific $\bar{x}$ for each integrand by the method outlined in connection with (15.42) is complicated by the fact that the $\bar{x}$ is now not only a function of β, but also of γ^L.

With the use of (15.88), the conductivity components can be put in the form

$$\sigma_{xx}(H) = |ne\mu_0^L K(\beta, \gamma)|, \tag{15.89}$$

$$\sigma_{xy}(H) = \mp \left| ne\mu_0^L \gamma^{1/2} \frac{\sqrt{\pi}}{2} L(\beta, \gamma) \right|,$$

$$H = H_z, \quad - \text{ for electrons, } + \text{ for holes,} \tag{15.90}$$

[241a] D. V. Gray, Rept. AFOSR–2665, Tables of the Transverse Magnetic Coefficients $K(\gamma)$ and $L(\gamma)$, April 30, 1962. The tables have subsequently been published in *J. Appl. Phys.* **34,** 291 (1963).

where

$$\gamma \equiv (9\pi/16)(\mu_0{}^L H/c)^2 \qquad \text{in Gaussian units,[236]}$$

and

$$\beta \equiv 6\mu_0{}^L/\mu_0{}^I, \tag{15.91}$$

$$K(\beta, \gamma) \equiv \int_0^\infty \frac{x^3(x^2 + \beta)e^{-x}}{(x^2 + \beta)^2 + \gamma x^3}\, dx, \tag{15.92}$$

$$L(\beta, \gamma) \equiv \frac{2}{\sqrt{\pi}} \int_0^\infty \frac{x^{9/2} e^{-x}}{(x^2 + \beta)^2 + \gamma x^3}\, dx. \tag{15.93}$$

The preceding relationships were first presented by Johnson and Whitesell,[242] who list numerical values for the integrals. More extensive tabulations have subsequently appeared in an article by Beer et al.[139] The functions $K(\beta, \gamma)$ and $L(\beta, \gamma)$ reduce to the $K(\beta)$ and $L(\beta)$ previously introduced, for $\gamma = 0$ and to the $K(\gamma)$ and $L(\gamma)$ of the preceding section when $\beta = 0$. Satisfactory power series representations, either in β or γ, are not possible since $\beta = 0$ and $\gamma = 0$ are singular points where derivatives do not exist. The sole exception is the first derivative with respect to γ, which does exist at $\gamma = 0$. One can therefore write

$$K(\beta, \gamma) \cong K(\beta, 0) + K'(\beta, 0)\gamma, \qquad \gamma \ll 1, \tag{15.94}$$

$$L(\beta, \gamma) \cong L(\beta, 0) + L'(\beta, 0)\gamma, \qquad \gamma \ll 1. \tag{15.95}$$

The function $K'(\beta, 0)$ $[\equiv \{\partial K(\beta, \gamma)/\partial \gamma\}_{\gamma=0}]$ has previously been introduced in connection with weak-field magnetoresistance. It can be evaluated analytically in terms of sine and cosine integrals,[243] or can be obtained from tables of the $K(\beta, \gamma)$ functions.[139]

Asymptotic representations for large values of γ, when β is small, are

$$K(\beta, \gamma) \approx (2 + \beta)/\gamma, \tag{15.96}$$

$$L(\beta, \gamma) \approx 3/2\gamma. \tag{15.97}$$

[242] V. A. Johnson and W. J. Whitesell, *Phys. Rev.* **89**, 941 (1953). The notation is such that J_1 and J_2 are identical, respectively, with our K and $\frac{1}{2}\pi^{1/2}L$. Typographical errors exist, some of which are apparent in comparing Tables I and II with IV.

[243] J. Appel, *Z. Naturforsch.* **9a**, 167 (1954).

The exact expressions for the galvanomagnetic effects follow from Eqs. (12.26) and (12.32) with (15.89) and (15.90):

$$R_H = \mp \frac{3\pi}{8} \frac{1}{n|e|c} \frac{L(\beta, \gamma)}{K^2(\beta, \gamma) + (\pi/4)\gamma L^2(\beta, \gamma)},\tag{15.98}$$

$-$ for electrons, $+$ for holes,

$$\frac{\Delta\rho}{\rho_0} = \frac{K(\beta, \gamma)K(\beta, 0)}{K^2(\beta, \gamma) + (\pi/4)\gamma L^2(\beta, \gamma)} - 1,\tag{15.99}$$

$$\left(\frac{\Delta\rho}{\rho_0}\right)_{E_y = 0} = \frac{K(\beta, 0)}{K(\beta, \gamma)} - 1.\tag{15.100}$$

In addition to the work of Johnson and Whitesell, a detailed investigation of the behavior of the Hall coefficient factor R_H/R_∞ and the magnetoresistance $\Delta\rho/\rho_0$ has been presented by Appel.[243] The relations between the parameters of Appel and those employed here are

$$\alpha^{(\text{Appel})} = \beta^{1/2},$$

$$\gamma^{(\text{Appel})} = \gamma/\beta^{1/2},$$

$$(\mu/C)^{(\text{Appel})} = \sqrt{30}\,\gamma^{1/2}/\beta^{1/2}.$$

The latter parameter μ/C — which, for the scattering processes considered in this development, is independent of temperature — is used by Appel as the independent variable in plots of the galvanomagnetic functions.

VI.
Multiband Conduction

16. GENERAL CONSIDERATIONS

We shall consider the transport properties of two or more noninteracting bands. Actually the importance of the two-band model, especially in analyzing galvanomagnetic phenomena, has been recognized for some time,[244] and an early application was made by Jones to bismuth.[48]

For the case of uncoupled bands, the conductivity components can be written as the sums of contributions from each band, for example,

$$\sigma_{xx}(H) = \sum_i \sigma_{xx}^{(i)}(H), \quad H \equiv H_z \tag{16.1}$$

$$\sigma_{xy}(H) = \sum_i (-1)^i |\sigma_{xy}^{(i)}(H)|, \tag{16.2}$$

electrons: i odd, holes: i even.

Each band is labeled by the index i, and our convention is such that i is odd for electron or conduction bands and even for hole or valence bands.[244a] This choice is consistent with the convention that $\sigma_{xy}(H)$ is negative for

---

[244] See, for example, the article by Chambers[135] and by Kohler[245] and the literature cited therein.

[244a] It is to be noted that relation (16.2) applies only when $\sigma_{xy}(H)$ is antisymmetric, as is true for spherical energy surfaces or for certain anisotropic solids when **H** is in a direction of high symmetry. If $\sigma_{xy}(H)$ has symmetric components (see, for example, Sections 11b or 23b), then those $\sigma_{xy}^s(H)$ components must be summed as in relation (16.1). It is also apparent that Eq. (16.3) and the relations derived from it are valid only under the condition that $\sigma_{xy}(H)$ has no symmetric components, inasmuch as our Hall effect is defined only in terms of the antisymmetric components of the resistivity tensor [Section 10a(3)]. Finally it is to be pointed out that the sign convention for (16.2) and (16.3) applies for standard bands. If re-entrant energy surfaces should become important, then a reversal of sign could occur.[34]

electron conduction, cf. Eq. (4.20). The bands may overlap, as in the case of metals, or they may be separated in energy, as is true for semiconductors. It is possible to put Eq. (16.2) into a somewhat more convenient form by introducing the Hall angle for each band, according to the definition (12.28). Thus,

$$\sigma_{xy}(H) = \sum_i \sigma_{xx}^{(i)}(H) \tan \theta_i, \qquad |\theta_i| \leqslant \pi \qquad (16.3)$$

$\theta_i < 0$ for electrons, > 0 for holes.

Also, in terms of the Hall coefficient and conductivity for each band, we have

$$\tan \theta_i = R_H^{(i)} \sigma^{(i)}(H) H. \qquad (16.4)$$

Another set of useful expressions follows from the application of (12.27):

$$\sigma_{xx}^{(i)}(H) = \sigma^i(H) [1 + \tan^2 \theta_i]^{-1}, \qquad (16.5)$$

$$\sigma_{xy}^{(i)}(H) = \sigma^i(H) \tan \theta_i [1 + \tan^2 \theta_i]^{-1}. \qquad (16.6)$$

The condition of uncoupled bands enunciated above is not so restrictive as it might appear at first glance. Physically, we may indeed have interaction in the form of interband scattering. It is apparent that, for example, if transport in each band can be described by a relaxation time and by a steady-state carrier density, then the bands are uncoupled mathematically. A carrier scattered from band 2 to band 1 is immediately replaced by a carrier scattered into 2 by the inverse transition. This point has been made by Ehrenreich and Overhauser[246] who have investigated transport by the heavy- and light-mass valence bands in germanium.

Since weak-field Hall effect and magnetoresistance include terms involving second and third powers, respectively, of the relaxation time averaged over energy (see Section 12d), it may be expected that the influence of multiband conduction on galvanomagnetic phenomena can be large if the individual characteristics of each band are widely different. In order

---

[245] M. Kohler, *Ann. Physik* [6] **5**, 89 (1949); **6**, 18 (1949).

[246] H. Ehrenreich and A. Overhauser, *Phys. Rev.* **104**, 649 (1956).

to obtain a better insight into what is involved, let us examine the expressions for Hall effect and magnetoresistance for a two-band model in terms of the characteristics of each band. These relationships follow from (16.1) to (16.6) with the use of (12.26) and (12.32). General developments, including the thermomagnetic effects, can be found in a number of the articles which have been cited. In addition, a number of specific implications are discussed in texts such as those by Jan[1], by Jones[247], and by Wilson.[9]

In terms of the conductivities σ_1 and σ_2 of each band, and the respective Hall coefficients R_1 and R_2, the expressions can be put in the form given by Chambers[135]:

$$R_H = \frac{\sigma_1^2 R_1 + \sigma_2^2 R_2 + \sigma_1^2 \sigma_2^2 R_1 R_2 H^2 (R_1 + R_2)}{(\sigma_1 + \sigma_2)^2 + \sigma_1^2 \sigma_2^2 H^2 (R_1 + R_2)^2} \tag{16.7}$$

where

$$\sigma_i \equiv \sigma^{(i)}(H), \qquad R_i \equiv R_H^{(i)}, \qquad i = 1, 2.$$

An equation similar to the above can be written for the transverse magnetoresistance. In terms of Hall angles, the result is

$$\frac{\Delta\rho}{\rho_0} = \tag{16.8}$$

$$= \frac{(\sigma_1 + \sigma_2)(\sigma^0 - [\sigma_1 + \sigma_2]) + \sigma^0(\sigma_1 \tan^2 \theta_2 + \sigma_2 \tan^2 \theta_1) - (\sigma_1 \tan \theta_2 + \sigma_2 \tan \theta_1)^2}{(\sigma_1 + \sigma_2)^2 + (\sigma_1 \tan \theta_2 + \sigma_2 \tan \theta_1)^2}$$

where

$$\sigma^0 = \sigma_1^0 + \sigma_2^0, \qquad \text{and} \qquad \tan \theta < 0 \text{ for electrons}, > 0 \text{ for holes}.$$

The influence of multiband transport in magnetoresistance is vividly brought out by considering the case of the constant-τ model or of a highly degenerate metal, so that the magnetoresistance of each spherical band vanishes [see (12.12), (12.13), (12.32), and (14.8)]. Then $\sigma_i(H) = \sigma_i^0$, $i = 1, 2$ so that (16.8) becomes

$$\frac{\Delta\rho}{\rho_0} = \frac{\sigma_1^0 \sigma_2^0 (\tan \theta_1 - \tan \theta_2)^2}{(\sigma_1^0 + \sigma_2^0)^2 + (\sigma_1^0 \tan \theta_2 + \sigma_2^0 \tan \theta_1)^2}, \qquad \sigma_i(H) = \sigma_i^0. \tag{16.9}$$

---

[247] See the "Handbuch" article by Jones (cited in footnote 67a).

Thus we see that the two-band model provides a nonvanishing magneto-resistance whenever the Hall angles are unequal in each band, even though the characteristics of either band alone ensure a zero magneto-resistance.

It is of interest to express results explicitly in terms of H for the case of electron and hole bands, having parameters designated, respectively, by subscripts n and p by the relations [cf. (12.28) and (12.51)]

$$\tan\theta_1 = -\frac{r_n\sigma_n H}{n|e|c}, \qquad \tan\theta_2 = \frac{r_p\sigma_p H}{p|e|c} \qquad (16.10)$$

where n and p are the respective electron and hole concentrations. To illustrate the principal points, it is sufficient to consider the simpler expression (16.9) which applies to the case where the conductivity in each band is field-independent. The result is

$$\frac{\Delta\rho}{\rho_0} = \frac{\dfrac{\sigma_n\sigma_p}{e^2 c^2(\sigma_n+\sigma_p)^2}\left(\dfrac{\sigma_n r_n}{n}+\dfrac{\sigma_p r_p}{p}\right)^2 H^2}{1+\dfrac{\sigma_n^2\sigma_p^2}{e^2 c^2(\sigma_n+\sigma_p)^2}\left(\dfrac{r_n}{n}-\dfrac{r_p}{p}\right)^2 H^2}, \qquad \sigma_i=\sigma_i^0,\quad i=n,p. \quad (16.11)$$

Thus, we see that the magnetoresistance at weak fields behaves as H^2 and in general tends to saturate at strong fields. In the special case when $r_p\, n = r_n\, p$, however, there is no saturation, and the magnetoresistance continues as H^2. In isotropic metals, the degeneracy ensures $r_n = r_p = 1$ [Eq. (14.7)] so that for certain pure divalent metals of high purity where overlapping bands occur and where $n \cong p$, large magnetoresistances can be measured at high fields. Of course, in many metals the Fermi surface topology may be far from spherical (see Section 26). The condition for nonsaturation of the magnetoresistance at strong magnetic fields follows generally from (16.8):

$$\sigma_1\tan\theta_2 + \sigma_2\tan\theta_1 = 0, \qquad \tan\theta_i \gg 1, \qquad (16.12)$$

or, using (16.4),

$$R_1 + R_2 = 0, \qquad R_i\sigma_i H \gg 1, \qquad i = 1, 2. \qquad (16.13)$$

Thus, the Hall coefficients of the two bands are equal and opposite. If the conductivities of each band at saturation are also equal, then it is apparent from Eq. (16.7) that relation (16.13) requires the strong-field Hall coefficient of the material to vanish.

The Hall coefficient will vanish in general when [cf. Eq. (9.18)]

$$\sigma_{xy}^{(1)}(H) + \sigma_{xy}^{(2)}(H) = 0. \tag{16.13a}$$

The above relation, together with Eqs. (16.4)–(16.6), yields immediately:

$$\sigma_1^2 R_1 (1 + \sigma_1^2 R_1^2 H^2)^{-1} + \sigma_2^2 R_2 (1 + \sigma_2^2 R_2^2 H^2)^{-1} = 0. \tag{16.13b}$$

This condition also follows directly from (16.7) for the Hall coefficient null. Thus if $\sigma_1 = \sigma_2$ at saturation, it is seen that condition (16.13) insures that the Hall coefficient and Hall angle vanish. For general values of σ_1 and σ_2, it is readily shown that condition (16.13) yields

$$R_H = \frac{(\sigma_1 - \sigma_2) R_1}{\sigma_1 + \sigma_2}, \qquad \tan\theta = \frac{(\sigma_1 - \sigma_2) R_1 H}{1 + \sigma_1 \sigma_2 R_1^2 H^2}, \qquad R_1 = - R_2 \tag{16.13c}$$

Here, at large fields, the Hall angle varies as $1/H$, and also as $1/R_1$.

17. Parabolic Conduction and Valence Bands

For spherical energy surfaces with the band edge at $\mathbf{k} = 0$, the energy of the electrons in the conduction band is given in terms of the wave vector $\mathbf{k}$ by

$$E - E_c \equiv \varepsilon_1 = \hbar^2 |\mathbf{k}|^2 / 2m_1, \tag{17.1}$$

and that of the deficit electrons, or holes, in the valence band by

$$E_V - E \equiv \varepsilon_2 = \hbar^2 |\mathbf{k}|^2 / 2m_2 \tag{17.2}$$

where m_1 and m_2 are the respective electron and hole effective masses. The energy of the carriers E, that of the edge at the bottom of the conduction band E_c, and that of the edge at the top of the valence band E_V are all measured from the same level, say the bottom of the valence band. The quantity ε_1, on the other hand, is the energy as measured positive upward from the bottom of the conduction band, while ε_2 is the energy as measured positive downward from the top of the valence band. Many authors prefer to express (17.2) in terms of ε_1 as follows:

$$\varepsilon_1 = - \Delta E_G - \hbar^2 |\mathbf{k}|^2 / 2m_2, \tag{17.3}$$

where $\Delta E_G (\equiv E_C - E_V)$, which is positive for semiconductors, is the band separation or energy gap. In the case of metals where there is overlap in the bands, ΔE_G is negative.

a. Two-Band Case

The equations for electrical and thermal currents in the case of mixed conduction, i.e., by both electrons and holes, follow from a straight-forward evaluation of (6.6) and (6.7) over the two bands defined by (17.1) and (17.2). Explicit expressions are given in a number of standard articles such as those by Sondheimer and Wilson,[248] Wilson,[9] Madelung,[170] and Samoilowitsch and Korenblit.[24] The terms representing hole transport are usually put in a form symmetrical to those of the electrons by introducing the hole distribution function and by using energy parameters measured from the top of the valence band. Thus

$$f_0^{(2)}(\varepsilon_2) = [e^{(\varepsilon_2 - \zeta_2)/kT} + 1]^{-1} \tag{17.4}$$

where ζ_2 is the Fermi energy of the system as measured from the top of the valence band, positive downward, in contrast to ζ_1 which is the same quantity but measured from the bottom of the conduction band, positive upward. Hence,

$$\zeta_2 = E_V - \zeta, \qquad \text{also} \qquad \zeta_1 = \zeta - E_c, \tag{17.5}$$

so that

$$\zeta_1 + \zeta_2 = -\Delta E_G. \tag{17.6}$$

Justification for treating transport in an almost-full band by the formalism of introducing deficit electrons or holes, where these particles are considered to possess positive charges, is contained in the works of a number of authors.[249–251] It follows that the integrals $\mathscr{D}_n$ of Eq. (7.16), which contain odd powers of the carrier charge, are of opposite signs for holes and electrons. This is not true of the $\mathscr{C}_n$ integrals, which depend on even powers of e. The expressions for the electric current densities thus follow from (7.13) to (7.17):

[248] E. H. Sondheimer and A. H. Wilson, *Proc. Roy. Soc.* **A190**, 435 (1947).
[249] W. Heisenberg, *Ann. Physik* [5] **10**, 888 (1931).
[250] R. Peierls, *Z. Physik* **53**, 255 (1929).
[251] See p. 318 of Seitz.[209]

$$J_x = [\mathscr{C}_1^{(1)} + \mathscr{C}_1^{(2)}]E_x{}^* - [\mathscr{D}_1^{(1)} - \mathscr{D}_1^{(2)}]\,E_y{}^* + \tag{17.7}$$

$$\frac{1}{|e|T}\,[\mathscr{C}_2^{(1)} - \mathscr{C}_2^{(2)} - \zeta_1\,\mathscr{C}_1^{(1)} + \zeta_2\,\mathscr{C}_1^{(2)}]\,\frac{\partial T}{\partial x} -$$

$$\frac{1}{|e|T}\,[\mathscr{D}_2^{(1)} + \mathscr{D}_2^{(2)} - \zeta_1\mathscr{D}_1^{(1)} - \zeta_2\mathscr{D}_1^{(2)}]\,\frac{\partial T}{\partial y},$$

$$J_y = [\mathscr{D}_1^{(1)} - \mathscr{D}_1^{(2)}]E_x{}^* + [\mathscr{C}_1^{(1)} + \mathscr{C}_1^{(2)}]\,E_y{}^* + \tag{17.8}$$

$$\frac{1}{|e|T}\,[\mathscr{D}_2^{(1)} + \mathscr{D}_2^{(2)} - \zeta_1\mathscr{D}_1^{(1)} - \zeta_2\mathscr{D}_1^{(2)}]\,\frac{\partial T}{\partial x} +$$

$$\frac{1}{|e|T}\,[\mathscr{C}_2^{(1)} - \mathscr{C}_2^{(2)} - \zeta_1\,\mathscr{C}_1^{(1)} + \zeta_2\,\mathscr{C}_1^{(2)}]\,\frac{\partial T}{\partial y}$$

where superscripts (1) and (2) refer to electrons and holes, respectively.

Similar equations could be written down for the heat currents. With both electrons and holes present, however, the thermal transport needs to be considered especially carefully. As was pointed out before [following Eq. (1.6)],, the condition $\mathbf{J} = 0$ is satisfied as long as $\mathbf{J}^{(1)} = -\mathbf{J}^{(2)}$,. Hence the individual electron and hole currents do not in general vanish, and energy transport by ambipolar diffusion can occur. Thus, the interpretation of measured quantities depends on the consideration of appropriate heat currents. To go into details is beyond the scope of this work. In addition to the literature already cited[11–15], the reader can consult subsequent articles by Madelung,[170,252] Price,[23,134] and Ioffe.[253] A more detailed treatment of basic transport effects when both electrons and holes are present has been recently carried out by Czaja,[254] using the thermodynamic theory of irreversible processes. Consideration is given to recombination and generation of the electron-hole pairs.

It is see from (17.7) and (17.8), or from (16.1) and (16.2), with (15.89) and (15.90) that the components of the conductivity tensor can be written for the case of mixed acoustic phonon and ionized impurity scattering as follows[254a]:

[252] O. Madelung, Z. Naturforsch. 11a, 478 (1956).
[253] A. F. Ioffe, Can. J. Phys. 34, 1342 (1956).
[254] W. Czaja, Helv. Phys. Acta 32, 1 (1959).
[254a] In these expressions all quantities are positive. The appropriate signs for electron and for hole transport have been taken into account in the signs governing each term.

$$\sigma_{xx}(H) = |e| [n\mu_{0,n}^L K(\beta_n, \gamma_n) + p\mu_{0,p}^L K(\beta_p, \gamma_p]] \qquad (17.9)$$

$$\sigma_{xy}(H) = - |e| [[\sqrt{\pi}/2] [n\mu_{0,n}^L \gamma_n^{1/2} L(\beta_n, \gamma_n) - p\mu_{0,p}^L \gamma_p^{1/2} L(\beta_p, \gamma_p)] \qquad (17.10)$$

where n and p refer to electron and hole concentrations, respectively, and when used as subscripts indicate quantities for conduction and valence bands, respectively. The assumptions concerning the treatment of the impurity scattering in connection with (17.9) and (17.10) were discussed in Section 15c(2).

The concentrations of the electrons and holes are determined by the position of the Fermi level, or more basically by the densities of states in the two bands and by the characteristics of the impurity levels. These relationships have been given in a number of publications, and the reader is referred to some of them for details.[255-259]

Equations of the type (17.9) and (17.10) have been used by a number of investigators to analyze Hall effect and transverse magnetoresistance in mixed semiconductors. Madelung treated the case of arbitrary concentrations of electrons and holes when pure lattice scattering existed ($\beta = 0$). Details of some of this work are given later.

The general expressions for Hall effect and transverse magnetoresistance, including that for the Corbino magnetoresistance, can be put in the following form [254a] for a consistent set of laboratory units[259a]:

---

[255] R. Hutner, E. Rittner, and F. Du Pré, *Philips Research Repts.* 5, 188 (1950).

[255a] A. Samoilowitsch and L. Korenblit, *Fortschr. Physik* 4, 630 (1956).

[256] See p. 230 ff. of Shockley.[32]

[257] J. S. Blakemore, *Elec. Commun.* 29, 131 (1952).

[258] See p. 34 ff. of Madelung's article in the "Handbuch."[132]

[259] E. H. Putley, *Proc. Phys. Soc. (London)* 72, 917 (1958).

[259a] The "consistent set" of laboratory units are: R_H in cm³/coulomb; σ in (ohm-cm)$^{-1}$; e in coulomb; μ in cm²/volt-sec; H in volt-sec/cm². For magnetic fields in gauss, the H's should be replaced by $H/10^8$. This is to be compared to the case where Gaussian units are used and the dimensionless magnetic-field factor γ involves the quantities $\mu H/c$, with the result that H in Eqs. (17.11) and (17.12) is replaced by H/c. A factor of c then also appears in the denominator of the expression for R_H since the numerator involved the quantity $\gamma^{1/2}$ — cf. Eq. (15.98).

$$R_H = -\qquad\qquad\qquad\qquad\qquad (17.11)$$

$$\frac{3\pi}{8}\left\{\frac{\sigma_{0,n}^L \mu_{0,n}^L L(\beta_n,\gamma_n) - \sigma_{0,p}^L \mu_{0,p}^L L(\beta_p,\gamma_p)}{[\sigma_{0,n}^L K(\beta_n,\gamma_n) + \sigma_{0,p}^L K(\beta_p,\gamma_p)]^2 + [3\pi/8]^2 H^2[\sigma_{0,n}^L \mu_{0,n}^L L(\beta_n,\gamma_n) - \sigma_{0,p}^L \mu_{0,p}^L L(\beta_p,\gamma_p)]^2}\right\}$$

$$\frac{\Delta\rho}{\rho_0} = \qquad\qquad\qquad\qquad\qquad (17.12)$$

$$\frac{[\sigma_{0,n}^L K(\beta_n,\gamma_n) + \sigma_{0,p}^L K(\beta_p,\gamma_p)][\sigma_{0,n}^L K(\beta_n,0) + \sigma_{0,p}^L K(\beta_p,0)]}{[\sigma_{0,n}^L K(\beta_n,\gamma_n) + \sigma_{0,p}^L K(\beta_p,\gamma_p)]^2 + [3\pi/8]^2 H^2[\sigma_{0,n}^L \mu_{0,n}^L L(\beta_n,\gamma_n) - \sigma_{0,p}^L \mu_{0,p}^L L(\beta_p,\gamma_p)]^2} - 1$$

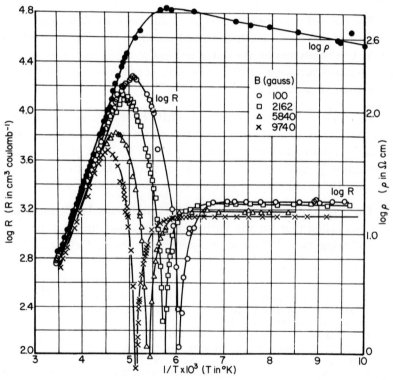

FIG. 17. Temperature dependence of the Hall coefficient of a p-type indium antimonide specimen at different magnetic field strengths (after Howarth *et al.*[267])

$$\left(\frac{\Delta\rho}{\rho_0}\right)_{E_y=0} = \frac{\sigma_{0,n}^L K(\beta_n,0) + \sigma_{0,p}^L K(\beta_p,0)}{\sigma_{0,n}^L K(\beta_n,\gamma_n) + \sigma_{0,p}^L K(\beta_p,\gamma_p)} - 1 \qquad (17.13)$$

where the zero-magnetic-field lattice conductivity of each band is given by

$$\sigma_{0,n}^L = n|e|\mu_{0,n}^L \quad \text{and} \quad \sigma_{0,p}^L = p|e|\mu_{0,p}^L. \tag{17.14}$$

Because of the opposing Hall fields created by electrons and holes, it is apparent that the galvanomagnetic effects can have unusually strong temperature variations in regions near the Hall null when the relative electron-hole population is temperature dependent.   Likewise, when $\mu_{0,n}$ and $\mu_{0,p}$ are significantly different, strong magnetic-field dependences will be observed.   This behavior is especially noticeable in the case of indium antimonide where $\mu_{0,n}/\mu_{0,p}$ is the order of 50 or more.[260] Experimental data on the Hall coefficient of p-type indium antimonide have been obtained by a number of investigators,[261-268] and a typical $1/T$ dependence of R_H is shown for several magnetic field strengths in Fig. 17. It is apparent that in the region of the crossover, the variation of R_H with magnetic field can be tremendous.

Because of the singular nature of the Hall field as a function of temperature (i.e., as a function of the ratio p/n), the magnetoresistance may be expected to exhibit a maximum.   Such a behavior is apparent in the data of Weiss,[262] Harman et al.,[263] and Champness.[268] Because of the reduced Hall voltage, saturation effects are delayed and quite large values of $\Delta\rho/\rho_0$ can be obtained, as is illustrated by several of the experimental results shown in Fig. 18.

---

[260] By $\mu_{0,p}$ here we mean the mobility in the heavy hole band. Because of valence band degeneracy, there are holes of both light and heavy masses in InSb. For quantitative investigations Eqs. (17.11)–(17.13) must include also the contribution of the light hole band.

[261] M. Tanenbaum and J. Maita, *Phys. Rev.* **91**, 1009 (1953).

[262] H. Weiss, *Z. Naturforsch.* **8a**, 463 (1953).

[263] T. Harman, R. Willardson, and A. Beer, *Phys. Rev.* **95**, 699 (1954). Note that the captions to Figs. 5 and 6 should be interchanged.

[264] R. Breckenridge, R. Blunt, W. Hosler, H. Frederikse, and W. Oshinsky, *Phys. Rev.* **96**, 571 (1954).

[265] H. Fritzsche and K. Lark-Horovitz, *Phys. Rev.* **99**, 400 (1955).

[266] H. Hrostowski, F. Morin, T. Geballe, and G. Wheatley, *Phys. Rev.* **100**, 1672 (1955).

[267] D. Howarth, R. Jones, and E. Putley, *Proc. Phys. Soc. (London)* **B70**, 124 (1957).

[267a] C. Hilsum and R. Barrie, *Proc. Phys. Soc. (London)* **71**, 676 (1958).

[268] C. H. Champness, *J. Electronics and Control* **4**, 201 (1958).

A number of authors present plots of Eqs. (17.11) and (17.12) for various values of $\mu^L_{0,n}/\mu^L_{0,p}$ For example, Johnson and Whitesell[242] discuss the behavior of magnetoresistance and magneto-Hall coefficient for intrinsic conduction $(n = p)$ and pure lattice scattering. The case

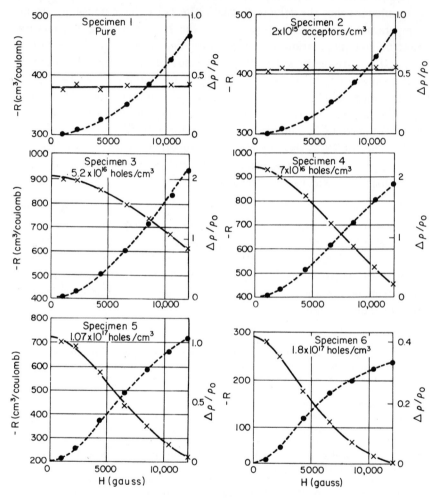

FIG. 18. Magnetic-field dependence of Hall coefficient (solid lines) and transverse magnetoresistance in p-type indium antimonide specimens having different impurity concentrations. Points represent experimental data at room temperature; curves are theoretical calculations (after Hilsum and Barrie[267a]).

for arbitrary electron-hole concentrations is examined by Madelung[269] and by Harman *et al.*[263] The problem has also been treated by Appel,[243] who gives special consideration to the cases of weak- and strong-field limits.

The Corbino magnetoresistance has an H^2 dependence in the region where simple theory is applicable, and measurements of that quantity as a function of magnetic field can yield useful information in the case of certain materials. An interesting example is an intrinsic semiconductor in which the electron mobility is substantially greater than that of the holes. In such a case, where $n = p$, Eq. (17.13) becomes

$$\left(\frac{\Delta\rho}{\rho_0}\right)_{E_y=0} = \frac{K(\beta_n, 0) + bK(\beta_p, 0)}{K(\beta_n, \gamma_n) + bK(\beta_p, \gamma_p)} - 1, \qquad n = p \qquad (17.15)$$

where $b = \mu_{0,p}^L / \mu_{0,n}^L$.

Thus, it is seen that in specimens where $b \ll 1$, the electron characteristics predominate at weak magnetic fields. As the field increases, however, $K(\beta_n, \gamma_n)$ decreases more rapidly than does $K(\beta_p, \gamma_p)$, since $\mu_{0,n}^L \gg \mu_{0,p}^L$, with the result that the effects due to hole transport predominate when the electronic transport is in the strong-field region. This behavior is readily illustrated by examining the case of $\beta = 0$ so that the expansions of $K(0, \gamma)$ and $L(0, \gamma)$, as given in (15.86) and (15.87), are applicable to (17.15) to yield:

$$\left(\frac{\Delta\rho}{\rho_0}\right)_{E_y=0} \simeq \frac{9\pi}{16} (\mu_{0,n} H)^2 \frac{1+b^2}{1+b}, \qquad \gamma_n, \ \gamma_p \ll 1 \qquad (17.16)$$

where $\mu_{0,n} = \mu_{0,n}^L$, that is $\beta = 0$. For the intermediate case when the electronic transport is in the strong-field region and the hole transport is in the weak-field region — a situation which can obviously occur only when $b \ll 1$ — the result becomes

$$\left(\frac{\Delta\rho}{\rho_0}\right)_{E_y=0} \simeq \frac{1}{b} + \frac{9\pi}{16} (\mu_{0,p} H)^2, \qquad \begin{array}{c} \gamma_n \gg 1 \\ \gamma_p \ll 1 \end{array}. \qquad (17.17)$$

Finally, at very high field strengths if both carriers are in the strong-field region, one obtains the symmetrical expression

---

[269] O. Madelung, *Z. Naturforsch.* 8a, 791 (1953).

$$\left(\frac{\Delta\rho}{\rho_0}\right)_{E_y = 0} \approx \frac{9\pi}{32}\mu_{0,n}\,\mu_{0,p}\,H^2, \qquad \begin{matrix} \gamma_n \gg 1 \\ \gamma_p \gg 1 \end{matrix}. \qquad (17.18)$$

In practice it may not always be possible to achieve strong-field limits without complicating the theory. This is especially true if data are taken at low temperatures. For if $\hbar\omega > kT$, charge carrier orbit quantization

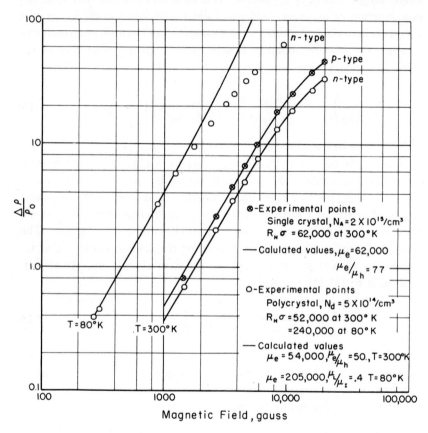

FIG. 19. Corbino magnetoresistance in indium antimonide (after Beer *et al.*[269a]).

effects can begin to become significant. The classical treatment of the charged particles in the magnetic field is then no longer adequate (see Section 28). Deviations in the Corbino magnetoresistance from an H^2 dependence at strong magnetic fields are, of course, evidence of the failure of the ordinary magnetoresistance to saturate (Section 12d). The influence of two-carrier transport on this effect is apparent from some unpublished data taken on InSb at the Battelle Institute,[269a] shown in Fig. 19. At room temperature, where the sample is intrinsic, the data are fit very well by a theoretical curve determined by Eq. (17.15), using the values of the parameters indicated. At 80°K, in the extrinsic range, the hole concentration is negligible. It appears there that quantum effects may in part be responsible for the break away from the H^2 line. This point was also made by Frederikse and Hosler in connection with their data.[269b]

To illustrate more specifically the use of singular points in the Hall coefficient to obtain information about mobilities of each carrier, consider a semiconductor having a single acceptor, level of density N_A and negligible activation energy. Then[255−258]

$$p = n + N_A \tag{17.19}$$

and in general

$$np \equiv n_i{}^2 = 16\pi^2 \left(\frac{2\sqrt{m_n m_p}\, kT}{h^2}\right)^3 F_{1/2}\left(\frac{\zeta - E_c}{kT}\right) F_{1/2}\left(\frac{E_V - \zeta}{kT}\right). \tag{17.20}$$

For classical statistics, one has

$$np = 4\left(\frac{2\pi\sqrt{m_n m_p}\, kT}{h^2}\right)^3 \exp\left(-\frac{\Delta E_G}{kT}\right). \tag{17.21}$$

If we define X as the ratio

$$X \equiv n/N_A, \tag{17.22}$$

then it is apparent that the parameter X is a measure of the degree to which the intrinsic region is approached. Small values of X indicate a small concentration of the minority carriers and hence a predominance

[269a] A. C. Beer, et al. Research and Development work on semiconducting materials of unusually high mobility, Office of Technical Services Rept. PB-121288 (unpublished).

[269b] H. P. R. Frederikse and W. R. Hosler, "Solid State Physics in Electronics and Telecommunications," Proceedings of the Brussels Conference (M. Désirant and J. Michiels, eds.). Vol. 2, p. 651. Academic Press, New York, 1960.

of extrinsic conduction, while large values of X indicate that $n \simeq p$ and that the conduction is preponderantly intrinsic. Thus an increase in X corresponds to an increase in temperature, the exact functional relationship being given by (17.19) and (17.21).

It is apparent from (17.11) and following equations that at the Hall coefficient null,

$$X = \frac{b^2 L(\beta_p, \gamma_p)}{L(\beta_n, \gamma_n) - b^2 L(\beta_p, \gamma_p)}, \qquad R_H = 0. \qquad (17.23)$$

Then for $b \ll 1$, $L(\gamma_n)$ decreases more rapidly with increasing H than does $L(\gamma_p)$, so that the null moves to larger X (higher T) with increasing magnetic field.

The expression for the Hall coefficient maximum is more complicated — except in the weak-magnetic-field region, where $L(\gamma) \to 1$, and when $\beta = 0$. For this case, the result is

$$X = \frac{b}{1-b}, \qquad R_H = R_0{}^{max}, \qquad \gamma_n, \gamma_p \ll 1; \qquad \beta = 0 \qquad (17.24)$$

$$R_0{}^{max} = -\frac{3\pi}{8|e|} \frac{1}{N_A} \frac{(1-b)^2}{4b} = -R_0{}^{ex} \frac{(1-b)^2}{4b} \qquad (17.25)$$

where $R_0{}^{ex}$ is the weak-field Hall coefficient at the extrinsic plateau. From (17.25) it is seen that the relative magnitude of the maximum Hall coefficient can be unusually great if the minority carrier mobility is comparatively large. The behavior of the Hall coefficient in the region of influence of intrinsic conduction has been examined in some detail by Putley.[269c]

In concluding this section, it appears desirable to emphasize a fact which has been vividly illustrated by both the theoretical developments and the experimental data which were presented. The point is that in any careful investigation of a semiconductor by means of galvano-magnetic measurements, information must be obtained about the temperature dependence and the magnetic-field dependence of the effects. Otherwise it is possible that erroneous conclusions will be drawn.

[269c] See p. 115 ff. of the monograph by Putley.[93]

b. Three-Band Conduction

Within the past 10 years band-structure calculations have been carried out for a number of semiconductors of the zincblende crystal system. The results indicate that in general the valence band is complicated. The most extensive work has been done in germanium and in silicon.[270-275] The states of maximum energy in the valence band occur at $k = 0$ in the Brillouin zone and would be sixfold degenerate there if there were no spin-orbit interaction. As a result of spin-orbit coupling, this level is split into a fourfold degenerate state at the top of the band and a doubly degenerate state, which is lowered by approximately 0.29 ev in germanium and 0.04 ev in silicon. Away from $k = 0$ the upper band is split into two bands having appreciably different curvatures. Thus in describing the valence band, one commonly refers to a heavy-mass band, a light-mass band, and the split-off band. This picture of the valence band in germanium has also been supported by infrared absorption studies[276-277] and by cyclotron resonance.[278-281] The latter technique has provided much quantitative information on the band structure in semiconductors.

Accurate transport calculations must obviously take into account the complex nature of the valence band. The influence of the light-mass band upon the galvanomagnetic effects is extremely large, and the two-band model for the valence band accounts semiquantitatively for a number of characteristics which appear anomalous when considered in connection with a single band for the valence states.

---

[270] F. Herman and J. Callaway, *Phys. Rev.* **89**, 518 (1953).

[271] F. Herman, *Phys. Rev.* **93**, 1214 (1954); **95**, 847 (1954).

[272] F. Herman, *Physica* **20**, 801 (1954); *Proc. I. R. E.* **43**, 1703 (1955).

[273] F. Herman, *Revs. Modern Phys.* **30**, 102 (1958).

[274] J. Callaway, *Solid State Phys.* **7**, 99 (1958).

[275] E. O. Kane, *Phys. and Chem. Solids* **1**, 82 (1956).

[276] H. B. Briggs and R. C. Fletcher, *Phys. Rev.* **91**, 1342 (1953).

[277] W. Kaiser, R. Collins, and H. Fan, *Phys. Rev.* **91**, 1380 (1953).

[278] G. Dresselhaus, A. Kip, and C. Kittel, *Phys. Rev.* **92**, 827 (1953); **95**, 568 (1954).

[279] B. Lax, H. Zeiger, R. Dexter, and E. Rosenblum, *Phys. Rev.* **93**, 1418 (1954).

[280] R. Dexter, H. Zeiger, and B. Lax, *Phys. Rev.* **95**, 557 (1954).

[281] The use of cyclotron resonance and other experimental techniques for determining band structure in solids has been reviewed by Lax. The article gives a thorough citation of the literature. B. Lax, *Revs. Modern Phys.* **30**, 122 (1958)

The possibility that the dual-valence-band model could account for the unusual behavior of the ratio $\mu/R_0\,\sigma_0$ as a function of temperature in extrinsic p-type germanium was pointed out by Shibuya[282] at the Amsterdam Conference. A similar scheme had been suggested to explain differences in the magnetic-field dependence of the temperature of the Hall coefficient null in indium antimonide and in germanium.[263] An analytical treatment of the problem was given by Willardson et al.[283] in which all energy surfaces were assumed to be spherical, and the mobilities and states densities in the two bands were determined from experimental data, including magnetic-field and temperature dependences of Hall coefficients and magnetoresistance. Data were also taken into the intrinsic region where all three bands contributed to the transport effects.

For transport by electrons (subscript 1) and by "slow" and "fast" holes (of respective mobilities μ_2, μ_3 and densities p_2, p_3), Eqs. (17.11) and (17.12) can be put in the form:

$$R_H = -\frac{3\pi}{8|e|p_2}\left\{\frac{a_1\,b_1\,L_1 - L_2 - a_3\,b_3\,L_3}{[a_1\,K_1 + K_2 + a_3\,K_3]^2 + \frac{1}{4}\pi\gamma_2[a_1\,b_1\,L_1 - L_2 - a_3\,b_3\,L_3]^2}\right\}$$

$$(17.26)$$

$$\frac{\varDelta\rho}{\rho_0} = \frac{[a_1\,K_1 + K_2 + a_3\,K_3][a_1 + 1 + a_3]}{[a_1\,K_1 + K_2 + a_3\,K_3]^2 + \frac{1}{4}\pi\gamma_2[a_1\,b_1\,L_1 - L_2 - a_3\,b_3\,L_3]^2} - 1$$

$$(17.27)$$

where

$$a_1 = \sigma_{0,1}^L/\sigma_{0,2}^L, \qquad b_1 = \mu_{0,1}^L/\mu_{0,2}^L, \qquad a_3 = \sigma_{0,3}^L/\sigma_{0,2}^L, \qquad b_3 = \mu_{0,3}^L/\mu_{0,2}^L,$$

$$\gamma_2 = 9\pi/16(\mu_{0,2}^L H)^2$$

for consistent laboratory units,[259a] and

$$L_i \equiv L(\beta_i, \gamma_i), \qquad K_i \equiv K(\beta_i, \gamma_i), \qquad i = 1, 2, 3.$$

An analysis of the above equations reveals how the high-mobility holes can strongly influence the dependence of the galvanomagnetic effects on temperature and on magnetic field.

---

[282] M. Shibuya, *Physica* **20**, 971 (1954).
[283] R. Willardson, T. Harman, and A. Beer, *Phys. Rev.* **96**, 1512 (1954). These authors will hereafter be designated as WHB.

For example, the condition for the Hall coefficient null is

$$n(\mu_{0,1}^L)^2 L(\beta_1, \gamma_1) - p_2(\mu_{0,2}^L)^2 L(\beta_2, \gamma_2) - p_3(\mu_{0,3}^L)^2 L(\beta_3, \gamma_3) = 0. \quad (17.28)$$

Consider now two examples:

(A) A typical two-band model for which $\mu_{0,1}^L > \mu_{0,2}^L$, $\mu_{0,3}^L = \mu_{0,2}^L$, $p_2 + p_3 > n$. Then it is apparent that as H increases from zero, the ratio

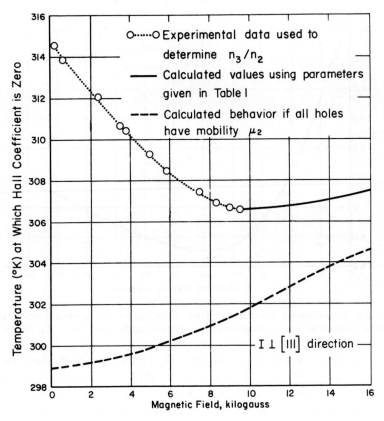

FIG. 20. Experimental data and calculated results of Hall coefficient crossover temperatures as a function of magnetic field (after WHB[283]).

$n/(p_2 + p_3)$ must increase to maintain the Hall coefficient at zero — i.e., the temperature must be increased. This state of affairs is indicated by the dashed curve in Fig. 20. A similar behavior would occur for the three-band model as long as $\mu_{0,3}^L < \mu_{0,1}^L$. On the other hand, if $\mu_{0,3}^L > \mu_{0,1}^L$, we have example B:

(B) When $\mu_{0,3}^L > \mu_{0,1}^L > \mu_{0,2}^L$, the third term can be controlling so that an increase in H requires n to decrease in order to maintain the zero Hall coefficient. This is the situation for germanium, as shown by the upper curve in Fig. 20, where the temperature at the Hall null decreases as H increases from zero to 8500 gauss.

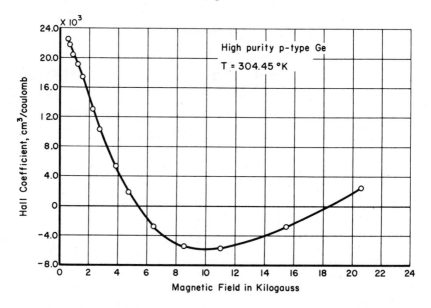

FIG. 21. Experimental data on the Hall coefficient in the neighborhood of the crossover region as a function of magnetic field (Willardson and Beer, unpublished).

It is also seen from the numerator of (17.26) that at constant temperature and in the neighborhood of the Hall null, R_H becomes more positive in example A, as H increases above zero; more negative (i.e., less positive), in example B. The latter situation is illustrated by some unpublished data by Willardson and Beer shown in Fig. 21.

The experimental data show that p-type indium antimonide is indicative of example A,[263] and that p-type germanium is indicative of example B. Actually InSb has light- and heavy-mass bands,[284] with

---

[284] C. H. Champness, *Phys. Rev. Letters* **1**, 439 (1958).

$\mu_{0,3}^L \sim 7.5\,\mu_{0,2}^L$, as is approximately the case for germanium. However, in InSb $\mu_{0,1}^L > \mu_{0,3}^L$, as compared to the opposite situation in germanium.

As the magnetic field is increased, the "fast" hole term in (17.26) may become sufficiently small in comparison to the other terms, that its effect is negligible. The situation is then essentially that of the two-band model and the magnetic field dependences should follow those of example A. This behavior is suggested for germanium by the experimental-theoretical curve in Fig. 20, and is verified by the experimental data above 10 kgauss in Fig. 21.

Another observed effect attributed to the fast holes is the augmentation of the magnetoresistance in the extrinsic region, so that the maximum in the curve as a function of temperature is not discernable[263, 283] or is relatively small.[284a]

c. Extrinsic p-Type Germanium and Similar Semiconductors

The inclusion of fast-hole transport produces especially striking effects in Hall and magnetoresistance phenomena at weak magnetic fields in the extrinsic region of the semiconductor. This is readily apparent from a study of the limiting forms of (17.26) and (17.27) at weak and at strong magnetic fields. For simplicity we assume here that $\beta = 0$ so that (17.26) and (17.27) reduce to

$$R_{H \to 0} = \frac{3\pi}{8|e|p_2} \frac{1 + (p_3/p_2)(\mu_3/\mu_2)^2}{[1 + (p_3/p_2)(\mu_3/\mu_2)]^2} \tag{17.29}$$

$$\lim_{H \to 0}\left(\frac{\Delta\rho}{\rho_0}\right) = \frac{9\pi}{16}\,(\mu_2\,H)^2\left[\frac{1 + (p_3/p_2)(\mu_3/\mu_2)^3}{1 + (p_3/p_2)(\mu_3/\mu_2)} - \frac{\pi}{4}\left(\frac{1 + (p_3/p_2)(\mu_3/\mu_2)^2}{1 + (p_3/p_2)(\mu_3/\mu_2)}\right)^2\right] \tag{17.30}$$

$$R_{H \to \infty} = 1/|e|(p_2 + p_3) \tag{}$$

$$\lim_{H \to \infty}\left(\frac{\Delta\rho}{\rho_0}\right) = \frac{32}{9\pi}\frac{[1 + (p_3/p_2)(\mu_3/\mu_2)][1 + (p_3/p_2)(\mu_2/\mu_3)]}{(1 + p_3/p_2)^2} - 1 \tag{17.31}$$

where we have assumed $\beta = 0$ and have written μ_i to mean $\mu_{0,i}^L$ $(i = 2, 3)$.

[284a] V. Stafeev and V. Tuckevich, *J. Tech. Phys. U.S.S.R.* **26**, 273 (1956) [translation: *Soviet Phys.-Tech. Phys.* **1**, 268 (1956)].

It is apparent from the above that the addition of high-mobility holes can influence substantially the weak-field galvanomagnetic effects, even though such holes are present only in a relatively small amount. In the case of the Hall effect, the mobility weighting factor enters to the square; for magnetoresistance, it appears as the cube. For example, if the density

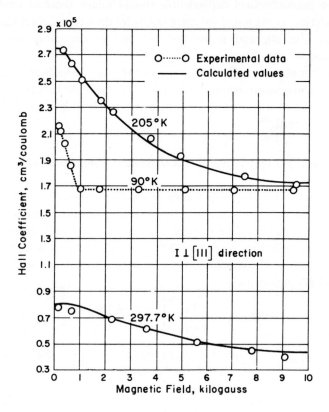

FIG. 22. Hall coefficient as a function of magnetic field for a *p*-type germanium specimen (after WHB[283]).

of the fast holes is two percent that of the others and their mobility 8 times as large, the Hall coefficient is increased by a factor of 1.7. In such a case, the factor in the brackets of (17.30) is increased from 0.21 to 6.7, producing an increase in magnetoresistance of over 30 times. In the strong-field limits, the mobility weighting factor is far less important —

in fact, as expected, the strong-field Hall coefficient involves only the sum of the carrier densities.

A semiconductor having dual hole bands with the characteristics indicated above can thus exhibit strong magnetic-field dependences in the galvanomagnetic properties. Such a situation has been demonstrated for p-type germanium by a number of investigators.[55,183,285,286]

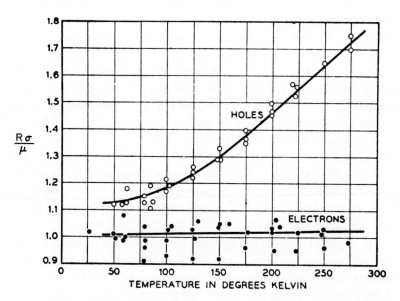

FIG. 23. Measured values of the parameter $R\sigma/\mu$ as a function of temperature for different specimens of n- and p-type germanium (after Morin[287]).

In the cases where the Hall coefficient changes significantly with magnetic field, especial care is necessary in interpreting Hall data obtained as a function of temperature. This is because the galvanomagnetic effects depend on the magnetic field through the parameter γ, which is proportional to μH. Although the experimenter may religiously maintain H constant as temperature is varied, in most cases the μ will change significantly with temperature. Thus, a substantial excursion

[285] W. C. Dunlap, *Phys. Rev.* **71**, 471 (1947); **79**, 286 (1950); **82**, 329 (1951).

[286] V. Stafeev and V. Tuckevich, *J. Tech. Phys. U.S.S.R.* **28**, 1642 (1958) [translation: *Soviet Phys.-Tech. Phys.* **3**, 1513 (1958)].

along the curve of R_H vs. μH can occur in a temperature run. If the resulting variation in r_H [defined in Eq. (12.51)] is not accounted for, it is obvious that erroneous conclusions can be made regarding the temperature dependence of the carrier concentration or of the mobility. An example is p-type germanium where the extrinsic Hall coefficient measured at a few kilogauss can decrease significantly as the temperature falls. This is apparent from a comparison of the data in Fig. 22 for the two temperatures. A similar behavior, over a much wider temperature range, is illustrated by the measurements of Morin,[287] who determined values of $R\sigma/\mu$ as a function of temperature for both n- and p-type germanium.[288] His data are shown in Fig. 23. Here the effect of the degenerate hole bands is quite striking. The behavior of the p-type specimens can be understood qualitatively by reference to Fig. 22. Assuming a constant magnetic field of several kilogauss was used at 90°K, the fast hole band is in the strong-field limit and, even for the slow holes, γ is greater than unity, so that r_H is only slightly above unity. The additional 17% in $R\sigma$ results from the increase in σ due to the contributions of the fast holes. At 205°K, R has increased by perhaps 25% due to the decreased γ in each band, raising $R\sigma$ to 1.47. Finally at 300°K, γ is still smaller so that R has been increased by 55% to give an $R\sigma/\mu$ of 1.8.

It is apparent from the preceding paragraphs that before one can draw firm conclusions from Hall-effect data, it is essential to know something about the magnetic-field dependence of the Hall coefficient. If a high-mobility band is involved, measurements at quite low values of magnetic field are necessary to determine the weak-field Hall coefficient plateau. For example, in high purity p-type germanium at 200°K, fields below 100 gauss are desirable; at 77°K, fields below 50 gauss are necessary. For high-purity indium antimonide ($\mu_1 \sim 5 \times 10^6$ cm²/volt-sec at 77°K), it may be desirable to measure at 20 gauss and below![289]

In order to emphasize further the importance of ascertaining magnetic-field dependencies of galvanomagnetic effects, we present some unpublished data on p-type indium antimonide contrasting the temperature

[287] F. J. Morin, *Phys. Rev.* **93**, 62 (1954).

[288] The quantity $R\sigma$ (expressed in practical units) is often referred to as "Hall mobility" in the literature. We shall restrict the latter term to applicability only when single-band transport occurs.[182]

[289] R. Bate, R. Willardson, and A. Beer, *Phys. and Chem. Solids* **9**, 119 (1959).

dependence of the Hall coefficient in the weak-field region with that in the strong-field case.   The results, shown in Fig. 24, reveal a completely opposite behavior in the two cases.   Sufficient investigation was not carried out to establish firmly the mechanisms involved in the two characteristics.   A reasonable explanation, however, is that R_H for the

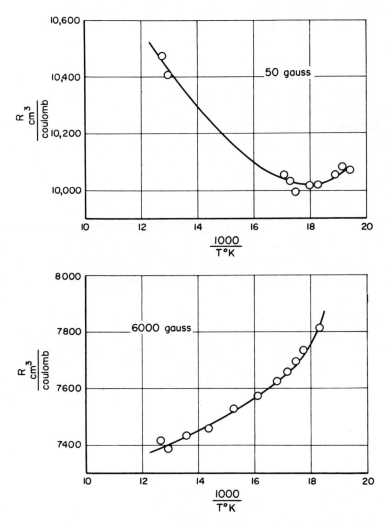

FIG. 24.   Temperature dependence of Hall coefficient of p-type InSb at 50 and 6000 gauss (Willardson and Beer, unpublished).

strong-field region reveals a drop in carrier concentration as the temperature is lowered from 77° to 55°K, presumably due to the activation energy of the acceptor level. In the weak-field region, on the other hand, the increase in r_0 due to the greater degree of ionized impurity scattering,[289] is able to offset the effect of decreased carrier concentration. Attempts to consider this behavior quantitatively in p-type indium antimonide do not seem worthwhile because of the complicated nature of the valence bands, which suggests that the heavy-mass band is nonparabolic near $k = 0$ and that the energy involves linear terms in the wave number.[290, 291] In addition, the scattering processes in those semiconductors where there are unlike atoms in the unit cell are more complicated and may involve polar scattering, piezoelectric scattering, etc.[215, 292]

In connection with the data in Fig. 24, the delineation of the weak- and strong-field regions was accomplished experimentally by ascertaining the field dependence of R_H at 77°K. The data are shown in Fig. 25, which also includes measurements on an n-type specimen. The effect of the fast holes in the p-type material is again apparent. It is seen that to achieve the weak-field plateau, magnetic fields as low as 50 gauss are desirable; and that for $H > 5000$ gauss, the strong-field region is realized. The fine structure in the curves, if it is real, is not a subject for discussion here. Part of it could be due to insufficiently precise determinations of H; the behavior might also result from impurity gradients across the specimen (see Section 27).

In applying Eqs. (17.26) and (17.27) to p-type germanium, WHB found that a mobility ratio for light and heavy holes of 7.5 to 8 was necessary to account for the magnetic-field dependence of the Hall coefficient and the magnetoresistance.[283]   This result was reasonable inasmuch as cyclotron resonance data predicted effective masses of approximately 0.34 m_0 and 0.043 m_0, respectively, for the heavy- and light-mass bands,[293] giving a ratio of 7.9. It is expected that the mobilities in the two bands would be in approximately the inverse ratio of the masses, since the relaxation times of the two kinds of holes are approximately equal. This follows from the fact, pointed out by Brooks,[294] that interband scattering

[290] E. O. Kane, *Phys. and Chem. Solids* 1, 249 (1957).
[291] F. Stern, *Phys. and Chem. Solids* 8, 277 (1959).
[292] W. A. Harrison, *Phys. Rev.* 101, 903 (1956).
[293] R. Dexter, H. Zeiger, and B. Lax, *Phys. Rev.* 104, 637 (1956).
[294] See p. 152 of reference 33.

is the principal mechanism which determines the mobility of the light holes, while intraband scattering is the predominant mechanism for the heavy holes. Thus the scattering depends essentially on the density of

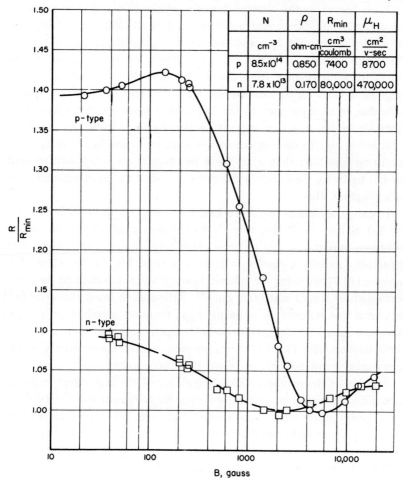

FIG. 25. Magnetic-field dependence of Hall coefficient of n- and p-type InSb at 77°K (Willardson and Beer, unpublished).

the final states, which in either case is principally in the band of large states' density (heavy mass). Thus the collision frequencies of the two types of holes are approximately equal. The approximate equality of relaxation times is consistent with estimates based on linewidths in cyclotron resonance measurements. Results suggested $\tau_3 \cong 7 \times 10^{-11}$ sec and $\tau_2 \gtrsim 5 \times 10^{-11}$ sec.[295]

With regard to the relative densities of the fast and slow holes, the galvanomagnetic data could be fit, using Eqs. (17.29) and (17.30), only for a density ratio of fast and slow holes, p_3/p_2, of approximately 2%. This figure is also consistent with the results of Mochan et al.[296] but differs by a factor of 2 from the results of cyclotron resonance, which suggests a value of approximately 4.2%.[297] This discrepancy appears to be due, in a major part, to the fact that account was not taken of the relatively larger degree of impurity scattering encountered by the light-mass holes, and to the neglect of the warping of the heavy-mass band. It will be seen later that when these two factors are taken into account, the 4% figure for the density ratio gives a good fit to the galvanomagnetic data (Section 21d).

If galvanomagnetic data are taken at temperatures still lower than the 205°K used by WHB, the effect of impurity scattering can become still more important. For example, Goldberg, Adams, and Davis would apparently require a carrier ratio of less than 1% to fit their data measured at 77°K, using the spherical energy surface model and equations developed for lattice scattering only.[55] Attempts to bring the weak-field data into line without so reducing p_3/p_2 required a reduction of μ_3/μ_2 to values such that the magnetic-field dependence was then too weak. These authors also found that the introduction of nonsphericity in the heavy-mass band tended to reduce the discrepancy.

A study of the magnetic-field dependence of the Hall effect in p-type germanium at room temperature was done by Baranskii and Vinetskii.[297a] These investigators carried out measurements at field strengths reaching as low as the neighborhood of one gauss! The existence of the weak-field plateau was verified experimentally to extend from the lowest field to the neighborhood of 200 gauss.

---

[295] G. Dresselhaus, A. Kip, and C. Kittel, *Phys. Rev.* **98**, 368 (1955).

[296] I. Mochan, Iu. Obraztsov, and T. Krylov, *J. Tech. Phys. U.S.S.R.* **27**, 242 (1957) [translation: *Soviet Phys.-Tech. Phys.* **2**, 213 (1957)].

[297] B. Lax and J. Mavroides, *Phys. Rev.* **100**, 1650 (1955).

[297a] P. I. Baranskii and R. M. Vinetskii, *Fiz. Tverd. Tela* **4**, 289 (1962) [translation: *Soviet Phys.-Solid State* **4**, 208 (1962)].

VII.
Nonquadratic Energy Surfaces

18. GENERAL CONSIDERATIONS

As was pointed out in Section 6b, it is not possible to obtain solutions of the Boltzmann equation in closed form for arbitrary values of magnetic field intensity when the energies of the charge carriers in the solid are not quadratic forms in the wave number. In these cases, one is forced to use series expansions in terms of the magnetic field intensity H, or to carry out a development in terms of the cyclotron frequencies and harmonics appropriate to the carriers in the band. The former method is applicable only in the weak-magnetic-field region; the latter technique has wider validity, but may require involved and tedious calculations.

The former procedure was used by Davis[298] to examine the transverse and longitudinal magnetoresistance in a highly-degenerate metal having cubic symmetry. It will be recalled that the single-band spherically-symmetric model predicts zero magnetoresistance in the limit of high charge-carrier degeneracy (Section 14) assuming an isotropic relaxation time. In Davis' treatment, the relaxation time was not assumed to be a function of energy only. A spherical coordinate system $(\varepsilon, \theta, \varphi)$, where ε is the energy and θ, φ are the customary angles, was used. The quantity $\tau(\varepsilon, \theta, \varphi)$ is then expanded in series of spherical harmonics, using only those terms having cubic symmetry.[298a] The result, to terms of first order in deviations from spherical symmetry, is

$$\tau = \tau_0(\varepsilon)Y_0^c + \tau_1(\varepsilon)Y_4^c \tag{18.1}$$

where $Y_0^c = 1$, and the fourth-order spherical harmonic having cubic symmetry is written by Davis in terms of the associated Legendre functions as

$$Y_4^c = P_4(\cos\theta) + (\cos 4\varphi/168)P_4^4(\cos\theta). \tag{18.2}$$

---

[298] L. Davis, *Phys. Rev.* **56**, 93 (1939).

[298a] For a discussion of these harmonics, consult F. C. von der Lage and H. A. Bethe, *Phys. Rev.* **71**, 612 (1947).

A similar expansion was used for the wave number $k(\varepsilon, \theta, \varphi)$, namely,

$$k = k_0(\varepsilon) + k_1(\varepsilon) Y_4^c. \tag{18.3}$$

The integrals were evaluated so as to yield expressions for the conductivity and the weak-field Hall coefficient, and transverse and longitudinal magnetoresistance. The departure from spherical symmetry had negligible influence on σ_0 and on R_0, but, as would be expected, provided the essential part of the magnetoresistance.

A similar approach was taken by Seitz in investigating the galvanomagnetic coefficients of a cubic semiconductor.[62] The classical Maxwell-Boltzmann distribution function was used, and the appropriate averages over energy were carried out. The calculations were simplified by neglecting the $k_1(\varepsilon)$ term in (18.3). Thus the approximation of spherical energy surfaces was used, the anisotropy being introduced through the relaxation time, namely, by the $\tau(\varepsilon) Y_4^c$ term of (18.1). Explicit results are presented for the phenomenological magnetoresistance coefficients occurring in the general relation between the electric field and the current density given below for a cubic material in a weak magnetic field:

$$\mathbf{J} = \sigma_0\,\mathbf{E} + \alpha(\mathbf{E} \times \mathbf{H}) + \beta H^2\,\mathbf{E} + \gamma(\mathbf{E}\cdot\mathbf{H})\mathbf{H} + \delta\mathbf{T}\mathbf{E} \tag{18.4}$$

for coordinate axes coincident with the cube directions, and where $\mathbf{T}$ is a diagonal tensor with the elements H_1^2, H_2^2, and H_3^2. The quantity σ_0 is the conductivity at zero field, α/σ_0^2 is the Hall coefficient R_0, and β, γ, and δ are special magnetoresistance coefficients. These coefficients were discussed in Sections 8a and 8b.

In a subsequent treatment by Olson and Rodriguez[298b] in connection with studies of the magnetoresistance in single crystals of copper, the expressions for the conductivity coefficients are determined for an anisotropic $\varepsilon(\mathbf{k})$, using expansions involving cubic harmonics of degrees 4 and 6, namely

$$\varepsilon = \frac{\hbar^2 k_0^2}{m^*}\left[\frac{1}{2}\left(\frac{k}{k_0}\right)^2 + s\left(\frac{k}{k_0}\right)^4\left\{K_4(\theta,\varphi) + t\left(\frac{k}{k_0}\right)^2 K_6(\theta,\varphi)\right\}\right], \tag{18.5}$$

where s and t are adjustable parameters. The integrals were evaluated under the assumptions of:

[298b] R. Olson and S. Rodriguez, *Phys. Rev.* 108, 1212 (1957).

(i) The metallic approximation of highly degenerate statistics.

(ii) A relaxation time which was constant over the Fermi surface. In view of (i), this is equivalent to the constant-τ approximation.

(iii) The Fermi surface being a single closed surface inside the first Brillouin zone and not touching its boundary.

(iv) The parameter s being $\ll 1$ so that s^4 and higher powers could be neglected.

The following results were obtained for the Seitz coefficients:

$$\sigma_0 = ne^2(\tau/m^*) \, [1 - s^2 \, (0.190 + 1.85 \, t^2)], \qquad\qquad (18.6)$$

$$\alpha = - n(e^3/c) \, (\tau/m^*)^2 \, [1 - s^2 \, (5.14 + 81.2 \, t^2)],$$

$$\beta = - n(e^4/c^2) \, (\tau/m^*)^3 \, [1 + s^2 \, (26.3 + 224 \, t^2)], \qquad e > 0 \text{ for electrons}$$

$$\gamma = n(e^4/c^2) \, (\tau/m^*)^3 \, [1 + s^2 \, (67.3 - 43.6 \, t + 716t^2)],$$

$$\delta = - n(e^4/c^2) \, (\tau/m^*)^3 \, 3s^2 \, [13.7 - 7.83 \, t + 368 \, t^2].$$

19. VALENCE BANDS OF GERMANIUM AND SILICON

Directional cyclotron resonance measurements on germanium and silicon have revealed anisotropy in the energy surfaces of the valence states. Although the effect is quite small, and in most respects negligible, for the light-mass band, it is significant for the heavy-mass band where m_2 may range from 0.29 to 0.36 m_0 in germanium[280, 299] and 0.46 to 0.56 m_0 in silicon.[300] Consequently, it is customary to refer to the energy surfaces of the heavy-mass bands as *warped* spheres. The general representation of the energy as a function of wave number for the valence bands of germanium and silicon near the band edge has been given by Dresselhaus, Kip, and Kittel for a **k** coordinate system along the cube axes[301, 302] and can be written as follows:

[299] B. Lax, H. Zeiger, and R. Dexter, *Physica* **20**, 818 (1954).
[300] R. Dexter and B. Lax, *Phys. Rev.* **96**, 223 (1954).
[301] G. Dresselhaus, A. Kip, and C. Kittel, *Phys. Rev.* **95**, 568 (1954).
[302] C. Kittel, *Physica* **20**, 829 (1954).

$$\varepsilon(\mathbf{k}) = - \frac{\hbar^2}{2m_0} \{Ak^2 \pm [B^2 k^4 + C^2(k_x{}^2 k_y{}^2 + k_x{}^2 k_z{}^2 + k_y{}^2 k_z{}^2)]^{1/2}\}$$

(19.1)

where the zero of energy has been taken at the top of the valence band, and ε increases positively in the direction toward the conduction band. In addition, our convention is such that the plus sign is associated with the light holes; the minus sign, with the heavy holes; and A, B, and C are all positive. These parameters can be related to the directional effective masses[295] and thus can be evaluated from the cyclotron resonance data. The results obtained by Dexter, Zeiger, and Lax[293] (DZL) and by Dresselhaus, Kip, and Kittel[295] (DKK) are:[302a—e]

		A	B	C
Ge:	DZL	13.1 ± 0.4,	8.3 ± 0.6,	12.5 ± 9.5,
	DKK	13.2 ± 0.1,	8.9 ± 0.5,	10.6 ± 0.2,
Si:	DZL	4.0 ± 0.1,	1.1 ± 0.4,	4.1 ± 0.4,
	DKK	4.0 ± 0.2,	1.1 ± 0.5,	4.0 ± 0.5.

(19.2)

The degree of the deviation of the heavy-mass surfaces of constant energy from spheres in k-space is illustrated in Fig. 26, which shows the contours near the band edge in the (110) plane.

In developing the expressions for charge-carrier densities and conductivity coefficients, the relationship of (19.1) is expressed in terms of spherical coordinates k, θ, φ as follows:

$$\varepsilon = - \frac{\hbar^2 k^2}{2m^*} g(\theta, \varphi)$$

(19.3)

[302a] See also, W. Mercouroff, *Physica Status Solidi* **2**, 282 (1962).

[302b] See also, J. Phillips, *Phys. Rev.* **125**, 1931 (1962).

[302c] Results have recently been obtained from studies in the region where quantum effects are observed. Consult J. Stickler, H. Zeiger, and G. Heller, *Phys. Rev.* **127**, 1077 (1962).

[302d] For data on germanium as a function of temperature, consult D. Bagguley, R. Stradling, and J. Whiting, *Proc. Roy. Soc.* **A262**, 340 (1961).

[302e] For data on silicon as a function of temperature, consult D. Bagguley, R. Stradling, and J. Whiting, *Proc. Roy. Soc.* **A262**, 365 (1961).

where the $g(\theta, \varphi)$ contains the variations from spherical symmetry and the m^*, the deviations of the effective mass from the free electron mass m_0. To first order in the deviations from spherical symmetry, $g(\theta, \varphi)$ can be written in the form

$$g(\theta, \varphi) = \{1 + (\Gamma/2)\,(\sin^4 \theta\,[\cos^4 \varphi + \sin^4 \varphi] + \cos^4 \theta - \tfrac{2}{3})\} \quad (19.4)$$

$$m^* = m_0/(A \pm B')$$

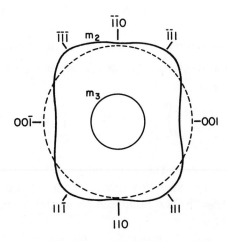

FIG. 26. Contours of constant energy in the (110) plane through $k = 0$ in k-space for the valence band of germanium (after Dexter *et al.*[293]).

where

$$B' \equiv (B^2 + C^2/6)^{1/2}, \qquad \Gamma \equiv \mp\, C^2/[2B'(A \pm B')]. \quad (19.5)$$

The upper sign is always associated with the holes of smaller effective mass, the lower sign with those of the large mass. The form given above for $g(\theta, \varphi)$ is, except for constant factors, identical with that used by Lax and Mavoides.[297]

The number of holes in each band is obtained by the use of Eq. (5.0) which, for uniform distribution in configuration space, yields the following expression for the number of charge carriers per unit volume of the crystal:

$$p = \frac{1}{4\pi^3} \int f_0(\mathbf{k}) d^3\, k = \frac{1}{4\pi^3} \int f_0(\mathbf{k}) k^2\, dk \sin \theta\, d\theta\, d\varphi \quad (19.6)$$

where, for the semiconductors in question, $f_0(\mathbf{k})$ can be the classical approximation to the Fermi-Dirac distribution function, namely, for the case of holes,[34e]

$$f_0(\mathbf{k}) \cong e^{(E_V - \zeta)/kT} e^{\varepsilon/kT}. \tag{19.7}$$

The energies at the top of the valence band E_V and at the Fermi surface ζ are both measured, positive upward, from some arbitrary position in the valence band. The energy of the holes ε in (19.7) is the same as that in (19.1) and (19.3) and is, therefore, a negative quantity since it is measured, positive upward, from the top of the valence band.

The integration over k can be carried out at once in (19.6) to yield

$$p = 2 \left(\frac{2\pi m^* kT}{h^2} \right)^{3/2} e^{(E_V - \zeta)/kT} \frac{1}{4\pi} \int_0^{2\pi} \int_0^{\pi} [g(\theta, \varphi)]^{-3/2} \, d\Omega \tag{19.8}$$

where $d\Omega = \sin \theta \, d\theta \, d\varphi$. The above integrals have been evaluated by Lax and Mavroides by expanding $[g(\theta, \varphi)]^{-3/2}$ in a power series in Γ and integrating termwise.[297] The result can be written in the form:

$$p = 2(2\pi m_0 kT/h^2)^{3/2} (A \pm B')^{-3/2} e^{(E_V - \zeta)/kT} a_d \tag{19.9}$$

where the anisotropy factor a_d is given by

$$a_d = 1 + 0.05 \, \Gamma + 0.01635 \, \Gamma^2 + 0.000908 \, \Gamma^3 + \ldots. \tag{19.10}$$

For $a_d = 1$, Eq. (19.9) is the well-known carrier-density relationship for classical statistics and effective mass of $m_0/(A \pm B')$ — as is apparent from a consideration of Eqs. (12.6) and (15.2). For convenience, we shall define a quantity p^s, the carrier density for a spherical energy surface:

$$p^s = 2 \{2\pi m_0 kT/h^2(A \pm B')\}^{3/2} e^{(E_V - \zeta)/kT} \tag{19.11}$$

so that Eq. (19.9) may be written in the form

$$p = p^s a_d. \tag{19.12}$$

20. WEAK-FIELD TRANSPORT COEFFICIENTS

For this limiting case, the usual procedure is to express the transport coefficients in power series of the magnetic field intensity so that the current-density components for a given energy band can be written as in (8.5), namely,[2]

$$J_i = \sigma_{ij}^0 E_j + \sigma_{ijl}^0 E_j H_l + \sigma_{ijlm}^0 E_j H_l H_m + \ldots \qquad (20.1)$$

where the coefficients are expressed in terms of the relaxation times and characteristics of the energy surfaces by relations (8.6) to (8.8). By the use of Eq. (19.3) for $\varepsilon(\mathbf{k})$, the coefficients can be evaluated for a given dependence of relaxation time on energy. To obtain the measured quantities it is then necessary to sum the coefficients for each band which contributes to the transport, as was discussed in Section 16.

a. Conductivity and Hall Effect

The coefficients for the conductivity and Hall terms in (20.1) are conveniently expressed for each band in question as follows:

$$\sigma_{ij}^0 = p^s |e| \mu_0^s \, a_{11} \, \delta_{ij}, \qquad (20.2)$$

$$\sigma_{ijl}^0 = p^s |e| \mu_0^s (\mu_0^{H,s}/c) a_{12} \, \varepsilon_{ijl} \qquad \text{(Gaussian units)} \qquad (20.3)$$

where δ_{ij} is the Kronecker delta and ε_{ijl} is the permutation tensor. The values of the anisotropy factors a_{11} and a_{12} for the valence bands in germanium and silicon will be given later. It is apparent from the above that the zero-field conductivity and the first-order Hall coefficient are nondirectional, as is expected for cubic symmetry. The quantities μ_0^s and $\mu_0^{H,s}$ are, respectively, the conductivity and Hall mobilities at zero-magnetic field for a spherical energy surface. It is seen from (20.2) that in the above notation the zero-magnetic-field conductivity mobility in the warped band, μ_0, is given by

$$\mu_0 = \mu_0^s \, a_{11}/a_d. \qquad (20.4)$$

Inasmuch as (20.3) can be obtained directly from (20.2) through the use of relation (12.30a), it also follows that the Hall mobility in the warped band, μ_0^H, is given by[303]

$$\mu_0^H = \mu_0^{H,s}\, a_{12}/a_{11}. \tag{20.5}$$

The anisotropy factors, as determined by Lax and Mavroides from integrations of (8.6) and (8.7) for a relaxation time which is a function of energy only, are given by[297]

$$a_{11} = 1 + 0.01667\, \Gamma + 0.041369\, \Gamma^2 + 0.00090679\, \Gamma^3 + 0.00091959\, \Gamma^4$$

$$+ 0.00002106\, \Gamma^5 + \ldots, \tag{20.6}$$

$$a_{12} = 1 - 0.01667\, \Gamma + 0.017956\, \Gamma^2 - 0.0069857\, \Gamma^3 + 0.0012610\, \Gamma^4 + \ldots \tag{20.7}$$

where the parameter Γ is given by (19.5).

For classical statistics and a simple power law dependence of relaxation time on energy, namely,

$$\tau = \tau_0(\varepsilon/kT)^\lambda, \tag{20.8}$$

one obtains the familiar expressions for μ_0^s and $\mu_0^{H,s}$ [cf. (15.9) and (15.10)],

$$\mu_0^s = \{|e|\tau_0/m^*\}\{4(\lambda + \tfrac{3}{2})!/3\sqrt{\pi}\}, \tag{20.9}$$

$$\mu_0^{H,s} = \{|e|\tau_0/m^*\}\{(2\lambda + \tfrac{3}{2})!/(\lambda + \tfrac{3}{2})!\} \tag{20.10}$$

where

$$m^* = m_0/(A \pm B') \qquad (+ \text{ for light-mass band}, - \text{ for heavy-mass band}). \tag{20.11}$$

---

[303] It should be pointed out that the relations derived in Section 12 are of general validity only in the case of isotropic systems. In the weak magnetic field limit, however, it is apparent that Eq. (12.30a) can be applied to each of the components in (20.2) and (20.3) to establish the relation given above. In the present case of cubic symmetry, the consideration is especially trivial because in the limit of vanishing magnetic field both the conductivity and the Hall coefficients are isotropic.

Expressions of the form (20.2) and (20.3) follow from the fact that integrals (8.6) to (8.8) can be evaluated by integrating first over the magnitude of $\mathbf{k}$, leaving an integral where the angular variations enter only through the function $g(\theta, \varphi)$. Thus, the restrictions to classical statistics and to a scattering process expressed by Eq. (20.8) were given for purposes of illustration rather than necessity. For example, Eq. (20.2) is valid for quantum statistics if (19.11) and (20.9) are replaced, respectively, by forms of (12.6) and (12.58), the expressions valid for Fermi-Dirac statistics. A corresponding change in Eq. (20.10) would provide the proper result for (20.3). Similarly, a more general scattering mechanism than that specified by Eq. (20.8) can be introduced by using the appropriate expressions for μ_0^s and $\mu_0^{H,s}$. Hence, for a case of classical statistics and mixed scattering where the relaxation time is given by (15.88), one has [cf. (15.89)]

$$\mu_0^s = \mu_0^{L,s} K(\beta, 0), \tag{20.12}$$

$$\mu_0^{H,s} = (3\pi/8)\mu_0^{L,s} L(\beta, 0)/K(\beta, 0). \tag{20.13}$$

The quantity $\mu_0^{L,S}$ is the lattice mobility for a band having spherical energy surfaces, and the functions $K(\beta, 0)$ and $L(\beta, 0)$ are defined in (15.92) and (15.93).

A quantity of special interest for investigating semiconductors is the ratio of Hall and conductivity mobilities. This parameter is sensitive to both the scattering mechanism and the band structure. For single-band transport, μ_0^H/μ_0 is equivalent to the ratio of the limiting values of Hall coefficient at weak and strong magnetic fields [Eq. (12.49)]. For multiband transport, the measured quantities obviously involve appropriate sums of the contributions from each band, as is shown in Section 16. For an individual band, we obtain at once, from (20.4) and (20.5),

$$\mu_0^H/\mu_0 = (\mu_0^{H,s}/\mu_0^s)(a_{12}\, a_d/a_{11}^2), \tag{20.14}$$

showing explicitly the effect of the anisotropy. The influence of the scattering mechanism is contained in the ratio $\mu_0^{H,S}/\mu_0^s$. When it is evaluated, using (20.9) to (20.13), one obtains

$$\frac{\mu_0^H}{\mu_0} = \frac{3\sqrt{\pi}}{4} \frac{(2\lambda + \tfrac{3}{2})!}{[(\lambda + \tfrac{3}{2})!]^2} \frac{a_{12}\, a_d}{a_{11}^2} \qquad \text{(Power-law scattering),} \tag{20.15}$$

the expression given by Lax and Mavroides,[297] or

$$\frac{\mu_0^H}{\mu_0} = \frac{3\pi}{8} \frac{L(\beta, 0)}{K^2(\beta, 0)} \frac{a_{12} a_d}{a_{11}^2} \qquad \text{(mixed lattice and impurity scattering).}$$

(20.16)

It is apparent that in the constant-τ model — $\lambda = 0$ in (20.15) — differences between μ_0^H and μ_0 will exist only as a result of deviations in the energy surfaces from sphericity. Thus

$$(\mu_0^H/\mu_0)_{\tau_0} = a_{12} a_d/a_{11}^2. \qquad (20.17)$$

Values of the anisotropy parameters representative of the light- and heavy-mass bands of germanium and silicon are given in Table II.

TABLE II. VALUES OF BAND STRUCTURE PARAMETERS FOR HEAVY- AND LIGHT-MASS VALENCE BANDS (V_2 AND V_3, RESPECTIVELY) FOR GERMANIUM AND SILICON[a]

	Germanium		Silicon	
Parameter	V_2	V_3	V_2	V_3
A	13.1		4.0	
B'	9.743		2.003	
m_2^*/m_3^* [b]	6.80		3.01	
Γ	2.389	-0.3510	2.101	-0.6991
a_d	1.225	0.984	1.186	0.973
a_{11}	1.318	0.999	1.244	1.008
a_{12}	1.008	1.008	1.004	1.023
$(\mu_0^H/\mu_0)_{\tau_0}$ [c]	0.711	0.994	0.769	0.979
p_3/p_2 [d]	0.045		0.157	

[a] Values of basic parameters A, B, and C taken from data of DZL [see (19.2)].
[b] Density of states masses: $m_2^*/m_3^* = (A + B')/(A - B')$.
[c] Constant-τ case. See Eq. (20.17).
[d] $p_3/p_2 = [(A - B')/(A + B')]^{3/2} a_{d,3}/a_{d,2}$, as obtained from (19.9).

The zero-field conductivity σ_0 and the weak-field limit of the Hall coefficient R_0 are obtained for p-type germanium and silicon by summing the contributions from each band, to yield

$$\sigma_0 = |e|\,[\{p^s\,\mu_0{}^s\,a_{11}\}_2 + \{p^s\,\mu_0{}^s\,a_{11}\}_3], \qquad (20.18)$$

$$R_0 = |e|\,\frac{\{p^s\,\mu_0{}^s(\mu_0{}^{H,s}/c)a_{12}\}_2 + \{p^s\,\mu_0{}^s(\mu_0{}^{H,s}/c)a_{12}\}_3}{\sigma_0{}^2} \qquad (20.19)$$

where $\{\ \}_2$ and $\{\ \}_3$ refer to the heavy- and the light-mass bands, respectively.

b. Magnetoconductivity and Magnetoresistance

The first-order magnetoconductivity coefficients, the σ^0_{ijlm} of relation (20.1), are determined directly from (8.8) and (8.10) with the use of (19.3). The algebra is quite involved and only an illustrative example will be given. For this purpose, we outline the calculation of σ^0_{xxyy}, the simplest transverse magnetoconductivity tensor component. This coefficient does not in general vanish when the energy surfaces are spherical.

Since τ is considered to be a function of energy only, one readily obtains

$$\sigma^0_{xxyy} = -\frac{e^4}{4\pi^3\,\hbar^6\,c^2}\int \tau^3 \frac{\partial f_0}{\partial \varepsilon}\frac{\partial \varepsilon}{\partial k_x}\left(\frac{\partial \varepsilon}{\partial k_z}\frac{\partial}{\partial k_x} - \frac{\partial \varepsilon}{\partial k_x}\frac{\partial}{\partial k_z}\right)\cdot$$

$$\left(\frac{\partial \varepsilon}{\partial k_z}\frac{\partial}{\partial k_x} - \frac{\partial \varepsilon}{\partial k_x}\frac{\partial}{\partial k_z}\right)\frac{\partial \varepsilon}{k_x}\,d^3k. \qquad (20.20)$$

For spherical symmetry in $\varepsilon(\mathbf{k})$, the above integrand reduces to a single term. Thus, for the more general energy surface defined by (19.3) to (19.5), we may approximate

$$\sigma^0_{xxyy} = \frac{e^4}{4\pi^3\,\hbar^6\,c^2}\int \tau^3 \frac{\partial f_0}{\partial \varepsilon}\left(\frac{\partial \varepsilon}{\partial k_x}\right)^2 \frac{\partial^2\varepsilon}{\partial k_x{}^2}\frac{\partial^2\varepsilon}{\partial k_z{}^2}\,[1 + G(\Gamma)]\,d\Omega\,k^2\,dk \quad (20.21)$$

where $d\Omega \equiv \sin\theta\,d\theta\,d\varphi$ and where $G(\Gamma)$ is a power series in Γ involving the angular variables, which vanishes when Γ is zero. We note that for the warped sphere the energy may be expressed as follows:

$$\varepsilon(\mathbf{k}) = -\frac{\hbar^2\,k^2}{2m^*}\,g(\theta,\varphi) \equiv -\frac{\hbar^2\,k^2}{2m^*}\,[1 + f(\Gamma,\theta,\varphi)]$$

$$\equiv -\frac{\hbar^2}{2m^*}\,[k_x{}^2 + k_y{}^2 + k_z{}^2][1 + f(\Gamma,\theta,\varphi)] \qquad (20.21a)$$

in which the leading term in $f(\Gamma,\theta,\varphi)$ is of at least the first power in Γ.

Use of (20.21a) enables Eq. (20.21) to be expressed in terms of a simple integral involving only ε, plus subsequent integrals containing Γ and angular coordinates. The result is

$$\sigma_{xxyy}^0 = \frac{2}{3}\frac{e^4}{\pi^{3/2} m^{*3} c^2}\left(\frac{2\pi m^*}{h^2}\right)^{3/2}\int \tau^3 \frac{\partial f_0}{\partial \varepsilon}\varepsilon^{3/2}\,d\varepsilon\,[1+F(\Gamma)]\,d\Omega$$

(20.21b)

where $F(\Gamma)$, which vanishes when Γ is zero, is a power series in Γ containing angular variables θ and φ. The integration of the terms not involving Γ is very familiar and as a result, Eq. (20.21b) can be written in the form

$$\sigma_{xxyy}^0 = -\frac{p^s e^4}{m^{*3} c^2}\langle \tau^3 \rangle\, a_{1122}$$

(20.22)

where p^s is given by (19.11), m^* by (20.11), and the average of τ^3 is given by Eq. (15.4). The anisotropy factor a_{1122} is a power series in Γ, where the leading term is unity. The isotropic part of (20.22) is, of course, identical with the magnetoconductive term in (12.14).

The determination of the anisotropic contributions in a_{1122} involves the evaluation of (20.20) as a power series in Γ. The algebra is extremely tedious, but has been carried out by ML (Mavroides and Lax).[304] Their results give

$$a_{1122} = 1 - 0.2214\,\Gamma + 0.3838\,\Gamma^2 - 0.0167\,\Gamma^3 + 0.00755\,\Gamma^4 + \quad (20.23)$$
$$0.000661\,\Gamma^5 - 0.000190\,\Gamma^6 - \ldots .$$

The other two of the three independent magnetoconductivity coefficients for a cubic system can be written explicitly in terms of ML's findings as follows:

$$\sigma_{xxxx}^0 = -\frac{p^s e^4}{m^{*3} c^2}\langle \tau^3 \rangle\, \mathscr{B}(\Gamma)$$

(20.24)

where

$$\mathscr{B}(\Gamma) = \frac{16}{1155}\,\Gamma^2\,(1 - 0.4295\,\Gamma + 0.0188\,\Gamma^2 + 0.0103\,\Gamma^3 + \quad (20.25)$$
$$+ 0.00249\,\Gamma^4 + 0.000474\,\Gamma^5 + 0.000085\,\Gamma^6 + \ldots),$$

---

[304] J. Mavroides and B. Lax, *Phys. Rev.* **107**, 1530 (1957); **108**, 1648 (1957).

$$\sigma^0_{xyxy} = \sigma^0_{xyyx} = \frac{p^s \, e^4}{m^{*3} \, e^2} \langle \tau^3 \rangle \left\{ \frac{a_{1212}}{2} + \frac{\mathscr{B}(\Gamma)}{4} \right\} \qquad (20.26)$$

where

$$a_{1212} = 1 - 0.0500 \, \Gamma - 0.0469 \, \Gamma^2 + 0.0040 \, \Gamma^3 - 0.00063 \, \Gamma^4 +$$

$$+ \, 0.000114 \, \Gamma^5 + 0.000004 \, \Gamma^6 + \dots .$$

It should be noted that the σ^0_{xyxy} above is not identical with the σ_{xyxy} of ML, inasmuch as we have chosen to use σ^0_{ijlm} which are symmetric in indices *lm* [see Eq. (8.10)], rather than the unsymmetrical form which results from use of, say, (8.8b), as was done by ML. The difference is merely formalistic since in all measurable quantities, the coefficients σ^0_{xyxy} and σ^0_{xyyx} occur in pairs.

A point of interest in the preceding equations is that for a nonvanishing longitudinal magnetoresistance along a cube axis, which enters via the anisotropy factor $\mathscr{B}(\Gamma)$, terms to at least the *second* order in the anisotropy parameter Γ are necessary.

Results for a specific scattering mechanism — as long as the process can be represented by a relaxation time, which in our approximation is a function of energy only — are obtained by evaluating $\langle \tau^3 \rangle$ for the process in question. Thus, for the simple power law case typified by (20.8), it follows from (15.4) that (20.22) becomes

$$\sigma^0_{xxyy} = - \frac{4}{3 \sqrt{\pi}} \frac{p^s \, e^4}{m^{*3} \, c^2} \tau_0^3 \, (3\lambda + \tfrac{3}{2})! \, a_{1122}. \qquad (20.28)$$

If p^s is expressed in terms of the Fermi-level energy as in (19.11), then (20.28) becomes identical with the result of ML when account is taken of their definition of l and λ.

For the case of mixed scattering where τ is given by (15.88), the expression for σ^0_{xxyy} becomes

$$\sigma^0_{xxyy} = \frac{9\pi}{16} \frac{(\mu_0^L)^3}{c^2} p^s |e| K'(\beta^M, 0) a_{1122} \qquad (20.29)$$

where the function K' is defined in (15.54).

In a similar fashion, the expressions for the magnetoconductivity coefficients σ^0_{xxxx} and σ^0_{xyxy} can be written down for the two scattering mechanisms considered above.

To apply the preceding equations to p-type germanium or silicon, it is necessary to calculate the coefficients for both the light- and heavy-mass bands and then to sum these quantities.

Expressions for the directional magnetoresistance coefficients as defined by Eqs. (11.1) and (11.3) can be written as relations involving the galvanomagnetic coefficients. These relations can then be expressed in terms of the conductivity coefficients developed in this section through the use of the inversion relations (8.29c) and relations (8.12a) and (8.12b). The results are

$$\Upsilon_{100} \equiv M_{100}/H^2 = - \{\sigma^0_{xxxx}\}_{2,3}/\sigma_0, \tag{20.30}$$

$$\Upsilon^{010}_{100} = - \{\sigma^0_{xxyy}\}_{2,3}/\sigma_0 - [\{\sigma^0_{xyz}\}_{2,3}/\sigma_0]^2, \tag{20.31}$$

$$\Upsilon_{110} = - \frac{1}{2\sigma_0} \{\sigma^0_{xxxx} + \sigma^0_{xxyy} + \sigma^0_{xyxy} + \sigma^0_{xyyx}\}_{2,3}, \tag{20.32}$$

$$\Upsilon^{\bar{1}10}_{110} = - \frac{1}{2\sigma_0} \{\sigma^0_{xxxx} + \sigma^0_{xxyy} - \sigma^0_{xyxy} - \sigma^0_{xyyx}\}_{2,3} - \left[\frac{\{\sigma^0_{xyz}\}_{2,3}}{\sigma_0} \right]^2 \tag{20.33}$$

where the notation $\{\ \}_{2,3}$ indicates that the coefficients in the braces are to be evaluated for heavy- and light-mass bands and summed. The conductivity σ_0 is given in (20.18). General relations between the directional magnetoresistance coefficients for cubic symmetry can be obtained through the use of Eqs. (11.4) and (11.5).

Expressions (20.30) to (20.33) were evaluated by ML[304] using parameters representative of germanium and silicon and compared with the experimental data of Pearson and Suhl[79] and Pearson and Herring.[305] The choice of τ was made by fitting theory and experiment for the coefficient Υ^{010}_{100}. Satisfactory agreement was then found for the other coefficients, with the exception of Υ_{100} — the longitudinal coefficient along the cube axis — for which the calculated value was significantly smaller. It is likely that it may be necessary to consider a greater degree of anisotropy — in particular that of the scattering process.

---

[305] G. L. Pearson and C. Herring, *Physica* **20**, 975 (1954).

21. ARBITRARY MAGNETIC FIELD STRENGTHS

a. General Considerations

Here we are interested in regions where $\omega\tau$ — cf. Eq. (6.10a) — may be the order of unity or larger. Therefore, a Jones-Zener series solution of the Boltzmann equation in powers of H is no longer possible. In such cases, it is necessary to introduce the magnetic-field dependence by a representation involving Fourier series expansions in harmonics of the frequency of the carrier around the curve (hodograph) determined by the intersection of a surface of constant energy in k-space with a plane normal to the magnetic field (see Section 6b). Such a development has been carried out by McClure.[54] The initial steps of the derivation were given in Eqs. (6.15) ff. The quantity $\mathbf{v}\phi$ in the integrand of the expression for current density is first averaged over the hodograph which passes through the particular point in k-space, thus

$$\mathbf{J} = \frac{e}{4\pi^3} \int \langle \mathbf{v}\phi \rangle_s \frac{\partial f_0}{\partial \varepsilon} d^3k, \qquad e > 0 \text{ for electrons.} \qquad (21.1)$$

To obtain expressions for the components of the conductivity tensor, we define a tensor having components $\mathscr{S}_{ij}$ such that[2]

$$[\langle \mathbf{v}\phi \rangle_s]_i = - e\tau \mathscr{S}_{ij} E_j. \qquad (21.2)$$

Hence

$$\sigma_{ij}(\mathbf{H}) = [e^2/4\pi^3] \int \tau \mathscr{S}_{ij}(\mathbf{H}) \left[- \partial f_0/\partial \varepsilon \right] d^3k. \qquad (21.3)$$

From Eqs. (21.2) and (6.23) it can be seen that

$$\mathscr{S}_{jk} = \sum_{m=-\infty}^{\infty} \frac{v_j(-m) v_k(m)}{1 + im\omega\tau}, \qquad (21.3a)$$

where $i = \sqrt{-1}$.

If now we choose an xyz coordinate system such that $\mathbf{H} \equiv (0, 0, H)$ and take into account the condition proved by McClure — that $v_x(0) = v_y(0) = 0$ — it follows directly from (21.3a) that

$$\mathcal{S}_{xx} = \sum_{m=1}^{\infty} \frac{2|v_x(m)|^2}{1 + (m\omega\tau)^2}, \tag{21.4}$$

$$\mathcal{S}_{xy} = \sum_{m=1}^{\infty} \left\{ \frac{v_x(m)v_y(-m) + v_x(-m)v_y(m)}{1 + (m\omega\tau)^2} - \right. \tag{21.5}$$

$$\left. im\omega\tau \frac{v_x(-m)v_y(m) - v_x(m)v_y(-m)}{1 + (m\omega\tau)^2} \right\}, \qquad \omega > 0, \text{ for electrons}$$

$$\mathcal{S}_{zz} = v_z^2(0) + \sum_{m=1}^{\infty} \frac{2|v_z(m)|^2}{1 + (m\omega\tau)^2}. \tag{21.6}$$

In the above, use was made of the fact that the reality of $\mathbf{v}$ in (6.20) requires that $\mathbf{v}(-m) = \mathbf{v}^*(m)$, where the asterisk denotes the complex conjugate.

In principle, the velocity amplitudes can be evaluated by taking appropriate gradients of the energy expressed as a Fourier series in cylindrical coordinates in k-space, with the azimuthal angle $\theta \ (\equiv \omega t_s)$ as the position around the hodograph. For complicated energy surfaces, an analytical determination of the Fourier components of the velocity can be very tedious. In such cases, the preceding equations may be used to establish the functional form of the conductivity components, the parameters being determined by analysis of experimental data. This procedure has been applied to graphite,[306] and its applicability to germanium and silicon will be considered shortly. On the other hand, exact determinations are possible for cylindrical energy surfaces,[58] or as will be seen later, in the case of cubical surfaces, where the hodograph is a square. Of course, if the surfaces are spheres, the series in (21.4) to (21.6) terminate with $m = 1$.

For hodographs with fourfold symmetry, only odd harmonics appear. In addition the mth term in $\mathcal{S}_{xy}$ is given by $\pm m\omega\tau$ times the mth term in $\mathcal{S}_{xx}$. Thus, for a cubic crystal with $\mathbf{H} \equiv (0, 0, H)$ and z along a cube axis, $\mathcal{S}_{ij}(H)$ is expressed by McClure in terms of coefficients $B(n)$ as follows:[54]

---

[306] J. W. McClure, *Phys. Rev.* **112**, 715 (1958).

$$\mathcal{S}_{xx} = \sum_{m \text{ odd}} \frac{B^2(m-1) + B^2(-m-1)}{1 + (m\omega\tau)^2} \tag{21.7}$$

$$\mathcal{S}_{xy} = - \sum_{m \text{ odd}} m\omega\tau \frac{B^2(m-1) - B^2(-m-1)}{1 + (m\omega\tau)^2}, \qquad \omega > 0 \text{ for electrons} \tag{21.8}$$

where $B(n) \neq 0$ only for $n = 0, \pm 4, \pm 8, \pm 12 \ldots$.

For convenience, we shall replace the coefficients in the above series by dimensionless quantities B_N, so normalized that $B_1 = 1$ for spherical energy surfaces. We note from McClure's equations that

$$B^2(0) = \frac{\hbar^2}{2m^{*2}} (k_x{}^2 + k_y{}^2), \tag{21.9}$$

$$B^2(n) = 0, \qquad n \neq 0 \tag{21.10}$$

when $\varepsilon = \hbar^2 k^2/2m^*$, $H \equiv H_z$. Also in the isotropic case, we may replace

$$k_x{}^2 = k_y{}^2 = k^2/3.$$

The result is that (21.7) and (21.8) can be written, for the general case of anisotropic energy surfaces having fourfold symmetry, in the form

$$\mathcal{S}_{xx} = \frac{1}{3} \left(\frac{\hbar k}{m^*} \right)^2 \sum_{N \text{ odd}} \frac{B_N}{1 + (N\omega\tau)^2} \tag{21.12}$$

$$\mathcal{S}_{xy} = \pm \frac{1}{3} \left(\frac{\hbar k}{m^*} \right)^2 \sum_{N \text{ odd}} \frac{(-1)^n N|\omega|\tau B_N}{1 + (N\omega\tau)^2}, \qquad n \equiv \tfrac{1}{2}(N-1). \tag{21.13}$$

The plus sign in front of the expression for $\mathcal{S}_{xy}$ is for holes, the negative sign for electrons. For spherical energy surfaces, $B_N = 0$ for $N > 1$. For anisotropic solids, the B_N are complicated functions of the parameters characterizing the energy surfaces. Also the cyclotron frequency ω, which for spherical energy surfaces is the ratio $eH/m^* c$, is a function of the components of the effective mass tensor and of the orientation of the magnetic field vector [see Eq. (6.19) and following discussion].

Because of the complexity of the parameters in (21.12) and (21.13), one can develop tractable expressions for the components of the conductivity tensor $\sigma_{ij}(\mathbf{H})$ only for special cases. Common examples are cubic, octahedral, or cylindrical energy surfaces or, to a certain approximation, slightly warped spheres. The former cases are discussed briefly in the next section. In the latter case one can perform an approximate evaluation of the Boltzmann average of $\mathscr{S}_{ij}(\mathbf{H})$, Eq. (21.3), to obtain a semiquantitative expression for the magnetic field dependence of $\sigma_{ij}(\mathbf{H})$. The result contains parameters which can most effectively be evaluated from experimental data. Thus, we write:

$$\sigma_{xx}(H) = p^s(e^2/m^*) \left\langle \tau \sum_{N \text{ odd}} B_N/[1 + (N\omega\tau)^2] \right\rangle \qquad (21.14)$$

$$\sigma_{xy}(H) = p^s(e^2/m^*) \left\langle |\omega|\tau^2 \sum_{N \text{ odd}} (-1)^n N B_N/[1 + (N\omega\tau)^2] \right\rangle$$

$$n \equiv \tfrac{1}{2}(N - 1) \qquad (21.15)$$

where p^s, the hole density in a band with spherical energy surfaces, is given by Eq. (19.11), the effective mass m^* by Eq. (20.11), and the averages by Eq. (15.4).

The above expressions are the analogues for the case of arbitrary magnetic field strengths of equations such as (20.2), (20.3), and (20.22). It is pointed out again that fourfold symmetry exists in the xy-plane, that the magnetic field is along the z-axis (a cube direction), and that τ is a function of energy only. The coefficients B_1 are unity, and the anisotropy is represented through the coefficients B_3, B_5,..., and by the cyclotron frequency factor. This quantity, ω, the angular frequency on the hodograph, is given by Eq. (6.19), namely,

$$\omega = 2\pi/T = [2\pi eH/\hbar c] \left[\oint dk_s/v_\perp \right]^{-1} \qquad (21.16)$$

where dk_s is an element of arc length along the hodograph and $v_\perp$ is the magnitude of the velocity component normal to $\mathbf{H}$. For spherical energy surfaces, the hodograph is a circle and (21.16) reduces to the familiar relation, $\omega = eH/m^* c$. In the general case, m^* is replaced by a function of the components of the effective mass tensor characterizing the energy surface which forms the hodograph in question.[54a, b]

b. Cubic Energy Surfaces

The advantage of a model consisting of cubic energy surfaces is that the relative amplitudes of the terms in the McClure expansion can be calculated exactly, so that an analytical determination of the magnetic-field dependence of the conductivity components is possible. Results have been presented by Goldberg, Adams, and Davis (GAD).[55] For $\mathbf{H} \equiv (0, 0, H)$ with the z-direction along a cube axis, relations (21.4) and (21.5) are applicable; and for fourfold symmetry in the xy-plane, they reduce to

$$\mathscr{S}_{xx} = \sum_{N \text{ odd}} 2v_{xN}^2 / [1 + (N\omega\tau)^2], \tag{21.17}$$

$$\mathscr{S}_{xy} = \sum_{N \text{ odd}} 2(-1)^n \omega\tau N v_{xN}^2 / [1 + (N\omega\tau)^2], \qquad n \equiv \tfrac{1}{2}(N - 1). \tag{21.18}$$

The hodograph is a square, and GAD have shown that the amplitudes of the harmonics are given by

$$v_{xN} = 2v \sin (N\pi/4)/N\pi, \qquad N \text{ odd} \tag{21.19}$$

where v is the magnitude of the velocity of the particle on the hodograph.

Thus, the magnetic-field dependence of the conductivity coefficients is represented by the following relations:

$$\mathscr{S}_{xx} = \frac{4v^2}{\pi^2} \sum_{N \text{ odd}} \frac{1}{N^2(1 + N^2 \omega^2 \tau^2)} \tag{21.20}$$

$$\mathscr{S}_{xy} = \frac{4v^2 \omega\tau}{\pi^2} \sum_{N \text{ odd}} \frac{(-1)^n}{N(1 + N^2 \omega^2 \tau^2)}. \tag{21.21}$$

The quantity ω — see Eq. (21.16) — is given by

$$\omega = (\pi/4)(eH/m_{001}^* c) \tag{21.22}$$

where m_{001}^* is the effective mass on the 001 cube axis.

The series can be summed in limiting cases of weak- and strong-magnetic fields to yield[306a]

[306a] The series have been summed for arbitrary values of $\omega\tau$ by Miyazawa.[164a] Expressions are also given for the case where H is along a [111] direction.

$$\left.\mathscr{S}_{xx} \cong (4v^2/\pi^2)(\pi^2/8) \right\} \omega\tau \ll 1 (21.23)$$

$$\left.\mathscr{S}_{xy} \cong (4v^2\,\omega\tau/\pi^2)(\pi/4) \right\} (21.24)$$

$$\left.\mathscr{S}_{xx} \approx (4v^2/\pi^2)(\pi^4/96\,\omega^2\,\tau^2) \right\}, \omega\tau \gg 1. (21.25)$$

$$\left.\mathscr{S}_{xy} \approx (4v^2/\pi^2)(\pi^3/32\,\omega\tau) \right\} (21.26)$$

A Boltzmann average over energy — cf. Eq. (21.3) — is performed by GAD for the case of constant τ, and they give the following expressions for the components of the conductivity tensor normal to **H**:

$$\sigma_{xx}(H) = \frac{8}{\pi^2}\,p\,\frac{e^2\,\tau}{m^*} \sum_{N\,\text{odd}} \frac{1}{N^2(1 + N^2\,\omega^2\,\tau^2)}, \qquad (21.27)$$

$$\sigma_{xy}(H) = \frac{8}{\pi^2}\,p\,\frac{e^2\,\tau}{m^*}\,\omega\tau \sum_{N\,\text{odd}} \frac{(-1)^n}{N(1 + N^2\,\omega^2\,\tau^2)}. \qquad (21.28)$$

By use of the sums given in (21.23) to (21.26), it is readily seen that the above relations lead to

$$\mu_0 = e\tau/m^* \qquad (21.29)$$

$$\mu_0^{H}/\mu_0 = \tfrac{1}{2} \qquad (21.30)$$

where $\sigma_0 = pe\mu_0$ and $\mu_0^{H} = R_0\,\sigma_0\,c$.[182]

A detailed comparison of (21.27) and (21.28) with the results obtained using expression (19.1) for $\varepsilon(\mathbf{k})$ and leading to (19.12), (20.2), and (20.3) does not seem possible unless an explicit representation of $\varepsilon(\mathbf{k})$ is available for the cubic surfaces to permit evaluation of such quantities as densities of states, etc.

c. Other Energy Surfaces

Application of the Fourier method in investigations of the galvano-magnetic properties of solids — principally metals — has been reported by a number of authors. These include Chambers,[38, 306b] Lifshitz et al.,[57] and Ziman.[58] The special application to a cylindrical Fermi surface was carried out by Ziman. The problems of the saturation Hall coefficient

---

306b See also, Herbert Budd, *Phys. Rev.* **127**, 4 (1962).

in strong magnetic fields in cases of equality of holes and electrons was examined by Bass and Kaganov.[307] A number of articles dealing with more complicated Fermi surfaces,[308] as well as with thermoelectric and thermomagnetic phenomena[309, 310] associated with such surfaces, can be found in the literature. Toroidal energy surfaces have been considered by Casella[310a] and by Rashba and Boiko.[310b] Expressions for the case of octahedral energy surfaces have been presented by Miyazawa.[164a]

d. Application to Germanium and Silicon

Although as we saw in Section 17c, the dual-valence-band model makes a tremendous improvement over the single-band scheme in accounting for the galvanomagnetic effects in germanium, it is clear from the cyclotron resonance data discussed in Section 19 that any approach to quantitative calculations must take into account the warped nature of the heavy-mass band. It is seen from Table II that for the example of a constant relaxation time, $(\mu_0^H/\mu_0)_{\tau_0}$ should be 0.71 for this band. A parabolic band of spherical symmetry, on the other hand, gives a μ_0^H/μ_0 of unity for the constant-τ case. The actual problem is further complicated by the necessity to take into account contributions from impurity scattering, even for quite pure samples so long as the temperature is below 200°K.

Determination of the magnetic-field dependence of the components of the conductivity tensor is a complicated procedure in the case of warped energy surfaces, and it is therefore necessary to resort to approximations. An interesting example, which was investigated by Goldberg et al.,[55] is the case where the heavy-hole surface is a cube, for which an

---

[307] F. Bass and M. Kaganov, *J. Exptl. Theoret. Phys. U.S.S.R.* **32**, 1233 (1957) [translation: *Soviet Phys.-JETP* **5**, 1002 (1957)].

[308] I. Lifshitz and V. Peschanskii, *J. Exptl. Theoret. Phys. U.S.S.R.* **35**, 1251 (1958) [translation: *Soviet Phys.-JETP* **8**, 875 (1959)].

[309] M. Azbel', M. Kaganov, and I. Lifshitz, *J. Exptl. Theoret. Phys. U.S.S.R.* **32**, 1188 (1957) [translation *Soviet Phys.-JETP* **5**, 967 (1957)].

[310] Yu. Bychkov, L. Gurevich, and G. Nedlin, *J. Exptl. Theoret. Phys. U.S.S.R.* **37**, 534 (1959) [translation: *Soviet Phys.-JETP* **10**, 377 (1960).

[310a] R. E. Casella, *Bull. Am. Phys. Soc.* **6**, 129 (1961).

[310b] E. I. Rashba and I. I. Boiko, *Fiz. Tverdogo Tela* **3**, 1277 (1961) [translation: *Soviet Phys.-Solid State* **3**, 927 (1961)].

exact calculation of the magnetic-field dependence of the conductivity components is possible. Their findings are that for such a surface the high harmonics of the velocity contribute too strongly. In fact, the value of $(\mu_0{}^H/\mu_0)_{\tau_0}$ was found to be 0.5. Thus the desired value of 0.7 turns out to be almost midway between that for a sphere and that for a cube. It was estimated by GAD that inclusion of only the third and fifth harmonics might represent the velocity variation fairly well. Their attempts to fit the observed magnetic-field dependence by use of such a scheme were not especially satisfying, perhaps due in part to the fact that the effect of impurity scattering was significant inasmuch as the measurements were done at 80°K.

A subsequent analysis by Beer and Willardson (BW) is also based on use of harmonics up to the fifth.[56] Additional parameters include one connecting the cyclotron frequencies with the magnetic field, and a coefficient associated with the density of states. A further modification is the replacement of the constant-τ treatment by the energy-dependent relation approximating scattering by acoustic phonons and ionized impurities. The expressions for the conductivity components due to a hole-band are written as follows:

$$\sigma_{xx}(H) = \frac{pe^2}{m^*}\alpha \left\langle \tau \sum_{N\,\mathrm{odd}} \frac{b_N}{[1+(N\omega\tau)^2]} \right\rangle, \qquad b_1 \equiv 1, \qquad (21.31)$$

$$\sigma_{xy}(H) = \frac{pe^2}{m^*}\alpha \left\langle \omega\tau^2 \sum_{N\,\mathrm{odd}} \frac{(-1)^n N b_N}{[1+(N\omega\tau)^2]} \right\rangle, \qquad n \equiv \tfrac{1}{2}(N-1) \qquad (21.32)$$

for the magnetic field vector along the z-axis, and fourfold symmetry in the xy-plane. The above expressions are equivalent to (21.14) and (21.15), although the parameters are somewhat differently defined. The average over energy is that given in Eq. (15.4), and differs by a weighting factor of ε/kT from that used in a number of places in the literature.[56, 164]

Relation (21.16) connecting the cyclotron frequency ω and the magnetic field intensity is written as

$$\omega = a|e|H/m^* c. \qquad (21.33)$$

Thus the anisotropy of the energy surfaces is expressed by means of the parameters α, a and b_3, b_5, ... In the BW treatment, all coefficients higher than b_5 are neglected. The values of the parameters for the heavy-mass bands of germanium and silicon are then determined by using the requirements that the values of these parameters be between those for spherical and cubic surfaces, that at low fields they agree with the Lax-Mavroides results (Section 19), and that at strong fields the Hall coefficient approaches $(pec)^{-1}$. Inasmuch as none of the above constraints is influenced by the variation of the relaxation time with energy, it is simplest to determine the band-structure constants by use of equations developed for the constant-τ case. Thus, by considering appropriate ratios of mobilities for the warped and for spherical energy surfaces, one obtains directly from (21.31) and (21.32)

$$\mu_0/\mu_0{}^s \equiv \sigma_{xx}[1/p|e|\mu_0{}^s] = \alpha(1 + b_3 + b_5 + \ldots) = a_{11}/a_d, \qquad H \to 0$$

$$(21.34)$$

$$\mu_0{}^H \mu_0/(\mu_0{}^s)^2 \equiv [\sigma_{xy}/H][c/p|e|(\mu_0{}^s)^2] \qquad (21.35)$$

$$= \alpha a(1 - 3b_3 + 5b_5 - \ldots + \ldots) = a_{12}/a_d, \qquad H \to 0.$$

The important equality in each of the above equations is the last one, since it provides a direct relation with the LM constants.

Mobilities can be defined in the warped band in the strong-field limit also: $\mu_\infty \equiv \sigma_\infty/p|e|$ and $\mu_\infty{}^H = R_\infty \sigma_\infty c$, and ratios chosen to give

$$\frac{\mu_\infty \mu_0{}^s}{(\mu_\infty{}^H)^2} \equiv \sigma_{xx}{}^\infty \frac{\mu_0{}^s H^2}{p|e|c^2} = \frac{\alpha}{a^2} \times \left[1 + \frac{b_3}{9} + \frac{b_5}{25} + \ldots\right], \qquad H \to \infty,$$

$$(21.36)$$

$$\frac{\mu_\infty}{\mu_\infty{}^H} \equiv \sigma_{xy}{}^\infty \frac{H}{p|e|c} = \frac{\alpha}{a} \times \left[1 - \frac{b_3}{3} + \frac{b_5}{5} - \ldots + \ldots\right], \qquad H \to \infty.$$

$$(21.37)$$

The values of parameters occurring in the preceding equations are tabulated for the cases of interest in Table III.

In evaluating (21.31) and (21.32) for the case of mixed scattering by lattice vibrations and ionized impurities, the expression for the relaxation time is taken as [cf. (15.88)]

TABLE III. VALUES OF PARAMETERS DETERMINING THE CONDUCTIVITY COEFFICIENTS FOR SEVERAL TYPES OF ENERGY SURFACES

			Value for type of surface indicated			
	Sphere	Cube[b]	Warped band in Ge[c]	Warped band in Si[c]	Choice of BW Ge	Choice of BW Si
Basic						
α	1	—	—	—	0.96	0.96[d]
a	1	—	—	—	0.935	0.935[d]
b_3	0	$1/9$	—	—	0.085	0.072
b_5	0	$1/25$	—	—	0.035	0.030
Derived[a]						
μ_0/μ_0^s	1	—	1.075	1.049	1.075	1.058
$\mu_0^H \mu_0/(\mu_0^s)^2$	1	—	0.823	0.847	0.826	0.838
μ_0^H/μ_0	1	$1/2$	0.713	0.769	0.714	0.749
$\mu_\infty/\mu_0^s/(\mu_\infty^H)^2$	1	—	—	—	1.110	1.108
μ_∞/μ_∞^H	1	1	—	—	1.005	1.008

[a] See Eqs. (21.34)–(21.37). For comparison with the LM results, an energy-independent relaxation time was used here.

[b] From GAD.[55]

[c] From Lax and co-workers.[293, 297]

[d] For simplicity in computation, the germanium values were used.

$$\tau = \frac{3\sqrt{\pi}}{4}\frac{m^*}{e}\,\mu_L^s\,\frac{x^{3/2}}{\beta + x^2} \tag{21.38}$$

where x is the reduced energy ($\equiv \varepsilon/kT$); μ_L^s, the lattice mobility for a spherical energy surface; and β, considered independent of energy, is given by $6\mu_{0,L}^s/\mu_{0,I}^s$. The effective mass m^* is related to band parameters A and B of LM as follows [Eq. (19.4)]:

$$m^* = m_0/(A \pm B') \qquad (\text{+ for light mass, } - \text{ for heavy mass}). \tag{21.39}$$

In terms of the functions $K(\beta, \gamma)$ and $L(\beta, \gamma)$ used in Eqs. (15.89) and (15.90), the conductivity components may be written in the form

$$\sigma_{xx}(H) = p|e|\mu_L^s \alpha \sum_{N\,\text{odd}} b_N\, K(\beta, a^2 N^2 \gamma^s) \tag{21.40}$$

$$\sigma_{xy}(H) = \tfrac{1}{2}(\pi)^{1/2} p|e|\mu_L^s \alpha a(\gamma^s)^{1/2} \sum_{N\,\text{odd}} (-1)^n N b_N\, L(\beta, a^2 N^2 \gamma^s) \tag{21.41}$$

where

$$\gamma^s = (9\pi/16)(\mu_L^s H/c)^2, \qquad \text{Gaussian units.} \tag{21.42}$$

When the above equations are used to determine the magnetic-field dependence of the Hall coefficient factor $r_H [\equiv R_H/R_\infty$, see Eq. (12.52)] for a single warped band characterized by the parameters given in Table III, the curves shown in Fig. 27 are obtained. It is seen that a significant lowering of the ratio $\mu_0^{\ H}/\mu_0 (\equiv R_0/R_\infty)$ results from the warping. Furthermore, as the degree of impurity scattering is increased, maxima begin to appear in the plots of r_H as a function of H.

In calculations on germanium and silicon, it is a good approximation to consider the light-mass band spherical. The Hall coefficient factor can then be written as follows:[56]

$$\frac{R_H}{R_\infty} = \frac{3\pi}{8}\left(1 + \frac{p_3}{p_2}\right) \times$$

$$\frac{\mathscr{L}(\beta_2, \gamma_2^s) +}{[\mathscr{K}(\beta_2, \gamma_2^s) + (p_3/p_2)(\mu_{L,3}^s/\mu_{L,2}^s)\, K(\beta_3, \gamma_3^s)]^2 +} \tag{21.43}$$

$$\frac{(p_3/p_2)\,(\mu_{L,3}^s/\mu_{L,2}^s)^2\, L(\beta_3, \gamma_3^s)}{\tfrac{1}{4}\pi\gamma_2^s\,[\mathscr{L}(\beta_2, \gamma_2^s) + (p_3/p_2)(\mu_{L,3}^s/\mu_{L,2}^s)^2\, L(\beta_3, \gamma_3^s)]^2}$$

where

$$\mathscr{L}(\beta_2, \gamma_2^s) \equiv a\alpha[L(\beta_2, \gamma_2^s) - 3b_3\, L(\beta_2, 9a^2\gamma_2^s) + 5b_5\, L(\beta_2, 25a^2\gamma_2^s)] \tag{21.44}$$

$$[\mathscr{K}(\beta_2, \gamma_2^s) \equiv \alpha[K(\beta_2, \gamma_2^s) + b_3\, K(\beta_2, 9a^2\gamma_2^s) + b_5\, K(\beta_2, 25a^2\gamma_2^s)]. \tag{21.45}$$

An expression for the transverse magnetoresistance containing the same parameters can readily be written down.

Predictions of the above theory are compared with experimental data in Figs. 28 and 29, for germanium. A certain arbitrariness exists in the

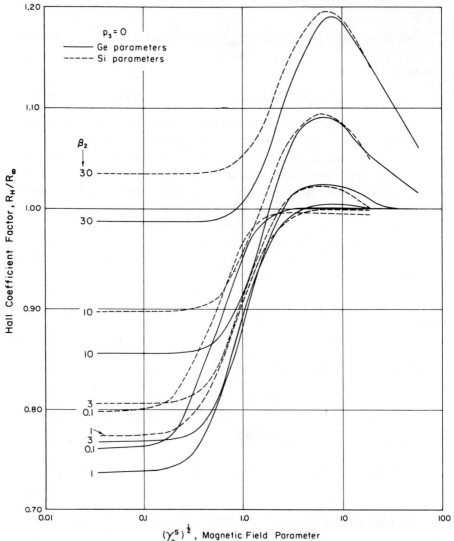

FIG. 27. Hall coefficient factor for a single warped band. The solid lines are for parameters representative of the heavy-mass band in germanium as determined from cyclotron resonance. The dashed lines are applied to silicon. The parameter β_2 measures the degree of impurity scattering (after BW[56]).

normalization of the observed data, and the references should be consulted for details. Reasonable agreement, however, appears to have been achieved, including the nature of the fine structure. These minima were first reported by Peterson et al.[311] The present theory suggests that their prominence is associated with the amount of warping and the degree

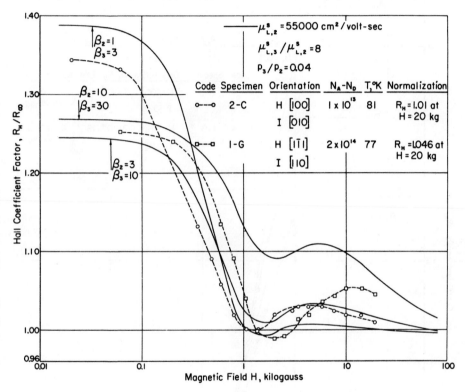

FIG. 28. Comparison of theoretical Hall coefficient factor (solid lines) with experimental data on germanium (dashed lines) for liquid nitrogen temperatures (after BW[56]).

of impurity scattering. This is borne out by the experimental data at different temperatures, impurity contents, and orientations, as is apparent from the measurements shown in Figs. 30 and 31. Inasmuch as γ_2^s contains the factor $\mu_{L,2}^s$, the bringing of the experimental and theoretical Hall

---

[311] E. Peterson, J. Swanson, and G. Tucker, *Bull. Am. Phys. Soc.* **1**, 117 (1956).

coefficient curves into coincidence at the minima yields values of $\mu_{L,2}^s$, independent of any measurement of $\sigma(H)$. This determination is somewhat distinct, and it therefore supplements the usual information on $\mu_{L,2}^s$

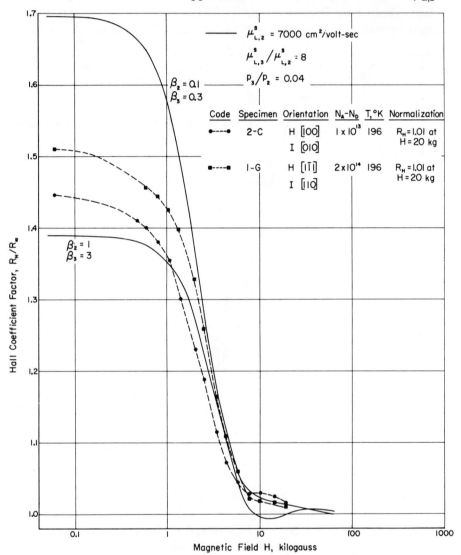

FIG. 29. Comparison of theoretical Hall coefficient factor (solid lines) with experimental data on germanium (dashed lines) for a temperature of 196°K (after BW[56]).

which results from magnetoresistance measurements and from $R_0 \, \sigma_0$ data. Unique values of $\mu^s_{L,2}$ for germanium and for silicon fit satisfactorily the three sets of data,[56] although the more recent work suggested an increase in the mobility values at liquid nitrogen temperature from 55,000 to

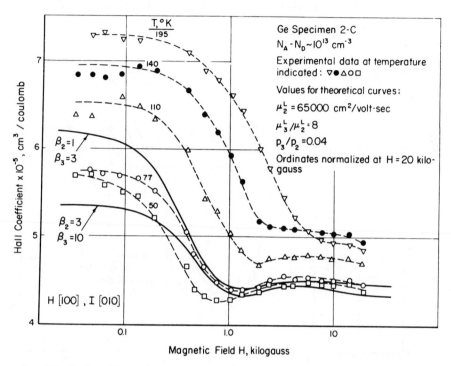

Fig. 30. Hall coefficient in p-type germanium. Theoretical curves (solid lines) are based on $\mu_2^L = 65{,}000$ cm²/volt-sec, representative of the mobility at 77°K and on normalization of ordinates at 20 kgauss for the $\beta_2 = 1$ curve to fit the experimental curves, the curve of $\beta_2 = 3$ being slightly depressed for clarity. Subscripts 3 and 2 refer to light- and heavy-mass bands, respectively (after Beer[164]).

65,000 cm²/volt-sec for germanium and from 12,000 to 14,000 cm²/volt-sec for silicon.[164]   If, however, one attempts to use the parameters representative of silicon for IIB diamond or for aluminium antimonide, this consistency does not exist. This point is discussed further in the next section. In regard to mobilities, consult recent work cited in Section 30a.

It is pointed out by BW that their calculations could be improved in a number of ways, at the expense of more onerous computation.

Perhaps the most obvious consideration involves the scattering mechanism. It is quite generally agreed that optical modes play an important role in the interaction of the carriers with the lattice in the valence bands of germanium and silicon, although this can be expected to be of diminished importance at temperatures of 77°K and below. For example, the

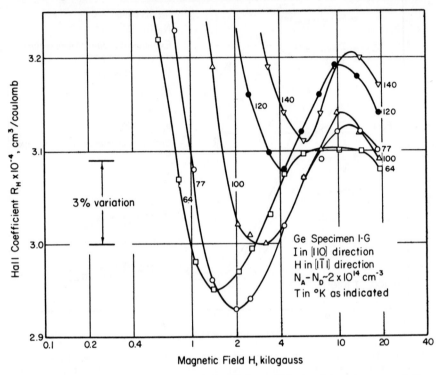

FIG. 31. Temperature dependence of the Hall coefficient minima in germanium. This sample has a larger carrier concentration and a different orientation than sample 2-C (after Beer[164]).

results of Bray and Brown indicate that the mobility in high-purity p-type germanium at temperatures below 70°K can be accounted for by a mixture of acoustical mode and ionized impurity scattering.[311a] Temperatures greater than 90°K were necessary for the $T^{-2.3}$ dependence

[311a] R. Bray and D. M. Brown *in* "Proc. Intern. Conf. on Semiconductor Phys. Prague 1960", p. 82. Publishing House Czech. Acad. Sci. Prague, 1961. See also D. M. Brown and R. Bray, *Phys. Rev.* **127**, 1593 (1962).

—indicative of optical modes in the scattering — to become apparent. The treatment of the impurity scattering, especially as regards its relative importance in the heavy- and light-mass bands, is another factor which might also be examined more thoroughly. These considerations could modify the numerical values associated with such parameters as $\mu_{L,2}^s$, β_2, and β_3, etc. When the impurity concentration is the order of 10^{15} cm^{-3} or greater, there are indications that hole-hole scattering is significant. This process has been studied by Appel and Bray.[311b] Further experimental data on mobility and Hall coefficient in p-type germanium over a range of temperature and impurity concentrations have been presented by Golikova and collaborators[311c] and by Miyazawa.[164a]

Actually, the simplified treatment does a surprisingly good job, especially in the case of germanium, in accounting for the behavior of the Hall coefficient and transverse magnetoresistance, not only in connection with over-all quantitative details, but also as regards the fine structure in the Hall-effect curves. It is noteworthy that this was done using mobility ratios for fast and slow holes of 8 and 3, respectively, for germanium and silicon, with corresponding carrier density ratios of 0.04 and 0.16. Although these are the values predicted from cyclotron resonance experiments, previous attempts to fit galvanomagnetic data, where warped bands and mixed scattering were not considered, required much smaller values of p_3/p_2 to achieve even a partial fit.[55, 283, 296]

In the case of silicon, the agreement between theory and experiment was not quite so good as for germanium. Although part of the discrepancy may be due to the fact that in several cases the orientation of the magnetic field was along directions of lower symmetry than a cube axis, it does appear that other considerations are important.[56, 164] It is possible that a higher degree of warping exists than is represented by the values given the parameters in Table III. This could account for the fact that the measured transverse magnetoresistance is definitely larger than the calculated value.[56] Also, it was found that at 77 °K, the ratio of longitudinal and transverse magnetoresistance is substantially larger in

[311b] J. Appel and R. Bray, *Phys. Rev.* **127**, 1603 (1962).

[311c] O. Golikova, B. Moizhes, and L. Stil'bans, *Fiz. Tverd. Tela* **3**, 3105 (1961); O. Golikova and L. Stil'bans, *ibid.* p. 3115. [Translations: *Soviet Phys.-Solid State* **3**, 2259 and 2266 (1962)].

silicon than in germanium.[312, 79]   This criterion needs to be used with care, however, inasmuch as the transverse magnetoresistance is augmented by the two-band effect, even for spherical energy surfaces [cf. Eq. (16.9)]. The increase can be expected to be greater in germanium than in silicon because of the larger value of $\mu_3{}^s/\mu_2{}^s$. Nevertheless, in the case of silicon, it is noted that the longitudinal coefficient is itself larger than that for germanium — and this is in spite of the fact the hole mobilities are substantially lower in silicon.

It should be noted that the cyclotron resonance measurements were done at $4\,°K$. One may therefore speculate on the possibility of a significant temperature dependence for the anisotropy parameters.   This point has been made by Long in connection with his magnetoresistance data on p-type silicon.[312−313a]

A very interesting feature is brought out in studies of the Hall coefficient in high-purity silicon (room temperature resistivity of $\sim 10^2$ ohm-cm, uncompensated) as compared to ultra-high-purity silicon (room temperature resistivity $\sim 10^3$ ohm-cm, uncompensated). It will be recalled, from Fig. 27, that the effect of warping on the characteristics of a single band is to reduce $\mu_0{}^H/\mu_0$, so that the Hall coefficient factor R_H/R_∞ increases with magnetic field once the weak-field plateau is exceeded. In germanium, due to the high mobility of the light-mass band ($\mu_{L,3}^s/\mu_{L,2}^s \cong 8$), the contributions from this spherical band overshadow the effect and the Hall coefficient factor is seen to decrease with H from the weak-field plateau. In silicon, however, the light holes are relatively less mobile ($\mu_{L,3}^s/\mu_{L,2}^s \cong 3$), and if a moderate amount of impurity scattering is present, the contributions of the light-mass band may not be sufficient to induce the germanium-like behavior. The result is that an increase in R_H/R_∞ with H is observed. The situation is depicted by the theoretical curves shown in Fig. 32, which are based on Eq. (21.43) with $\mu_{L,3}^s/\mu_{L,2}^s = 3$ and $p_3/p_2 = 0.16$.   At the time the manuscripts of the published articles quoted herein were sent to the press, no data were available on silicon sufficiently pure to exhibit the "germanium-like" behavior. The state of affairs is illustrated by Fig. 33. It will be noted

---

[312] D. Long, *Phys. Rev.* **107**, 672 (1957).

[313] D. Long and J. Myers, *Phys. Rev.* **109**, 1098 (1958).

[313a] Measurements of Bagguley et al. fail, however, to indicate a temperature dependence in the effective mass parameters for holes up to $50°K$.[302e]

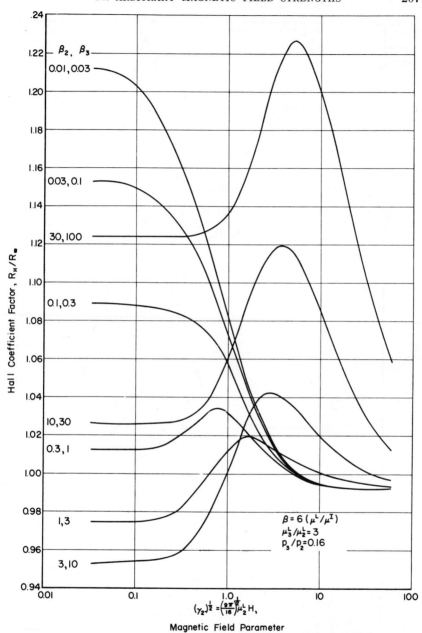

FIG. 32. Hall coefficient factor for degenerate valence bands representative of silicon. The anisotropy parameters used for the heavy-mass band are those given in Table III. For the light-mass band, the energy surfaces are spherical. The variable parameter is the degree of impurity scattering (after Reid and Willardson[314]).

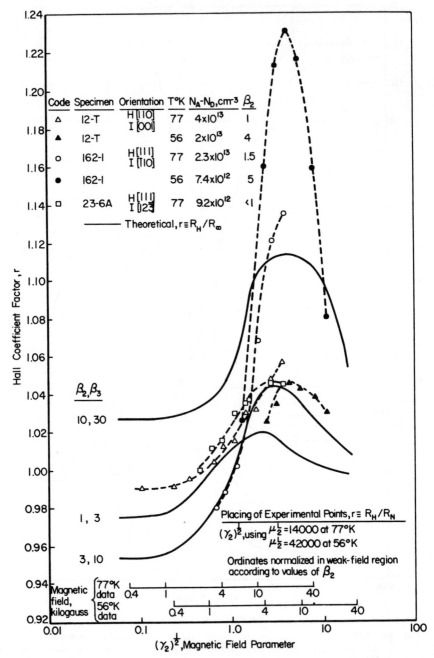

FIG. 33. Experimental data (dashed lines) indicating magnetic-field variation of normalized Hall coefficient factor in extrinsic p-type silicon for two temperatures. Theoretical predictions, for different amounts of impurity scattering, are shown by solid lines (after Beer[164]).

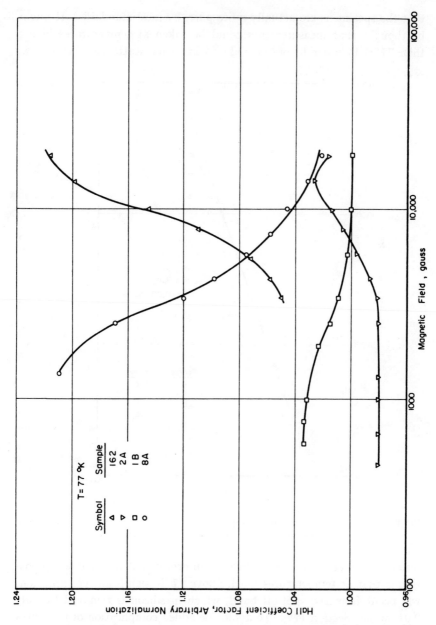

Fig. 34. Magnetic-field dependence of relative Hall coefficient in several p-type silicon samples of different purity (after Reid and Willardson[314]). The ultra-pure specimens 8A and 1B have room-temperature resistivities of 2700 and 5400 ohm-cm, respectively. Sample 1B appears to have more compensation than does 8A, a postulate borne out by the $R\sigma$ data shown in Fig. 35.

that the specimens are actually quite pure, by most standards. It might be thought that measurements could be taken at temperatures higher than 77°K in order to obtain reduced impurity scattering. This gives

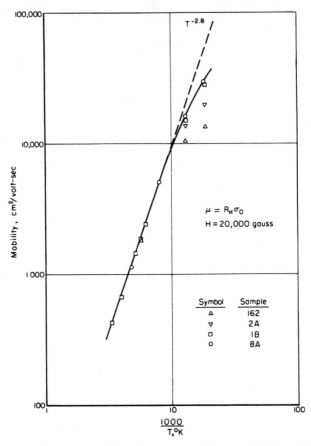

FIG. 35. Mobility as a function of temperature for several high-purity p-type silicon specimens (after Reid and Willardson[314]).

results, however, which are not readily interpreted. A reasonable explanation is that at temperatures much above 77°K significant contributions will occur from the split-off band, which in silicon is removed by only 0.04 ev [see Section 17b]. To avoid the added complication of this extra band, it is felt necessary to restrict measurements to 77°K and below.

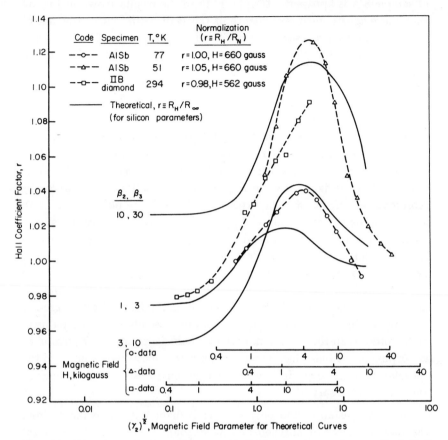

FIG. 36. Experimental data on magnetic-field dependence of normalized Hall coefficient factor (dashed lines) for p-type diamond and AlSb. Superimposed are solid-line theoretical curves (cf. Fig. 32) representative of silicon (after Beer[164]).

Unpublished data, now available on two ultra-pure specimens of p-type silicon,[314] are shown in Fig. 34, along with the data on sample 162 and one other specimen, for comparison. The germanium-like behavior

---

[314] F. J. Reid and R. K. Willardson (unpublished). These data are presented in the report entitled "Investigations and Measurements of Properties of Single-Crystal Silicon", from Battelle Memorial Institute to AFCRC, TR–59–125, Astia AD212539, edited by A. C. Beer (March 31, 1959). Available from Office of Technical Services, Rept. No. PB–140634.

of sample 8 A is apparent. It appears from the results shown in Fig. 34 that the magnetic-field dependence of the Hall coefficient can be a sensitive criterion for assessing the purity of p-type silicon. This postulate is supported by the $R\sigma$-data on the same specimens shown in Fig. 35.

e. Structure in Hall Coefficient Curves of Other Materials

Measurements of the magnetic-field dependence of the Hall coefficient in p-type specimens of II-B diamond[315] and aluminum antimonide[316] reveal maxima of the type commonly found in silicon. This behavior is illustrated by the data shown in Fig. 36, which includes theoretical curves representative of silicon. The experimental points are plotted so that all maxima occur at similar values of $\gamma_2{}^s$. If the theoretical curves for silicon are applicable to the diamond and the AlSb, then the relationship between H and $\gamma_2{}^s$ for each specimen yields a value for the mobility $\mu_{L,2}^s$. This procedure, however, gives an unrealistic value of $\mu_{L,2}^s$ — in each case about eight times as large as expected on the basis of $R\sigma$ data or magnetoresistance values. Such behavior could result from a greater warping of the heavy-mass band, necessitating use of anisotropy terms of higher order than those containing the b_5 coefficients. Another possibility is warping in the light-mass band. In order to remove this point from the speculation stage, quantitative information on the shapes of the energy surfaces is necessary.

Magnetoresistance data on p-type II-B diamonds are available from the measurements of Mitchell and Wedepohl.[317] They find a ratio of longitudinal to transverse magnetoresistance of between $\frac{1}{3}$ and $\frac{1}{2}$. A more extensive study was subsequently carried out by Kemmey and Mitchell.[317a] Attention is given to the anisotropy of the magnetoresistance, and results are quoted for all the weak-field directional coefficients.

---

[315] R. Bate and R. Willardson, *Proc. Phys. Soc. (London)* **74**, 363 (1959).

[316] F. Reid and J. Duga (unpublished).

[317] E. W. J. Mitchell and P. T. Wedepohl, *Proc. Phys. Soc. (London)* **B70**, 527 (1957).

[317a] P. J. Kemmey and E. W. J. Mitchell, *Proc. Roy. Soc.* **A263**, 420 (1961).

VIII.
Quadratic Energy Surfaces of the Many-Valley Type

22. GENERAL DISCUSSION

The use of the ellipsoidal model to approximate anisotropic conditions has the advantage that solutions of the Boltzmann equation can be obtained which are exact, mathematically, in the magnetic field strength. Such solutions have been available for some time (see Section 6a), and early calculations of the galvanomagnetic effects in bismuth were based on such a model.

Representation of an energy surface by a *single* ellipsoid centered about $\mathbf{k} = 0$ [see Eq. (6.2)] will not in general satisfy the symmetry of the crystal. Such a surface, to possess cubic symmetry, for example, would need to degenerate to a sphere. It is, therefore, necessary to represent the anisotropic energy surfaces by a *system* of ellipsoids, so arranged in the Brillouin zone as to provide the symmetry of the crystal. These ellipsoids, centered about a number of equivalent band-edge points in k-space, provide an energy band such that $\varepsilon(\mathbf{k})$ has a number of minima or "valleys," and the system is often referred to as a "many-valley" structure.[65]

a. Case of Isotropic Scattering on a Surface of Constant Energy

A detailed analysis of the transport properties of a many-valley semiconductor has been given by Herring,[65] for the case where the charge-carrier scattering process can be represented by a relaxation time, assumed to be a function of energy only.

The components of the conductivity tensor due to the carriers in all the valleys are given by sums of the contributions from each single valley, thus

$$\sigma_{ij}(\mathbf{H}) = \sum_{r}{}' \sigma_{ij}^{(r)}(\mathbf{H}) \tag{22.1}$$

213

where $\sigma_{ij}^{(r)}(\mathbf{H})$ is the conductivity tensor component due to the carriers in the rth valley. The expressions for $\sigma_{ij}^{(r)}(\mathbf{H})$, in this case of ellipsoidal energy surfaces and a relaxation time which is independent of position over a surface of constant energy, differ from those given in Chapter V only in that the effective mass is a tensor quantity rather than a scalar. If, as is customary, the coordinate axes are chosen to be coincident with the principal axes of the energy ellipsoid [cf Eq. (6.2)] — designated by subscripts 1, 2, and 3 — for the valley in question, then the mass tensors are diagonal with elements usually written as[45f]

$$\mathsf{M}_{ij} \equiv m_i{}^* \, \delta_{ij}, \qquad (\mathsf{M}^{-1})_{ij} \equiv (1/m_i{}^*) \, \delta_{ij}, \qquad i, j = 1, 2, 3 \qquad (22.2)$$

where δ_{ij} is the Kronecker symbol.

The diagonal terms are thus abbreviated $m_{11}^* \equiv m_1{}^*$, etc. For this choice of coordinate directions, the conductivity coefficients and other transport quantities discussed in Sections 8 and 12 assume, in the limiting case as the magnetic field approaches zero, the forms which are given below. The zero-field coefficient is

$$\sigma_{ij}^{0(r)} = n^{(r)} \left| e\mu_{ij}^{0(r)} \right| = n^{(r)}(e^2/m_i{}^*) \langle \tau \rangle \, \delta_{ij} \qquad (22.3)$$

where, for classical statistics, $n^{(r)}$ is given in terms of the reduced Fermi level η (measured positive from the band edge into the band, and η is therefore negative for nondegenerate semiconductors) by the following expression [cf. Eq. (15.3)]:

$$n^{(r)} = 2(2\pi kT/h^2)^{3/2} \, (m_1{}^* \, m_2{}^* \, m_3{}^*)^{1/2} \, e^\eta. \qquad (22.3a)$$

The average of τ over energy, $\langle \tau \rangle$, is given by (15.4) and therefore differs from that used by Herring and others by the weighting factor ε (energy) and the appropriate normalizing factor.[318] For an arrangement of ellipsoids possessing cubic symmetry, the zero-magnetic-field mobility is the same in all directions and is given by[319]

---

[318] If an average defined as
$$\langle g \rangle \equiv \int_0^\infty g(\varepsilon)\varepsilon^{1/2} \, e^{-\varepsilon/kT} \, d\varepsilon \Big/ \int_0^\infty \varepsilon^{1/2} \, e^{-\varepsilon/kT} \, d\varepsilon,$$
as often appears in the literature,[56,65] is used in place of (15.4) then the $\langle \tau \rangle$ in (22.3) is to be replaced by $\langle \varepsilon\tau \rangle/\langle \varepsilon \rangle$.

[319] It has been pointed out by Blatt (p. 281 of ref. 44) that symmetry requirements in a cubic crystal impose the condition that two of the three effective masses be equal if the energy minimum lies along a symmetry axis. The ellipsoids are thus figures of revolution (spheroids).

$$\mu_0 = e \langle \tau \rangle \left\{ \frac{1}{3} \left[\frac{1}{m_1^*} + \frac{1}{m_2^*} + \frac{1}{m_3^*} \right] \right\}, \qquad e < 0 \text{ for electrons, } (22.4)$$

an expression which reduces to (12.25) in the case of isotropic systems.

For the first-order contribution to the Hall effect [see Eq. (8.5)], one obtains for the rth valley — choosing again a coordinate system such that the mass tensor is diagonal — the following expression:

$$\sigma_{ijl}^{0(r)} = \mp n^{(r)} (|e^3|/c \, m_i^* \, m_j^*) \langle \tau^2 \rangle \varepsilon_{ijl}, \qquad - \text{ for electrons; } + \text{ for holes}$$

$$(22.5)$$

where ε_{ijl} is the permutation tensor [see (6.13)]. Except for the changes in notation, the above results are those presented by Herring.[65] In the limiting case of isotropic energy surfaces, they reduce to the expressions for $\sigma_{xx}(0)$ and $\lim_{H \to 0} \sigma_{xy}(H)/H$ given in (12.14) and (12.15).

It is of interest to carry out the summation over r for an arrangement of ellipsoids possessing cubic symmetry, and to examine the expression for the rather fundamental ratio μ_0^H/μ. The result is given by Herring and it can be written in terms of the familiar isotropic factors [Eq. (12.40)] multiplied by an anisotropy factor, thus

$$\mu_0^H/\mu_0 \equiv r_0 = \{ \langle \tau^2 \rangle / \langle \tau \rangle^2 \} \cdot a^H \qquad (22.6)$$

where[65]

$$a^H \equiv 3 \left(\frac{1}{m_1^* \, m_2^*} + \frac{1}{m_2^* \, m_3^*} + \frac{1}{m_3^* \, m_1^*} \right) \Bigg/ \left(\frac{1}{m_1^*} + \frac{1}{m_2^*} + \frac{1}{m_3^*} \right)^2.$$

$$(22.7)$$

The anisotropy factor in (22.6), which is unity for the isotropic case, is, in general, less than unity. It has been plotted by Herring for the case

$$m_1^* = m_2^* = m_\perp^*, \qquad m_3^* = m_\parallel^* \qquad (22.8)$$

where the subscripts $\perp$ and $\parallel$ refer, respectively, to directions which are perpendicular and parallel to the axis of revolution of the ellipsoid. The ratio $m_\parallel^*/m_\perp^*$ is often designated as K, and the anisotropy factor will be written here as $a^H(K)$. The behavior is illustrated in Fig. 37.

The expressions for the weak-field magnetoconductivity coefficients follow from an evaluation of (8.8). Although the procedure is straightforward, the algebra is involved. The reader is referred to the literature for details. The form of the expression for each σ^0_{ijlm} involves the carrier density in the valley, $n^{(r)}$, an average over energy involving the relaxation

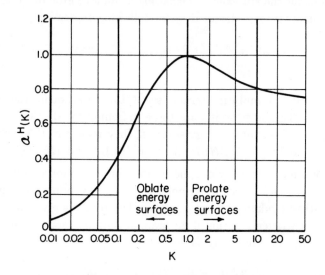

FIG. 37. Dependence of anisotropy factor in μ_0^H/μ_0 on the anisotropy of the effective mass for a family of spheroidal energy surfaces arranged so as to possess cubic symmetry (after Herring[65]). The quantity K, here, is the ratio $m_\parallel*/m_\perp*$.

time, namely $\langle \tau^3 \rangle$, and an anisotropic factor $a^{(r)}_{ijlm}$ which takes into account the ratios of the effective masses in the valley. The general form of the relationship is given in Section 22b. Along the principal directions of a valley, the longitudinal magnetoconductivity vanishes, i.e., $\sigma^{0(r)}_{iiii} = 0$.

Even in the case of cubic symmetry the results are somewhat complicated. For unlike the zero-magnetic-field conductivity and the first-order Hall coefficient, which are nondirectional in cubic systems, the σ^0_{ijlm} are, of course, anisotropic. This means that these magnetoconductivity coefficients cannot be expressed in terms of a nondirectional anisotropy factor such as the a^H of (22.6). Not only are the $a^{(r)}(K)$ for magnetoconductivity dependent on the directions $ijlm$, but the resulting $a(K)$ — obtained by summing over r — is dependent on the *particular* arrangement of ellipsoids which was used to satisfy the requirement of cubic symmetry. For example, the arrangements possessing cubic symmetry, which commonly appear in the literature, are (a) 3 or 6 spheroids with major axes along the [100] directions, (b) 6 or 12 spheroids along [110] directions, and (c) 4 or 8 spheroids along [111] directions. For all three of these models the anisotropic terms for the conductivity and weak-field Hall effect are those given in (22.4) and (22.6), respectively. For the σ_{ijlm}^0, however, the factor is different for each model. Directional magnetoresistance measurements can therefore provide information for determining which model is applicable. A particularly significant point is that in the case of [100] valleys — model (a) — the longitudinal magnetoconductivity vanishes along the cubic axes. Further discussion of systems of specific symmetry is given in the sections to follow.

In addition to the commonly considered scattering mechanisms — those by acoustic phonons (*intra*valley) and ionized impurities — the relaxation time in a many-valley semiconductor may be significantly affected by *inter*valley scattering processes. This type of scattering involves phonon wave numbers of the order of the **k** vector between two different band edge points, i.e., $\mathbf{k}^{(i)} - \mathbf{k}^{(j)}$, where the superscripts denote two different valleys. This involves phonon energies considerably larger than those involved in the intravalley acoustical processes. Therefore, intervalley scattering would be expected to be unimportant for the very low temperatures, but can augment the temperature dependence of the mobility in the intermediate temperature regions. At still higher temperatures, where the energy of the intervalley phonon is considerably less than either kT or the charge-carrier energy, the intervalley processes approach the same characteristics as the intravalley acoustic scattering. For quantitative consideration, the reader is referred to the original article by Herring[65] or to review papers by Brooks[185] or Blatt.[44] The effect of different admixtures of intervalley scattering on the conductivity mobility is shown in Fig. 38. In the case of n-type germanium, the mobility varies[287] approximately as $T^{-1.66}$ in the temperature interval 100°–300°K. It has been suggested that the steeper temperature dependence from the $T^{-1.5}$ behavior representative of intravalley acoustic phonon scattering might result from contributions of intervalley processes as well as from optical modes.[192] Admixture of either intravalley optical modes or intervalley acoustical or optical modes

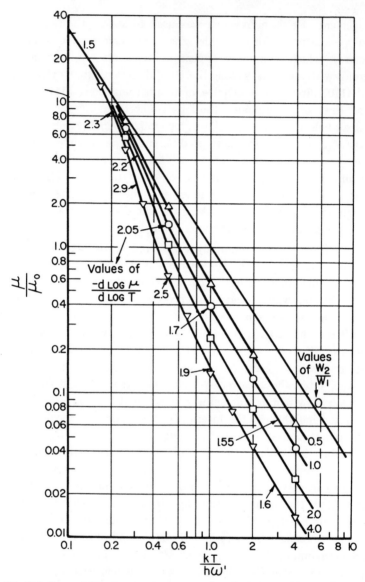

Fig. 38. Relative mobility-temperature curves for admixtures of intervalley scattering and intravalley scattering by acoustical modes. The quantities w_1 and w_2 measure the strength of the coupling of the carriers to the intra- and intervalley modes, respectively. The abscissa is a dimensionless temperature parameter; when $w_2 \neq 0$, ω' is the frequency of the intervalley mode. When $w_2 = 0$, the mobility is given by the familiar $T^{-3/2}$ curve, namely, by

$$\mu = (4/3\sqrt{\pi})(e/3w_1)(2/m_\perp{}^* + 1/m_\parallel{}^*)(kT/\hbar\omega')^{-3/2}.$$

The normalization parameter μ_0 is the value of the above expression for $(kT/\hbar\omega') = 1$ (after Herring[65]).

produces the same type of perturbation to the $T^{-1.5}$ variation of the intravalley acoustic-mode mobility. The magnitudes to be expected are illustrated in Fig. 38, or, in more detail, in several plots given by Adawi.[320]

As a result of symmetry considerations in n-type germanium, where the band-edge points are believed to occur at the centers of the hexagonal faces of the Brillouin zone, there are theoretical reasons, as advanced by Herring and Vogt,[321] for expecting the intervalley scattering to be small. These predictions are in agreement with the experimental findings of Keyes, who has concluded, on the basis of elastomagnetoresistance measurements, that the coupling constant in n-type germanium for intervalley scattering is considerably less than that for the intravalley process.[322] He estimates that at room temperature only 10–20% of the scattering is of the inter-valley type.

For n-type silicon, on the other hand, where the mobility[323] appears to go as $T^{-2.5}$ in the region $160° < T < 400°K$, an analysis of the scattering by Harrison[324] indicates that the zero-order contribution to the optical-mode matrix element vanishes identically, and therefore intervalley scattering seems to be the most promising mechanism to explain the steep temperature variation. Subsequent investigations by Dumke[325] indicate also that intervalley scattering is the dominant mechanism at 300°K for electrons in silicon. On the other hand, Klose finds that if instead of a modified Bloch potential one uses the Nordheim potential in calculating the electron-phonon interaction, one finds the influence of optical modes for intravalley scattering to be greater in n-type silicon than in n-type germanium.[325a, b] He quotes support for such a finding from the relative values in germanium and silicon of the critical fields which mark the beginning of "hot-electron" behavior.[325a]

In Hall conductivity and magnetoconductivity, where averages of τ^2 and τ^3, respectively, are involved, the effect of admixtures of intervalley

[320] I. Adawi, *Phys. Rev.* **120**, 118 (1960).
[321] C. Herring and E. Vogt, *Phys. Rev.* **101**, 944 (1956); **105**, 1933 (1957).
[322] R. W. Keyes, *Phys. Rev.* **103**, 1240 (1956).
[323] G. W. Ludwig and R. L. Watters, *Phys. Rev.* **101**, 1699 (1956).
[324] W. A. Harrison, *Phys. Rev.* **104**, 1281 (1956).
[325] W. P. Dumke, *Phys. Rev.* **118**, 938 (1960).
[325a] W. Klose *in* "Proc. of the Intern. Conf. on Semiconductor Phys., Prague 1960," p. 78. Publishing House Czech. Acad. Sci., Prague, 1961.
[325b] W. Klose, *Ann. Physik* **7**, 233 (1961).

scattering can be fairly large. For example, the curves shown by Herring[65] for $\langle \tau^2 \rangle / \langle \tau \rangle^2$ as a function of $(kT/\hbar\omega')$ deviate from the acoustic-mode scattering value of 1.18 to values as low as 1.15 and as high as 1.5. The quantity $\langle \tau^3 \rangle / \langle \tau \rangle^3$, which for acoustic-mode scattering is 1.77, is seen to vary from around 1.4 to 2.8. If conditions are such that the value of $(kT/\hbar\omega')$ corresponds to regions of largest slope on the curves, then one might expect to find that the intervalley scattering has introduced a significant temperature dependence to r_0 and to the magnetoconductivity.

b. Anisotropic Scattering

In the preceding section, the properties of the many-valley semiconductor were discussed for the case where the collision mechanism could be described by a relaxation time which depended only on energy. The implications of this restriction have been considered by Herring[326] who concludes that such a treatment is probably good for intervalley lattice scattering, optical mode scattering in nonpolar crystals, and neutral impurity scattering; but is not very satisfactory for intravalley scattering by acoustic modes, and can be quite poor when ionized impurity scattering is important and the energy surfaces are highly anisotropic.

A theory which takes into account anisotropy in the scattering processes has been developed by Herring and Vogt.[321] Their treatment is applicable to scattering processes which either conserve energy or randomize velocity. These include most of the situations which are prevalent in semiconductors, the notable exception being polar scattering and electron-electron collisions. Under the restrictions on the scattering processes given above, there is essentially no mixing of the distribution functions of each energy shell, and therefore it is possible to solve the Boltzmann equation independently for each shell of a valley and to obtain the resulting current contributions from said shell. These shell current contributions are then combined in the appropriate manner.

The Herring-Vogt development leads to three relaxation times $\tau_1(\varepsilon)$, $\tau_2(\varepsilon)$, and $\tau_3(\varepsilon)$ associated, respectively, with the three principal directions of the energy surfaces of a valley. It turns out that for static fields, i.e., dc effects, the transport properties can be described by equations

---

[326] Reference 65, Appendix A.

identical with those for the isotropic scattering case given in the preceding section except that each component of the effective mass tensor is weighted by the reciprocal of the corresponding relaxation time tensor, i.e., the combination τ_i/m_i^* always occurs. Thus the expressions for the contributions of the rth valley to the first three conductivity coefficients are, in the principal axis system of this valley, as follows[45f, 321]:

$$\sigma_{ij}^{0(r)} = n^{(r)} (e^2/m_i^*) \langle \tau_i \rangle \, \delta_{ij} \tag{22.9}$$

$$\sigma_{ijl}^{0(r)} = \mp \, n^{(r)} (|e^3|/cm_i^* \, m_j^*) \langle \tau_i \, \tau_j \rangle \, \varepsilon_{ijl}, \qquad - \text{ for electrons}; \ + \text{ for holes} \tag{22.10}$$

$$\sigma_{ijlm}^{0(r)} = n^{(r)} (e^4/2c^2 \, m_i^* \, m_j^* \, m_q^*) \langle \tau_i \, \tau_j \, \tau_q \rangle \, (\varepsilon_{qlj} \, \varepsilon_{qim} + \varepsilon_{qmj} \, \varepsilon_{qil}) \tag{22.11}$$

where the average of τ over energy $\langle \tau \rangle$, is given by Eq. (15.4).

If results are specialized to the case where the ellipsoids are so arranged as to yield cubic symmetry, then (22.9) and (22.10) are nondirectional, and a summation over r results only in the change of $n^{(r)}$ into n where $n = \Sigma_r \, n(r)$, and in an average over the valleys for the remaining factors. Furthermore, if the minima be along a symmetry axis so that two of the effective masses are equal[319], we may use the notation of (22.8), and the expression for the conductivity mobility (at zero magnetic field) assumes the form

$$\mu_0 = \mp \, \frac{|e|}{3} \, \frac{\langle \tau_\parallel \rangle}{m_\parallel^*} \, [2K + 1] \tag{22.12}$$

where we have assumed that

$$\frac{\tau_\perp}{m_\perp^*} \, \frac{m_\parallel^*}{\tau_\parallel} = K, \tag{22.13}$$

and that $\tau_\parallel$ and $\tau_\perp$ have the same dependence on energy.

Now the zero-field Hall mobility $[\mu_0^H \equiv R_0 \, \sigma_0 \, c]$ for a cubic crystal is related to the σ_{ijl}^0 of the crystal by means of the following expression [cf. Eqs. (8.15), (8.31), and (8.31a)]:

$$\sigma_{ijl}^0 = \sigma_0^2 \, R_0 \, \varepsilon_{ijl} = [\sigma_0 \, \mu_0^H/c] \, \varepsilon_{ijl}. \tag{22.14}$$

The summing of (22.10) over axially symmetric valleys yields

$$\sigma_{ijl}^{0} = \mp\, n\,[\,|e^3|/cm_{\parallel}^{*2}]\, \langle \tau_{\parallel}^2 \rangle\, [K(K+2)/3]\, \varepsilon_{ijl}.\qquad (22.15)$$

Hence,

$$\frac{\mu_0^H}{\mu_0} = \frac{\langle \tau_{\parallel}^2 \rangle}{\langle \tau_{\parallel} \rangle^2}\, \frac{3K[K+2]}{[2K+1]^2}.\qquad (22.16)$$

For the magnetoconductivity tensor, the summing over axially symmetric valleys yields an expression of the form

$$\sigma_{ijlm}^{0} = n\, \frac{e^4}{c^2}\, \frac{\langle \tau_{\parallel}^3 \rangle}{m_{\parallel}^{*3}}\, K\,[g_{ijlm}^{30}\, K^2 + g_{ijlm}^{21}\, K + g_{ijlm}^{12}].\qquad (22.17)$$

The g_{iilm}^{pq} depend on the arrangement of the ellipsoids in the Brillouin zone. Values, as given for [100] and [111] valleys by Herring and Vogt, are tabulated in Table IV.

TABLE IV. Low-Field Magnetoconductivity Components for Cubic Crystals with Axially Symmetric Valleys, Referred to the Crystal Axes[a]

Component, referred to crystal axes	Type of valleys (direction of $\mathbf{k}^{(r)}$)	
	[100]	[111]
$\sigma_{1111}^{0} = -\sigma_0(b + c + d)$ $= -\sigma_0\, \Upsilon_{100}$	0, 0, 0	$-2/9,\ 4/9,\ -2/9$
$\sigma_{1122}^{0} = -\sigma_0 b - \sigma_0(\mu_0^H/c)^2$ $= -\sigma_0\, \Upsilon_{100}^{010} - \sigma_0(\mu_0^H/c)^2$	$-1/3,\ -1/3,\ -1/3$	$-2/9,\ -5/9,\ -2/9$
$\sigma_{1212}^{0} = -\tfrac{1}{2}\sigma_0 c + \tfrac{1}{2}\sigma_0(\mu_0^H/c)^2$ $= -\tfrac{1}{2}\sigma_0^2\, \mathscr{R}_0^p + \tfrac{1}{2}\sigma_0(\mu_0^H/c)^2$	0, 1/2, 0	1/9, 5/18, 1/9

[a] Tabulated quantities are the coefficients g_{ijlm}^{30}, g_{ijlm}^{21}, and g_{ijlm}^{12}, respectively, in Eq. (22.17) for the components σ_{ijlm}^{0} indicated (after Herring and Vogt). The σ_{ijlm}^{0} are also given in terms of the magnetoresistance coefficients of Eq. (8.30), and the measurable quantities Υ_{hkl}^{mnp} of Eq. (11.3), or of the planar "Hall" coefficient $\mathscr{R}_0^p$ of (11.27). The divisor of μ_0^H is, of course, not a coefficient but represents the velocity of light.

A general solution of the kinetic equation for a system of electrons in external electric and magnetic fields for the case in which the collision term cannot be expressed by means of a relaxation-time tensor — as, for example, in the strict case of ionized impurity scattering when the electrons have an anisotropic energy distribution — has been carried out by Korenblit.[326a] The equations are developed for the case where the energy surfaces are ellipsoids. It is found that in strong magnetic fields, one gets, to a good approximation, the same results which are obtained from the Herring-Vogt theory. In weak magnetic fields, expansions are possible, and results are obtained which are similar in form to those of Herring and Vogt. However, the tensor components involved in the two treatments, although equal in magnitude for phonon scattering, can differ in the case of ionized impurity scattering by as much as 70% in the case of maximum anisotropy, by 30% for anisotropy representative of n-type germanium, and by 10% for n-type silicon. Inasmuch as the components of the relaxation-time tensor can occur to the second or third power in the lower-order galvanomagnetic effects, the differences can be significant. For the case of intermediate magnetic fields in a solid having a strongly anisotropic mass tensor — such as n-type germanium — Korenblit points out that the expressions do not reduce to the usual form involving components of a relaxation-time tensor.

23. APPLICATION TO SPECIFIC SEMICONDUCTORS

The many-valley theory has found its most extensive use in connection with n-type germanium and silicon, where the conduction band minima lie along axes of symmetry, and the band is described by a set of ellipsoids of revolution. Detailed investigations of this case were made by Abeles and Meiboom[157, 327] and by Shibuya.[154, 282]

Although, as pointed out before, solutions of the Boltzmann equation which are exact in the magnetic-field parameter are possible for quadratic

[326a] I. Korenblit, *Fiz. Tverd. Tela* **4**, 168 (1962) [translation: *Soviet Phys.-Solid State* **4**, 120 (1962)].

[327] An earlier account is given in S. Meiboom and B. Abeles, *Phys. Rev.* **93**, 1121 (1954).

energy surfaces with certain restrictions on the scattering, the results for the directional quantities are rather cumbersome, and therefore considerable space in the literature has been devoted principally to the weak-field effects. We consider these first.

a. Weak Magnetic Fields

The contributions of an individual valley to each of the principal magnetoconductivity coefficients were considered in the preceding section, where results are given in terms of anisotropy factors and Boltzmann averages of the relaxation times. As mentioned above, expressions are given by Abeles and Meiboom and by Shibuya for the electrical transport properties of arrangements of the ellipsoids which possess cubic symmetry. The numerical constants are evaluated for a scattering process represent- ative of that by acoustical phonons, although of course results are readily modified for any scattering where τ is a function only of energy, by using the appropriate $\tau(\varepsilon)$ in the Boltzmann averages. For completeness, we shall reproduce expressions similar to those developed by Abeles- Meiboom (A–M) and Shibuya (S), using a notation consistent with Section 22. The effective masses in directions parallel and normal to the axis of revolution of the spheriod are designated by $m_\parallel^*$ and $m_\perp^*$, respectively. A comparison of the notations used herein with those of A–M and S is given in Table V.

Use of this table enables us to write down readily from the works of A–M, S, or of Herring (cf. Section 22), the principal conductivity coefficients expressing the transport properties of systems of spheroidal energy surfaces.

(1) *Single spheroid with principal axes along coordinate directions.* Although this system does not possess cubic symmetry, we discuss it here since we shall achieve cubic symmetry by suitable arrangements of spheroids in the Brillouin zone. For the case where direction 3 is parallel to the axis of revolution of the spheroid $(m_3^* = m_\parallel^*)$, the coefficients can be expressed by[327a]

[327a] In compliance with the convention used in Section 22, the coefficients represen- tative of a single spheroid ("r"th valley) should be written $\sigma_{ij}^{0(r)}$, $\sigma_{ijk}^{0(r)}$, etc. Such a superscript is implied here, although it is omitted for simplicity.

TABLE V. EQUIVALENCE OF SYMBOLS USED IN THIS ARTICLE AND THOSE OF ABELES-MEIBOOM AND SHIBUYA[a]

Quantity	This article	A–M	S
Longitudinal effective mass (direction parallel to axis of revolution of spheroid)	$m_\parallel^*$	m_3	m_1
Transverse effective mass	$m_\perp^*$	m_1	m_2
Ratio of masses $m_\parallel^*/m_\perp^*$	K	K	r^{-1}
Scalar mass (for spherical energy surfaces)	m_s^*	—	m_0
Conductivity mobility (for spherical energy surfaces)	$\mu_0^s \equiv e\langle\tau\rangle/m_s^*)$	—	μ_0
Carrier density, per ellipsoid ("r"th valley)	$n^{(r)}$	n	—
Total carrier density	n	N	N
Longitudinal valley mobility[b]	$\mu_0^l (\equiv e\langle\tau\rangle/m_\parallel^*)$	—	—
Transverse valley mobility[b]	$K\mu_0^l$	—	A
B	$\mp (3\sqrt{\pi}/4c)K\mu_0^l$	—	B
u	$n^{(r)}e\mu_0^l$	u	—
v	$(3\sqrt{\pi}/4c)\mu_0^l$	v	—
$K(X)$	$K(X)^c$ or $\bar{K}(X)$	$\alpha(\sqrt{X})$	$1 - XQ(X)$
$L(X)$	$L(X)^c$	$(2/\sqrt{\pi})\beta(\sqrt{X})$	$2P(X)$
$Q(X)$	$X^{-1}[1 - K(X)]$	$\gamma(\sqrt{X})$	$Q(X)$

[a] There seems to be a misprint in Eq. (6) of S; the quantity A should apparently be defined by $\mu_0 M_1^{-1} r^{-1}$, where $M_1 \equiv m_1/m_0$, $r \equiv m_2/m_1$.

[b] These quantities are sometimes called "partial mobilities" (see Section 23c).

[c] See Eqs. (15.85). The K function is not to be confused with $K \equiv m_\parallel^*/m_\perp^*$.

$$\sigma_{ij}^0 = n^{(r)} e^2 \langle\tau\rangle \nu_{ij}(m^*), \tag{23.1}$$

$$= n^{(r)}|e\mu_0^l|\xi_{ij}(K), \tag{23.2}$$

$$\sigma_{ijl}^0 = \mp n^{(r)}(|e^3|/c)\langle\tau^2\rangle\nu_{ijl}(m^*), \quad \text{— for electrons; + for holes} \tag{23.3}$$

$$= \mp (3\pi/8c)n^{(r)}|e|(\mu_0^l)^2 \xi_{ijl}(K), \quad \tau \sim \varepsilon^{-1/2} \tag{23.4}$$

$$\sigma^0_{ijlm} = n^{(r)} \left(e^4 | c^2\right) \langle \tau^3 \rangle v_{ijlm}(m^*),\tag{23.5}$$

$$= (9\pi/16c^2)n^{(r)}|e| \, |\mu_0{}^l|^3 \, \xi_{ijlm}(K), \qquad \tau \sim \varepsilon^{-1/2},\tag{23.6}$$

where the averages of τ over energy are given by (15.4). The longitudinal valley mobility $\mu_0{}^l$ is defined in Table V, and the values of the anisotropy factors $v(m^*)$ and $\xi(K)$ are listed in Table VI.

All other conductivity coefficients of the orders tabulated in the table but not listed therein are zero. An important point to note is the vanishing of the longitudinal magnetoresistance in the directions of the principal axes of the energy ellipsoid. It is stressed by Keyes that this is not a general consequence, however, but results in part from the relaxation time approximation.[328]

(2) *Systems of spheroids possessing cubic symmetry, coordinate axes along cube axes.* The commonly studied arrangements, representative respectively of conduction bands in silicon and germanium, are: (1) three or six spheroids, the main axes of which are directed along the cube axes of the reciprocal lattice ([100] valleys); (2) four or eight spheroids, with main axes along the body diagonals of the unit cell of the reciprocal lattice ([111] valleys). The additional case of twelve [110] type spheroids was included by Shibuya.

The transformation of the tensor components given in Table VI from coordinate systems in the principal axes of each valley to a system coincident with the cube axes, and summation over the valleys is discussed in the literature previously cited, and by Keyes.[328] It should be noted that because of our symmetry convention in the indices representing magnetic field directions, the Ω_{44} component of Keyes differs by a factor of 2 from the corresponding component in Table VI; that is,

$$\Omega_{44} \equiv \Omega_{2323} = \sigma^0_{2323} + \sigma^0_{2332} = 2\sigma^0_{2323}.\tag{23.6a}$$

In expressing the conductivity coefficients, it is convenient to use as a normalizing factor the longitudinal mobility of a single valley (spheroid). The anisotropy is then described by a function of the parameter

---

[328] R. W. Keyes, *Phys. Rev.* 111, 34 (1958).

K, similar to the procedure employed in the case of the single spheroid. We therefore write

$$\sigma_{ij}^0 = n|e\mu_0^l|\xi_{ij}(K) \tag{23.7}$$

$$\sigma_{ijl}^0 = \mp (3\pi/8c)n|e|(\mu_0^l)^2\,\xi_{ijl}(K), \qquad \tau \sim \varepsilon^{-1/2}, \tag{23.8}$$

$$\sigma_{ijlm}^0 = (9\pi/16c^2)n|e|\,|\mu_0^l|^3\,\xi_{ijlm}(K), \qquad \tau \sim \varepsilon^{-1/2}. \tag{23.9}$$

The total carrier density n is given by summing the contribution from each spheroid, thus

$$n = \sum_r n^{(r)} \tag{23.10}$$

TABLE VI. VALUES OF ANISOTROPY FACTORS FOR CONDUCTIVITY COEFFICIENTS IN CASE OF SINGLE SPHEROID[a]

Conductivity coefficient [b, c]	$1/\nu(m^*)$	$\xi(K)$
$\sigma_{11}^0 = \sigma_{22}^0$	$m_\perp^*$	K
σ_{33}^0	$m_\parallel^*$	1
$\sigma_{123}^0 = -\sigma_{213}^0$	$m_\perp^{*2}$	K^2
$\sigma_{231}^0 = \sigma_{312}^0 = -\sigma_{132}^0 = -\sigma_{321}^0$	$m_\parallel^* m_\perp^*$	K
$\sigma_{1122}^0 = \sigma_{2211}^0$	$-m_\parallel^* m_\perp^{2}$	$-K^2$
$\sigma_{1133}^0 = \sigma_{2233}^0$	$-m_\perp^{*3}$	$-K^3$
$\sigma_{3311}^0 = \sigma_{3322}^0$	$-m_\parallel^{*2} m_\perp^*$	$-K$
$\sigma_{1212}^0 = \sigma_{2121}^0 = \sigma_{2323}^0$ $= \sigma_{3232}^0 = \sigma_{3131}^0 = \sigma_{1313}^0$	$2m_\parallel^* m_\perp^{*2}$	$\tfrac{1}{2}K^2$
Also, $\sigma_{1221}^0 = \sigma_{2112}^0 = \sigma_{2332}^0$, etc.		

[a] The axis of revolution is along direction 3, i.e., $m_\parallel^* \equiv m_3^*$. All other coefficients of comparable order but not listed in the table are zero.

[b] Our convention introduces a factor of $\tfrac{1}{2}$ into A-M's expression for such coefficients as σ_{1212}^0 inasmuch as our symmetry convention regarding indices lm for σ_{ijlm} requires, for example, in σ_{1212}^0 that the coefficient of the $H_1\,H_2$ term is $\sigma_{1212}^0 + \sigma_{1221}^0 = 2\sigma_{1212}^0$.

[c] See footnote 327a.

where $n^{(r)}$ is given by (22.3a). The anisotropy factors are given, for each arrangement, in Table VII. Although the numerical factors in (23.8) and (23.9) apply only for acoustic phonon scattering (i.e., for $\tau \sim \varepsilon^{-1/2}$), it is clear that the other quantities — including the anisotropy factor $\xi(K)$ — are valid for any scattering mechanism for which τ depends only on energy. In fact, it was shown by Herring and Vogt that the anisotropy factor $\xi(K)$ may be applied in a number of cases where τ is anisotropic over a surface of constant energy when τ has the same symmetry as the energy ellipsoids [see Section 22b]. In such cases, one merely needs

TABLE VII. Anisotropy Factors for Systems of Spheroids Having Cubic Symmetry[a - c]

Conductivity coefficient	$\xi(K)$ [100] type spheroids	$\xi(K)$ [111] type spheroids	$\xi(K)$ [110] type spheroids
σ^0_{11}	$(2K + 1)/3$	$(2K + 1)/3$	$(2K + 1)/3$
σ^0_{123}	$K(K + 2)/3$	$K(K + 2)/3$	$K(K + 2)/3$
σ^0_{1111}	0	$-2K(K - 1)^2/9$	$-K(K - 1)^2/6$
σ^0_{1122}	$-K(K^2 + K + 1)/3$	$-K(2K + 1)(K + 2)/9$	$-K(K + 1)^2/4$
σ^0_{1212}	$\frac{1}{2}K^2$	$K(2K + 1)(K + 2)/18$	$K(K^2 + 4K + 1)/12$
$\sigma_0/n|e\mu_0{}^l|$	$(2K + 1)/3$	$(2K + 1)/3$	$(2K + 1)/3$
$\alpha/[\mp (3\pi/8c)n|e|(\mu_0{}^l)^2]$	$K(K + 2)/3$	$K(K + 2)/3$	$K(K + 2)/3$
$\beta/[(9\pi/16c^2)n|e||\mu_0{}^l|^3]$	$-K(K^2 + K + 1)/3$	$-K(2K + 1)(K + 2)/9$	$-K(K + 1)^2/4$
$\gamma/[(9\pi/16c^2)n|e||\mu_0{}^l|^3]$	K^2	$K(2K + 1)(K + 2)/9$	$K(K^2 + 4K + 1)/6$
$\delta/[(9\pi/16c^2)n|e||\mu_0{}^l|^3]$	$K(K - 1)^2/3$	$-2K(K - 1)^2/9$	$-K(K - 1)^2/12$

[a] Coefficients of the same order as those listed but not shown are either equal to one of those listed or are zero [see, for example, Eqs. (8.12a) and (8.12b)].

[b] For reference purposes, values of the Seitz coefficients [Eq. (8.13)] are also given, using numerical constants representative of $\tau \sim \varepsilon^{-1/2}$ scattering.

[c] For a listing of equivalent coefficients in cubic systems, see Eq. (8.12b). It is to be noted that by convention our coefficients σ^0_{ijlm} are symmetric in l and m, and are therefore equivalent to a symmetrical combination of A–M's, namely, $\frac{1}{2}(\sigma^0_{ijlm} + \sigma^0_{ijml})$.

to define K as shown in (22.13). Use of this expression for K and the assumption that both $\tau_\parallel$ and $\tau_\perp$ have the same dependence on energy, permits Eqs. (23.7) to (23.9) to be written in a general form, namely,

$$\sigma_{ij}^0 = ne^2 [\langle \tau_\parallel \rangle / m_\parallel{}^*] \xi_{ij}(K), \tag{23.11}$$

$$\sigma_{ijl}^0 = \mp\, n\,[|e|^3/c]\,[\langle \tau_\parallel{}^2 \rangle / m_\parallel{}^{*2}] \xi_{ijl}(K), \tag{23.12}$$

$$\sigma_{ijlm}^0 = n\,[e^4/c^2]\,[\langle \tau_\parallel{}^3 \rangle / m_\parallel{}^{*3}] \xi_{ijlm}(K) \tag{23.13}$$

where the averages over energy are given by (15.4). The $\xi(K)$ are the same functions given in Table VII. The relaxation-time tensor is diagonal in the coordinate system of the principal axes of the energy ellipsoid, and it has the components

$$\tau_\parallel = \tau_\parallel{}^0\, \tau(\varepsilon),$$

$$\tau_\perp = \tau_\perp{}^0\, \tau(\varepsilon). \tag{23.14}$$

The relaxation time anisotropy, K_τ, is therefore independent of energy, namely,

$$K_\tau \equiv \tau_\parallel / \tau_\perp = \tau_\parallel{}^0 / \tau_\perp{}^0. \tag{23.15}$$

The anisotropy parameter K is therefore given by the ratio

$$K \equiv \frac{K_m}{K_\tau} = \frac{m_\parallel{}^*\, \tau_\perp{}^0}{m_\perp{}^*\, \tau_\parallel{}^0}. \tag{23.16}$$

Inasmuch as most laboratory techniques yield a measurement of *magnetoresistivity* (current density vector $\mathbf{J}$ is maintained constant during variations in H, while the electric field $\mathbf{E}$ is allowed to change direction) rather than *magnetoconductivity* ($\mathbf{E}$ is constant under variations in H), it is desirable to have available the expressions also for the components of the resistivity tensor, i.e., the galvanomagnetic coefficients. In terms of the longitudinal mobility of a valley $\mu_0{}'[\equiv |e|\langle\tau\rangle/m_\parallel{}^*]$, the inverse Seitz coefficients [see Eq. (8.31)] can be expressed by

TABLE VIII. INVERSE SEITZ COEFFICIENTS[a] FOR SYSTEMS OF SPHEROIDS HAVING CUBIC SYMMETRY[b]

Coefficient	Value		
	[100] type spheroids	[111] type spheroids	[110] type spheroids
$\rho_0 \cdot n\lvert e\mu_0^l\rvert$	$3/(2K+1)$	$3/(2K+1)$	$3/(2K+1)$
$a/[\pm (3\pi/8c)\lvert\mu_0^l\rvert] \equiv A(K)$	$K(K+2)/(2K+1)$	$K(K+2)/(2K+1)$	$K(K+2)/(2K+1)$
$b/[(9\pi/16c^2)(\mu_0^l)^2]$	$\left[\dfrac{K(K^2+K+1)}{2K+1} - \dfrac{\pi}{4}A^2(K)\right]$	$\left[\dfrac{K(K+2)}{3} - \dfrac{\pi}{4}A^2(K)\right]$	$\left[\dfrac{3K(K+1)^2}{4(2K+1)} - \dfrac{\pi}{4}A^2(K)\right]$
$c/[(9\pi/16c^2)(\mu_0^l)^2]$	$-\left[\dfrac{3K^2}{2K+1} - \dfrac{\pi}{4}A^2(K)\right]$	$-\left[\dfrac{K(K+2)}{3} - \dfrac{\pi}{4}A^2(K)\right]$	$-\left[\dfrac{K(K^2+4K+1)}{2(2K+1)} - \dfrac{\pi}{4}A^2(K)\right]$
$d/[(9\pi/16c^2)(\mu_0^l)^2]$	$\dfrac{-K(K-1)^2}{(2K+1)^2}$	$\dfrac{2K(K-1)^2}{3(2K+1)}$	$\dfrac{K(K-1)^2}{4(2K+1)}$

[a] Defined by Eq. (8.30).

[b] Numerical constants $3\pi/8$, $9\pi/16$, and $\pi/4$ are representative of $\tau \sim \varepsilon^{-1/2}$ scattering. For a general $\tau(\varepsilon)$, they should be replaced, respectively, by $\langle\tau^2\rangle/\langle\tau\rangle^2$, $\langle\tau^3\rangle/\langle\tau\rangle^3$, and $\langle\tau^2\rangle^2/\langle\tau\rangle\langle\tau^3\rangle$.

$$a = \pm \frac{|\mu_0^l|}{c} \frac{\langle \tau^2 \rangle}{\langle \tau \rangle^2} \frac{\xi_{123}(K)}{\xi_{11}(K)}$$

$$b = \left[\frac{\mu_0^l}{c} \right]^2 \left\{ - \frac{\langle \tau^3 \rangle}{\langle \tau \rangle^3} \frac{\xi_{1122}(K)}{\xi_{11}(K)} - \left[\frac{\langle \tau^2 \rangle}{\langle \tau \rangle^2} \right]^2 \left[\frac{\xi_{123}(K)}{\xi_{11}(K)} \right]^2 \right\}$$

$$c = - \left[\frac{\mu_0^l}{c} \right]^2 \left\{ 2 \frac{\langle \tau^3 \rangle}{\langle \tau \rangle^3} \frac{\xi_{1212}(K)}{\xi_{11}(K)} - \left[\frac{\langle \tau^2 \rangle}{\langle \tau \rangle^2} \right]^2 \left[\frac{\xi_{123}(K)}{\xi_{11}(K)} \right]^2 \right\}$$

(23.16a)

$$d = \left[\frac{\mu_0^l}{c} \right]^2 \frac{\langle \tau^3 \rangle}{\langle \tau \rangle^3} \frac{1}{\xi_{11}(K)} [- \xi_{1111}(K) + \xi_{1122}(K) + 2\xi_{1212}(K)].$$

These coefficients are listed in Table VIII for three cubically symmetrical arrangements of spheroids.

Measurement of directional magnetoresistance coefficients permits one, in principle, to distinguish between the various arrangements of spheroids in the Brillouin zone. From Table VIII it is apparent that for the development presented here, the symmetry of the energy surfaces imposes the following conditions on the inverse Seitz coefficients:

Spherical symmetry [see Eq. (8.18a), or in Eqs. (23.16a),

place $K = 1$]: $b + c = 0$, $d = 0$

[100] type spheroids: $b + c + d = 0$, $d < 0$

[111] type spheroids: $b + c = 0$, $d > 0$ (23.17)

[110] type spheroids: $b + c - d = 0$, $d > 0$.

These "symmetry conditions" are independent of the particular form of $\tau(\varepsilon)$ — or of (23.14), if τ is a tensor having the symmetry of the energy ellipsoids. It is important to note, however, that the expressions (23.17) were developed using the assumption of the existence of a relaxation time, and therefore the relations are perhaps not of such general validity as the commonly applied designation "symmetry conditions" might imply.

Explicit expressions for Hall and magnetoresistance quantities are given by Abeles and Meiboom for the case of $\tau \sim \varepsilon^{-1/2}$ scattering. These relationships are

$$R_0 = \mp (3\pi/8)(1/nec)[3K(K+2)/(2K+1)^2] \qquad (23.18)$$

$$\mu_0{}^H/\mu = (3\pi/8)[3K(K+2)/(2K+1)^2]. \qquad (23.19)$$

In establishing the weak-field magnetoresistance coefficients [see Eq. (11.3)], the quantities $\mu_0{}^l$ occurring in the expressions in Table VIII are eliminated by use of the relationship

$$R_0 \sigma_0 = (3\pi/8c)\mu_0{}^l K(K+2)/(2K+1). \qquad (23.20)$$

The results are:

System of [100] type spheroids

$$\Upsilon_{100} = 0 \qquad (23.21)$$

$$\Upsilon_{100}^{010} = (4/\pi)R_0{}^2 \sigma_0{}^2\{[(2K+1)(K^2+K+1)/K(K+2)^2] - \pi/4\} \qquad (23.22)$$

$$\Upsilon_{110} = (2/\pi)R_0{}^2 \sigma_0{}^2[(2K+1)(K-1)^2/K(K+2)^2] \qquad (23.23)$$

$$\Upsilon_{110}^{1\bar{1}0} = \Upsilon_{100}^{010} - \Upsilon_{110}. \qquad (23.24)$$

The latter relation is apparent from Eq. (11.5) and either (23.17) or Table VIII, and does not require $\tau \sim \varepsilon^{-1/2}$ scattering for its validity.

System of [111] type spheroids

$$\Upsilon_{100} = (8/3\pi)R_0{}^2 \sigma_0{}^2[(2K+1)(K-1)^2/K(K+2)^2] \qquad (23.25)$$

$$\Upsilon_{100}^{010} = (4/3\pi)R_0{}^2 \sigma_0{}^2\{[(2K+1)^2/K(K+2)] - 3\pi/4\} \qquad (23.26)$$

$$\Upsilon_{110} = \tfrac{1}{2}\Upsilon_{100}$$

$$\Upsilon_{110}^{1\bar{1}0} = \tfrac{1}{2}\Upsilon_{100} + \Upsilon_{100}^{010}. \qquad (23.27)$$

The last two relations are again obvious from Eqs. (11.5) and (23.17) and are not tied to a specific scattering law. One further relation, which is valid in general for cubic symmetry [see Eqs. (11.5)] and therefore holds for [100], [111], or [110] spheroids, is

$$\Upsilon_{110}^{001} = \Upsilon_{100}^{001}. \tag{23.28}$$

A plot of the anisotropy coefficients for the Hall effect and the transverse and longitudinal magnetoresistances is given in Fig. 39 for the case of [111] spheroids.

In the case of n-type germanium, the [111] ellipsoid model was found to fit reasonably well the experimental data of Morin[287] for μ_0^H/μ_0 and the directional magnetoresistance data of Pearson and Suhl.[79] Prolate spheroids are indicated, with Abeles and Meiboom suggesting a value of

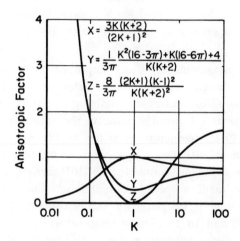

Fig. 39. Anisotropic factors for weak-field Hall coefficient and magnetoresistances as a function of K for [111] spheroids. The function X refers to the Hall effect [Eq. (23.18)]; Y to the transverse magnetoresistance [Eq. (23.26)]; Z to the longitudinal magnetoresistance [Eq. (23.25)]. The ratio of effective masses characterizing the energy surfaces, or of masses divided by corresponding relaxation times as in Eq. (23.16), is given by K (after Abeles and Meiboom[157]).

K of 20, and Shibuya implying a value of around 13 — assuming in both cases acoustic phonon scattering. For p-type germanium, although these authors find the [100] model preferable to the [111] arrangement, the fit with experiment is not satisfactory. This is understandable in view of the valence band degeneracy and warping (see Section 19 ff).

Experimental tests of the symmetry relation $b + c = 0$, $d > 0$ [see Eqs. (23.17)] and determinations of K were carried out by a number of investigators. The earlier data[329-333] suggested room temperature values of K of about 10 to 15, appreciably lower than the cyclotron resonance value[295] of 19.3 (this being at 4°K). It is to be noted, of course, that cyclotron resonance experiments yield directly the mass ratio $m_\parallel^*/m_\perp^*$, or K_m, while the galvanomagnetic studies provide a ratio of the anisotropies of effective mass and relaxation time, $(m_\parallel^*/m_\perp^*)/(\tau_\parallel/\tau_\perp)$, as was discussed in Section 22b. Although at room temperature the relaxation time anisotropy in pure samples is not likely to be significant, at lower temperatures and in more highly doped material the anisotropic scattering of ionized impurities can be expected to be noticeable.[65, 334] In fact, the experimental values obtained for K appear definitely to decrease as the temperature is lowered or as the impurity content of the specimens is increased.

Subsequent measurements, using improved techniques and purer crystals, have yielded room temperature values of K between 17.5 and 20.[153,156] On the purest specimen containing 7×10^{13} carriers/cm³, the data of Goldberg and Howard[153] indicate the anisotropy parameter to remain around 19 for temperatures as low as 125°K. This result is in excellent agreement with the values obtained by magnetoconductance measurements on a specimen containing 4×10^{12} carriers/cm³.[152] Goldberg and Howard also made a special examination of the symmetry relation $b/c = -1$, and find it obeyed with carrier concentrations as high as 6×10^{15} cm⁻³, and to the lowest temperatures used, namely, 77°K. Evidence of deviations exists for $n = 4 \times 10^{17}$ cm⁻³ and above, but the ratio always remains negative.

These values of K in the range 17.5 to 20 obtained by the later measurements of weak-field magnetoresistance are in agreement with the values obtained from measurements done at strong magnetic fields, as we shall see in Section 23b. Thus the [111] ellipsoid model appears now to be firmly established for n-type germanium, and the values of

---

[329] G. Benedek, W. Paul, and H. Brooks, *Phys. Rev.* **100**, 1129 (1955).

[330] M. Glicksman, *Phys. Rev.* **100**, 1146 (1955).

[331] C. Goldberg and R. Davis, *Phys. Rev.* **102**, 1254 (1956).

[332] M. Glicksman, *Phys. Rev.* **108**, 264 (1957).

[333] M. Glicksman, in "Progress in Semiconductors" (A. Gibson, ed.), Vol. 3, p. 3, Wiley, New York, 1958.

[334] F. Ham, *Phys. Rev.* **100**, 1251(A), (1955).

K as obtained from cyclotron resonance and from galvanomagnetic phenomena are in good agreement.

If one makes the reasonable assumption that the mass anisotropy varies only slightly with temperature, then by measuring $K(\equiv K_m/K_\tau)$ as a function of temperature one can obtain information on the anisotropy

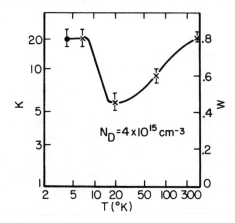

Fig. 40. Temperature dependence of the effective anisotropy parameter K in n-type germanium (after Laff and Fan[335]).

of various scattering mechanisms which predominate at different temperatures. Such experiments were done by Laff and Fan.[335] Values of K were determined from temperatures above 300°K to as low as 4.2°K on a specimen of germanium containing 4×10^{15} donors. The results are shown in Fig. 40.

The decrease in K from 300° to 20°K is attributed to the increase in scattering by the ionized impurities. Below 20°K, the carriers freeze out rapidly, reducing the ionized impurity density. The Hall coefficient suggested that 20% of the effective donors were ionized at 20°K, but that the number was negligible at 7°K. The scattering at temperatures below 7°K seems to be due to neutral impurities, and for this process the τ is apparently isotropic. The supposition that the decrease in K in the range 300°K < T < 7°K was actually due to increased impurity scattering was strengthened by subsequent experiments in which

335   R. A. Laff and H. Y. Fan, *Phys. Rev.* **112**, 317 (1958).

compensating impurities were introduced into the specimen. It was found that the scattering anisotropy value, K_τ, of 12 calculated by Ham[334] for a mass anisotropy of 19, was consistent with the extrapolation of the data to the limit of total ionized impurity scattering.

In the case of n-type silicon, it is the [100] arrangement of spheroids which is applicable. The earliest data on directional magnetoresistance appears to be that of Pearson and Herring.[305] They found Υ_{100} to be essentially zero — being perhaps 5% of Υ_{100}^{001}. The calculated value of K is 4.9 at room temperature and 4.6 at 68°K. These compare with Glicksman's room temperature value of 5.5.[330, 333] Other investigators have also measured magnetoresistance and Hall effect at intermediate magnetic field strengths, and obtain similar results for K. For example, Broudy and Venables[159] quote a value of 5.2 at 80°K. Krag[163] also finds that such a value fits his magnetoresistance data reasonably well, although the magnetic field dependence of the Hall coefficient seems to call for a K of 3.2. This is understandable, however, inasmuch as the theoretical curves were based on a constant-τ approximation. We have seen before that the particular form of $\tau(\varepsilon)$ can exert considerable influence on R_H/R_∞.

The early cyclotron resonance results suggested[293, 295] $m_\perp{}^*/m_0$ $= 0.19 \pm 0.01$, $m_\parallel{}^*/m^0 \simeq 0.98 \pm 0.04$ — giving a mass ratio K of 5.2. More recent experiments,[335a] using wavelengths of 2 mm, confirm the value of $m_\perp{}^*/m_0$ (namely, 0.192 ± 0.001) but yield a value of 0.90 ± 0.02 for $m_\parallel{}^*/m_0$, and therefore give a mass anisotropy ratio K_m of 4.7. No explanation could be given of the discrepancy.

Long and Myers[336] carried out determinations of K at various temperatures from 273° to 77°K on a number of specimens of n-type silicon of differing impurity contents using weak-field and saturation values of magnetoresistance. By extrapolating their data at 77°K to the limit of zero impurity content they estimated a value for K of 6.7 when the scattering is due to lattice vibrations. For a K_m of 4.7, this gives a value for the lattice scattering anisotropy of 0.7. The authors estimate that intervalley scattering — which is isotropic — makes up 15% of the total lattice scattering at 77°K, and the anisotropic ratio $K_\tau(\equiv \tau_\parallel/\tau_\perp)$ for intravalley scattering by acoustic modes is approximately 2/3. Their

[335a] C. Rauch, J. Stickler, H. Zeiger, and G. Heller, *Phys. Rev. Letters* **4**, 64 (1960).
[336] D. Long and J. Myers, *Phys. Rev.* **120**, 39 (1960).

data are not especially sensitive to the value of K_r for ionized impurity scattering, but the ratio definitely appears to be larger than unity. In fact it is suggested that the value of 4, as deduced by Ham[334], seems consistent with the measurements. The symmetry condition for [100] spheroids [see Eq. (23.24) and (23.28)], namely, $\Upsilon_{110}/[\Upsilon_{110}^{001} - \Upsilon_{110}^{\bar{1}10}] = 1$, is satisfied to within 10%. The authors suggest that the discrepancy here might be due to errors in the $\Upsilon_{110}^{\bar{1}10}$ coefficient inasmuch as this was measured with the magnetic field lying in the plane of the side-arms on the sample.

We have seen that the directional galvanomagnetic phenomena support the theoretical predictions of band structure, namely that in germanium the conduction band has minima along [111] axes in reciprocal lattice space and that in silicon the conduction minima are along the [100] directions. It is therefore of interest to examine the behavior of single crystal germanium-silicon alloys. This has been done by Glicksman[330], who finds that in the region 11.5–14% silicon, the magnetoresistance exhibits the changes in symmetry conditions to be expected for a competition of conduction in [111] and [100] minima. It is pointed out that if x is the mole fraction of silicon in the germanium, the findings of Johnson and Christian[337] on the optical band gap can be represented by

$$E_G = 0.72 + 1.5x \text{ ev}, \qquad 0 \leqslant x \leqslant 0.14 \qquad (23.29)$$

$$E_G = 0.89 + 0.31x \text{ ev}, \qquad 0.14 \leqslant x \leqslant 1. \qquad (23.30)$$

These findings are consistent with the suggestion of Herman[271] that in germanium, besides the lowest conduction minima, which have [111] symmetry, there are [100] minima about 0.17 ev above the [111] states. As silicon is added, both sets of minima move farther away from the valence band, and at different rates, as given respectively by Eqs. (23.29) and (23.30). Thus, in alloys of less than 14% silicon, conduction by the [111] minima predominates, but in alloy compositions containing more silicon the greater contribution is from the [100] minima. Subsequent investigations by Glicksman and Christian reveal that in the region 0 to 8% silicon the measured magnetoresistance data satisfy the symmetry conditions for [111]-type surfaces; in the region 20–100% silicon the

---

[337] E. R. Johnson and S. M. Christian, *Phys. Rev.* **95**, 560 (1954).

magnetoresistance is consistent with [100]-type surfaces; but that in the range 8–20% silicon, neither of the symmetry conditions is satisfied.[337a] The latter case is treated theoretically by Glicksman with a two-band model, using one set of [100] spheroids and another set oriented in the [111] directions in reciprocal lattice space.[337b]   Relationships among the magnetoresistance constants now involve the shape of the valleys, their energy separation, and the relaxation times.   A comparison of theory and experiment provides evidence to support the existence of additional scattering mechanisms, such as interband scattering and scattering from lattice disorder.[337b,c]

Another group of cubic semiconductors for which directional magneto-resistance coefficients have been measured comprises lead telluride, selenide, and sulfide.   In each case there is considerable anisotropy, with the longitudinal magnetoresistance often being substantially larger than the transverse.[338] Little difference seemed to exist between n- and p-type material.   By far the largest quantity of data is available for PbTe[338–343]. Several investigators conclude independently that in this compound the data favor [111] prolate spheroids for both conduction and valence band energy surfaces.   Anisotropy ratios, K, ranging from 3.3 to 6 were indicated, depending on temperature and other factors.[338, 342, 343]   More recent investigations tend to confirm the [111] spheroid structure, but also suggest that two-band conduction may occur, perhaps in both the conduction and the valence bands.[343a-d] In the case of PbS and PbSe, some recent data[342] indicate a substantial decrease in both the transverse and the longitudinal coefficients at room temperature from the values at 77° and 4.2°K.   This behavior is quite different from that observed

[337a] M. Glicksman and S. Christian, *Phys. Rev.* **104**, 1278 (1956).
[337b] M. Glicksman, *Phys. Rev.* **102**, 1496 (1956).
[337c] M. Glicksman, *Phys. Rev.* **111**, 125 (1958).
[338] R. S. Allgaier, *Phys. Rev.* **112**, 828 (1958).
[339] E. H. Putley, *Proc. Phys. Soc.* (*London*) **B68**, 22 (1955).
[340] K. Shogenji and S. Uchiyama, *J. Phys. Soc. Japan* **12**, 1164 (1957).
[341] K. Shogenji, *J. Phys. Soc. Japan* **14**, 1360, 1835 (1959).
[342] R. S. Allgaier, *Phys. Rev.* **119**, 554 (1960).
[343] M. Ellett, K. Cuff, and C. Kuglin, *Bull. Am. Phys. Soc.* **6**, 18 (1961).
[343a] P. Stiles, E. Burstein and D. Langenberg, *J. Appl. Phys.* **32**, 2174 (1961).
[343b] K. Cuff, M. Ellett, and C. Kuglin, *J. Appl. Phys.* **32**, 2179 (1961).
[343c] R. S. Allgaier, *J. Appl. Phys.* **32**, 2185 (1961).
[343d] R. H. Rediker and A. R. Calawa, *J. Appl. Phys.* **32**, 2189 (1961).

in the PbTe.   Piezoresistance studies of Ilisavskii[343e] yield results in agreement with a [111] spheroid structure for both the conduction and valence bands of PbTe.   In the case of PbSe, however, there is a reasonable possibility that the surfaces of constant energy are spheres.

(3) *System of ellipsoids possessing cubic symmetry.* We have previously discussed the cubically symmetric models where each valley was an ellipsoid of revolution (spheroid).   It was pointed out by Allgaier[344] that although cubic symmetry required the valleys in the [100] and [111] arrangements to be spheroids, this need not be so for the [110] model. The cubic symmetry is satisfied for a system of general ellipsoids with appropriate orientation of the principal axes — for example, the ellipsoid in the first quadrant of the $k_x k_y$-plane has axes along the [00$\bar{1}$], [1$\bar{1}$0], and [110] directions.   These directions correspond respectively to effective masses m_1^*, m_2^*, and m_3^*.   The coordinate directions are, of course, along the cube axes.

The procedure, as in the case of spheroids, is first to evaluate the components of the conductivity tensor for a single ellipsoid, with a coordinate system directed along the principal axes of the ellipsoid. The general expressions were presented before, namely, Eqs. (22.9) to (22.11). The nonzero components have been given by Allgaier, and are as follows[327a, 345]:

$$\sigma_{11}{}^0 = n^{(r)} e^2 \langle \tau \rangle / m_1^*, \qquad \sigma_{22}{}^0 = (1/L)\sigma_{11}{}^0, \qquad \sigma_{33}{}^0 = (1/K)\sigma_{11}{}^0 \qquad (23.31)$$

$$\sigma_{123}^0 = - \sigma_{213}^0 = \mp n^{(r)} [|e|^3/c] \langle \tau^2 \rangle / m_1^* m_2^* \qquad (23.32)$$

$$\sigma_{231}^0 = - \sigma_{321}^0 = (1/K)\sigma_{123}^0, \qquad \sigma_{312}^0 = - \sigma_{132}^0 = (L/K)\sigma_{123}^0 \qquad (23.33)$$

$$\sigma_{1122}^0 = - n^{(r)}(e^4/c^2)\langle \tau^3 \rangle / m_1^{*2} m_3^*, \qquad \sigma_{1133}^0 = (K/L)\sigma_{1122}^0 \qquad (23.34)$$

$$\sigma_{2233}^0 = (K/L^2)\sigma_{1122}^0, \qquad \sigma_{2211}^0 = (1/L^2)\sigma_{1122}^0 \qquad (23.35)$$

[343e] Yu. V. Ilisavskii, *Fiz. Tverd. Tela* **4**, 918 (1962) [translation: *Soviet Phys.-Solid State* **4**, 674 (1962)].

[344] R. S. Allgaier, *Phys. Rev.* **115**, 1185 (1959).

[345] The relation between certain quantities used by Allgaier and those here is $aFG_k = - n^{(r)} e^2 \langle \tau^k \rangle$, where the Boltzmann average is defined by Eq. (15.4). Another consideration is the factor of $\frac{1}{2}$ introduced into our σ_{ijlm}^0, which are symmetrical in indices l, m.

$$\sigma^0_{3311} = (1/KL)\sigma^0_{1122}, \qquad \sigma^0_{3322} = (1/K)\sigma^0_{1122} \tag{23.36}$$

$$\sigma^0_{1212} = \sigma^0_{2121} = \sigma^0_{1313} = \sigma^0_{3131} = \sigma^0_{2323} = \sigma^0_{3232} \tag{23.37}$$

$$= \sigma^0_{1221} = \sigma^0_{2112} = \sigma^0_{1331} = \sigma^0_{3113} = \sigma^0_{2332} = \sigma^0_{3223} = -(1/2L)\sigma^0_{1122}$$

where[346]

$$K = m_3{}^*/m_1{}^*, \qquad L = m_2{}^*/m_1{}^*. \tag{23.38}$$

The matrices of the transformations from coordinate systems coincident with each of the ellipsoid axes to one along the cube axes are given by Allgaier.[344] The result for the magnetoconductivity coefficients, after summations over the system of ellipsoids, is as follows:

$$\sigma^0_{ii} = ne^2 \frac{\langle \tau \rangle}{m_3{}^*} \left[\left(1 + K + \frac{K}{L} \right) \bigg/ 3 \right] \tag{23.39}$$

$$\sigma^0_{ijl} = \mp n \frac{|e^3|}{c} \frac{\langle \tau^2 \rangle}{m_3{}^{*2}} \left[K \left(1 + \frac{K}{L} + \frac{1}{L} \right) \bigg/ 3 \right] \varepsilon_{ijl} \tag{23.40}$$

$$\sigma^0_{iiii} = -n \frac{e^4}{c^2} \frac{\langle \tau^3 \rangle}{m_3{}^{*3}} \left[K \left(1 - \frac{K}{L} \right)^2 \bigg/ 6 \right] \tag{23.41}$$

$$\sigma^0_{iijj} = -n \frac{e^4}{c^2} \frac{\langle \tau^3 \rangle}{m_3{}^{*3}} \cdot \tag{23.42}$$

$$\left[K \left\{ \frac{1}{2} \left(1 + \frac{K^2}{L^2} \right) + K + \frac{1}{L} \left(1 + K + K^2 + \frac{K}{L} \right) \right\} \bigg/ 6 \right]$$

$$\sigma^0_{ijij} + \sigma^0_{ijji} = n \frac{e^4}{c^2} \frac{\langle \tau^3 \rangle}{m_3{}^{*3}} \left[K \left(1 + 4 \frac{K}{L} + \frac{K^2}{L^2} \right) \bigg/ 6 \right]. \tag{23.43}$$

In the above, we have chosen $m_3{}^*$ as reference mass, so that the anisotropic factors for the case when $m_2{}^* = m_1{}^*$, i.e., $L = 1$, reduce to the expressions given in Table VII.

In presenting the inverse Seitz magnetoresistance coefficients, Allgaier uses a dimensionless form obtained by removing the factor $(\mu_0{}^H/c)^2$. We designate these dimensionless parameters by b', c', d'. Thus

$$b' \equiv b \bigg/ \left[\frac{\mu_0{}^H}{c} \right]^2 \equiv b \bigg/ \left\{ \left(\frac{\mu_0{}^{(3)}}{c} \right)^2 \left(\frac{\langle \tau^2 \rangle}{\langle \tau \rangle^2} \frac{\xi_{123}(K, L)}{\xi_{11}(K, L)} \right)^2 \right\} \tag{23.44}$$

---

[346] The quantity L used in this section is not to be confused with the function $L(X)$ defined in Eq. (15.85).

where our reference mobility $\mu_0^{(3)}$ $[\equiv |e|\langle\tau\rangle/m_3^*]$ is the valley mobility in the direction of the ellipsoidal axis 3. This convention affects only our definition of the anisotropy parameters K and L in the functions $\xi(K, L)$, which are given by the factors in the brackets in each of Eqs. (23.39) to (23.43) [including the negative sign for the σ_{iiii}^0 and the σ_{iijj}^0]. It obviously will not affect the overall expressions for the conductivity and magnetoresistance coefficients. The results can be put into the form

$$b' = \frac{\langle\tau^3\rangle\langle\tau\rangle}{\langle\tau^2\rangle^2} \frac{(K + L + LK)}{2KL(K + L + 1)^2}. \tag{23.45}$$

$$[6KL + L(K - 1)^2 + K(L - 1)^2 + \tfrac{1}{2}(K - L)^2] - 1$$

$$c' = -\frac{\langle\tau^3\rangle\langle\tau\rangle}{\langle\tau^2\rangle^2} \frac{(K + L + LK)}{2KL(K + L + 1)^2} [6KL + (K - L)^2] + 1 \tag{23.46}$$

$$d' = -\frac{\langle\tau^3\rangle\langle\tau\rangle}{\langle\tau^2\rangle^2} \frac{(K + L + LK)}{2KL(K + L + 1)^2} [L(K - 1)^2 + K(L - 1)^2 - \tfrac{3}{2}(K - L)^2]. \tag{23.47}$$

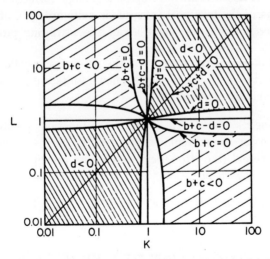

FIG. 41. Relations among the weak-field magnetoresistance coefficients as a function of the mass ratios $K(\equiv m_3^*/m_1^*)$ and $L(\equiv m_2^*/m_1^*)$. The quantity $b + c$ is negative only in the lightly shaded regions, and d is negative only in the more darkly shaded regions (after Allgaier[344]).

The symmetry conditions relating b, c, and d for the ellipsoid model are quite varied. These are discussed in some detail by Allgaier. For $L = 1$, and also for $K = 1$, the model reduces to the [110] spheroid model. Also, for $K = L$ it can be seen that the arrangement is equivalent to the [100] spheroid. A number of other interesting conditions on b, c, and d result from special relations between K and L. These are illustrated in Fig. 41, which is a logarithmic plot in the KL-plane of the loci of a number of special symmetry relations. Several distinct regions are outlined, namely, where $b + c < 0$ [which does not occur for any spheroid model], and where $d < 0$. Other features of interest are the lines along which $b + c = 0$ and $d = 0$. The latter situation implies that the magneto-resistance depends only on $\mathbf{J} \cdot \mathbf{H}$ and not on the orientation of these vectors with respect to the crystal axes, as is apparent from the first of relations (23.17).

b. Arbitrary Magnetic Field Strengths

In principle, the components of the conductivity tensor $\sigma_{ij}(H)$ can be expressed in closed form for ellipsoidal energy surfaces. In practice, the evaluation of the transport integrals is quite arduous, unless various simplifying assumptions are made about the scattering process.

(1) Constant mean free path. For the case of a constant mean free path, that is, $\tau \sim \varepsilon^{-1/2}$ scattering, explicit results are given by Abeles-Meiboom[157] and by Shibuya.[154]

Case of single ellipsoid. To illustrate the functions involved, we give the expression for the current density $\mathbf{J}(\mathbf{E}, \mathbf{H})$ when the energy surface is a single spheroid (the rth valley), having its principal axes along the coordinate axes, with $m_3^* = m_\parallel^*$ and $m_1^* = m_2^* = m_\perp^*$:

$$J_i^{(r)} = \sigma_{ij}^{(r)}(\mathbf{H})E_j = n^{(r)}|e|(\mathbf{\mu E})_i^{(r)}, \qquad i = 1, 2, 3 \qquad (23.48)$$

where

$$(\mathbf{\mu E})_1^{(r)} = K\mu_0^l \bar{K}(X)E_1 \mp \frac{3\pi}{8c}(\mu_0^l)^2 L(X)K[KE_2 H_3 - E_3 H_2] + \qquad (23.49)$$

$$\frac{9\pi}{16c^2}(\mu_0^l)^3 K^2 Q(X)\mathbf{E} \cdot \mathbf{H}H_1$$

$$(\boldsymbol{\mu}\mathbf{E})_2{}^{(r)} = K\mu_0{}^l \bar{K}(X)E_2 \mp \frac{3\pi}{8c} (\mu_0)^2 L(X)K[E_3 H_1 - KE_1 H_3] + \qquad (23.50)$$

$$\frac{9\pi}{16c^2} (\mu_0{}^l)^3 K^2 Q(X)\mathbf{E}\cdot\mathbf{H}H_2$$

$$(\boldsymbol{\mu}\mathbf{E})_3{}^{(r)} = \mu_0{}^l \bar{K}(X)E_3 \mp \frac{3\pi}{8c} (\mu_0{}^l)^2 L(X)K[E_1 H_2 - E_2 H_1] + \qquad (23.51)$$

$$\frac{9\pi}{16c^2} (\mu_0{}^l)^3 K^2 Q(X)\mathbf{E}\cdot\mathbf{H}H_3$$

where the functions[347] $\bar{K}(X)$ and $L(X)$ are defined in Eq. (15.85) and where

$$Q(X) \equiv X^{-1}[1 - \bar{K}(X)], \qquad (23.52)$$

$$X = \frac{9\pi}{16c^2} (\mu_0{}^l)^2 K[H_1{}^2 + H_2{}^2 + KH_3{}^2]. \qquad (23.53)$$

The anisotropy parameter $K[\equiv m_\parallel{}^*/m_\perp{}^*]$ may be generalized to include anisotropic relaxation times, as indicated in Eq. (23.16). The longitudinal valley mobility, $\mu_0{}^l$, is defined in Table V, and the numerical constants in (23.49) to (23.52) are valid for $\tau \sim \varepsilon^{-1/2}$ scattering. In the Hall terms the $-$ sign is for electron conduction, the $+$ sign for hole conduction.

Case of cubically symmetric arrangement of spheroids: By carrying out appropriate transformations of the above quantities, expressions for cubically symmetric arrangements of spheroids can be obtained. This was done by Abeles-Meiboom and by Shibuya for coordinate axes coincident with the cube axes. The equations are rather cumbersome and will not be presented here. Instead we shall specialize their general relationships for cases where currents and magnetic fields lie in simple crystallographic directions. In particular when $\mathbf{H} \equiv (H_1, H_2, 0)$, the components of the conductivity tensor reduce to:

---

[347] We are using the barred expression $\bar{K}(X)$ in this section to avoid confusion of the function $K(X)$ of (15.85) with the mass anisotropy parameter $K[\equiv m_\parallel{}^*/m_\perp{}^*]$.

[100] *spheroids*, $\mathbf{H} \equiv (H_1, H_2, 0)$:

$$\sigma_{11}(\mathbf{H}) = \tfrac{1}{3}n|e\mu_0{}^l|\left\{[\bar{K}(X_1) + K\bar{K}(X_2) + K\bar{K}(X_3)] + \right.$$

$$(9\pi/16c^2)(\mu_0{}^l)^2 K^2 H_1{}^2 \sum_i Q(X_i)\Big\}$$

$$\sigma_{12}(\mathbf{H}) = \tfrac{1}{3}n|e\mu_0{}^l|(9\pi/16c^2)(\mu_0{}^l)^2 K^2 H_1 H_2 \sum_i Q(X_i)$$

$$\sigma_{22}(\mathbf{H}) = \tfrac{1}{3}n|e\mu_0{}^l|\left\{[K\bar{K}(X_1) + \bar{K}(X_2) + K\bar{K}(X_3)] + \right. \qquad (23.54)$$

$$(9\pi/16c^2)(\mu_0{}^l)^2 K^2 H_2{}^2 \sum_i Q(X_i)\Big\}$$

$$\sigma_{23}(\mathbf{H}) = \mp \tfrac{1}{3}n|e\mu_0{}^l|(3\pi/8c)|\mu_0{}^l|KH_1[KL(X_1) + L(X_2) + L(X_3)]$$

$$\text{—, electrons; +, holes}$$

$$\sigma_{33}(\mathbf{H}) = \tfrac{1}{3}n|e\mu_0{}^l|[K\bar{K}(X_1) + K\bar{K}(X_2) + \bar{K}(X_3)]$$

$$\sigma_{31}(\mathbf{H}) = \mp \tfrac{1}{3}n|e\mu_0{}^l|(3\pi/8c)|\mu_0{}^l|KH_2[L(X_1) + KL(X_2) + L(X_3)]$$

$$\sigma_{ij}(\mathbf{H}) = \sigma_{ji}(-\mathbf{H})$$

$$X_1 = (9\pi/16c^2)(\mu_0{}^l)^2 K[KH_1{}^2 + H_2{}^2]$$

$$X_2 = (9\pi/16c^2)(\mu_0{}^l)^2 K[H_1{}^2 + KH_2{}^2]$$

$$X_3 = (9\pi/16c^2)(\mu_0{}^l)^2 K[H_1{}^2 + H_2{}^2].$$

[111] *spheroids*, $\mathbf{H} \equiv (H_1, H_2, 0)$:

$$\sigma_{11}(\mathbf{H}) = n|e\mu_0{}^l|\{\{\tfrac{1}{6}[2K + 1][\bar{K}(X_+) + \bar{K}(X_-)] + $$

$$\tfrac{1}{2}[9\pi/16c^2](\mu_0{}^l)^2 K^2 H_1{}^2 [Q(X_+) + Q(X_-)]\}$$

$$\sigma_{22}(\mathbf{H}) = n|e\mu_0{}^l|\{\{\tfrac{1}{6}[2K + 1][\bar{K}(X_+) + \bar{K}(X_-)] + $$

$$\tfrac{1}{2}[9\pi/16c^2](\mu_0{}^l)^2 K^2 H_2{}^2 [Q(X_+) + Q(X_-)]\}$$

$$\sigma_{33}(\mathbf{H}) = n|e\mu_0{}^l|\{\{\tfrac{1}{6}[2K + 1][\bar{K}(X_+) + \bar{K}(X_-)]\}$$

$$\sigma_{12}(\mathbf{H}) = n|e\mu_0^l|\{ -\tfrac{1}{6}[K-1][\bar{K}(X_+) - \bar{K}(X_-)] +$$
$$\tfrac{1}{2}[9\pi/16c^2](\mu_0^l)^2 K^2 H_1 H_2 [Q(X_+) + Q(X_-)]\}$$

$$\sigma_{23}(\mathbf{H}) = \mp \tfrac{1}{6}n|e\mu_0^l|(3\pi/8c)|\mu_0^l|K\{[(K-1)H_2 +$$
$$(K+2)H_1]L(X_+) - [(K-1)H_2 - (K+2)H_1]L(X_-)\}$$

$$\sigma_{31}(\mathbf{H}) = \mp \tfrac{1}{6}n|e\mu_0^l|(3\pi/8c)|\mu_0^l|K\{[(K-1)H_1 + (K+2)H_2]L(X_+) -$$
$$[(K-1)H_1 - (K+2)H_2]L(X_-)\}$$

$$\sigma_{ij}(\mathbf{H}) = \sigma_{ji}(-\mathbf{H}) \qquad\qquad (23.55)$$

$$X_\pm = (3\pi/16c^2)(\mu_0^l)^2 K[(K+2)(H_1^2 + H_2^2) \pm 2(K-1)H_1 H_2].$$

In the above relationships, K is the ratio of longitudinal and transverse masses in the energy spheroid [see Table V, also Eq. (23.16)], the functions[347] $\bar{K}(x)$ and $L(x)$ are defined by (15.85), and $Q(x)$ by (23.52). Again, the numerical constants are supplied for $\tau \sim \varepsilon^{-1/2}$ scattering. The $\mp$ signs introducing the expressions for σ_{23} and σ_{31} refer, respectively, to conduction by electrons and by holes. An examination of Eqs. (23.54) and (23.55) reveals that for the less highly symmetric directions of $\mathbf{H}$, off-diagonal components of the conductivity tensor may include terms which are even in H. Thus to determine the Hall coefficient, it may be necessary to average measurements over both directions of H to eliminate the symmetric terms in the off-diagonal components of the resistivity tensor. This point will be illustrated subsequently by an explicit expression for $R_{111}^{1\bar{1}0}(H)$ [see Eq. (23.79)].

The expressions given in (23.54) and (23.55) are sufficiently general to allow us to evaluate transport coefficients when the magnetic field is along a cube axis or in $[1\bar{1}0]$ or $[110]$ directions, thus

$$H[100]: \qquad H_1 = H, H_2 = 0$$

$$H[010]: \qquad H_1 = 0, H_2 = H$$

$$H[1\bar{1}0]: \qquad H_1 = H/\sqrt{2}, H_2 = -H/\sqrt{2} \qquad (23.56)$$

$$H[110]: \qquad H_1 = H_2 = H/\sqrt{2}.$$

In these cases the conductivity tensors assume the following forms:

$$\boldsymbol{\sigma}(H, 0, 0) = \begin{pmatrix} \sigma_{11} & 0 & 0 \\ 0 & \sigma_{22} & \sigma_{23} \\ 0 & -\sigma_{23} & \sigma_{22} \end{pmatrix} \quad \text{where } \sigma_{ij} \equiv \sigma_{ij}(H, 0, 0),$$

$$(23.57)$$

$$\boldsymbol{\sigma}(0, H, 0) = \begin{pmatrix} \sigma_{11} & 0 & -\sigma_{31} \\ 0 & \sigma_{22} & 0 \\ \sigma_{31} & 0 & \sigma_{11} \end{pmatrix} \quad \text{where } \sigma_{ij} \equiv \sigma_{ij}(0, H, 0),$$

$$(23.58)$$

$$\boldsymbol{\sigma}\left(\frac{H}{\sqrt{2}}, \frac{-H}{\sqrt{2}}, 0\right) = \begin{pmatrix} \sigma_{11} & \sigma_{12} & \sigma_{23} \\ \sigma_{12} & \sigma_{11} & \sigma_{23} \\ -\sigma_{23} & -\sigma_{23} & \sigma_{33} \end{pmatrix} \quad \text{where } \sigma_{ij} \equiv \sigma_{ij}\left(\frac{H}{\sqrt{2}}, \frac{-H}{\sqrt{2}}, 0\right),$$

$$(23.59)$$

$$\boldsymbol{\sigma}\left(\frac{H}{\sqrt{2}}, \frac{H}{\sqrt{2}}, 0\right) = \begin{pmatrix} \sigma_{11} & \sigma_{12} & -\sigma_{23} \\ \sigma_{12} & \sigma_{11} & \sigma_{23} \\ \sigma_{23} & -\sigma_{23} & \sigma_{33} \end{pmatrix} \quad \text{where } \sigma_{ij} \equiv \sigma_{ij}\left(\frac{H}{\sqrt{2}}, \frac{H}{\sqrt{2}}, 0\right).$$

$$(23.60)$$

The directional Hall coefficients and magnetoresistances [see Eqs. (11.18) and (11.1)] which are associated with the above tensors are as follows:

$$R_{100}^{010}(H) = \frac{\sigma_{31}}{H[\sigma_{11}{}^2 + \sigma_{31}{}^2]} = R_{101}^{010}(H), \tag{23.61}$$

$$R_{110}^{1\bar{1}0}(H) = \frac{\sqrt{2}\,\sigma_{23}}{H[\sigma_{33}(\sigma_{11} + \sigma_{12}) + 2\sigma_{23}{}^2]},$$

$$M_{100}(H) = \frac{\sigma_{11}(0)}{\sigma_{11}} - 1, \quad M_{110}(H) = \frac{\sigma_{11}(0)}{\sigma_{11} + \sigma_{12}} - 1, \tag{23.62}$$

$$M_{100}^{010}(H) = \frac{\sigma_{11}\,\sigma_{11}(0)}{\sigma_{11}{}^2 + \sigma_{31}{}^2} - 1 = M_{101}^{010}\,(H), \tag{23.63}$$

$$M_{110}^{1\bar{1}0}(H) = \frac{\sigma_{33}\,\sigma_{11}(0)}{\sigma_{33}(\sigma_{11} + \sigma_{12}) + 2\,\sigma_{23}{}^2} - 1. \tag{23.64}$$

Explicit values of the above coefficients for the two popular models can be obtained through use of relations (23.54) and (23.55). The results, for $\tau \sim \varepsilon^{-1/2}$ scattering, are:

[100] *type spheroids:*

$$R_{100}^{010}(H) = \mp \frac{3\pi}{8} \frac{1}{n|e|c} \times \tag{23.65}$$

$$\frac{3K\,[2L(X_1) + KL(X_2)]}{[(1 + K)\bar{K}(X_1) + K\bar{K}(X_2)]^2 + (3\pi/8c)^2(\mu_0{}^l H)^2\,K^2\,[2L(X_1) + KL(X_2)]^2}\,,$$

$$R_{110}^{1\bar{1}0}(H) = \mp \frac{3\pi}{8} \frac{1}{n|e|c} \times \tag{23.66}$$

$$\frac{3K\,[(K + 1)L(\bar{X}_1) + L(\bar{X}_3)]}{[2K\bar{K}(\bar{X}_1) + \bar{K}(\bar{X}_3)][(K + 1)\bar{K}(\bar{X}_1) + K\bar{K}(\bar{X}_3)] + (3\pi/8c)^2(\mu_0{}^l H)^2 \cdot}$$
$$K^2[(K + 1)L(\bar{X}_1) + L(\bar{X}_3)]^2$$

where $-$ is for electrons and $+$ is for holes.

The magnetoresistances are

$$M_{100}(H) = 0, \tag{23.67}$$

$$M_{110}(H) = \{(2K + 1)(K + 1)/[K^2 + 5K + (K - 1)^2\,\bar{K}(\bar{X}_1)]\} - 1,$$

$$M_{100}^{010}(H) = \tag{23.68}$$

$$\frac{(2K + 1)\,[(K + 1)\bar{K}(X_1) + K\bar{K}(X_2)]}{[(K + 1)\bar{K}(X_1) + K\bar{K}(X_2)]^2 + (3\pi/8c)^2(\mu_0{}^l H)^2\,K^2\,[2L(X_1) + KL(X_2)]^2} - 1,$$

$$M_{110}^{1\bar{1}0}(H) = \tag{23.69}$$

$$\frac{(2K + 1)\,[2K\bar{K}(\bar{X}_1) + \bar{K}(\bar{X}_3)]}{[2K\bar{K}(\bar{X}_1) + \bar{K}(\bar{X}_3)][(K + 1)\bar{K}(\bar{X}_1) + K\bar{K}(\bar{X}_3)] + (3\pi/8c)^2\,(\mu_0{}^l H)^2 \cdot} - 1.$$
$$K^2[(K + 1)L(\bar{X}_1) + L(\bar{X}_3)]^2$$

The arguments of the functions $\bar{K}(x)$ and $L(x)$ in the above expressions are given by

$$X_1 = (9\pi/16c^2)(\mu_0{}^l H)^2 K, \qquad X_2 = KX_1 \qquad (23.70)$$

$$\bar{X}_3 = (9\pi/16c^2)(\mu_0{}^l H)^2 K, \qquad \bar{X}_1 = \tfrac{1}{2}(K+1)\bar{X}_3$$

[111] *type spheroids:*

$$R_{100}^{010}(H) = \mp \frac{3\pi}{8} \frac{1}{n|e|c} \times \qquad\qquad (23.71)$$

$$\frac{3K(K+2)L(X)}{[(2K+1)\bar{K}(X)]^2 + (3\pi/8c)^2(\mu_0{}^l H)^2[K(K+2)L(X)]^2},$$

$$R_{110}^{1\bar{1}0}(H) = \mp \frac{3\pi}{8} \frac{1}{n|e|c} \times$$

$$\frac{6K[3L(X_+) + (2K+1)L(X_-)]}{(2K+1)[\bar{K}(X_+) + \bar{K}(X_-)][(K+2)\bar{K}(X_+)\,3K\bar{K}(X_-)] +}$$

$$\qquad (3\pi/8c)^2(\mu_0{}^l H)^2 K^2\,[3L(X_+) + (2K+1)L(X_-)]^2$$

$$(23.72)$$

where $-$ is for electron conduction, $+$ for hole conduction;

$$M_{100}(H) = \frac{(2K+1)(K+2)}{9K + 2(K-1)^2\,\bar{K}(X)} - 1, \qquad (23.73)$$

$$M_{110}(H) = \frac{(2K+1)^2}{3K^2 + 6K + (K-1)^2\,\bar{K}(X^+)} - 1, \qquad (23.74)$$

$$M_{100}^{010}(H) = \frac{(2K+1)^2\,\bar{K}(X)}{[(2K+1)\bar{K}(X)]^2 + (3\pi/8c)^2(\mu_0{}^l H)^2\,[K(K+2)L(X)]^2} - 1,$$

$$(23.75)$$

$$M_{110}^{1\bar{1}0}(H) = \qquad\qquad (23.76)$$

$$\frac{2(2K+1)^2[\bar{K}(X_+) + \bar{K}(X_-)]}{(2K+1)[\bar{K}(X_+) + \bar{K}(X_-)][(K+2)\bar{K}(X_+) + 3K\bar{K}(X_-)] +} - 1.$$

$$\qquad (3\pi/8c)^2\,(\mu_0{}^l H)^2\,K^2[3L(X_+) + (2K+1)L(X_-)]^2$$

In the above relations, the arguments of the functions $\bar{K}(x)$ and $L(x)$ are given by

$$X = (3\pi/16c^2)(\mu_0{}^l H)^2 K(K + 2)$$

$$X_+ = (3\pi/16c^2)(\mu_0{}^l H)^2 (3K)$$

$$X_- = X^+ = (3\pi/16c^2)(\mu_0{}^l H)^2 K(2K + 1). \qquad (23.77)$$

Throughout this section, we have chosen to express results in terms of the longitudinal mobility of one of the spheroidal energy surfaces. This quantity is readily expressed in terms of parameters representative of the cubic crystal through the use of isotropic properties such as conductivity and weak-field Hall coefficient [see Eq. (23.20)].

The preceding relationships, which are exact in the magnetic field strength H, are laborious to evaluate numerically. They simplify greatly in the weak-field case — to yield expressions (23.18) to (23.27) — and also for the strong field saturation. In the latter situation, the limit as $H \to \infty$

TABLE IX. SATURATION VALUES OF MAGNETORESISTANCE[a]

Coefficient	Limiting values as $H \to \infty$	
	[100] spheroids	[111] spheroids
M_{100}	0	$\dfrac{2(K-1)^2}{9K}$
M_{110}	$\dfrac{(K-1)^2}{K(K+5)}$	$\dfrac{(K-1)^2}{3K(K+2)}$
M_{100}^{010}	$\dfrac{32}{9\pi}\dfrac{(2K+1)(K+2)}{9K} - 1$	$\dfrac{32}{9\pi}\dfrac{(2K+1)^2}{3\,K(K+2)} - 1$
$M_{110}^{1\bar{1}0}$	$\dfrac{32}{9\pi}\dfrac{(5K+1)(2K+1)}{9K(K+1)} - 1$	$\dfrac{32}{9\pi}\dfrac{(2K+1)(K+2)}{9K} - 1$

[a] The numerical constants in the expressions for the transverse magnetoresistances are for $\tau \sim \varepsilon^{-1/2}$ scattering. The strong field limiting values of the Hall coefficients are, of course, $(nec)^{-1}$.

can be evaluated through the use of the asymptotic expansions for $K(x)$ and $L(x)$ as given in Eqs. (15.87). The results are summarized in Table IX.

Additional coefficients have been tabulated by Shibuya,[154] including results for the [110] spheroid model.

Several points are noteworthy about the strong field limits, namely: (1) The Hall coefficient is $(nec)^{-1}$ and does not depend on $\tau(\varepsilon)$ or on the particular model approximating the band structure. This relationship is actually of more general applicability than is implied here [see Section 12b]. (2) The magnetoresistances are independent of the Hall mobility. (3) In addition, the longitudinal magnetoresistance is independent of the scattering, that is, of the dependence of the relaxation time on energy, and therefore provides a direct indication of the band structure.

On the basis of these findings, it would appear to be of distinct advantage to carry out measurements at the strong magnetic field limit, where possible. This procedure calls, however, for great care. Even the slightest perturbation of the Hall field, whether by shorting contacts, multiband conduction, or by nonuniformities in the specimen, can significantly alter the saturation of the magnetoresistance. Some of these considerations were discussed in Section 9b, and a further account is given in Section 27. An additional factor at low temperatures is the possibility of quantum effects (Section 28).

The Hall coefficients and magnetoresistances discussed thus far in this section have been evaluated for currents and magnetic field orientations of fairly high symmetry, so as to reduce the complexity of the expressions. It is of interest to examine the result for an arrangement of lower symmetry. In particular we shall evaluate the Hall coefficient $R_{111}^{1\bar{1}0}(H)$, say, for the [111] type spheroid model. From (11.18) and (23.59) we obtain

$$R_{111}^{1\bar{1}0}(H) = \frac{\sqrt{2}}{3H} \left[\frac{\sigma_{11} + \sigma_{12} - \sigma_{33} + 3\sigma_{23}}{\sigma_{33}(\sigma_{11} + \sigma_{12}) + 2\sigma_{23}{}^2} \right]^a, \qquad (23.78)$$

where the superscript on the bracket indicates the antisymmetric part, that is, the part which is odd in H [cf. Eq. (11.12)]. Now from (23.55) or (23.54) it is seen that the denominator is symmetric with respect to the sign of H, and that the σ_{23} in the numerator is odd in H. This was precisely the state of affairs in the case of the Hall coefficients given in (23.61), so that the transverse voltage consisted there of a pure

Hall voltage and in theory it was not necessary to obtain differences for reversed magnetic field in order to eliminate unwanted galvanomagnetic voltages.[348] In the $R_{111}^{1\bar{1}0}(H)$ coefficient shown above, however, we see that the numerator contains a nonvanishing part, $\sigma_{11} + \sigma_{12} - \sigma_{33}$, which is even in H. Therefore, to determine the Hall coefficient as defined in Section 11b, we must take the difference for reversed directions of the magnetic field.

By using equations (23.55) we obtain an explicit expression for (23.78) for the case of [111] type spheroids. The result is

$$R_{111}^{1\bar{1}0}(H) = \frac{3\pi}{8}\frac{1}{n|e|c}\frac{1}{\mu_0{}^l H} \times \tag{23.79}$$

$$\frac{\{-\sqrt{2}(16c/3\pi)(K-1)[\bar{K}(X_+) - \bar{K}(X_-)] \mp}{\phantom{(2K+1)[\bar{K}(X_+) + \bar{K}(X_-)]}}$$

$$\frac{6\mu_0{}^l HK[3L(X_+) + (2K+1)L(X_-)]\}^a}{(2K+1)[\bar{K}(X_+) + \bar{K}(X_-)][(K+2)\bar{K}(X_+) + 3K\bar{K}(X_-)] +}$$

$$(3\pi/8c)^2(\mu_0{}^l H)^2 K^2[3L(X_+) + (2K+1)L(X_-)]^2$$

where the $-$ sign is for electron conduction and the $+$ sign for hole conduction. In the above expression, the first term in the numerator is even in H and starts out as H^2. It is therefore negligible at sufficiently weak magnetic fields, but can become substantial at intermediate field strengths, as was seen in Fig. 9.[349] When one takes the difference of the transverse electric fields for opposite directions of H — corresponding to the choice of the antisymmetric part of the numerators — the term is removed and one obtains an expression for $R_{111}^{1\bar{1}0}(H)$ which is identical with that for $R_{110}^{1\bar{1}0}(H)$, as given in Eq. (23.72).

(2) *Scattering processes other than* $\tau \sim \varepsilon^{-1/2}$. If the relaxation time for scattering by ionized impurities is assumed to be isotropic on a surface of constant energy — a situation known from the evidence presented in Sections 22b and 23a not to be true, so that the procedure to be outlined

---

[348] This statement, of course, has nothing to do with the reasons for reversing H in Hall measurements in order to get rid of various other spurious effects [see Section 9b].

[349] From the manner in which the symmetric and antisymmetric terms combine, it is apparent that the plot in Fig. 9 refers to $R_{111}^{\bar{1}10}(H)$ rather than the $R_{111}^{1\bar{1}0}(H)$ of Eq. (25.79).

can be applied only in the case of relatively small amounts of impurity scattering — then one can account for the admixture of a small percentage of scattering by ionized impurities to that due to $\tau \sim \varepsilon^{-1/2}$ processes by the expedient of introducing the functions $\bar{K}(\beta, X)$ and $L(\beta, X)$ as was done in Section 15c(2) for the case of isotropic conduction. This procedure increases the arithmetical labor, even though the functions $\bar{K}(\beta, X)$ and $L(\beta, X)$ are tabulated; and, in addition, the effect of the slowly varying term in the Brooks-Herring expression for τ_I is not taken into account. The presence of a magnetic field of arbitrary intensity complicates the dealing with this term by the method of Mansfield (Section 13b). Nevertheless, the admixture of a small amount of impurity scattering into the theory, even if rather superficially treated, is probably a good thing since it provides a cutoff on τ for the low energy carriers. One can, of course, introduce arbitrary cutoffs as has been done by several investigators.[156, 329]

In doing galvanomagnetic measurements on semiconductors, one is usually interested in getting the most information out of a single specimen. This invariably involves the taking of data for the different directions of **H**, as the magnetic field vector is rotated in various planes. It is of interest therefore to have expressions for Hall coefficient and magnetoresistance as a function of the angle which the field makes with a fixed crystallographic direction. A number of such calculations have been carried out for [100] and [111] spheroidal models, representative of silicon and germanium, respectively. In many cases the constant-τ approximation was used. Although such treatment cannot be considered physically realistic, it has the advantage of reducing somewhat the complexity of the arithmetical calculations, while still preserving many of the features resulting from the anisotropy of the energy surfaces. Explicit results for several high-symmetry directions of the current may be found, for example, in the articles by Gold and Roth[155, 158] Bullis,[156, 161] and Krag.[163]

Broudy and Venables[159] discuss a technique for the experimental determination of the components of the resistivity tensor $\rho_{ik}(\mathbf{H})$. In the general case, three samples are required with **J** being in the x-, y-, and z-directions respectively. By means of this arrangement one can determine all nine components of the resistivity tensor for a given orientation of **H** with respect to the crystal lattice. Since $\boldsymbol{\rho}(\mathbf{H})$ contains only six independent terms, there is a desirable redundancy which can be used to check homogeneity of the specimens. In a cubic crystal, the coordinate axes are chosen coincident with the cube axes, so that the three current directions are equivalent, and only one sample is required. In this case, Broudy and Venables rotate $\mathbf{H}$ in a (100) plane, obtaining values of $\rho_{ik}(\phi)$, where ϕ is the angle between the [001] direction and $\mathbf{H}$. The $\boldsymbol{\rho}(\phi)$ are then inverted to yield the conductivity tensor $\boldsymbol{\sigma}(\phi)$. Explicit theoretical expressions are developed for $\boldsymbol{\sigma}(\phi)$ for the three common cubically symmetric arrangements of the spheroids. Results are valid for an energy-dependent relaxation time $\tau(\varepsilon)$, and can be extended to the case of anisotropic relaxation times as long as τ has the symmetry of m^*, in the manner indicated by relation (23.16).

The angular dependence of the $\sigma_{ik}(\phi)$ allows one to distinguish between the various spheroidal arrangements. For example, [100] type spheroidal energy surfaces yield maxima in $\sigma_{11}(\phi)$ at $\sin 2\phi = 0$, i.e., at $\phi = 0, \pi/2, \pi, \ldots$ and minima at $\phi = \pi/4, 3\pi/4, \ldots$; the [111] type arrangement has maxima at $\phi = \pi/4, 3\pi/4, \ldots$ and minima at $\phi = 0$, $\pi/2, \pi$, etc. In the case of [110] type spheroids, the maxima and minima are more complicated. Excellent verification of these predictions was found in the data on n-type silicon and n-type germanium taken at 80°K and at fields of 7720 gauss.[159]

The symmetry conditions enunciated above are not affected by the particular form of $\tau(\varepsilon)$ or by the magnitude of the magnetic field. The same statement applies to the following expressions which can be used to determine K:

[100] type spheroids:

$$\frac{K-1}{2K(K+2)} = \left[\frac{\sigma_{11}{}^0 - (\sigma_{22} + \sigma_{23})}{K(\sigma_{11}{}^0 - \sigma_{11}) - 2\,\sigma_{23}} \right]_{\phi\,=\,\pi/4} \tag{23.80}$$

[111] type spheroids:

$$\frac{9K}{(K+2)(2K+1)} = \left[\frac{\sigma_{22} - \sigma_{11}}{\sigma_{11}{}^0 - \sigma_{11}} \right]_{\phi\,=\,\pi/2} \tag{23.81}$$

where $\sigma_{11}^0 \equiv [\sigma_{11}]_{H\,=\,0}$. The geometrical arrangement of currents and magnetic fields implied in the above relationships is included in Eqs. (23.54) and (23.55) if each subscript in (23.80) and (23.81) is cyclically permuted twice; and the relationships can of course be established from those equations.

By using (23.81) and (23.80), Broudy and Venables have determined K for germanium and silicon.[159] For germanium they obtain 19.5 for $150°\text{K} < T < 210°\text{K}$, and 15.5 at $80°\text{K}$. The result for silicon is 5.2 at $80°\text{K}$. Experiments, using pulsed magnetic fields up to 600 kgauss, were done by Furth and Waniek,[350] who determined strong-field saturation longitudinal magnetoresistances in germanium. Their data yield a value of K of 17.2 for the conduction band of germanium at room temperature.

Recently, a series of careful measurements of the strong-field longitudinal magnetoresistance of n-type silicon was reported by Neuringer and Little.[350a] Data were taken at $78°\text{K}$ in d–c magnetic fields up to 90 kgauss. A variety of samples was used, so that the resistance could be measured for **H** lying along the [100], [110], or [111] type directions. Donor concentrations ranged from 10^{14} to 10^{16} cm^{-3}, and both float-zone and Czochralski-pulled crystals were used. Especial care was taken to guard against erroneous results which could arise from inhomogeneities in specimen or in magnetic field, from perturbation of Hall field by contacts, or from other "geometrical" effects. The data yielded values of the anisotropy parameter K at $78°\text{K}$ ranging from 6.0 to 3.9 for donor concentrations ranging from 1.3×10^{14} to 1.3×10^{16} cm^{-3}. The data revealed an anomalous size effect, occurring in fields above 40 kgauss.

c. Noncubic Crystals

A number of the investigations of galvanomagnetic effects in noncubic crystals reported on in the literature are concerned with semimetals or metals. The case of bismuth was examined by Abeles and Meiboom,[85] who applied ellipsoidal models to the conduction and valence bands. Results are given for arbitrary magnetic field strengths, using the constant-τ approximation. This assumption is considered adequate at low temperatures where charge-carrier degeneracy is significant, and it simplifies calculations of the magnetic-field dependence. The conductivity

---

[350] H. P. Furth and R. W. Waniek, *Phys. Rev.* **104**, 343 (1956).
[350a] L. J. Neuringer and W. J. Little, *in* "Proc. of the Intern. Conf. on the Physics of Semiconductors, Exeter, July, 1962," p. 614. The Institute of Physics and the Physical Society, London, 1962.

coefficients for a single ellipsoid, with principal axes along the coordinate directions, can be expressed for the constant-τ case as follows:

$$\sigma_{11}^{(r)}(\mathbf{H}) = n^{(r)} e \mu_1 [1 + (\mu_2 \mu_3 H_1{}^2/c^2)]/F, \qquad (23.82)$$

$$\sigma_{12}^{(r)}(\mathbf{H}) = \mp n^{(r)} e \mu_1 \mu_2 [(H_3/c) \mp (\mu_3 H_1 H_2/c^2)]/F, \qquad (23.83)$$

$$F \equiv 1 + (\mu_2 \mu_3 H_1{}^2 + \mu_3 \mu_1 H_2{}^2 + \mu_1 \mu_2 H_3{}^2)/c^2. \qquad (23.84)$$

The other components of $\sigma_{ik}^{(r)}$ are obtained by cyclic permutation of the indices and use of the Kohler-Onsager relation.

$$\sigma_{ik}(\mathbf{H}) = \sigma_{ki}(-\mathbf{H}). \qquad (23.85)$$

The preceding expressions were given by Abeles and Meiboom in a slightly different notation. In our convention both e and μ_i are positive, account being taken of electron or hole conduction by the choice of the $-$ or $+$ signs in Eq. (23.83). The μ_i, called partial mobilities by A–M, are related to the effective masses characterizing the ellipsoidal surfaces by

$$\mu_i = e\tau/m_i \qquad \text{where } \tau \text{ is independent of energy.}$$

The components given in (23.82)ff for the different valleys must now be referred to a common coordinate system and then summed. The result depends on what particular model is used to represent the energy surface of the solid. The operation carried out by A–M is for the case of three ellipsoids having one axis of each parallel (chosen for simplicity) to the trigonal axis of the crystal and another axis parallel to a binary axis. A given ellipsoid transforms into the others by rotations of $\pm 120°$ around the trigonal axis. This arrangement is applied to the conduction band; the valence band being approximated by a single ellipsoid of revolution (spheroid) with axis of revolution parallel to the trigonal axis. It has been pointed out subsequently[88a, 351] that the existence of inversion symmetry calls for a doubling of each set of ellipsoids in the case of a more general model. The six minima of the conduction band coalesce into three only if they happen to lie at the centers of zone faces. By examining the published data which give information on (1) the carrier density per ellipsoid and (2) the total carrier density in bismuth at liquid

---

351 M. H. Cohen and E. I. Blount, *Phil. Mag.* [8] 5, 115 (1960).

helium temperatures, Jain and Koenig conclude that there are three electron ellipsoids and one light-hole ellipsoid.[351a] It is suggested that the electron band consists of six half-ellipsoids centered on the pseudo-hexagonal faces of the Brillouin zone. The light-hole band presumably is composed of two half-ellipsoids centered on the hexagonal faces of the Brillouin zone. The uncertainty in the analysis allows for a possible existence of heavy holes with a concentration no greater than 0.15 of the light-hole concentration, assuming the nonexistence of heavy electrons. Recent investigations by Mase, von Molnar, and Lawson do not, however, support the postulate of a heavy-hole band.[351b] These studies involved the determination of components of the galvanomagnetic tensor as a function of magnetic field at 20.4° K for the intermediate-field region. The particular temperature was chosen so that the scattering was predominantly by long-wavelength acoustical phonons. The 20° K region was considered low enough so that optical phonons and interband and intervalley transitions could be neglected. It was high enough to avoid concern for scattering from static imperfections. Subsequent measurements of the components of the galvanomagnetic tensor at 4.2° K in the weak-magnetic-field region were reported by Zitter.[351c] It was necessary to restrict the magnetic field intensity to the order of 1 gauss, and to use a superconducting chopper to measure the minute voltages. The results indicate an electron concentration of 2.5×10^{17} cm^{-3} and a hole concentration of nearly the same — tending to rule out a three-band model having any significant concentration in the third band. On the other hand, oscillatory-magnetoresistance measurements of Lerner indicate the presence of heavy carriers with isotropic mass.[351d] A possible reconciliation of these results with Zitter's findings would be the existence of *both*, heavy holes and heavy electrons.[351d] Such a 4-carrier model would also supply the heavy-mass carriers which are desirable for explaining the specific heat data.

The results, after the necessary transformations and the summing over all the valleys, including the electron and hole bands, are rather lengthy and will not be reproduced here. Abeles and Meiboom determined

[351a] A. Jain and S. Koenig, *Phys. Rev.* **127**, 442 (1962).
[351b] S. Mase, S. von Molnar, and A. Lawson, *Phys. Rev.* **127**, 1030 (1962).
[351c] R. Zitter, *Phys. Rev.* **127**, 1471 (1962).
[351d] L. Lerner, *Phys. Rev.* **127**, 1480 (1962).

all the parameters — the partial mobilities for electrons and holes and the electron or hole density $(n = p)$ — from weak-field Hall and magnetoresistance data, with the exception of an ambiguity in assignment of μ_1 and μ_2 which was resolved by use of strong-field information. It was then found that the theory predicted reasonably well the magnetic-field dependence of the galvanomagnetic effects which they measured, thus giving support to the validity of the model chosen to approximate the band structure. Further information regarding the applicability of the A–M model is given by Tinkham,[352] who points out that interpretation of de Haas-van Alphen measurements by Shoenberg[353] requires the conduction band ellipsoids to be tilted slightly (6° from the trigonal axis). Such a band structure is also consistent with the interpretation of other data, including cyclotron resonance measurements.[352, 353a]

Also of interest is the analysis of piezoresistance by Keyes,[354] and the studies by Jain done on bismuth-antimony alloys.[88a] In addition, a study has been made by Mase[355] of the energy bands in bismuth-type crystals, taking into account spin-orbit interaction. He also indicates an angle of inclination between the principal axes of the ellipsoids and the trigonal axes. As will be discussed subsequently in connection with antimony, a zero angle of inclination results in an energy-surface structure of higher symmetry than that of the crystal and yields only six independent second order magnetoconductivity coefficients instead of the eight representative of the crystal symmetry. In particular, the A–M model leads to a vanishing longitudinal magnetoresistance in the direction of the trigonal axis, as well as zero values for certain other coefficients.

An investigation was made of the Hall field in bismuth, including the oscillatory part, at liquid helium temperature by Coldwell-Horsfall and ter Haar,[86] using Dingle's expression for the Fermi level in a magnetic field[356] generalized to the case of ellipsoidal energy surfaces representative

[352] M. Tinkham, *Phys. Rev.* **101**, 902 (1956).
[353] D. Shoenberg, *Phil. Trans. Roy. Soc. London* **245**, 1 (1952); *Proc. Roy. Soc.* **A170**, 341 (1939).
[353a] See, for example, J. Galt, W. Yager, F. Merritt, B. Cetlin, and A. Brailsford, *Phys. Rev.* **114**, 1396 (1959); J. E. Aubrey and R. G. Chambers, *J. Phys. and Chem. Solids* **3**, 128 (1957).
[354] R. W. Keyes, *Phys. Rev.* **104**, 665 (1956).
[355] S. Mase, *J. Phys. Soc. Japan* **13**, 434 (1958); **14**, 584 (1959).
[356] R. B. Dingle, *Proc. Roy. Soc.* **A211**, 500 (1952).

of the bands in bismuth. The expression for the conductivity coefficients is formulated for a relaxation time assumed to be a function of energy only,[357] with specific calculations being done for $\tau \sim \varepsilon^{-1/2}$. This treatment is able to account satisfactorily for the behavior of the oscillatory part of the Hall field, but does not adequately predict the magnetic-field dependence of the nonoscillatory part even when account is taken of the contribution of the hole band. For a detailed discussion of the oscillatory behavior of the conductivity and the diamagnetic susceptibility in bismuth and related materials, the reader is referred to the review article by Kahn and Frederikse.[357a] A comparison of the results of different methods used to determine the characteristics of the Fermi surface in bismuth can be found in the paper by Smith,[357b] which deals with investigations of the anomalous skin effect.

A general treatment of electrical conductivity and elastoresistance for multivalley models of the energy bands in crystals having an axis of three-, four-, or sixfold symmetry is given by Keyes.[358] The components of the magnetoconductivity tensor are developed through coefficients of the H^2 terms. This tensor is then inverted to yield the galvanomagnetic coefficients. A discussion is given of the application of the results to crystals having additional elements of symmetry.

The general model used by Abeles and Meiboom for the conduction band of bismuth was adapted by Freedman and Juretschke to explain the galvanomagnetic data on antimony.[82] These authors point out, however, that the specific scheme calculated by A–M, where an axis of the ellipsoids is parallel to the trigonal axis, needs to be modified to accommodate their measurements. This comes about since the A–M simplification results in an energy-surface symmetry of $\bar{6}m$, which is higher than the crystal point symmetry $\bar{3}m$. Symmetry $\bar{6}m$ allows only six independent magnetoconductivity coefficients of the second order in H, while $\bar{3}m$ calls for eight. In particular, the higher symmetry requires a vanishing of coefficients of the type σ_{1123}^0 and σ_{3211}^0.[359] In addition, the specific

[357] R. Coldwell-Horsfall and D. ter Haar, *Physica* **23**, 1126 (1957).

[357a] A. Kahn and H. Frederikse, *Solid State Phys.* **9**, 257 (1959).

[357b] G. E. Smith, *Phys. Rev.* **115**, 1561 (1959).

[358] R. W. Keyes, *J. Electronics* **2**, 279 (1956).

[359] The indices are based on a coordinate system having direction 3 along the trigonal axis and direction 1 along a binary axis.

ellipsoidal model yields a zero value for σ^0_{3333}, and therefore a vanishing magnetoresistance in the direction of the trigonal axis. Since these conditions are not verified experimentally, Freedman and Juretschke introduce a $\bar{3}m$ symmetry for the energy surfaces. This is done by tilting the ellipsoids so their axes are out of the base plane. As in the case of the arrangement of A–M, one axis of each ellipsoid is parallel to a binary axis of the crystal. The x_1 coordinate direction is chosen parallel to one of the three equivalent binary axes. A similar scheme is adopted for the valence band. The constant-τ approximation is used, and therefore the parameters to be determined from experiment consist of three partial mobilities and an angle of tilt for each band, plus the carrier concentration ($n = p$). Expressions for the galvanomagnetic coefficients, through the quadratic terms in H, are compared with appropriate experimental data, taken at room temperature. By the use of an electronic computer it was possible to find unique values for the 9 parameters which provided a "best fit" to all the data. The values so found were also seen to be in good agreement with the predictions from de Haas-van Alphen data taken at 4°K. An interesting observation, pointed out by Freedman and Juretschke, is that the largest partial mobility turned out to be that of the electrons ($\mu_2^e \sim 4000$ cm^2/volt-sec, compared to $\mu_1^h \sim 3600$ cm^2/volt-sec), yet both the weak-field Hall coefficients were *positive*. A simple estimate of mobility based merely on Hall data would therefore be quite misleading. This example illustrates vividly the importance of securing adequate data when attempting to analyze materials where the band-structure is not simple.

Introduction of the angle of tilt ψ, as was done by Freedman and Juretschke, means of course that for an orthogonal coordinate system with two axes coincident with the two crystal axes, namely, the trigonal and the binary axes, the effective mass tensor of none of the valleys is any longer diagonal. In particular, the ellipsoid having a principal axis along the crystal binary axis which is coincident with a coordinate direction has a normalized effective mass tensor of the form:

$$\mathsf{M}/m_0 = \begin{pmatrix} m_{11} & 0 & 0 \\ 0 & m_{22} & m_{23} \\ 0 & m_{23} & m_{33} \end{pmatrix} \tag{23.86}$$

where m_0 is the free electron mass and where coordinate direction x_1 is along the binary axis; x_3 along the trigonal axis. In the A–M scheme, where the angle of tilt is zero and an ellipsoid axis coincides with the trigonal axis, the off-diagonal component m_{23} vanishes. For the above ellipsoid one may write the relation between energy and wave vector in a manner similar to that used by Shoenberg, namely,

$$\varepsilon = (\hbar^2/2m_0)(\alpha_{11} k_1{}^2 + \alpha_{22} k_2{}^2 + \alpha_{33} k_3{}^2 + 2\alpha_{23} k_2 k_3) \qquad (23.87)$$

where the α_{ij} are components of the normalized reciprocal mass tensor, that is

$$\alpha_{ij} m_{jl} = \delta_{il}. \qquad (23.88)$$

Hence the α_{ij} occurring in (23.87) are related to the components of the normalized effective mass tensor, (23.86), as follows:

$$\alpha_{11} = 1/m_{11}, \qquad \alpha_{22} = m_{33}/[m_{22} m_{33} - m_{23}^2], \qquad (23.89)$$

$$\alpha_{33} = m_{22}/[m_{22} m_{33} - m_{23}^2], \qquad \alpha_{23} = -m_{23}/[m_{22} m_{33} - m_{23}^2].$$

By transforming the ellipsoid in (23.87) to its principal axes, one readily finds that θ, the angle of inclination to the trigonal axis and to coordinate direction 3, is given by

$$\tan 2\theta = \frac{2\alpha_{23}}{(\alpha_{22} - \alpha_{33})}, \qquad (23.90)$$

Explicit expressions for the conductivity coefficients in terms of the dimensionless effective mass parameters shown in (23.86) are presented by Lax and collaborators for H of arbitrary magnitude in the directions of all the crystallographic axes.[360] A constant-τ treatment is used, and results are given which include high-frequency as well as d-c fields.

Cyclotron resonance studies of the Azbel'-Kaner type and also electron spin resonance studies have been carried out on antimony crystals by Datars and Dexter.[360a–c] Results support the tilted-ellipsoid model for

[360] B. Lax, K. Button, H. Zeiger, and L. Roth, *Phys. Rev.* **102**, 715 (1956).
[360a] W. Datars and R. Dexter, *Phys. Rev.* **124**, 75 (1961).
[360b] W. Datars, *Can. J. Phys.* **39**, 1922 (1961); *ibid.* **40**, 1784 (1962).
[360c] W. Datars, *Phys. Rev.* **126**, 975 (1962).

the Fermi surface of electrons. It is suggested, however, that the hole band may be quite complex. Indications support the presence of both light-mass and heavy-mass holes, with perhaps a significant amount of warping of the heavy-hole band.[360b] Non-ohmic behavior has been observed in high-purity antimony specimens at 4.2°K in a magnetic field when the electric field had been increased such that a certain critical value of E/H was exceeded.[360d] Subsequent investigations by Nanney[360e] suggest that the effect is thermal in nature and results from a steep temperature rise in the specimen. This is occasioned by poor heat transfer from the specimen to the liquid helium at the point at which the specimen becomes coated with a film of thermally insulating vapor. These experiments point out the importance of considering the heat transfer between the specimen and the bath whenever significant power might be dissipated in the specimen.

A many-valley model of the type discussed in the preceding paragraphs was applied by Drabble and collaborators[67,87,87a] to the conduction and valence bands of bismuth telluride. They considered six ellipsoids centered on the reflection planes. The coordinate system is slightly different from the arrangement that has been discussed heretofore, in that the $x_1 x_3$ coordinate plane is parallel to a mirror plane of the crystal, that is, x_2 is along one of the binary axes. Again, an angle of inclination θ is introduced, this being the angle of rotation about the x_2 coordinate axis which makes the principal axes of the rth valley coincide with the coordinate axes. As before, x_3 is along the threefold crystallographic axis.

Since bismuth telluride is a semiconductor and can be measured in the extrinsic region, the joint contribution from conduction and valence bands does not necessarily need to be considered, as was the case with semimetals bismuth and antimony. On the other hand, the constant-τ approximation is probably not too good. For this reason, a relaxation time is considered, which is a function of energy. In addition, results are given for an arbitrary charge carrier degeneracy.[87a]

Explicit expressions are presented for the 12 components of the conductivity tensor through the H^2 coefficients. The energy-surface

---

[360d] W. Datars and P. Eastman, *Can. J. Phys.* **40**, 670 (1962); *ibid.* **41**, 161 (1963).
[360e] C. Nanney, *Appl. Phys. Letters* **1**, 71 (1962).

anisotropy is expressed by means of three principal effective masses characterizing the ellipsoids, and the orientation angle θ.[67, 87]   An alternative scheme is to use the four components of the normalized reciprocal mass tensor,[87a] as appear in relation (23.87). Since the orientation used by Drabble places the x_2 coordinate direction along one of the twofold crystallographic axes, the expression for the energy ellipsoid for the electron band is slightly different from (23.87), namely,

$$\varepsilon = (\hbar^2/2m_0)(\alpha_{11} k_1{}^2 + \alpha_{22} k_2{}^2 + \alpha_{33} k_3{}^2 + 2\alpha_{13} k_1 k_3). \qquad (23.91)$$

The α_{ij} tensor here is nondiagonal because of the angle of tilt θ between the axis of the ellipsoid and the x_3 coordinate direction. To express the α_{ij} in terms of the principal masses characterizing the energy ellipsoid, it is necessary to diagonalize the α_{ij} matrix. This is done, of course, by rotating the coordinate system through an angle θ about the x_2-axis, so that it coincides with the principal directions of the valley. In such case relation (23.91) becomes

$$\varepsilon = (\hbar^2/2m_0)(a_1 k_1{}'^2 + a_2 k_2{}'^2 + a_3 k_3{}'^2) \qquad (23.92)$$

where the a_i are now the normalized reciprocal effective masses, cf. (6.2), namely,

$$a_i = m_0/m_i{}^*, \qquad i = 1, 2, 3. \qquad (23.93)$$

By performing the transformation

$$k_1 = k_1{}' \cos\theta + k_3{}' \sin\theta,$$

$$k_3 = -k_1{}' \sin\theta + k_3{}' \cos\theta,$$

$$k_2 = k_2{}',$$

and requiring that the coefficient of the $k_1{}' k_3{}'$ term vanish, one finds readily that

$$\alpha_{11} = a_1 \cos^2\theta + a_3 \sin^2\theta$$

$$\alpha_{22} = a_2$$

$$\alpha_{33} = a_1 \sin^2\theta + a_3 \cos^2\theta$$

$$2\alpha_{13} = (a_3 - a_1) \sin 2\theta. \qquad (23.94)$$

Drabble shows that the anisotropy factors assume a rather pleasant form when, for example, the conductivity tensor components are expressed in terms of three anisotropy parameters and the partial mobility along a coordinate direction. We shall choose this mobility in the x_2 direction, expressing it in the form

$$\mu_{22}^0 = (e/m_0)\langle\tau\rangle\alpha_{22}, \qquad \alpha_{22} = m_0/m_2^*. \tag{23.95}$$

The three anisotropy parameters, which we shall designate by K, L, and M, are defined as follows:

$$K = \alpha_{11}/\alpha_{22}, \qquad L = \alpha_{33}/\alpha_{22}, \qquad M = (\alpha_{11}\alpha_{33} - \alpha_{13}^2)/\alpha_{22}^2. \tag{23.96}$$

This convention is different from that followed by Drabble, in that our reference partial mobility is μ_{22}^0 instead of μ_{11}^0. This is done since the tensor component α_{22} is equal to m_0/m_2^* of the energy ellipsoid. Such a simple reciprocal relationship does not apply in the case of α_{11} inasmuch as the tensor α_{ij} has off-diagonal components α_{13}. Also, it is desirable to point out that Drabble's definition of the ρ_{ijl}^0 includes a minus sign.

The 12 independent components of the conductivity tensor through second-order terms in H for a coordinate system with the $x_1 x_3$-plane parallel to a mirror plane of the crystal, may be written in our notation as follows:

$$\sigma_{ij}^0 = n(e^2/m_0)\langle\tau\rangle\alpha_{22}\,\xi_{ij}(K, L, M),$$

$$\sigma_{ijl}^0 = \mp\, n(|e^3|/m_0^2\, c)\langle\tau^2\rangle\alpha_{22}^2\,\xi_{ijl}(K, L, M), \tag{23.97}$$

$$\sigma_{ijlm}^0 = n(e^4/m_0^3\, c^2)\langle\tau^3\rangle\alpha_{22}^3\,\xi_{ijlm}(K, L, M)$$

where the average of τ^n over energy is defined by (12.11) in the general case of Fermi-Dirac statistics. It reduces to the simplified expression (15.4) for classical statistics. The values of the anisotropy factors $\xi(K, L, M)$ are listed in Table X.

If the angle of tilt of the ellipsoids with the trigonal axis, θ, is zero — as in the A–M model — then $M = KL$, and it is seen from Table X that three of the magnetoconductivity components vanish. This point was discussed before in connection with the Freedman-Juretschke calculations for antimony. The relationship between the anisotropic parameters of

TABLE X. VALUES OF ANISOTROPY FACTORS FOR CONDUCTIVITY COEFFICIENTS[a]

Conductivity coefficient	$\xi(K, L, M)$
$\sigma_{11}^{0} = \sigma_{22}^{0}$	$(K + 1)/2$
σ_{33}^{0}	L
σ_{123}^{0}	K
$\sigma_{231}^{0} = \sigma_{312}^{0}$	$(L + M)/2$
$\sigma_{1111}^{0} = \sigma_{2222}^{0}$	$-(3KL + L + KM - 5M)/8$
σ_{3333}^{0}	$-(KL - M)$
$\sigma_{1122}^{0} = \sigma_{2211}^{0}$	$-(KL + 3L + 3KM + M)/8$
$\sigma_{1133}^{0} = \sigma_{2233}^{0}$	$-K(K + 1)/2$
$\sigma_{3311}^{0} = \sigma_{3322}^{0}$	$-L(L + M)/2$
$\sigma_{1313}^{0} = \sigma_{2323}^{0}$	$\frac{1}{2}KL$
$\sigma_{3111}^{0} = -\sigma_{3122}^{0} = -\sigma_{3221}^{0}$	$-(L - M)(KL - M)^{1/2}/4$
$\sigma_{1113}^{0} = -\sigma_{2213}^{0} = -\sigma_{1223}^{0}$	$-(1 - K)(KL - M)^{1/2}/4$

[a] Energy surfaces are a set of three or six ellipsoids arranged to exhibit $\bar{3}m$ symmetry. Coordinate direction x_3 is along the threefold axis; x_2 is along a twofold axis. All other coefficients of comparable order but not listed are zero, except for $\sigma_{1212}^{0} \equiv \frac{1}{2}(\sigma_{1111}^{0} - \sigma_{1122}^{0})$, and those satisfying the relations $\sigma_{ijk} = -\sigma_{jik}$ or $\sigma_{ijkl} = \sigma_{ijlk} = \sigma_{jikl} = \sigma_{jilk}$. It is to be noted from relations (23.96) that the quantity $(KL-M)$ is never negative.

(23.96) and the principal masses of the energy ellipsoid is readily established by means of (23.93) and (23.94) to be

$$K = (m_2^*/m_1^*) \cos^2 \theta + (m_2^*/m_3^*) \sin^2 \theta,$$

$$L = (m_2^*/m_1^*) \sin^2 \theta + (m_2^*/m_3^*) \cos^2 \theta,$$

$$M = m_2^{*2}/m_1^* m_3^*. \tag{23.98}$$

The case of anisotropic scattering in a crystal such as Bi_2Te_3 was studied by Korenblit.[360f] Equations were developed for ellipsoidal energy

[360f] I. Korenblit, *Fiz. Tverd. Tela* **2**, 3083 (1960) [translation: *Soviet Phys.-Solid State* **2**, 2738 (1961)].

surfaces, and scattering processes were described by an anisotropic relaxation-time tensor of the form

$$\tau_{ij} = \phi(\varepsilon)a_{ij}, \tag{23.99}$$

where $\phi(\varepsilon)$ is an isotropic function of energy. The anisotropic factor, a_{ij}, is independent of the electron energy *and* the wave vector. Therefore the τ_{ij} is not necessarily diagonal in the coordinate system in which the effective mass of a given valley is diagonal. Korenblit's treatment is, therefore, more general than that given in Section 22b, where τ_{ij} was assumed to be diagonal in the principal coordinate system of the mass tensor. The galvanomagnetic coefficients representative of each ellipsoid are summed over the six equivalent valleys representative of the band structure postulated for bismuth telluride. Two fundamental relations between several galvanomagnetic coefficients are shown to exist, independent of the form of $\phi(\varepsilon)$ and the statistics of the electron gas. It is pointed out that in the case of a mixed scattering process it will, in general, no longer be possible to split the τ_{ij} into the two factors as in Eq. (23.99). In such a case, one of the fundamental relations must fail. The relaxation-time tensor given in Eq. (23.99) was used by Efimova et al. in their analyses of experimental data on p-type bismuth telluride.[360g] Measurements were taken over the temperature range from 4° to 290°K, and the more general form of the relaxation-time tensor allowed an estimate of the anisotropy of the relaxation time for impurity scattering.

Tellurium is another semiconductor for which a reasonable amount of information is available. The solid consists of a hexagonal array of chains containing a threefold screw axis. The point group symmetry is 32, and hence the number of independent galvanomagnetic coefficients is the same as that for $\bar{3}m$ crystals.[67b] Pure tellurium has been consistently found to be p-type; and therefore, except for indications available from studies in the intrinsic range, the available information concerns essentially the valence band.[360h] Attempts have been made to fit the galvanomagnetic properties by a six-ellipsoidal valence band.[361, 362] The problem is rendered

[360g] B. Efimova, I. Korenblit, and V. Novikov, *Fiz. Tverd. Tela* **3**, 2746 (1961) [translation: *Soviet Phys.-Solid State* **3**, 2004 (1962).]

[360h] See, for example, R. W. McKay and W. E. Gravelle, *Can. J. Phys.* **39**, 534 (1961).

[361] H. Roth, *J. Phys. & Chem. Solids* **8**, 525 (1959).

[362] A. Nussbaum and D. Long *in* "Proc. of the Intern. Conf. on Semiconductor Phys. Prague 1960," p. 990. Publishing House Czech. Acad. Sci., Prague, 1961.

difficult, however, by the fact that the relative importance of certain of the galvanomagnetic coefficients appears to depend on the degree of doping or other details of preparation.[362–364] A subsequent paper by Nussbaum and Hager presents data on the 12 galvanomagnetic coefficients over the temperature range 77°–300°K.[364a] The proposed band structure invokes the six-ellipsoidal model, with light- and heavy-hole bands separated sufficiently in energy so that the light-hole band is not activated until the temperature approaches 300°K. Such a model is consistent with observed pressure effects and with the optical properties reported by Caldwell and Fan.[364b] Galvanomagnetic and thermoelectric effects were measured on extrinsic tellurium, using bismuth-doped samples, between 77° and 250°K by Rigaux.[364c] The results are quantitatively interpreted by a twelve-ellipsoid model for the constant energy surfaces of the valence band. The principal effective masses and the angular orientation of ellipsoids in the Brillouin zone are determined. In the intrinsic range, the second Hall and Seebeck reversals are explained by the existence of two conduction bands separated by an energy of about 0.36 ev.

Galvanomagnetic effects have been investigated in single-crystal specimens of n-type bismuth selenide at 90°K by Hashimoto.[364d] Results are reasonably consistent with a six-valley model of the conduction band with the energy minima situated on the reflection planes. Values of the effective mass ratios for the ellipsoidal energy surfaces are given as $m_2/m_1 = 0.33$ and $m_3/m_1 = 4.2$, with the long axis being tilted only slightly from the threefold crystallographic axis.

---

[363] W. Teutsch, H. Roth, and H. Harper, *Bull. Am. Phys. Soc.* **6**, 27 (1961).

[364] A. Nussbaum and R. Hager, *Bull. Am. Phys. Soc.* **6**, 130 (1961).

[364a] A. Nussbaum and R. Hager, *Phys. Rev.* **123**, 1958 (1961).

[364b] R. S. Caldwell and H. Y. Fan, *Phys. Rev.* **114**, 664 (1959).

[364c] C. Rigaux, *J. Phys. and Chem. Solids* **23**, 805 (1962).

[364d] K. Hashimoto, *J. Phys. Soc. Japan* **16**, 1970 (1961).

IX.
Special Bands and Scattering Processes

24. Nonparabolic Bands and Nonequivalent Valleys

a. Nonparabolic Bands and Nonequivalent Valleys, with Special Considera-tion of III–V Compound Semiconductors

The representation of $\varepsilon(\mathbf{k})$ by a quadratic form, as is usually done for nondegenerate bands [Eq. (6.1a)], is recognized as the utilization of the initial terms of a more general expansion about the energy minimum, or band edge. It is apparent that for sufficiently large energies above the band edge, higher order terms in k will be necessary to represent the energy. This statement has nothing to do with the symmetry of the energy surface and is equally applicable to spherical energy surfaces, where $\varepsilon(\mathbf{k}) = \varepsilon(k)$. The *nonparabolic* characteristic of the band is manifest through a change in apparent effective mass with increase in population of the band. In the case of silicon and germanium, it appears that these effects become noticeable when the carrier concentration is in the 10^{18} cm^{-3} range and higher. Evidence for this is found in the effective mass determinations from reflectivity data by Cardona *et al.*[365] These authors also cite diamagnetic susceptibility measurements by several investigators, which yield results consistent with their findings. Some recent reflectivity measurements of Spitzer, Trumbore, and Logan on n-type germanium fail, however, to yield the large change in effective mass with carrier concentration indicated by the data of Cardona.[365a] At most a variation of perhaps 20% is suggested for the range $6 \times 10^{18} \leqslant n \leqslant 8 \times 10^{19}$ cm^{-3}.

In a number of the III-V compound semiconductors, several factors occur which cause nonparabolic effects to be important at substantially lower carrier concentrations. This behavior is exemplified in indium

---

[365] M. Cardona, W. Paul, and H. Brooks, *Helv. Phys. Acta* **33**, 329 (1960).
[365a] W. Spitzer, F. Trumbore, and R. Logan, *Bull. Am. Phys. Soc.* **6**, 155 (1961).

antimonide, where the pertinent considerations have been discussed by Kane.[290] The conduction-band surfaces of constant energy may be considered as spheres, that is, the energy depends only on $|\mathbf{k}|$, for electron energies as high perhaps as 0.1 ev above the band edge. The conduction band does, however, become nonparabolic for energies the order of only a fraction of 0.1 ev above the minimum at $k = 0$. This characteristic, which results from the interaction of the conduction band with the light-mass valence band, is revealed experimentally in a number of ways including infrared absorption studies,[366, 367] thermoelectric power measurements,[368,a] infrared cyclotron resonance data,[369] the Faraday rotation studies,[370−371a] and magnetic susceptibility measurements. The latter measurements of Bowers[372] reveal deviations from parabolicity for electron concentrations in indium antimonide as low as 10^{16} cm^{-3}.

In the valence bands of the zincblende semiconductors, the situation is more complicated than in the case of the diamond-type lattices, such as germanium and silicon, due to the lack of inversion symmetry resulting from the fact that all atoms are no longer identical. Furthermore, spin-orbit interaction can remove the degeneracy due to time reversal symmetry $[\varepsilon(\mathbf{k}) = \varepsilon(-\mathbf{k})]$, and therefore the possibility of contributions to energy from terms linear in k exists.[45b,c,290] For sufficiently small energies, such linear terms would dominate the k^2 terms and one might then expect to observe unusual effects. A review article presenting most of the available information on the valence-band structure of the common III–V compounds has been written by Braunstein and Kane.[372a]

---

[366] H. J. Hrostowski, G. H. Wheatley, and W. F. Flood, *Phys. Rev.* **95**, 1683 (1954).

[367] G. W. Gobeli and H. Y. Fan, *Phys. Rev.* **119**, 613 (1960).

[368] R. P. Chasmar and R. Stratton, *Phys. Rev.* **102**, 1686 (1956).

[368a] O. Emel'yanenko, F. Kesamanly, and D. Nasledov, *Fiz. Tverd. Tela* **3**, 1161 (1961) [translation: *Soviet Phys.-Solid State* **3**, 845 (1961)]. For InAs, consult, F. Gashimzade and F. Kesamanly, *ibid.* **3**, 1255 (1961) [translation: *ibid.* **3**, 910 (1961)].

[369] R. J. Keyes, S. Zwerdling, S. Foner, H. Kolm, and B. Lax, *Phys. Rev.* **104**, 1804 (1956).

[370] T. S. Moss, S. D. Smith, and K. W. Taylor, *J. Phys. and Chem. Solids* **8**, 323 (1959).

[371] S. D. Smith, T. S. Moss, and K. W. Taylor, *J. Phys. and Chem. Solids* **11**, 131 (1959).

[371a] For a recent review of the Faraday and the Voigt effects in semiconductors, consult I. M. Boswarva, R. E. Howard, and A. B. Lidiard, *Proc. Roy. Soc.* **A269**, 125 (1962).

[372] R. Bowers, *J. Phys. and Chem. Solids* **8**, 206 (1959).

[372a] R. Braunstein and E. O. Kane, *J. Phys. and Chem. Solids* **23**, 1423 (1962).

Transport properties of nonparabolic bands have been discussed by a number of investigators. For example, Radcliffe[373] considered the effect of k^n terms, in bands which were spherically symmetric, on the temperature dependence of mobility due to lattice scattering. Calculations were made by Barrie and Edmond[374] of the electrical properties, as well as optical absorption, to be expected of a spherically symmetric band for which

$$\varepsilon = ak^2(1 - bk^2).$$

The extra term in the $\varepsilon(k)$ appears to be in the right direction for explaining the observations on indium antimonide; but from a quantitative standpoint, trouble was experienced in connection with the thermoelectric power data.

A more general treatment of conduction in spherically symmetric bands was subsequently given by Barrie,[375] who assumed only the existence of a minimum at $\mathbf{k} = 0$ and a monotonic increase in ε with $|\mathbf{k}|$. A relaxation time is also assumed, and the transport quantities are obtained from the equations applicable to a standard (parabolic) band (equations in Section 12) by replacing[375a] m^* by $\hbar^2 k(d\varepsilon/dk)^{-1}$. Expressions for τ are developed for commonly encountered scattering mechanisms, and requirements for the existence of a unique relaxation time are discussed.

The mobility and thermoelectric power of intrinsic InSb were analyzed by Ehrenreich,[215] who took into account scattering by optical phonons through polar modes as well as acoustical phonon scattering, and also the effects of electron-hole scattering, using the conduction band characteristics postulated by Kane.[290] A subsequent calculation[376] examines the screening effects of the carriers on the electron-phonon interaction. The Hall coefficient factor $r_0 [\equiv \mu_0^H/\mu_0]$ is obtained by the use of a variational treatment which applies where a small magnetic field is present. The dominant scattering mechanisms, namely, lattice scattering by polar modes and electron-hole scattering, are properly combined to

[373] J. M. Radcliffe, Proc. Phys. Soc. (London) **A68**, 675 (1955).
[374] R. Barrie and J. T. Edmond, J. Electronics **1**, 161 (1955).
[375] R. Barrie, Proc. Phys. Soc. (London) **B69**, 553 (1956).
[375a] T. C. Harman and J. M. Honig, J. Phys. and Chem. Solids **23**, 913 (1962).
[376] H. Ehrenreich, J. Phys. and Chem. Solids **9**, 129 (1959).

provide the values of the transport coefficients. The results for the Hall coefficient factor for electrons in intrinsic InSb are plotted as a function of temperature in Fig. 42.

The values obtained by Ehrenreich for conductivity mobility and thermoelectric power agree very well with experiment in the region $250° \leqslant T \leqslant 500°$K. This is the region where the scattering mechanisms

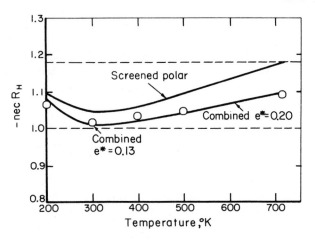

FIG. 42. Hall coefficient factor for electrons in intrinsic InSb $(n = p \equiv n_i)$. Since $\mu_e \gg \mu_h$, it follows that $r_0{}^{(e)} \equiv - nec R_0{}^{(e)} \cong - n_i ec R_0$. Curves are given for screened polar scattering alone and for combined screened polar scattering and electron-hole scattering. An effective ionic charge e^* of 0.13 is used for the open circles; an e^* of 0.20 for the line. The "screened polar" curve is independent of e^* (after Ehrenreich[376]).

incorporated in the theory can be expected to dominate. At lower temperatures, ionized impurity scattering may become noticeable, while at the higher temperatures it is suggested that electron-electron collisions may influence significantly the electron-hole scattering process. Other approximations, concerned with the position of the Fermi level in the band, are also less valid at the higher temperatures. Actually the agreement of Ehrenreich's results with experiment is quite remarkable in that essentially no adjustable parameters are involved. The only constant capable of significant variation is the effective ionic charge, and values of this quantity are fairly well bracketed through the use of optical data. Furthermore, the likely uncertainty in e^* produces only a relatively small uncertainty in some of the electrical properties. Ehrenreich also solves the Boltzmann equation for high-frequency conduction, and thus is able to calculate the reflectivity minimum in the far infrared, obtaining again good agreement with experiment.

In connection with the valence bands of InSb, there is considerable uncertainty about how far away from $\mathbf{k} = 0$ the possible linear term in the expression $\varepsilon(\mathbf{k})$ might dominate. A study of the infrared absorption by Gobeli and Fan[367] fails to reveal maxima of the valence band away from $k = 0$. Their data on a sample containing about 5×10^{17} holes cm^{-3} suggest that any such maxima must lie less than 0.013 ev above the value of the energy at $k = 0$. This finding is consistent with theoretical estimates which give a figure the order of 10^{-4} ev.[290]

In the case of indium arsenide, conditions are more favorable for observation of the linear term in $\varepsilon(k)$. Matossi and Stern[377] obtained optical absorption data on a specimen having an acceptor concentration in the 10^{16} cm^{-3} range, and analysis of these data suggests that the energy maximum in the heavy-hole band lies around 0.003 ev above the energy at the center of the Brillouin zone. One might expect the linear term in $\varepsilon(k)$ to exert a pronounced influence on certain of the electrical transport characteristics. These effects have been considered by Stern, who carried out calculations for band structure parameters which approximated the situation in InAs. Because of considerable warping of the heavy-mass band near $\mathbf{k} = 0$, there are regions where principal effective mass components can change sign. Since the Hall conductivity tensor involves a product of reciprocal masses in two perpendicular directions, such behavior can produce anomalous Hall effects. The calculations of Stern[291] show that $\mu_0{}^H/\mu_0$ can vary widely, and may become negative for certain positions of the Fermi level.

Another III-V semiconductor which has been studied fairly extensively is gallium arsenide. Here the band separation E_G at room temperature, as obtained from optical data, is approximately 1.35 ev[378-380] and the spin orbit splitting of the valence bands, Δ, is 0.33 ev[381] — as compared

[377] F. Matossi and F. Stern, *Phys. Rev.* **111**, 472 (1958).
[378] R. Barrie, F. Cunnell, J. Edmond, and I. Ross, *Physica* **20**, 1087 (1954).
[379] F. Oswald and R. Schade, *Z. Naturforsch.* **9a**, 611 (1954).
[380] W. Spitzer and J. Whelan, *Phys. Rev.* **114**, 59 (1959).
[381] R. Braunstein, *J. Phys. and Chem. Solids* **8**, 280 (1959).

to an E_G in InSb of 0.18 ev and a Δ which is much larger than E_G, perhaps the order of 0.9 ev.[290] In regard to the conduction band, nonparabolic effects, although present, are less important in GaAs than in InSb. Another characteristic of the conduction band is of interest, however, and is revealed quite strikingly when the Hall coefficient of n-type GaAs is measured as a function of temperature. One finds an increase in the extrinsic Hall coefficient as the temperature is raised, leading to a pronounced maximum just before the typical drop at the onset of intrinsic conduction.[382, 383] Gray and Ehrenreich[384] pointed out that such a behavior could be expected on the basis of a conduction band structure proposed by Callaway.[274, 385] His considerations suggest that the lowest minimum is at the center of the Brillouin zone and that another minimum, in the [111] direction, lies only a few tenths of an electron volt above the [000] minimum. Furthermore, a [100] minimum can also be expected to be close by, as in germanium. Thus, at temperatures around 500°K, electrons begin to be excited into a higher band, so that two-band conduction occurs. Aukerman and Willardson[386] showed that simple two-band theory predicted in first approximation that the quantity $(R_{obs} - R^0)/R^0$ (where R_{obs} is the Hall coefficient for the two-band case, and R^0 is the Hall coefficient at the temperature where all carriers are confined to the one band) should depend only on the ratio of mobilities and effective masses in the two bands and on the separation in energy. Thus the ratio should be nearly independent of carrier density, for small or moderate carrier densities. Experimental data on three specimens where R^0 values were 10, 59, and 193 cm³/coulomb verified this prediction (Fig. 43) and yielded a value of the energy separation ΔE of 0.38 ev at absolute zero, and a value of m_1^*/m_2^* of 0.04. These results were based on a mobility ratio μ_1/μ_2 of 10. Subsequently, Ehrenreich[387] has made a thorough analysis of band structure and electron transport in GaAs, taking into account also some unpublished data from pressure experiments. These results suggest that μ_1/μ_2 is considerably larger than 10; that a

[382]　O. Folberth and H. Weiss, *Z. Naturforsch.* **10a**, 615 (1955).
[383]　J. Edmond, R. Broom, and F. Cunnell, *in* "Report of the Meeting on Semiconductors, Rugby, April, 1956," p. 109. The Physical Society, London, 1956.
[384]　P. Gray and H. Ehrenreich, *Bull. Am. Phys. Soc.* **3**, 255 (1958).
[385]　J. Callaway, *J. Electronics* **2**, 330 (1957).
[386]　L. Aukerman and R. Willardson, *J. Appl. Phys.* **31**, 939 (1960).
[387]　H. Ehrenreich, *Phys. Rev.* **120**, 1951 (1960).

good choice is probably to assume the ratio to be infinite.   Ehrenreich thus obtains a value for ΔE of 0.36 ev.   This is still substantially larger than 0.25 ev, the value suggested from the optical absorption studies of Spitzer and Whelan.[380] The most likely explanation involves the observa-

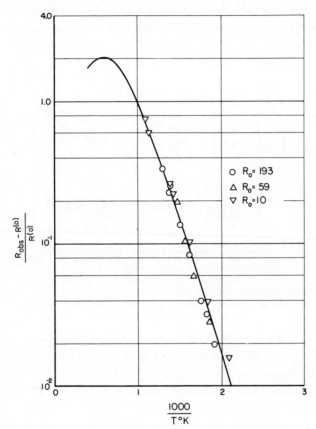

FIG. 43. The fractional increase in Hall coefficient with temperature of three n-type specimens of GaAs of different carrier concentrations. The solid curve is a theoretical fit given by the two-band model, using the parameters given in the text (after Aukerman and Willardson[386]).

tion that most of the specimens used in the optical absorption studies were more heavily doped than were the Hall samples, and thus possessed Fermi levels perhaps as great as 0.15 ev above the band edge.[387] The principal conduction band is of course a [000] minimum. The symmetry of the subsidiary band is perhaps open to some discussion.   It was originally thought to be a [111] type valley.[384] Subsequent experimental evidence from the behavior of the optical band gap in GaAs-GaP alloys and the high pressure data on GaAs has, however, led Ehrenreich to favor the postulate that the subsidiary band minima lie along [100] directions.

Another III-V semiconductor possessing a complex conduction band such as that found in gallium arsenide is gallium antimonide. Confirmation of this type structure results from broad investigations carried out by

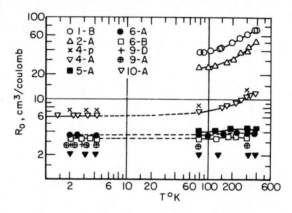

FIG. 44.   Hall coefficient as a function temperature for tellurium-doped GaSb samples of different electron concentrations (after Sagar[388]).

Sagar,[388, 388a] which include (1) Hall effect and conductivity between 1.5° and 370°K; (2) resistance and Hall effect of the samples under hydrostatic pressure up to 1.4×10^4 kg/cm[2] at room temperature; and (3) piezoresistance as a function of temperature between 77° and 370°K. The increase with temperature in the Hall coefficient of n-type material (doped with tellurium, inasmuch as undoped GaSb has always been found to be p-type) at temperatures above 100°K for the samples of lowest carrier concentration is reminiscent of gallium arsenide, and suggests initiation of conduction in a second band. This behavior of the Hall coefficient (ascertained to be independent of magnetic field strength in the range of fields used — namely, 0.5 to 6 kgauss) is shown in Fig. 44.

[388]   A. Sagar, *Phys. Rev.* **117**, 93 (1960).
[388a] A. Sagar and R. C. Miller, *J. Appl. Phys.* **32**, 2073 (1961).

An increase in resistivity is found, associated with the rise in Hall coefficient, indicating a decrease in average mobility when the carriers are excited into the subsidiary band. The values of the piezoresistance coefficients and their temperature dependences suggest that the subsidiary band is germanium-like, having ellipsoidal energy surfaces and minima along [111] directions, and that the principal conduction band (i.e., the one which is lowest in energy) is at the center of the Brillouin zone and has spherical energy surfaces. This latter band was studied by Zwerdling and collaborators,[389] using high-resolution magnetoabsorption techniques. They quote an effective mass of 0.047 m_0, and a separation from the valence band of 0.813 ev. By assuming characteristics of the [111] band similar to those in germanium, particularly in regard to the density of states, Sagar obtains a density of states ratio in the [111] and [000] bands of approximately 40.[388] Using this value, he estimates the energy separation ΔE between the two bands to be 0.074 ev at room temperature. The temperature dependence of the piezoresistance then calls for a temperature variation of the separation, $d(\Delta E)/dT$, of approximately $- 3 \times 10^{-4}$ ev/°C. It was verified that the model predicted reasonably well the measured Hall coefficients and resistivity values; the calculations having been carried out, however, with the constant-τ approximation for each band. Subsequent experiments by Strauss[390] on GaSb doped with tellurium and with selenium yielded data which were consistent with the two-band model of Sagar, although systematic differences were observed between the properties of the samples doped with selenium and those doped with tellurium. The results suggest that the nature of the donor impurity, as well as the conduction band structure, are important in determining the electrical properties of· n-type GaSb when the donor concentrations are relatively high ($> 10^{17}$ cm^{-3}). The likelihood of the importance of impurity conduction is pointed out. In the case of the samples which were less heavily doped with tellurium, an anomaly is apparent in that the Hall mobility at 77°K appears to increase with increasing carrier concentration. An alternative explanation has subsequently been proposed by Bate.[390a] This is based on the consideration

[389] S. Zwerdling, B. Lax, K. Button and L. Roth, *J. Phys. and Chem. Solids* **9**, 320 (1959).
[390] A. J. Strauss, *Phys. Rev.* **121**, 1087 (1961).
[390a] R. T. Bate, *J. Appl. Phys.* **33**, 26 (1962).

of hydrogenic ground states associated with electrons in each of the conduction band minima. Owing to the small effective mass in the [000] minimum, the radius of the Bohr orbit for electrons in this minimum is large, and the electron wave functions for neighboring impurities overlap at relatively low concentrations. These states are undoubtedly merged with the [000] conduction band minimum for donor concentrations of the order of 10^{17} cm^{-3} or greater. In the [111] minima, on the other hand, the effective masses are much larger, and less overlapping of the wave functions occurs. It thus appears that even a relatively large concentration of a group VI impurity could introduce a discrete level or narrow impurity band at some energy below the [111] band edge. This postulated impurity level would be expected to lie above the principal [000] conduction band minimum, and its presence could account for the dependence of the conductivity in n-type GaSb on the nature and concentration of the impurities. As the impurity content of the specimens becomes larger, the importance of scattering by neutral impurities increases. Bate's calculations show that the general shape of the curve depicting Hall mobility at 77°K as a function of carrier concentration can be accounted for by mixed scattering involving ionized impurities and neutral impurities.

In addition to the influence of subsidiary extrema on electrical properties of semiconductors as a result of the redistribution of carriers between the principal and the subsidiary extrema, a significant effect can also occur from scattering between the two extrema. This interband scattering has been discussed in some detail by Nathan, Paul, and Brooks in connection with pressure measurements on n-type germanium.[390b] Although at zero pressure, the energy separation between the [111]-type principal minima of the conduction band and the [100]-type subsidiary minima is the order of 0.2 ev, this separation decreases with increasing pressure. To account for the observed decrease in electron mobility with pressure, the authors consider, in addition to the sharing of electrons between states in the two sets of minima, a relaxation process involving the scattering of carriers from one type of minimum to the other type. This interband scattering is in addition to the regular intravalley acoustic mode scattering. The point that scattering between nonequivalent

---

[390b] M. Nathan, W. Paul, and H. Brooks, *Phys. Rev.* **124**, 391 (1961).

valleys can also play a role in determining the optical absorption constant at photon energies of sufficient magnitude to bridge the gap between the minima was made by Rosenberg and Lax.[390c]   A theoretical treatment of such processes has been presented by Risken and Meyer.[390d]

A review of the available information concerning the band structure of a number of semiconductors, including many III–V, IV–VI, and other common compounds, has been presented by Long.[390e]   A large bibliography is supplied.

b. Structurally-Equivalent Valleys Rendered Nonequivalent by Perturbations

An important example of this case can occur when a semiconductor having the many-valley band structure is subjected to shear strains. The phenomenon was reported by Smith[390f] in connection with piezoresistance studies in germanium and silicon, and has been discussed theoretically by Herring,[65, 321] Keyes,[322] Price,[23] and others.[390g] Another interesting consequence of the removal of the equivalence of the valleys is the splitting of the degeneracies of the ground states of impurity levels. This has been discussed by Kohn,[390h] and the technique has been used to study impurity levels (see Section 31b). Strong fields can also disturb the equivalence of the various valleys. For example, a strong magnetic field and the resulting Landau splitting can cause a carrier-transfer effect among the various ellipsoids, depending upon the relative orientation of the magnetic field vector and the principal axes of the ellipsoid (see Section 28c). Also, a strong electric field which leads to non-ohmic conductivity — and, therefore, "hot-carriers" — can produce unequal degrees of "hotness" in the different valleys [see Section 32a(2)]. Finally, it has been pointed out that if the intervalley scattering rate is low enough, the different valleys — even though crystallographically equivalent — can lead to anisotropies in directional phenomena. The effect of the

390c R. Rosenberg and M. Lax, *Phys. Rev.* **112**, 843 (1958).
390d H. Risken and H. J. G. Meyer, *Phys. Rev.* **123**, 416 (1961).
390e D. Long, *J. Appl. Phys.* **33**, 1682 (1962).
390f C. S. Smith, *Phys. Rev.* **94**, 42 (1954).
390g Additional literature is cited in Section 30a.
390h W. Kohn, *Solid State Phys.* **5**, 257 (1957).

many-valley structure in such a case on the diffusion of excess carriers was investigated by Conwell.[390i] A study of the Hall effect in a many-valley semiconductor for finite values of the intervalley scattering rate was done by Koenig.[390j] It is interesting to note that a somewhat similar problem involving charge carriers of different signs can exist when the electron-hole recombination rate is low [see Section 9b(3)]. In that case, since different carrier types are involved, the effect persists even for isotropic conduction for each carrier. In the present case, it is apparent that the anomaly will vanish if the valley mobility is isotropic.

Although it is estimated that the intervalley scattering rate in germanium is so high that one or both of the effects discussed above might not be experimentally discernable, it is suggested that the phenomena might appear as an anomalous behavior of the diffusion constant or the Hall coefficient when the crystal is strained. In connection with anisotropic mobilities and diffusivities in semiconductors, van Roosbroeck and Pfann have discussed the existence of photovoltaic phenomena.[390k] The anisotropy might be obtained by elastic strain in a cubic semiconductor or could occur without strain in certain noncubic structures. A detailed analysis is made of this "photopiezoresistance" effect in a slab with strongly absorbed radiation on one surface.

25. Inapplicability of the Relaxation Time Approximation

a. General Discussion — Use of Variational Technique

The explicit expressions for the transport coefficients, which have been presented thus far, were based on the use of the relaxation time approximation in the solution of the Boltzmann equation. As discussed in Section 5, the collision term is represented by the expression

$$(\partial f/\partial t)_{\text{coll}} = - (f - f_0)/\tau \tag{25.1}$$

where f, f_0, and τ are functions of $\mathbf{k}$. The quantity f_0 is actually a function

[390i] E. M. Conwell, *Phys. Rev.* **127**, 1493 (1962).
[390j] S. Koenig, *Helv. Phys. Acta* **34**, 765 (1961).
[390k] W. van Roosbroeck and W. Pfann, *J. Appl. Phys.* **33**, 2304 (1962).

only of energy, as is τ when the scattering is isotropic over a surface of constant energy.

The relaxation time assumption, which is used quite widely in transport theory, results in substantial simplification. The treatment is applicable to most scattering processes occurring in elemental semiconductors.[321] The principal exception is electron-electron scattering, which is of concern only for relatively high carrier concentrations. In the case of scattering of charge carriers by lattice vibrations in metals, expression (25.1) is reasonably applicable only at temperatures large compared to the Debye temperature.[391] A general discussion of various implications of the relaxation time is given in some of the literature cited in Section 5. Further information can be found in the books by Ziman and by Wannier.[392]

In those cases where the relaxation time assumption is not applicable, solutions of the Boltzmann equation are usually obtained by means of a variational method. This technique was used by Kohler in studies of transport phenomena in the electron gas in metals.[393] Explicit results are given for the leading terms in the series expressions for thermal conductivity and thermoelectric power, and also for additional terms in the series expressing the electrical conductivity. A treatment of the electrical conductivity in metals has also been given by Rhodes.[394] His procedure is to obtain a numerical solution of the integral equation by successive approximations. A comparison by Rhodes of his results with those obtained by Kohler reveals certain differences, which are attributed, at least in part, to an algebraic error in one of Kohler's expressions. Kohler's variational treatment was developed further by Sondheimer and used to provide exact expressions, in the form of infinite determinants, for the electrical and thermal conductivities and the thermoelectric power in a metal.[395] The expressions are valid for all temperatures, and it was found, in particular, that the Grüneisen-Bloch formula for the ideal electrical resistance is appreciably in error in the region of the Debye

---

[391] See, for example, p. 264 of Wilson's book,[9] or p. 297 of Blatt's review article[44]; also p. 334 ff. of Ziman's book.[38b]

[392] Chapter VII, ref. 38b; Chapter 7, ref. 45a.

[393] M. Kohler, *Z. Physik* **124**, 772 (1948); **125**, 679 (1949).

[394] P. Rhodes, *Proc. Roy. Soc.* **A202**, 466 (1950).

[395] E. H. Sondheimer, *Proc. Roy. Soc.* **A203**, 75 (1950).

temperature. An additional finding is that the residual and ideal resistances of an impure metal are not strictly additive in the region where the two are of the same order of magnitude. These deviations from Matthiessen's rule cannot be expressed by a simple relation, and are evaluated numerically for several cases. Variational procedures were also used by Tsuji in connection with the electrical and thermal conductivities and the thermoelectric power of an isotropic metal.[395a] Although the initial determination was based on the assumption of spherical energy surfaces, a subsequent calculation was done for anisotropic solids.[359b] Particular attention is paid to the conditions under which a positive thermoelectric power can be realized at low temperatures in monovalent metals. Electrical and thermal conductivities and thermoelectric power of a metal were also treated by Klein[395c] through the use of a variational principle.

The variational procedure has been applied by a number of investigators to cases where more complicated interactions between the charge carriers and the lattice are considered. For example, Dorn has calculated the effects of deviations in electron-lattice interactions in semiconductors from the usual assumption of elastic collisions.[396] The principal effect is that the mobility resulting from elastic collisions is multiplied by a factor of the form $[1 + a(\theta/T)]$, where θ is a characteristic temperature which, for most semiconductors, is in the neighborhood of $1\,°K$. The third approximation yields the value $2153/765$ for the coefficient a. It is thus seen that negligible effects are expected at high temperatures, but that in the low temperature range a significant variation in the temperature dependence of the mobility from the $T^{-3/2}$ behavior characteristic of acoustic phonon scattering might be expected. The interaction of the electrons and lattice vibrations in an anisotropic metal has been considered by Appel,[397] who took into account the directional dependence and the dispersion of phase and group velocities of the lattice vibrations. Explicit expressions are developed for transition probabilities, under the assumption of spherical energy surfaces, and with the neglect of umklapp

[395a] M. Tsuji, *J. Phys. Soc. Japan* **13**, 133, 655 (1958).
[395b] M. Tsuji, *J. Phys. Soc. Japan* **13**, 818 (1958).
[395c] R. Klein, *Z. Naturforsch.* **16a**, 116 (1961).
[396] D. Dorn, *Z. Naturforsch.* **12a**, 18 (1957).
[397] J. Appel, *Z. Naturforsch.* **14a**, 379 (1959).

processes[398] and of deviations of the lattice from thermal equilibrium. The resulting integral equation, which involves the perturbed electron distribution function, is formulated as a variational problem, and solutions are obtained which lead to expressions for the electrical conductivity, the thermoelectric power, and the electronic component of the thermal conductivity.

Although the question of the deviation of the lattice from thermal equilibrium is discussed to some extent in Section 29, it also deserves mention here. As is pointed out by Sondheimer,[59] and in the literature cited in his article, the assumption of thermal equilibrium of the lattice cannot be strictly valid when a temperature gradient exists. To be more specific, a rigorous development of the transport relationships requires that one determine not only the deviation of the electron distribution $f(\mathbf{k})$ from the equilibrium value $f_0(\mathbf{k})$, as is always done in the case of external electrical and thermal gradients, but that one also take into account in the case when temperature gradients exist, the deviation of the phonon distribution $N(\mathbf{q})$ from the equilibrium value $N_0(\mathbf{q})$. This renders the problem much more complicated than in the case usually treated, where it is assumed that $N(\mathbf{q}) = N_0(\mathbf{q})$. One is now faced with the task of solving simultaneously two Boltzmann equations. The solution of the simultaneous integral equations by means of the variational procedure is discussed by Hanna and Sondheimer[399] and by Dorn,[400] and expressions for the transport coefficients are obtained for a number of special cases of interest. The problem was also investigated by Bailyn,[400a] with particular attention to scattering processes. An interesting conclusion from his analysis is that the importance of umklapp processes in metals at low temperatures has been greatly underestimated, and that in the alkali metals this mechanism is important down to the lowest measurable temperatures. In fact, it is probably the dominant thermal scattering process. In particular, his calculations suggest — subject to the validity of the Born-von Kármán spectrum and the assumed isotropy of the collision process over a surface of constant energy — that the

---

[398] For a discussion of umklapp processes, see, for example, p. 293 of Blatt's article.[44]

[399] I. I. Hanna and E. H. Sondheimer, *Proc. Roy. Soc.* **A239**, 247 (1957).

[400] D. Dorn, *Z. Naturforsch.* **12a**, 739 (1957).

[400a] M. Bailyn, *Phys. Rev.* **112**, 1587 (1958); **120**, 381 (1960).

electrical resistivity is dominated by umklapp processes at all temperatures down to the limit of the calculations (20°K for lithium, 8°K for sodium, 2°K for cesium) and that the thermal resistivity has about equal contributions from umklapp and nonumklapp processes, the latter beginning to become relatively less important at the lowest temperatures. Similar conclusions were reached by Pfennig,[400b] who made a special study of the relative importance of umklapp and normal processes in alkali metals, taking into account the anisotropy in elastic behavior.

Tsuji has treated the case of a nonequilibrium distribution of phonons,[400c] and in addition has developed equations which take into account the presence of an external magnetic field.[400d] From this, he establishes the validity of the Onsager reciprocal relations [Eqs. (1.7)] for the case of a magnetic field and deviations in phonon distribution from the equilibrium value. By assuming spherical energy surfaces and the Debye model for the phonons, he obtains equations for most of the galvanomagnetic, thermoelectric, and thermomagnetic coefficients.

b. Application to Semiconductors

(1) General considerations. Specific applications of the variational technique to transport in semiconductors involve electron-electron scattering[220a,400e,f] [see Section 15a(4)], "warm" electrons[320, 401] [discussed briefly in Section 32a(2)], and lattice scattering in polar semiconductors. In these polar materials, the optical modes of the lattice vibrations can be expected to exert a controlling factor in the scattering over a substantial temperature range. Common examples are found in the III–V series of semiconductors, where there are two unlike atoms in the unit cell, and the optical vibrations may produce significant electric polarization. Howarth and Sondheimer[45] point out that for such collisions, where

---

[400b] H. Pfennig, *Z. Physik* **155**, 332 (1959).

[400c] M. Tsuji, *J. Phys. Soc. Japan* **13**, 426 (1958).

[400d] M. Tsuji, *J. Phys. Soc. Japan* **14**, 618 (1959).

[400e] P. M. Tomchuk, *Fiz. Tverd. Tela* **3**, 1258 (1961) [translation: *Soviet Phys.-Solid State* **3**, 913 (1961)].

[400f] J. Appel, *Phys. Rev.* **125**, 1815 (1962).

[401] I. Adawi, *Phys. Rev.* **115**, 1152 (1959).

the energy changes are large compared to the initial average energy of the charge carrier, a universal time of relaxation cannot be defined.

(2) Criteria for applicability of relaxation time concept.[402]   Although it is not the purpose of this monograph to examine in detail the form of the collision operator, it is desirable to consider certain aspects of its representation in order to understand the differences resulting from such scattering processes as acoustic phonons, optical phonons in nonpolar semiconductors, and optical phonons in polar semiconductors.   If we define a transition probability $S(\mathbf{k}, \mathbf{k}')$ as the probability per unit time of a transition of an electron from an initial state defined by wave vector $\mathbf{k}$ to a final state in unit volume of k-space centered on $\mathbf{k}'$, then the collision term of the Boltzmann equation (cf. Section 5) for classical statistics may be written as follows[403]:

$$(\partial f/\partial t)_{\text{coll}} = - \int [f(\mathbf{k})S(\mathbf{k}, \mathbf{k}') - f(\mathbf{k}')S(\mathbf{k}', \mathbf{k})]\, d^3k'. \qquad (25.2)$$

Strictly speaking, each term in the integrand should involve a factor of the type $[1 - f(\mathbf{k})]$.[404]   These factors give the probability that there are vacant levels in the final states.   In the case of semiconductors where classical statistics apply, we may replace this factor by unity, since $f(\mathbf{k})$ is small.   Where degeneracy may be important, the factor is of course included.[59, 404]   Borrowing somewhat from the notation of Sondheimer[59] and Jones,[404a] we may write, for a single phonon process

$$S(\mathbf{k}, \mathbf{k}') = U(\mathbf{k}, \mathbf{k}')N_{\mathbf{q}}\, \delta(\varepsilon_{\mathbf{k}'} - \varepsilon_{\mathbf{k}} - \hbar\omega_{\mathbf{q}}), \qquad \text{absorption}, \qquad (25.3)$$

$$S(\mathbf{k}, \mathbf{k}') = U(\mathbf{k}, \mathbf{k}')(N_{\mathbf{q}} + 1)\delta(\varepsilon_{\mathbf{k}'} - \varepsilon_{\mathbf{k}} + \hbar\omega_{\mathbf{q}}), \qquad \text{emission}$$

where the lattice vibrations are characterized by the wave vector $\mathbf{q}$ of the phonons, and the conservation of energy for the process is expressed by the Dirac δ-function.[405]   The quantity $\varepsilon_{\mathbf{k}}$ is the energy of the electron

---

[402]   The author is indebted to Dr. I. Adawi for the arguments presented in this section.

[403]   See, for example, Appendix A of Herring's article.[65]

[404]   See p. 194 of Wilson's book.[9]

[404a] See p. 288 of the "Handbuch" article by Jones[67a]

[405]   For more details concerning these transition processes, the reader is referred to the standard texts, for example, Chapter XV of Seitz's book.[209]

in the state characterized by wave number $\mathbf{k}$ (here, the initial state); and the energy of the phonon, $\hbar\omega_q$, is given in terms of its angular frequency ω_q. The quantity N_q is the phonon distribution function — the number of lattice quanta for the mode characterized by wave number $\mathbf{q}$ — which will subsequently be assumed to be the equilibrium distribution given by

$$N_q = N_{0q} = 1/[\exp{(\hbar\omega_q/kT)} - 1]. \tag{25.4}$$

The conservation of momentum for the collision process requires that

$$\mathbf{k}' - \mathbf{k} = \pm \mathbf{q}, \qquad +, \text{ absorption}; \quad -, \text{ emission}. \tag{25.5}$$

Finally, the quantity $U(\mathbf{k}, \mathbf{k}')$ is proportional to the square of the interaction-potential matrix element between electronic states $\mathbf{k}$ and $\mathbf{k}'$, and it also includes the factor $1/\omega_q$.[403] Because the interaction matrix is Hermitian, it follows that

$$U(\mathbf{k}, \mathbf{k}') = U(\mathbf{k}', \mathbf{k}). \tag{25.5a}$$

It is pointed out by Sondheimer that the validity of the above relation, which expresses the principle of microscopic reversibility, is sufficient to establish quite generally the Kelvin relations [that is, the Kohler-Onsager relations of Eq. (1.7) when $H = 0$].[59]

In expressing the collision term, Eq. (25.2), in terms of relations (25.3), we must keep in mind that the state $\mathbf{k}'$ in $S(\mathbf{k}, \mathbf{k}')$ is realized from state $\mathbf{k} \equiv \mathbf{k}' - \mathbf{q}$ by absorption of a phonon and from state $\mathbf{k} \equiv \mathbf{k}' + \mathbf{q}$ by emission of a phonon. The final result can be put in the form

$$(\partial f/\partial t)_{\text{coll}} = -\int \{f(\mathbf{k})U(\mathbf{k}, \mathbf{k}')N_q - f(\mathbf{k}')U(\mathbf{k}'\,\mathbf{k})[N_q + 1]\}\, \delta(\varepsilon_{\mathbf{k}'} - \varepsilon_{\mathbf{k}} - \hbar\omega_q)$$

$$+ \{f(\mathbf{k})U(\mathbf{k}, \mathbf{k}')[N_{-q} + 1] - f(\mathbf{k}')U(\mathbf{k}', \mathbf{k})N_{-q}\}\delta(\varepsilon_{\mathbf{k}'} - \varepsilon_{\mathbf{k}} + \hbar\omega_{-q})\, d^3k'$$

$$\tag{25.6}$$

where $\mathbf{q}$ now is given by

$$\mathbf{q} = \mathbf{k}' - \mathbf{k}. \tag{25.7}$$

Actually ω_{-q} can be replaced by ω_q since the frequency is even in $\mathbf{q}$, but the same cannot be said for N_{-q} unless we assume the lattice to be in thermal equilibrium.[406] Equation (25.6) is identical with that given by Sondheimer,[59] except for the approximations $1 - f(\mathbf{k}) \simeq 1, 1 - f(\mathbf{k}') \simeq 1$. The integration over $\mathbf{k}'$ space is performed by integrating over a surface of constant energy, followed by an integration over energy, thus

$$d^3k' = dS' \, d\varepsilon / |\text{grad}_{\mathbf{k}'} \varepsilon| \tag{25.8}$$

$$= (m^*/\hbar^2) \, d\varepsilon_{k'} \, k' \, d\Omega', \quad \text{for spherical energy surfaces} \tag{25.8a}$$

where Ω' is the element of solid angle. The delta functions permit the integration over energy to be written at once, and with the use of (25.5a) one obtains

$$(\partial f/\partial t)_{\text{coll}} = - \frac{m^*}{\hbar^2} \left[\int_{S_+} \{f(\mathbf{k})N_q - f(\mathbf{k}')[N_q + 1]\}U(\mathbf{k}, \mathbf{k}')k' \, d\Omega' + \right. \tag{25.9}$$

$$\left. \int_{S_-} \{f(\mathbf{k})[N_{-q} + 1] - f(\mathbf{k}')N_{-q}\}U(\mathbf{k}, \mathbf{k}')k' \, d\Omega' \right]$$

where the surface integrals are evaluated over the surfaces of constant energy, S_+ and S_-, defined as follows:

$$S_\pm : \quad \varepsilon_{k'} = \varepsilon_k \pm \hbar\omega_q. \tag{25.10}$$

It will be noted that for simplicity we have restricted ourselves to spherical energy surfaces with ε parabolic in k [cf. Eq. (25.8a)]. It is therefore convenient to expand the distribution function $f(\mathbf{k})$ in spherical harmonics, and we write[407]

$$f(\mathbf{k}) = \sum_l f_l(k)P_l(\cos \alpha) \tag{25.11}$$

where the polar axis has been chosen along $\mathbf{E}$, and where α is the angle between $\mathbf{k}$ and $\mathbf{E}$.[407a] In the usual transport theories, only the terms $l = 0$ and $l = 1$ are retained.

---

[406] See p. 259 of Wilson's book.[9]

[407] I. Adawi, *J. Appl. Phys.* **32**, 1101 (1961), Appendix A.2.

[407a] The vector $\mathbf{E}$ denotes some preferential direction, for example, that of an electric field or thermal gradient.

In applying (25.11) to Eq. (25.9), the collision term assumes the form

$$(\partial f/\partial t)_{\text{coll}} = \sum_l \mathscr{L}_l f_l(k) \tag{25.12}$$

where the collision operator $\mathscr{L}_l$ is given by the relation

$$\mathscr{L}_l f_l = -\frac{m^*}{\hbar^2} \left\{ \int_{S_+} [N_{0q} f_l(k) P_l(\cos\alpha) - (N_{0q} + 1)f_l(k') P_l(\cos\alpha')] \times \right.$$

$$U(\mathbf{k}, \mathbf{k}')k'\, d\Omega' + \int_{S_-} [(N_{0q} + 1)f_l(k) P_l(\cos\alpha) - N_{0q} f_l(k'') \times$$

$$\left. P_l(\cos\alpha'')U(\mathbf{k}, \mathbf{k}'')k''\, d\Omega'' \right\}. \tag{25.12a}$$

In arriving at the above expression, we have assumed the phonon distribution to be that at equilibrium, given by Eq. (25.4). In carrying out the integrations over $\mathbf{k}'$ and $\mathbf{k}''$, it is convenient to transform so that direction $\mathbf{k}$ is the polar axis. The P_l $(\cos\alpha')$ is expressed in terms of Legendre functions of $\cos\alpha$ and $\cos\theta'$ — where θ' is the angle between $\mathbf{k}'$ and $\mathbf{k}$ — by means of the addition theorem for Legendre polynomials.[408] Integration over the azimuthal angle produces zero for the coefficients of all the terms containing associated Legendre functions, and one is left with the product $P_l(\cos\alpha)$ $P_l(\cos\theta')$. The quantity $P_l(\cos\alpha)$ is a constant factor insofar as the integration is concerned, and it occurs in all terms of the integrand. It can therefore be factored out, to yield the result

$$(\partial f/\partial t)_{\text{coll}} = \sum_l P_l(\cos\alpha)L_l f_l(k) \tag{25.13}$$

where

$$L_l f_l = -\frac{2\pi m^*}{\hbar^2} \left\{ \int [N_{0q} f_l(k) - (N_{0q} + 1)f_l(k') P_l(\cos\theta')] \times \right.$$

$$U(\mathbf{k}, \mathbf{k}')k' \sin\theta'\, d\theta' + \int [(N_{0q} + 1)f_l(k) - N_{0q} f_l(k'') P_l(\cos\theta'')] \times$$

$$\left. U(\mathbf{k}, \mathbf{k}'')k'' \sin\theta''\, d\theta'' \right\}. \tag{25.13a}$$

---

[408] E. T. Whittaker and G. N. Watson, "A Course of Modern Analysis," 4th ed., p. 395. Cambridge Univ. Press, London and New York, 1940.

The quantity θ' is the angle between $\mathbf{k}$ and $\mathbf{k}'$ on the energy surface S_+ [Eq. (25.10)], and θ'' is that quantity for the energy surface S_-.

A generalized relaxation time can always be introduced when $L_l f_l(k)$ reduces to the form[407]

$$L_l f_l(k) = - f_l(k)/\tau_l(k), \qquad l \geqslant 1. \tag{25.14}$$

The condition enunciated above is somewhat more general than that given in (25.1). If account is taken of the fact that for the equilibrium distribution (absence of electrical and thermal gradients), $L_0 f_0$ vanishes, we see from Eq. (25.13) that[408a]

$$(\partial f/\partial t)_{\text{coll}} = \sum_{l=1} P_l(\cos \alpha) L_l f_l(k), \tag{25.15}$$

and from (25.14)

$$(\partial f/\partial t)_{\text{coll}} = - \sum_{l=1} f_l(k) P_l(\cos \alpha)/\tau_l(k). \tag{25.16}$$

From the above relation it is apparent that Eq. (25.1) ensues if all $\tau_l(k)$ are equal $(l \geqslant 1)$, or if the $f_l(k)$ are negligible for $l > 1$.

We shall now proceed to examine the forms assumed by Eq. (25.13a) for various scattering mechanisms of interest.

Acoustical modes (intravalley): In these cases the energy change of the charge carrier during a collision is small compared to its average energy. Therefore $f_l(k')$ does not differ appreciably from $f_l(k)$, and it can be expanded in a Taylor's series:

$$f_l(k') = f_l(k) + (\partial f_l/\partial k)(k' - k) + \dots . \tag{25.17}$$

The condition for the validity of this procedure, namely, that the second term on the right be small compared to the first, is equivalent to requiring that $\hbar\omega_q \ll kT$. This is readily established by assuming the behavior of f_l to be similar to that of the Maxwellian equilibrium distribution,[408a] and expressing $(k' - k)$ in terms of q and k by means of the energy

---

[408a] It is to be emphasized that only small departures from the equilibrium distribution f_0 are here considered.

conservation expression given by the δ-functions in (25.3). For acoustic phonon scattering, $U(\mathbf{k}, \mathbf{k}')$ is proportional to $|\mathbf{q}|^2/\omega_{\mathbf{q}}$.[406] It is not necessary for our purposes, however, to evaluate the integral (25.13a). It is sufficient to note that the approximation of $f_l(k')$ by the first term in (25.17) insures that $f_l(k)$ occur as a common factor throughout the integrand in (25.13a). The collision integral thereby assumes the form of (25.14), and a relaxation time can be defined. Thus, although the relaxation concept cannot be rigorously justified for the case of acoustic phonon scattering, its applicability is reasonably satisfactory because of the low energy of the average phonon compared to the thermal energy kT. In solids having nonspherical energy surfaces where the effective mass is very anisotropic, it may be necessary to introduce a relaxation time tensor, as was done by Herring and Vogt[321] or by Korenblit.[360f]

Optical modes, also intervalley scattering: In this case, the optical phonons can all be treated as having the same frequency. Thus the integrals over k', i.e., over q, reduce to finite differences. Furthermore, N_{0q} is now independent of q. Owing, however, to the large changes in energy in a collision, the difference $f_l(k') - f_l(k)$ is not expected to be small compared to $f_l(k)$, so that the expression in brackets in (25.13a) cannot be expanded. For polar materials, the function $U(\mathbf{k}, \mathbf{k}')$ goes approximately as $|\mathbf{q}|^{-2}/\omega_l$,[45] where ω_l is the frequency of the longitudinal optical mode. It therefore follows that a relaxation time cannot be introduced. The exception is at sufficiently high temperatures, where realization of the condition $\hbar\omega_l \ll kT$ permits an approximation of the type outlined for acoustic phonons.

In the limit at very low temperatures, $kT \ll \hbar\omega_l$, an expression for a relaxation time has been derived by Davydov and Shmushkevitch.[408b] This expression follows by consideration only of the *absorption* of phonons by the conduction electrons having energy much less than $\hbar\omega_l$. It has been verified by Howarth and Sondheimer[45] that such an expression is identical to the low temperature limit of their variational calculation. The implications associated with relaxation approximations in the low-temperature cases are not, however, so unambiguously established as for the high-temperature limit. For example, the point is made by Howarth

---

[408b] B. Davydov and I. Shmushkevitch, *J. Phys. USSR* **3**, 359 (1940).

and Sondheimer[45] that other authors, using a somewhat different concept, have developed an expression differing by a factor of 3 from the one cited above.

In the case of nonpolar solids, it turns out that $U(\mathbf{k}, \mathbf{k}')$ is independent of $\mathfrak{q}$ and is therefore constant throughout the integration. The $f_l(k')$ terms then drop out for $l > 0$ because the coefficients are integrals of the Legendre polynomials, which are orthogonal, and it is established that a relaxation time exists always. The same statement applies for intervalley scattering.

Scattering by impurities and lattice defects: For all scattering processes involving no energy losses, $f_l(k') = f_l(\kappa)$. This term can therefore be factored out and a generalized relaxation time can always be defined. [Note that $U(\mathbf{k}', \mathbf{k}) = U(\mathbf{k}, \mathbf{k}')$, and no phonons are involved.] Examples of this are impurity scattering (ionized or neutral) and lattice defects.

(3) Application of the variational method to polar semiconductors. Here we consider only semiconductors where the charge carriers interact weakly with the phonon field. The strength of this interaction is measured by an interaction parameter, or coupling constant, which is given by the relation[409]

$$\alpha = \frac{e^2}{\hbar}\left(\frac{1}{\varepsilon_\infty} - \frac{1}{\varepsilon_0}\right)\left(\frac{m^*}{2\hbar\omega_l}\right)^{1/2} \tag{25.18}$$

where ω_l is the angular frequency of the longitudinal optical mode; m^*, the effective mass of the charge carriers; ε_0, the static dielectric constant; and ε_∞ is the dielectric constant for infinite frequencies (i.e., at frequencies so high that the ionic motion cannot follow), equal to the square of the optical refractive index. It is clear that only longitudinal vibrations have a polar interaction with the charge carriers, inasmuch as any transverse polarization wave would have zero divergence and could therefore not give rise to a polarization electric field.[410, 410a]

409 H. Fröhlich, H. Pelzer, and S. Zienau, *Phil. Mag.* [7] **41**, 221 (1950).
410 H. Fröhlich and N. F. Mott, *Proc. Roy. Soc.* **A171**, 496 (1939).
410a H. Fröhlich, *Proc. Roy. Soc.* **A160**, 230 (1937).

In the case of weak interactions, $\alpha < 1$, perturbation methods can be used to derive an expression for the energy of the system consisting of the charge carrier in the polarized medium.[409, 411] This treatment is applicable to those semiconductors where the degree of ionicity is small. A further consideration is a large high-frequency dielectric constant. Examples are the III-V compounds and the PbS,-Se,-Te series. For the more ionic crystals, such as the alkali halides, α may range as high as 6. In these cases, other procedures have been employed[411-413] (see also Section 31d). Recent values of some of the optical constants appearing in Eq. (25.18) for the common III-V compounds have been given by Hass and Henvis.[413a] The Debye characteristic temperatures and certain elastic constants are presented by Joshi and Mitra for a number of crystals.[413b] Information is also available from studies of nuclear quadrupole spin-lattice relaxation times carried out by Mieher.[413c] On the basis of parameters deduced from far infra-red restrahlen spectra, refractive indices, dielectric constants, and effective masses, Hilsum has calculated the mobility which might be expected from polar scattering at 290°K in the common III-V compounds.[413d] The interaction of charge carriers with the polar-optical vibrations in weakly-polar cubic semiconductors — such as the III-V compounds — is considered theoretically by Gurevich et al. in connection with the infrared absorption by free carriers.[413e] The observation of special threshold effects is predicted when a definite relationship exists between the infrared frequency and the frequency of the longitudinal optical vibrations.

A phenomenon which can reduce the electron-phonon interaction significantly below that given by relation (25.18) is the screening effect of the conduction electrons.[414] This can be important at low temperatures where the Debye length is small compared to the reciprocal of the phonon

---

[411] H. Fröhlich, *Advances in Physics* **3**, 325 (1954).

[412] T. Lee, F. Low, and D. Pines, *Phys. Rev.* **90**, 297 (1953).

[413] F. Low and D. Pines, *Phys. Rev.* **91**, 193 (1953).

[413a] M. Hass and B. Henvis, *Phys. and Chem. Solids* **23**, 1099 (1962).

[413b] S. Joshi and S. Mitra, *Proc. Phys. Soc.* (*London*) **76**, 295 (1960).

[413c] R. Mieher, *Phys. Rev.* **125**, 1537 (1962).

[413d] C. Hilsum, *Proc. Phys. Soc.* (*London*) **76**, 414 (1960).

[413e] V. Gurevich, I. Lang, and Yu. Firsov, *Fiz. Tverd. Tela* **4**, 1252 (1962) [translation: *Soviet Phys.-Solid State* **4**, 918 (1962)].

[414] H. Ehrenreich, *J. Phys. and Chem. Solids* **8**, 130 (1959).

wave number. It was calculated by Ehrenreich[414] that in the case of PbS containing 10^{18} carriers/cm³, the screening would reduce the coupling constant by a factor of two at 100°K for a phonon of wave number equal to that of an electron having energy kT. Thus, weak-coupling theory may be applicable in certain cases to materials having appreciable carrier concentration, where the results obtained by use of Eq. (25.18) might tend to rule it out.

For the case of electron-phonon interactions via polar optical modes, however, it is suggested by Doniach[415] that owing to the high frequency of the optical mode, the static Debye treatment of screening breaks down, and the polarization of conduction-electron space charge by the lattice must be treated in a dynamic way. In the limit of long lattice waves, the classical Drude formula for the response to an oscillating applied electric field is applied, and it leads to Drude dielectric constant of less than unity. The space-charge screening may, in this case, *increase* the electron-phonon scattering — in contrast to the quenching expected for low-frequency phonons to which the Debye theory is applied. A self-consistent-field approximation is used by Doniach in calculations of the wave number and frequency dependence of the space charge polarization by the lattice.[415] Calculations, made under the approximations of low temperatures, $kT \ll \hbar\omega$, and fairly low electron concentrations, yield a mobility which decreases with increasing carrier density.

General expressions for the electrical conductivity and thermoelectric power of semiconductors where the electron-lattice interaction is weak are given in the article by Howarth and Sondheimer,[45] cited previously, for the case where there is no magnetic field. Exact expressions are presented as ratios of infinite determinants. By breaking off the determinants at a finite number of elements, results valid to a specified order may be obtained. The temperature is introduced through the parameter $z \equiv \hbar\omega_l/kT$, and the degree of charge-carrier degeneracy by the parameter $\xi \equiv \zeta/kT$.

The theory of Howarth and Sondheimer, as well as the polaron theory of Low and Pines, has been applied by Petritz and Scanlon[416] to mobility of electrons and holes in PbS. For this material, the coupling constant α

---

[415] S. Doniach, *Proc. Phys. Soc. (London)* **73**, 849 (1959).
[416] R. L. Petritz and W. W. Scanlon, *Phys. Rev.* **97**, 1620 (1955).

is calculated to be the order of 0.28, and both theories give essentially the same results for temperatures below the Debye temperature (194°K) — the expected range of validity of the expressions derived from use of the

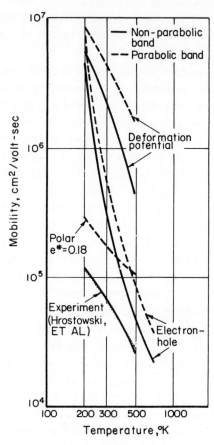

FIG. 45.   Electron mobility vs. temperature for deformation potential, electron-hole, and polar scattering in indium antimonide.   Solid lines refer to calculations using the theoretical nonparabolic conduction band structure.   Dashed lines refer to calculations using a parabolic conduction band corresponding to a mass $m^* = 0.013\, m_0$ and the correct Fermi level.   The experimental data by Hrostowski et al.[266] are represented by the dotted line (after Ehrenreich[215]).

polaron theory.   Comparison with the experimental data reveals fairly good agreement as to temperature dependence of the mobility for

$100°K \leqslant T \leqslant \theta$, but noticeable disagreement at the higher temperatures, where the theory gives a much weaker temperature dependence than the approximately $T^{-2.5}$ behavior, which is observed. The theoretical behavior in the vicinity of 77°K is markedly improved by the admixture of a small amount of acoustic mode scattering — a process which may be expected to become important inasmuch as the polar optical modes are being frozen out as T drops below θ. The reasons for the discrepancy at the higher temperatures appear to be more involved, and it was not possible to arrive at specific conclusions.

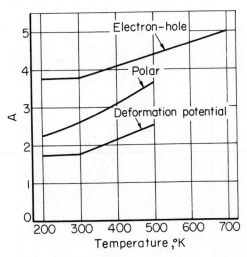

FIG. 46. Thermoelectric transport term A for various scattering mechanisms in intrinsic InSb (after Ehrenreich[215]).

Electron scattering in intrinsic indium antimonide has been investigated by Ehrenreich[215], who took into account the nonparabolic density of states. Specific curves were calculated giving the mobility as a function of temperature for polar scattering, for acoustic-mode scattering treated by the usual deformation potential technique, and for electron-hole scattering.[215] These results are shown in Fig. 45, along with some experimental data by Hrostowski and co-workers.[266] The polar mobility was calculated by means of the variational method, while the relaxation-time approximation was applied to the acoustic mode and the electron-hole scattering. The strong interaction between the light-mass valence band and the conduction band in InSb, which is responsible for the non-parabolic characteristic in the conduction band, complicates the calculation of the matrix elements for scattering in that it mixes an appreciable amount of wave function having p-symmetry into the total wave func-

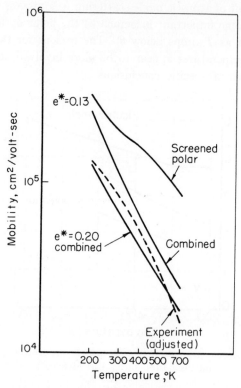

FIG. 47. Electron mobility in intrinsic InSb for screened polar scattering, and for combined screened polar and electron-hole scattering. The experimental value $e^* = 0.13$ for the effective ionic charge is used. An additional curve for $e^* = 0.20$ and combined scattering is also shown. The dashed line represents the Hall mobility data of Hrostowski and co-workers, adjusted for the change in Hall coefficient factor due to polar scattering (Fig. 42) from the value of $3\pi/8$ representative of acoustic phonon scattering (after Ehrenreich[376]).

tion, as one moves away from the band edge, which is characterized by pure s-symmetry. This p-function admixture is neglected for the results given in Fig. 45 (and for the thermoelectric transport terms shown in Fig. 46). Calculations are carried out, however, which enable one to obtain an estimate of the error involved for temperatures ranging from 300° to 700°K. Below room temperature, the effect of the admixture is probably negligible in the intrinsic InSb, especially inasmuch as the acoustic phonon scattering appears to make an insignificant contribution

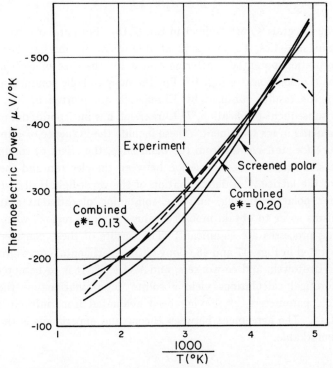

FIG. 48. Thermoelectric power in intrinsic InSb for screened polar scattering and for combined screened polar and electron-hole scattering for two values of the effective ionic charge e^*. The "screened polar" curve is independent of e^*. The dashed curve represents the experimental data of Weiss[418] (after Ehrenreich[376]).

there. It is noted from Fig. 45 that polar scattering is the dominant mechanism between 200° and 500°K, while at higher temperatures, electron-hole collisions become important.

Although a specific discussion of thermoelectric phenomena is outside the scope of this work, it is desirable to reproduce Ehrenreich's results for the scattering term A in the one-band expression for the thermoelectric power shown below:

$$\alpha = - (k/e)(A - \zeta/kT), \qquad e > 0 \text{ for electrons.} \qquad (25.19)$$

When the relaxation time approximation is applicable, it is seen from Eqs. (2.6), (2.7), (7.13), and (7.17) that

$$A = \mathscr{C}_2/\mathscr{C}_1 kT \qquad (25.20)$$

where the integrals $\mathscr{C}_n$ are defined in Eq. (7.15). For parabolic bands and Boltzmann statistics, A is independent of temperature and has the value 2 for deformation potential scattering and 4 for the case of electron-hole collisions (Coulomb scattering).[417] For the nonparabolic conduction band in InSb, the results obtained by Ehrenreich are plotted in Fig. 46.

In a subsequent publication,[376] Ehrenreich has incorporated a number of refinements in his treatment. These include the influence of p-function admixture for states away from the band edge, the effect of conduction-electron screening on the interaction between the electron and the polar modes of the lattice,[414] a determination of the weak-field Hall coefficient factor for polar scattering, and the combining of different scattering mechanisms so as to obtain mobility values in those regions where both scattering processes are significant. The results of these considerations are illustrated in Figs. 47 and 48, along with experimental curves from the data of Hrostowski and co-workers, and Weiss.[418] It is to be noted that the theoretical calculations yield absolute determinations — the only adjustable parameters, e^*, having been evaluated from infrared reflectivity data. The agreement between theory and experiment is therefore quite remarkable.

c. The Variational Principle in the Presence of a Magnetic Field

The procedure for dealing with the problem when a magnetic field exists is more complicated inasmuch as the symmetry requirements for Kohler's variational principle are destroyed. The difficulty is that the operators involving the magnetic field are antisymmetric in the field vector $\mathbf{H}$. This characteristic is manifest in the Kohler-Onsager relations

---

[417] The value 4 neglects effects of electron-electron interactions. If these are considered, one obtains 3.2. See, for example, C. Herring, *Phys. Rev.* **96**, 1163 (1954).

[418] H. Weiss, *Z. Naturforsch.* **11a**, 131 (1956).

(see Section 1). Implications of this state of affairs have been discussed by Ziman[419] and by Tauber[420] in articles dealing with the use of the variational principle in transport theory. A fundamental consideration is the principle of microscopic reversibility [cf. Eq. (25.5a)]. To retrace the motion, it is necessary not only to reverse velocities, but also to reverse the direction of the magnetic field.

Various procedures have been used by different investigators in obtaining explicit results for certain of the galvanomagnetic phenomena. The initial work by Lewis and Sondheimer[421] arrived at an expression for the Hall coefficient which was obtained by applying the requirement that the equations must reduce to the correct form — that is, the form determined by the variational method — when H became zero. Ehrenreich,[376] in his analysis of InSb, employed a scheme which remained a variational treatment in the case of small (but nonzero) magnetic fields. The possibility of taking the magnetic field into account by means of an iteration process is discussed by Seeger.[422] This consideration is occasioned by the fact that the use of iteration has been applied in studies of asymmetric scattering from crystal defects.[423, 424]

The weak-field Hall coefficient, the mobility, the thermoelectric power, and, to a reduced accuracy, the Lorenz number and the weak-field Ettingshausen coefficient have been computed for optical mode scattering in a polar semiconductor by Delves.[425] The technique was to integrate numerically the Boltzmann equation on an electronic computer. Results were obtained for the temperature range $\frac{1}{2}\hbar\omega_l \leqslant kT \leqslant 2\hbar\omega_l$, and the degeneracy range $-2 \leqslant (\zeta/kT) \leqslant 5$.

Details involved in the formulation of a variational principle which takes into account the presence of a magnetic field are presented in several publications. These include an article by García-Moliner and Simons,[426,a] who also consider the case of boundary scattering — another

---

[419] J. M. Ziman, *Can. J. Phys.* **34**, 1256 (1956).

[420] G. E. Tauber, *J. Franklin Inst.* **268**, 175 (1959).

[421] B. F. Lewis and E. H. Sondheimer, *Proc. Roy. Soc.* **A227**, 241 (1955).

[422] A. Seeger, *Can. J. Phys.* **34**, 1278 (1956).

[423] A. W. Sáenz, *Phys. Rev.* **91**, 1142 (1953).

[424] H. Bross and A. Seeger, *J. Phys. and Chem. Solids* **4**, 161 (1958); **6**, 324 (1958).

[425] R. T. Delves, *Proc. Phys. Soc.* (*London*) **73**, 572 (1959).

[426] F. García-Moliner and S. Simons, *Proc. Cambridge Phil. Soc.* **53**, 848 (1957).

[426a] See also, R. Englman, *Proc. Phys. Soc.* (*London*) **76**, 909 (1960).

situation in which the principle of microscopic reversibility breaks down. A generalized variation technique is also used by Tauber to develop expressions for the electrical and thermal transport coefficients,[427] taking into account also the phonon distribution functions. Inclusion of interband scattering into the variational scheme has also been done.[420]. The variational principle has also been used for establishing the transport properties of anisotropic solids. Specific application to a metal possessing cubic symmetry has been made by García-Moliner.[428] Expressions are developed for Hall fields and magnetoresistance effects, and the coefficients are evaluated to higher orders than those for the Seitz relationship given in Section 8a. The dependence of the transverse magnetoresistance on crystallographic orientation is found to be quite similar to that actually measured on certain metals — tungsten, for example. Another interesting observation is the fact that if H is along a direction of lower symmetry than [001] or [011], a Hall voltage for longitudinal magnetic fields [see Section 11b(2)], with the leading term going as H^3, can enter. The application of the variational procedure to studies of transport phenomena in semiconductors having degenerate energy surfaces with a certain degree of warping, such as silicon and germanium, is outlined by Tauber and Soffer.[429] The interband scattering effects are inherently included by the particular form of the collision operator.

Application of the variational technique to the weak-field magnetoresistance in metals is discussed by Hajdu[430] for isotropic dependence, and also for a more general quadratic dependence of energy on wave number. The question of convergence of approximation solutions to the Bloch integral equation, and therefore the convergence of series expressions for the transport coefficients, is investigated by Langbein through the use of variational formulations.[431]

A variational method is used by Tsuji[432] in which the variational function satisfies a different subsidiary condition. Results are obtained which yield the exact solution in the case of spherical energy surfaces.

---

[427] G. E. Tauber, *Can. J. Phys.* **36**, 1308 (1958).
[428] F. García-Moliner, *Proc. Roy. Soc.* **A249**, 73 (1959).
[429] G. E. Tauber and L. Soffer, *J. Phys. and Chem. Solids* **8**, 138 (1959).
[430] János Hajdu, *Z. Physik* **160**, 47 (1960).
[431] D. Langbein, *Z. Physik* **162**, 542 (1961).
[432] M. Tsuji, *J. Phys. Soc. Japan* **13**, 979 (1958).

For the case of cubic symmetry, the method gives an approximate solution which coincides with the exact solution through linear terms in H when an energy-dependent relaxation time exists. In a subsequent paper (see Section 25a), Tsuji takes into account a deviation in the phonon distribution from the equilibrium value.[400d]

Considerations involved in attempts to produce a maximum variational principle that applies to conduction problems in a magnetic field are discussed by Bailyn.[432a] The comment is made that many of the previous formulations were able to lead to an extremal principle, but that a maximum principle remained elusive. In the words of the author, "it has appeared as if a conspiracy exists against a true maximum principle in the presence of a magnetic field." Bailyn's result is that a maximum principle does hold in the presence of a magnetic field, but that what is maximized is the part of the diagonal conductivity tensor element that is even in the magnetic field. The procedure involves a separation of the Boltzmann equation into two parts, one which arises from terms which are odd in the magnetic field, and the other which arises from terms even in **H**. The point is made that for symmetry considerations it is not the operator $L + M$ — where L is the collision operator (which can also include phonon-drag and magnon-drag effects) and M the "magnetic" operator — but rather the operator $L - ML^{-1}M$, which is the important one. The relation between the "high-field" work of Chambers, Lifshitz, and co-workers and the variational method is pointed out, the latter being applied to accommodate open-orbit effects, and to obtain interpolation formulas to span high- and low-field solutions (keeping in view the phonon-drag effects). It was found that standard operator expansion techniques are useful for obtaining solutions for the high-field limit. Because scattering by spin waves is analogous to the scattering of phonons, it is indicated that the theory of "magnon drag" follows that of phonon drag, and the effects can automatically be incorporated in all the expressions.

Bailyn's theory yields an apparently new and very interesting symmetry relation under special cases. If drag effects are negligible and if a time of relaxation exists for the collision operator L, then a symmetry relation is found to occur between the cross coefficients connecting the

---

[432a] M. Bailyn, *Phys. Rev.* **126**, 2040 (1962).

electrical and thermal quantities in the phenomenological equations
[Eqs. (1.1) and (1.2)]; namely, that the following equalities are satisfied:

$$\mathscr{M}_{ij}(\mathbf{H}) = \mathscr{M}_{ji}(-\mathbf{H}),\tag{25.21}$$

$$\mathscr{N}_{ij}(\mathbf{H}) = \mathscr{N}_{ji}(-\mathbf{H}),\tag{25.22}$$

that is, the cross-effect coefficients satisfy the same relations as do $\sigma_{ij}(\mathbf{H})$
and $\mathscr{L}_{ij}(\mathbf{H})$ [cf. Eq. (1.7)]. It then follows from Eqs. (2.7) and (2.8) that
the same statement may therefore be made for the thermoelectric and
Peltier tensors, namely,

$$\alpha_{ij}(\mathbf{H}) = \alpha_{ji}(-\mathbf{H})\tag{25.23}$$

$$\pi_{ij}(\mathbf{H}) = \pi_{ji}(-\mathbf{H})\tag{25.24}$$

A noteworthy feature, which is a consequence of the above, is that the
diagonal elements of the thermoelectric and the Peltier tensors are even
in $\mathbf{H}$.   The conditions, again, under which Bailyn's relations hold are
that phonon-drag effects are negligible and that the charge-carrier energy
commutes with the operator $L+M$ — the latter condition being certainly
true if a time of relaxation exists for L.[432a] Before Bailyn's theoretical
development, relations such as (25.23) and (25.24) could apparently be
justified only for cases of sufficient symmetry of the crystal.[432b]

In conclusion, it seems desirable to illustrate the power of the variational principle in establishing certain relations or conclusions on a very
general basis.   To do this we quote verbatim from comments made by
Herring[433]: "The question has occasionally been raised as to whether
peculiar types of scattering interactions or peculiar types of warped
energy surfaces might be capable of giving a negative magnetoresistance.
Now Kohler's general variational principle states that the distribution
function which occurs for conduction in the absence of a magnetic field
is one which minimizes the dissipation for a given current.   The dissipation is a certain quadratic functional of the distribution function
which does not depend on the external fields explicitly.   So if for a given
current the distribution which occurs in the presence of a magnetic field
differs from that in the absence of such a field, the former must give the

[432b] See comments following Eq. (1.9) in Section 1.
[433] C. Herring, *J. Phys. and Chem. Solids* 8, 543 (1959).

higher dissipation. The conclusion from this is that it is not possible to obtain a negative magnetoresistance from any theory based on a Boltzmann equation with scattering interactions in crystal-momentum space. Negative magnetoresistance can arise only from an effect of the magnetic field on the carrier concentration, from phenomena peculiar to quantum transport theory, or as a consequence of a transport equation which treats transport not in momentum space alone but in momentum and position space together."

26. GENERAL TREATMENT OF CONDUCTIVITY IN ANISOTROPIC METALS

There exists in the literature a number of articles dealing with the application of Bloch theory and the Boltzmann equation to the conductivity in anisotropic crystals, in which the electron-lattice interaction is considered in substantially more detail than is usually the case for the theoretical treatment of conductivity in most semiconductors. Various general references have been cited previously including the "Handbuch" articles,[67a, 434] that by Blatt,[44] and the texts of Seitz[435] and Wilson.[9] There are, however, a number of specific articles which it seems desirable to discuss briefly here. These include the work of Baroody[436] on the directional dependence of the electrical conductivity, at zero magnetic field, in a general metallic crystal. Special attention is given to the electron-lattice interaction. In particular, the treatment of this interaction is taken further than is done in the customary procedure which assumes spherical distributions and spherically symmetric wave functions and treats the lattice waves as either longitudinal or transverse. As a special case, the propagation of elastic waves in solids of hexagonal symmetry is investigated. Finally, the directional dependence of the conductivity is examined for several models, namely, the case of spheroidal energy surfaces and isotropic interaction function, and that of anisotropic interaction function and spherical energy surfaces. Elliptical anisotropies

---

[434] A. Sommerfeld and H. Bethe *in* "Handbuch der Physik", referenced in footnote 34c.

[435] F. Seitz in text referenced in footnote 209.

[436] E. M. Baroody, *Phys. Rev.* **58**, 793 (1940).

in **k** space are considered by Langbein [436a] with regard to their effect on electrical conductivity in connection with (a) electron energies, (b) dispersion of sound waves, and (c) electron-phonon interactions. In two subsequent papers, particular attention is paid to the behavior of the magnetoresistance.[436b] Cases of multiply-connected Fermi surfaces have been considered by Gerlach, and the influence upon the resistivity investigated.[436c] A simple model for graphite is examined, whereby two nearly cylindrical Fermi surfaces are joined.

The problem of defining a free path, or relaxation time, is discussed by Supek[437] for normal collisions with the lattice and for umklapp processes. A treatment based on specific definitions of relaxation processes is compared with Bloch theory. The influence of deviations from spherical symmetry in the energy surfaces is discussed. Theoretical studies of the interaction between the electrons and the lattice in metals have been carried out by a number of investigators. Some of the contributions which are too recent to appear in the general references by Jones and Blatt include the articles by Supek,[437a] Bailyn,[438] Whitfield,[439] Chester,[439a] and Stolz,[440] and literature cited therein.

The magnetoresistance effect in metals has been considered quite broadly by Hajdu, both under the conditions where the simple concept of the relaxation time is applicable, and also where anisotropic energy surfaces require a more sophisticated treatment of the relaxation process.[430] The application of the variational principle by Appel[397] to problems involving interactions of charge carriers and the lattice in anisotropic metals has already been discussed.

In many metals, the Fermi surfaces are highly distorted, with a number of thick "necks" passing through the zone boundaries. Such a Fermi surface is multiply connected, and extends throughout **k**-space. Intersection of such surfaces by a plane determined by the motion of an

---

[436a] D. Langbein, *Z. Physik* **166**, 22 (1962).

[436b] D. Langbein, *Z. Physik* **167**, 83, 96 (1962).

[436c] Eckard Gerlach, *Z. Physik* **166**, 81 (1962).

[437] I. Supek, *Z. Physik* **117**, 125 (1941).

[437a] I. Supek, *Z. Physik* **149**, 324 (1957); *Nuovo Cimento* **12**, 290 (1959).

[438] M. Bailyn, *Phys. Rev.* **117**, 974 (1960).

[439] G. D. Whitfield, *Phys. Rev.* **121**, 720 (1961).

[439a] G. V. Chester, *Advances in Phys.* **10**, 357 (1961).

[440] H. Stolz, *Ann. Physik* **7**, 353 (1961).

electron in electric and magnetic fields can produce closed or open curves, depending on the orientation of the plane. The behavior of strong-field galvanomagnetic effects is quite different for these two types of orbits. As pointed out by Chambers,[441] for weak-magnetic fields, an electron in its orbit in k-space will transverse only a small part of the Fermi surface before colliding, and therefore its transport properties are determined principally by the local characteristics of the surface. In strong fields, $\omega\tau \gg 1$, on the other hand, the electron will traverse a large orbit before colliding, so that the topology of the Fermi surface becomes of paramount importance. The importance of open orbits on the galvanomagnetic effects of metals was stressed by Lifshitz, Azbel', and Kaganov[57, 177] in 1956. Further calculations were carried out by Lifshitz and Peschanskii, with special attention to the cases of the open orbits.[308, 442] Considerations pertinent to the direct observation of open magnetic orbits were also discussed by Blount.[443] An interesting example of the changing of open orbits into closed orbits as the magnetic field is increased, with resultant disappearance of the H^2 term in the magnetoresistance, has been discussed by Cohen and Falicov.[443a] The authors point out that in studies of the behavior of electrons in a magnetic field, the regimes of interest have been characterized by the relation of the cyclotron frequency ω to such quantities as $1/\tau$, $kT/\hbar$, and $\zeta/\hbar$ (see Section 28). The relation of ω to $E_G/\hbar$, where E_G is an energy gap has received little attention. This condition can, however, be realized in some metals where, because of spin-orbit splitting of points of accidental degeneracy at or near the Fermi level, there exist gaps of the order of 10^{-3} ev or less. In such cases, the electron motion changes with increasing H, from orbits determined semiclassically from the entire band structure to those determined semiclassically by ignoring the gaps. Cohen and Falicov call this phenomenon *magnetic breakdown*. The effect can cause a change of any orbit — closed, extended, or open — into any other of the same or different category. Consequently, as the field is varied, one may expect to observe

[441] R. G. Chambers, *in* "The Fermi Surface" (Proc. Intern. Conf. Fermi Surface of Metals, Cooperstown, 1960) (W. Harrison and M. Webb, eds.), p. 100. Wiley, New York, 1960.

[442] I. M. Lifshitz and V. G. Peschanskii, *J. Exptl. Theoret. Phys. USSR* **38**, 188 (1960) [translation: *Soviet Phys. — JETP* **11**, 137 (1960)].

[443] E. I. Blount, *Phys. Rev. Letters* **4**, 114 (1960).

[443a] M. H. Cohen and L. M. Falicov, *Phys. Rev. Letters* **7**, 231 (1961).

the disappearance of certain phenomena and the appearance of others. Possible experimental evidence for magnetic breakdown in magnesium is discussed, and several other metals in which occurrence of the effect is anticipated are cited.

The anisotropy of the magnetoresistance in a number of metals has been measured by Alekseevskii and Gaidukov in order to determine the topology of the Fermi surfaces. Results suggest the presence of open Fermi surfaces in gold, tin, lead, copper, silver, thallium, and gallium, while indium, sodium, and perhaps aluminum have closed surfaces.[444, 445] Hall effect measurements by Kachinskii[446] on tin, and Hall and magneto-resistance measurements by Borovik on zinc suggest also that these elements possess open Fermi surfaces.[447]   On the other hand, the galvanomagnetic data on indium and aluminum by Borovik and Volotskaya are indicative of the group of metals having closed Fermi surfaces.[448] Pippard has made a study of the Fermi surface in copper by measuring as a function of crystal orientation the anomalous skin resistance of plane surfaces.[449] His results are also consistent with the postulate of open Fermi surfaces. Supporting evidence for this conclusion in the case of copper, and also for silver and gold, is available from de Haas-van Alphen effect measurements by Shoenberg.[450] Calculations based on Pippard's data were carried out for copper by García-Moliner,[451] and by Priestley[452] on the magnetoresistance data by Alekseevskii and Gaidukov for copper, silver, and gold.

---

[444] N. Alekseevskii and Yu. Gaidukov, *J. Explt. Theoret. Phys. USSR* **35**, 554 (1958); **36**, 447 (1959); **37**, 672 (1959); **38**, 1720 (1960) [respective translations: *Soviet Phys.-JETP* **8**, 383 (1959); **9**, 311 (1959); **10**, 481 (1960); **11**, 1242 (1960)].

[445] Yu. Gaidukov, *J. Exptl. Theoret. Phys. USSR* **37**, 1281 (1959) [translation: *Soviet Phys.-JETP* **10**, 913 (1960)].

[446] V. Kachinskii, *Doklady Akad. Nauk SSSR* **135**, 818 (1960) [translation: *Soviet Phys.-Doklady* **5**, 1260 (1961)].

[447] E. Borovik, *J. Exptl. Theoret. Phys. USSR* **30**, 262 (1956) [translation: *Soviet Phys.-JETP* **3**, 243 (1956)].

[448] E. Borovik and V. Volotskaya, *J. Exptl. Theoret. Phys. USSR* **38**, 261 (1960) [translation: *Soviet Phys.-JETP* **11**, 189 (1960)].

[449] A. B. Pippard, *Phil. Trans. Roy. Soc.* (*London*) **A250**, 325 (1957).

[450] D. Shoenberg, *Phil. Mag.* **5**, 105 (1960).

[451] F. García-Moliner, *Phil. Mag.* **3**, 207 (1958).

[452] M. G. Priestley, *Phil. Mag.* **5**, 111 (1960).

A number of thorough review articles, which discuss the state of affairs as of around 1960 are to be recommended. The work of Pippard[453] includes a discussion of various experimental techniques which have been useful in providing information on Fermi surface topology, namely, transport phenomena, de Haas-van Alphen and related effects, anomalous skin effect, cyclotron resonance, ultrasonic attenuation and magneto-acoustic effects,[453a] and specimen size effects. A review of some of the theoretical problems of the electron theory of metals is presented by Lifshitz and Kaganov.[454] They give particular attention to the topology of the surfaces of constant energy, including the case of open orbits in the motion of charge carriers in electric and magnetic fields. Quantum-mechanical aspects of the problem are also considered, in addition to a quasi-classical treatment of the energy levels in a magnetic field. A general quantum theory of scattering of charge carriers having an arbitrary relationship between energy and wave number is outlined. The ordinary transport properties of the noble metals are discussed by Ziman.[455] A quantitative investigation is presented of the effects of the distorted Fermi surfaces on such quantities as densities of states, optical masses, galvanomagnetic effects, and thermoelectric properties. Discussion is also devoted to thermal conductivity at low temperatures. A review article on the many-body theory of electrons in a metal has recently been written by Falicov and Heine.[456] The authors discuss the electron theory of metals, taking the Coulomb force into account from the beginning. The point is made that all properties which depend only on the electrons at or near the Fermi level can be understood in terms of quasi-particle excitations at the Fermi level. In first approximation these excitations are independent, so that the independent-electron model has a broad justification. An excellent source of information in the areas being discussed here is the Proceedings of the International Conference on the Fermi Surface of Metals held at Cooperstown, New York, in 1960 and published in book form.[457] In connection with galvanomagnetic phenom-

[453] A. B. Pippard, *Repts. Progr. Phys.* **23**, 176 (1960).
[453a] See also, A. B. Pippard, *Proc. Roy. Soc.* **A257**, 165 (1960).
[454] I. M. Lifshitz and M. I. Kaganov, *Uspekhi Fiz. Nauk* **69**, 419 (1959) [translation: *Soviet Phys.-Uspekhi* **2**, 831 (1960)].
[455] J. M. Ziman, *Advances in Phys.* **10**, 1 (1961).
[456] L. Falicov and V. Heine, *Advances in Phys.* **10**, 57 (1961).
[457] "The Fermi Surface" (W. Harrison and M. Webb, eds.). Wiley, New York, 1960.

ena, there is an article by Chambers[441] which reviews the effect of energy surface topology on magnetoresistance. Consideration is given to the weak-magnetic-field region and to the strong-field classical region, with some comments on the quantum oscillation region at strong fields.

Further investigations of the effect of Fermi surface topology on galvanomagnetic effects are reported by Klauder and Kunzler[458, 459] and by Fawcett.[460] The anisotropy of the relaxation time of the conduction electrons in noble metals is examined by Ziman,[461] and the effect on the Hall coefficient is discussed. Also of interest are theoretical calculations by Ham,[462] by Harrison,[463, 464] and by Cornwell[464a] on band structure, the importance of spin-orbit splitting pointed out by Cohen and Falicov,[465] and the effect of electron-electron and electron-phonon interactions on a number of measured quantities pointed out by Stern,[466] Falicov,[467] Quinn,[467a] and others.

Additional literature on the Fermi surfaces of metals includes articles by Gold and Priestley,[467b] Alekseevskii and Gaidukov,[467c] and Khaikin on tin;[467d] and by Khaikin and Mina on lead.[467e] Results of high-field de Haas-van Alphen experiments on aluminum have been presented by Priestley.[467f] The magnetoresistance anisotropy studies on nickel reported by Fawcett and Reed suggest similarities between the Fermi surface of

[458] J. R. Klauder and J. E. Kunzler,[457] p. 125.

[459] J. R. Klauder and J. E. Kunzler, *J. Phys. and Chem. Solids* 18, 256 (1961); *Phys. Rev. Letters* 6, 179 (1961).

[460] E. Fawcett, *Phys. Rev. Letters* 6, 534 (1961); 7, 370 (1961).

[461] J. M. Ziman, *Phys. Rev.* 121, 1320 (1961).

[462] F. S. Ham,[457] p. 9.

[463] W. A. Harrison,[457] p. 28.

[464] W. A. Harrison, *Phys. Rev.* 118, 1182, 1190 (1960).

[464a] J. F. Cornwell, *Phil. Mag.* 6, 727 (1961).

[465] M. H. Cohen and L. M. Falicov, *Phys. Rev. Letters* 5, 544 (1960).

[466] E. A. Stern,[457] p. 50; *Phys. Rev.* 122, 1773 (1961).

[467] L. M. Falicov,[457] p. 39.

[467a] J. J. Quinn,[457] p. 58.

[467b] A. V. Gold and M. G. Priestley, *Phil. Mag.* 5, 1089 (1960).

[467c] N. Alekseevskii and Yu. Gaidukov, *J. Exptl. Theoret. Phys. USSR* 41, 1079 (1961) [translation: *Soviet Phys.-JETP* 14, 770 (1962)].

[467d] M. S. Khaikin, *J. Exptl. Theoret. Phys. USSR* 42, 27 (1962); 43, 59 (1962) [translation: *Soviet Phys.-JETP* 15, 18 (1962); *ibid.* 16, 42 (1963).

[467e] M. S. Khaikin and R. T. Mina, *J. Exptl. Theoret. Phys. USSR* 42, 35 (1962) [translation: *Soviet Phys.-JETP* 15, 24 (1962).

[467f] M. G. Priestley, *Phil. Mag.* 7, 1205 (1962).

nickel and that of copper.[467g]   A discussion concerning Fermi surfaces in certain alloys of the noble metals is given by Sato and Toth.[467h] Recent theoretical papers are concerned with energy bands in periodic lattices,[467i] in aluminum[467j] and in lithium.[467k] The Fermi surface and energy bands of copper have also been studied by Segall.[467l]

[467g] E. Fawcett and W. A. Reed, *Phys. Rev. Letters* **9**, 336 (1962).
[467h] H. Sato and R. S. Toth, *Phys. Rev. Letters* **8**, 239 (1962).
[467i] F. S. Ham and B. Segall, *Phys. Rev.* **124**, 1786 (1961).
[467j] B. Segall, *Phys. Rev.* **124**, 1797 (1961).
[467k] J. Callaway, *Phys. Rev.* **124**, 1824 (1961).
[467l] B. Segall, *Phys. Rev.* **125**, 109 (1962).

X.
Miscellaneous Items

27. INHOMOGENEITIES

It was pointed out in Section 9b that any perturbation of the Hall field — be it due to contacts applied to the specimen, to surface conduction, to two-carrier effects (including recombination processes), or to inhomogeneities — can exert a strong influence on galvanomagnetic voltages. In this section, the question of inhomogeneities is considered in greater detail.

a. Random Inhomogeneities in Measurement Sample

That impurity concentration gradients can strongly affect a galvanomagnetic measurement was pointed out by Herring some time ago.[468] More recently, he has given a theoretical treatment of the effect of random inhomogeneities on electrical and galvanomagnetic properties of materials.[469] Formulae are developed which are asymptotically exact in the limit of small fractional fluctuations of the local conductivity. The scale of the inhomogeneities is small compared with the size of the specimen but large compared to such quantities as a Debye length or suitably defined mean free path. Herring points out that nonuniformities of a larger scale require consideration of the boundary conditions of a specific geometry, while those of a smaller scale call for a microscopic transport theory involving position as well as momentum variables.

Even under the assumptions delineated above, the expressions are quite cumbersome. We shall present here the results only for the case where the fluctuations are statistically isotropic and involve only the carrier concentration n, and not the mobility. The weak-field magneto-conductivity ratios then assume the following forms[469]:

---

[468] C. Herring, T. H. Geballe, and J. E. Kunzler, *Bell. System Tech. J.* **38**, 657 (1959).
[469] C. Herring, *J. Appl. Phys.* **31**, 1939 (1960).

$$\left(\frac{\sigma^0_{xxzz}}{\sigma_0}\right)_{\text{eff}} = \left(\frac{\sigma^0_{xxzz}}{\sigma_0}\right)\left\{1 + \left[-\frac{2}{15} + \frac{1}{15}\left(\frac{\sigma^0_{yyzz} + \sigma^0_{zzzz}}{\sigma^0_{xxzz}}\right) + \right.\right. \tag{27.1}$$

$$\left.\left.\frac{1}{3}\frac{(\mu_0{}^H/c)^2 \sigma_0}{\sigma^0_{xxzz}}\right]\frac{\langle(n - \langle n\rangle)^2\rangle}{\langle n\rangle^2}\right\} \qquad \text{(isotropic fluctuations in } n\text{)},$$

$$\left(\frac{\sigma^0_{zzzz}}{\sigma_0}\right)_{\text{eff}} = \left(\frac{\sigma^0_{zzzz}}{\sigma_0}\right)\left\{1 + \left[-\frac{2}{15} + \frac{1}{15}\left(\frac{\sigma^0_{xxzz} + \sigma^0_{yyzz}}{\sigma^0_{zzzz}}\right)\right]\frac{\langle(n - \langle n\rangle)^2\rangle}{\langle n\rangle^2}\right\}$$

$$\text{(isotropic fluctuations in } n\text{).} \tag{27.2}$$

where $\langle n\rangle$ denotes the spatial average of n, and the last factor in the above expressions is the mean square fractional departure of the local n from the mean n. Herring's notation is such that his magnetoconductivity is related to the coefficient used above (see Section 8a) by the expression

$$\sigma^{(2)}_{\nu\nu} = \sigma^0_{\nu\nu zz} H^2, \qquad H \equiv H_z. \tag{27.3}$$

The effective conductivity or resistivity tensors — which are the measured quantities — are defined by the relations

$$\langle \mathbf{J}\rangle = \boldsymbol{\sigma}_{\text{eff}}\langle \mathbf{E}\rangle \qquad \text{or} \qquad \langle \mathbf{E}\rangle = \boldsymbol{\rho}_{\text{eff}}\langle \mathbf{J}\rangle. \tag{27.4}$$

We note from Eqs. (27.1) and (27.2) that, in addition to making a significant difference in the observed magnetoresistance, the inhomogeneities produce an intermixing of transverse and longitudinal effects. This behavior can be especially important in the case of the longitudinal magnetoresistance, which may be very small or zero in crystals of high symmetry. From (27.2), however, it is apparent that inhomogeneities lead to a nonzero effective longitudinal magnetoresistance.

For the strong-field magnetoresistance, where the local transverse magnetoresistance saturates, Herring obtains

$$\left[\frac{\rho(\infty)}{\rho(0)}\right]_{\text{eff}} = \frac{\rho(\infty)}{\rho(0)}\left[1 + \frac{2}{3}\frac{\langle(n - \langle n\rangle)^2\rangle}{\langle n\rangle^2}\right] \qquad \text{(isotropic fluctuations in } n\text{)}$$

$$\tag{27.5}$$

for the longitudinal case. The behavior of the transverse magneto-resistance at strong fields is somewhat more complicated inasmuch as the directional distribution of the fluctuations is especially important. If the fluctuations are statistically isotropic,

$$\left[\frac{\rho_{yy}(H)}{\rho(0)}\right]_{\text{eff}} \sim \frac{\rho_{yy}(H)}{\rho(0)}\left[1 + \lambda\,\frac{|RH|}{\rho_{yy}(H)}\,\frac{\langle(n - \langle n\rangle)^2\rangle}{\langle n\rangle^2}\right] \tag{27.6}$$

(isotropic fluctuations in n; $H \equiv H_z \gg c/\mu_0$)

where the factor λ is the order of unity, being approximately 0.9 for n-type germanium. It is seen that the inhomogeneity factor is multiplied by $(RH)/\rho$, the tangent of the Hall angle, which may be the order of 10 or more in high-mobility materials. Thus it is apparent that the strong-field transverse magnetoresistance can be greatly affected by inhomogeneities. We note in Eq. (27.6) that the measured magneto-resistance does not saturate but is asymptotically proportional to H. This behavior is a result of the assumption of statistical isotropy in the fluctuations. If, on the other hand, the carrier fluctuations are limited to the directions normal to the direction of the magnetic field through the sample, then Eq. (27.6) is replaced by

$$\left[\frac{\rho_{yy}(H)}{\rho(0)}\right]_{\text{eff}} \sim \frac{\rho_{yy}(H)}{\rho(0)}\left\{1 + \lambda'\left[\frac{RH}{\rho_{yy}(H)}\right]^2\frac{\langle(n - \langle n\rangle)^2\rangle}{\langle n\rangle^2}\right\} \tag{27.7}$$

$(H \equiv H_z \gg c/\mu_0;$ fluctuation in n limited to x- and y-directions)

where λ' is the order of unity. We see that in this case the influence of the inhomogeneities is even greater since the square of the tangent of the Hall angle is involved, and the transverse magnetoresistance continues as H^2 in strong fields.

Actually there must occur at high fields a substantial distortion of the current lines. This is necessary since otherwise the variation in Hall field in different regions would cause a violation of the basic requirement that curl **E** vanish throughout the specimen. Herring points out that when the distortions of the current lines do become large, the small fluctuation treatment is not adequate to describe the state of affairs. Thus one should not expect Eqs. (27.6) and (27.7) to be quantitatively accurate when the inhomogeneity in the current distribution is large.

It turns out though that the formulae developed on the basis of small fluctuations yield fairly good results for a number of examples where the fluctuations are sizable. This can be seen from a comparison with equations developed for cases involving large fluctuations and special geometries of fluctuations: a random mixture of two phases, the stratified or laminated medium, and certain types of inclusions. Of particular interest is the stratified medium, i.e., the situation where n is a function of a single coordinate, for example, x. Here exact calculations are possible, and Herring shows that for grad n and $\mathbf{J}$ in the x-direction and the magnetic field in the z-direction the strong-field magnetoresistance does indeed have the form of (27.7), regardless of the degree of distortion of the current lines. For the case of isolated inclusions or for inclusions so dense that overlap occurs, the problem is not so clear cut. Nevertheless, it appears that the transverse magnetoresistance increases without limit at strong fields when the local Hall constant and magnetoresistance saturate, in qualitative agreement with Eq. (27.6) or (27.7) developed by the small fluctuation theory.[469]

To illustrate a case where the small fluctuation formulae break down seriously at strong magnetic fields, Herring considers occasional rod-like inclusions having a different Hall coefficient from that of the surrounding continuum with axes along the magnetic field direction and extending the full thickness of the sample. It is in this latter respect that the example differs from the case of isolated inclusions mentioned previously. The present example is therefore a two-dimensional problem, and at strong magnetic fields the distortion is such that the current lines avoid the rods altogether. The galvanomagnetic properties at strong fields are thus determined only by the characteristics of the continuum and by the extent to which the current lines are squeezed in their avoidance of the rods. Hence the effective magnetoresistance in this model will saturate at strong fields (provided of course that the local magnetoresistance in the continuum does likewise) — in contrast to the H^2 dependence predicted by Eq. (27.7).

Actually, isolated inclusions in three dimensions lead to current distributions which become more and more nearly two-dimensional as $H \to \infty$, inasmuch as the current distortions continue to spread above and below the inclusion in the magnetic field direction. If we designate by Δz the distance beyond the cylinder for which this distortion persists, Herring obtains an expression for Δz which is asymptotically the order of

$$\Delta z \approx a(H/H_0) \, [\ln (H/H_0)]^{-1} \tag{27.7a}$$

where a is the radius of the cylindrical inclusion having its axis along the z-direction and H_0 is the field at which RH equals the resistivity. Herring points out that throughout most of this region j_z is $\gg j_x$ and j_y and that the extra dissipation introduced by this current distortion is, for fixed current density infinitely far from the distortions, proportional to Δz. Thus in a medium with a dilute sprinkling of such three-dimensional inclusions the macroscopic resistivity transverse to **H** should be a constant plus a term behaving like Eq. (27.7a). This behavior resembles qualitatively that of the weak-fluctuation expression (27.6), differing only by the presence of the logarithmic factor. Herring's derivation of relation (27.7a), which is based on interesting physical considerations, is given in the Appendix to his article.[469]

Application of some of the consequences of the small fluctuation theory to related problems of practical interest for semiconductors is also discussed by Herring. These include dislocations, statistical inhomogeneity phenomena (including impurity scattering effects), and magnetoresistance in polycrystalline specimens of material where the single crystal properties are anisotropic.[469]

b. Gross Inhomogeneities in Measurement Sample

When gross inhomogeneities exist, it is necessary to take into account the distortion of the current lines, and therefore each specific geometry must be considered separately. The case of nonconducting cylinders or spheres in uniform media ("pores") has been examined by Juretschke *et al.*[470] in connection with the conductivity and the weak-field Hall coefficient. The behavior of certain other types of inclusions was discussed in the preceding section. It was shown by Samoilovich and Korenblit that a nonuniform temperature field in an anisotropic medium can lead to thermoelectric eddy currents.[470a]

(1) Continuous variations in conductivity. The boundary conditions determining the electric field and the current distribution are

---

[470] H. Juretschke, R. Landauer, and J. Swanson, *J. Appl. Phys.* **27**, 838 (1956).
[470a] A. G. Samoilovich and L. L. Korenblit, *Fiz. Tverdogo Tela* **3**, 2054 (1961) [translation: *Soviet Phys.-Solid State* **3**, 1494 (1962)].

$$\text{curl } \mathbf{E} = 0, \tag{27.8}$$

$$\text{div } \mathbf{J} = 0. \tag{27.9}$$

In addition, there are the defining equations for the electric potential and the conductivity or resistivity, namely,

$$\mathbf{E} = - \text{ grad } V, \tag{27.10}$$

$$\mathbf{J} = \boldsymbol{\sigma} \mathbf{E}, \qquad \mathbf{E} = \boldsymbol{\rho} \mathbf{J} \tag{27.11}$$

where the tensors $\boldsymbol{\sigma}$ and $\boldsymbol{\rho}$ are in general functions of $\mathbf{H}$. If they are independent of position, relations (27.9) – (27.11) yield Laplace's equation. Consider the local conductivity to be isotropic at each point with $\mathbf{H} \equiv (0, 0, H)$ so that the conductivity tensor is given by

$$\boldsymbol{\sigma} \equiv \begin{pmatrix} \sigma_t & \beta\sigma_t & 0 \\ -\beta\sigma_t & \sigma_t & 0 \\ 0 & 0 & \sigma_l \end{pmatrix} \tag{27.12}$$

where $\beta = RH/\rho$ is the tangent of the Hall angle. The components of the tensor transverse and parallel to the magnetic field, σ_t and σ_l, respectively, and β are, in general, functions of position and magnetic field. In this case, Laplace's equation is replaced by

$$\nabla^2 V + \left[\frac{\sigma_l}{\sigma_t} - 1\right] \frac{\partial^2 V}{\partial z^2} + \frac{1}{\sigma_t} \left[\frac{\partial \sigma_t}{\partial x} - \frac{\partial}{\partial y} \beta\sigma_t\right] \frac{\partial V}{\partial x} + \tag{27.13}$$

$$\frac{1}{\sigma_t} \left[\frac{\partial \sigma_t}{\partial y} + \frac{\partial}{\partial x} \beta\sigma_t\right] \frac{\partial V}{\partial y} + \frac{1}{\sigma_t} \frac{\partial \sigma_l}{\partial z} \frac{\partial V}{\partial z} = 0.$$

The boundary conditions are that the normal component of the current density, J_n, vanish at all bounding surfaces except of course at the ends where the current leads are attached. To avoid the complications of the end electrodes — this problem having been discussed in Section 9b — we shall consider long thin parallelepipeds of length l much greater than width w or thickness b.

To handle Eq. (27.13) analytically we must consider special cases.

J *and* grad σ *exist along the z-direction:* The differential equation (27.13), far from the current contacts to the specimen, is then solved by a potential of the form

$$V = c \int_0^z \exp\left(-\int_0^{z'} K(z'') \, dz''\right) dz'$$

$$= c \int_0^z \frac{dz'}{\sigma_l(z')}, \qquad\qquad K(z) \equiv \sigma_l^{-1} \frac{\partial \sigma_l}{\partial z}. \qquad (27.14)$$

The current density is given by

$$J = I/A$$

where I is the total current and A is the cross-sectional area. We note that there is no distortion of the current lines. This is expected, inasmuch as no Hall field exists.

J *exists along x; grad* σ *in yz-plane;* β *constant:* The differential equation is solved by

$$V = c(x + \beta y), \qquad \beta = \text{const} \qquad (27.15)$$

assuming again that the current contacts are far removed (as regards cross-sectional dimensions) from the region in which knowledge of the potential is sought.

One finds again for this case that there are no strong perturbations in the current distribution caused by the magnetic field. The expression for the current density is simply

$$J_x = I\sigma_t(y, z) \Big/ \int_A \sigma_t(y', z') \, dy' \, dz'. \qquad (27.16)$$

The condition that β be constant is not unrealistically severe. It is satisfied if the inhomogeneity is one of carrier concentration only, and the Hall mobility R/ρ is uniform.

J *and* grad σ *exist along the x-direction:* If again we assume the inhomogeneity to be one of carrier concentration, with β a constant, Eq. (27.13) becomes

$$\frac{\partial^2 V}{\partial x^2} + \frac{\partial^2 V}{\partial y^2} + K(x)\left[\frac{\partial V}{\partial x} + \beta \frac{\partial V}{\partial y}\right] = 0 \qquad (27.17)$$

where $K(x) [\equiv n^{-1} \, dn/dx]$ is the fractional change in carrier concentration per unit distance along the x-axis. It turns out that the above equation is separable in Cartesian coordinates if $K(x)$ is a constant. This case, which implies an exponential variation of n, was examined by Bate and Beer.[471] Solutions for the potential, far from the ends of a sample which is long compared to its width and thickness $(l \gg w, l \gg b)$, are

$$V = c_1 e^{-K(x + \beta y)}, \qquad K \neq 0, \qquad (27.18)$$

$$V = c_2(x + \beta y), \qquad K = 0.$$

The current density, again far from the ends of the sample, is given by

$$J_x = \frac{I}{wb} \frac{\gamma/2}{\sinh \gamma/2} e^{-\gamma y/w}, \qquad J_y = J_z = 0, \qquad (27.19)$$

where I is the total current and $\gamma \equiv Kw\beta$.

We see from (27.19) that the effect of the magnetic field is to "move" the current toward one side of the sample. Since an exponential function is involved, the distortion of the current lines can be quite severe at strong magnetic fields. This is illustrated in Fig. 49, which shows the current distribution across the sample for different values of γ. We note that for $\gamma \sim 10$, the current effectively avoids half of the sample. As will be seen later, such behavior can yield negative contributions to the transverse magnetoresistance. It is important to note from (27.19) that even though the gradient in carrier density be small, a sufficiently large Hall angle can cause noticeable effects.

For the particular model being discussed, where K is a constant and therefore J_y is zero, the measured Hall coefficient is the local value at the point of measurement,[471] namely,

$$V(x, w/2) - V(x, -w/2) = R(x)IH/b. \qquad (27.20)$$

It is in the magnetoresistance where the distortion of the current lines leads to the most conspicuous effects. For example, the measured resistivity for $H > 0$ is given by the curves in Fig. 49 if the ordinate is interpreted as $\rho_0(V_1 - V_2)_H / \rho_H(V_1 - V_2)_0$ where the subscripts, $0, H$ denote, respectively, field-off and field-on conditions. Obviously, the inhomogeneity contribution to the magnetoresistance is not the same for both directions of the magnetic field unless the probes are located at the center $(y = 0)$.

---

[471] R. T. Bate and A. C. Beer, *J. Appl. Phys.* **32**, 800 (1961).

After an average over both directions of H, the expression for the voltage across the resistivity probes assumes the following form:

$$\frac{(V_1 - V_2)_H}{(V_1 - V_2)_0} \equiv \frac{[V(x_1, y, z) - V(x_2, y, z)]_H}{[V(x_1, y, z) - V(x_2, y, z)]_0} = \frac{\rho_H}{\rho_0} \frac{\gamma/2}{\sinh \gamma/2} \cosh(\gamma y/w).$$

(27.21)

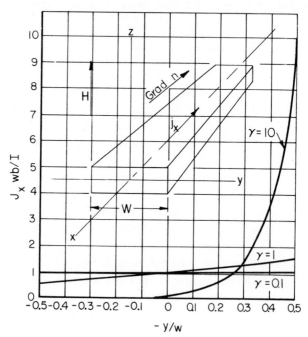

Fig. 49. Effect of transverse magnetic field on longitudinal current density in the presence of a longitudinal gradient in carrier density. $[\gamma = Kw\beta,\ K \equiv (1/n)(dn/dx),\ \beta \equiv 10^{-8} \mu_0 H\rho_0/\rho$ for H in gauss, μ_0 in cm^2/volt-sec (after Bate and Beer[471])].

Under the assumptions inherent in this model, the *material* magneto-resistivity ratio ρ_H/ρ_0 does not depend on x. The magnetic-field dependence of the inhomogeneity factor depends on the location of the potential probes. If they are at the center ($y = 0$), the factor becomes $(\gamma/2)/\sinh(\gamma/2)$, so that the apparent magnetoresistance is reduced and, as a matter of fact, can readily become negative. On the other hand, for probes at the edges ($y = \pm w/2$), the inhomogeneity contribution at large γ will vary as $|\gamma|/2$, that is, linearly with H. That a negative apparent magneto-resistance is also possible at the weakest magnetic field strengths can be seen by developing the hyperbolic functions in Eq. (27.21) for small values of their arguments. The result can be put in the form

$$\left[\frac{\Delta\rho}{\rho_0(\mu_0 H)^2}\right]_{\text{eff}} = \frac{\Delta\rho}{\rho_0(\mu_0 H)^2} + \tfrac{1}{2}(Kw)^2[(y/w)^2 - \tfrac{1}{12}], \qquad \gamma \ll 1.$$

$$(27.22)$$

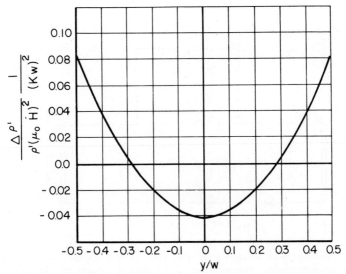

FIG. 50. Inhomogeneity contribution to the weak-field transverse magnetoresistance as a function of the y-coordinate of the probe positions. The probes are on a face perpendicular to the magnetic field (after Bate and Beer[471]).

On the right-hand side, the first term is the material magnetoresistance coefficient and the second term is the inhomogeneity contribution. This increment, designated by $\Delta\rho'/\rho'(\mu_0 H)^2$, is plotted in Fig. 50. We note that it is negative over a substantial part of the sample. If the material magnetoresistance coefficient is small, due, for example, to spherical energy surfaces and degenerate carrier densities — as is true in certain III-V semiconductors — a negative transverse magnetoresistance coefficient can occur even in the limit of zero field.

(2) *The step-function model.* The example discussed in the preceding section could be handled analytically because of our assumption of an exponential variation in carrier concentration $[(1/n)(dn/dx)$ a constant] and a constant β. These conditions insured the vanishing of J_y. It is of interest of course to examine a situation for which the transverse current density does not vanish. To obtain tractable results, however, we are forced to restrict ourselves to a step-function model in which resistivity and Hall coefficient change discontinuously, so that Laplace's equation is valid almost everywhere. This is the case of the stratified medium treated by Herring.[469] The solution of the boundary value

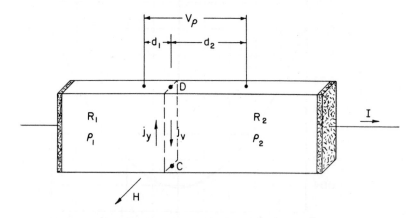

FIG. 51. Arrangement of resistivity and Hall voltage contacts in step-function model of inhomogeneous semiconductor. The length of the specimen in the direction of the current $\mathbf{I}$ is l, the width in the y-direction is w, and the thickness in the direction of $\mathbf{H}$ is b.

problem for a single planar discontinuity in resistivity and Hall coefficient between two long uniform parallelepipeds is outlined by Bate *et al.*[472] One finds that in order to satisfy relations (27.8) and (27.9) a circulating current must exist at the discontinuity between regions 1 and 2. In particular, the boundary conditions at the discontinuity (located at $x = 0$) are seen to be

---

[472] R. T. Bate, J. C. Bell, and A. C. Beer, *J. Appl. Phys.* **32**, 806 (1961).

$$J_{x_1}(0, y) = J_{x_2}(0, y) \equiv J_x(0, y)$$
$$J_{y_1}(0, y) = -J_{y_2}(0, y) \qquad (27.23)$$
$$E_{y_1}(0, y) = E_{y_2}(0, y).$$

For points far removed from the boundary — but not too close to the end electrodes — we must of course have

$$J_y(x, y) \to 0, \qquad x \to \infty$$

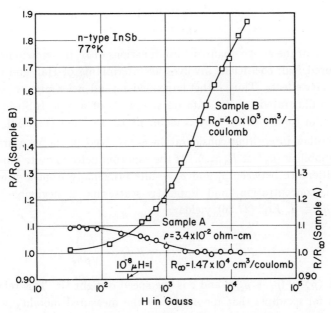

FIG. 52. Magnetic-field dependence of the normalized Hall coefficient of two high-purity n-type InSb samples. Carrier concentrations are: sample A: 4.3×10^{14} cm^{-3}; sample B: 5×10^{14} to 5×10^{15} cm^{-3} (after Bate et al.[472]).

Consider a resistivity tensor of the form

$$\boldsymbol{\rho}_i \equiv \begin{pmatrix} \rho_i & -\beta_i \rho_i \\ \beta_i \rho_i & \rho_i \end{pmatrix}, \qquad \mathbf{E}_i = \boldsymbol{\rho}_i \, \mathbf{J}_i \qquad (27.24)$$

where i refers to region 1 or 2, and the Hall angle tangent, β, is given by $\beta_i \equiv R_i H / \rho_i$ — all the above quantities being functions of magnetic field H. The relationship (27.24) and Eqs. (27.23) yield at once

$$J_{y_1}(0, y) = \frac{R_2 - R_1}{\rho_1 + \rho_2} J_x(0, y) \tag{27.25}$$

$$E_y(0, y) = \frac{R_1 \rho_2 + R_2 \rho_1}{\rho_1 + \rho_2} H J_x(0, y).$$

Thus, for Hall probes located at points C and D of the boundary (see Fig. 51), the expression for the measured Hall coefficient is simply

$$R_{\text{eff}} = \frac{R_1 \rho_2 + R_2 \rho_1}{\rho_1 + \rho_2}, \qquad x = 0. \tag{27.26}$$

Since all of the above quantities are functions of H, it is apparent that the measured Hall coefficient involves an intermixing of Hall and magneto-resistivity effects. Thus, rather large field dependencies might be expected. This is illustrated by the data on sample B of n-type InSb in which a change in carrier density by a factor of 10 occurred (Fig. 52).

Another interesting consideration is involved in the measurement of Hall mobility ($\mu_0{}^H \equiv R_0 \sigma_0 c$). If the semiconductor is quite pure so that the difference between ρ_1 and ρ_2 results principally from a difference in carrier concentration, and impurity scattering is negligible, so that $\mu_1 = \mu_2 \equiv \mu$, Eq. (27.26) yields

$$(\mu_0{}^H)_{\text{eff}} \equiv \frac{(R_0)_{\text{eff}}\, c}{\langle \rho_0 \rangle} = \mu \, \frac{4(n_1/n_2)}{[1 + (n_1/n_2)]^2} \tag{27.27}$$

where $\langle \rho \rangle = (\rho_1 + \rho_2)/2$ and c is the speed of light.[473] This relationship shows for example that for $n_1/n_2 = 6$ the measured mobility value will be less than half the actual value. It is suggested by Bate and co-workers[472] that considerations such as this may be responsible for a certain amount of scatter which is sometimes found in plots of mobility as a function of carrier concentration in some materials for which there is no obvious source of compensation.

In the case of the transverse magnetoresistance, much depends, as we have seen before, on the location of the potential probes. With the

---

[473] In laboratory units where ρ is in ohm-cm, μ in cm²/volt-sec, and R in cm³/coulomb, the constant c is replaced by unity. In such a system, when H is in gauss, the tangent of the Hall angle is given by $RH/(10^8 \rho)$.

arrangement shown in Fig. 51, an approximate expression for the measured magnetoresistance is

$$\left[\frac{\Delta\rho}{\rho_0}\right]_{\text{eff}} = \left\langle\frac{\Delta\rho}{\rho_0}\right\rangle + \frac{d_2 R_2 - d_1 R_1}{d_2 \rho_2{}^0 + d_1 \rho_1{}^0} \frac{(R_2 - R_1)H^2}{\rho_1 + \rho_2} \qquad (27.28)$$

where ρ_0 and $\rho_i{}^0$ denote zero-magnetic-field values. The above expression is a first-order approximation obtained by neglecting the x-variations of the electric fields $E_{x_1}(x, y)$ and $E_{x_2}(x, y)$ from the values in the neighborhood of the discontinuity $(x = 0)$. The approximation should be good as long as the distance between the probes is much less than the width of the sample, and the Hall angle is not too large. Higher approximations can be computed from the complete expressions for the potential given in the literature.[472]

The term $\langle\Delta\rho/\rho_0\rangle$ in Eq. (27.28) is a weighted average of the material magnetoresistance, namely,

$$\left\langle\frac{\Delta\rho}{\rho_0}\right\rangle = \frac{d_1\rho_1 + d_2\rho_2}{d_1\rho_1{}^0 + d_2\rho_2{}^0} - 1. \qquad (27.29)$$

The last term in the expression for $[\Delta\rho/\rho_0]_{\text{eff}}$ is the inhomogeneity contribution which results from the perturbation of the Hall field. We note that it vanishes if $R_1 = R_2$ and that in the weak-magnetic-field limit it varies as H^2. In strong fields, if R and ρ saturate, it also has an H^2 dependence. The term may be positive or negative, depending on the location of the potential probes with respect to the discontinuity.

c. Experimental Data

The type of behavior predicted in the preceding sections has been qualitatively confirmed in the experimental data of a number of investigators. Inhomogeneity effects have been most noticeable in the high-mobility III-V semiconductors. For example, Frederikse and Hosler point to anomalies observed in their measurements on indium antimonide[109]; Dixon[474] suggests that microscopic inclusions of n-type material might be responsible for anomalies found in the Hall coefficient

---

[474] J. R. Dixon, *J. Appl. Phys.* **30**, 1412 (1959).

of lightly doped p-type indium arsenide. If these microscopic n-type inhomogeneities were confined principally to the surface, then the findings of Rupprecht[475] — namely, that the anomalies could be introduced and removed cyclically by appropriate surface treatment — would be explained.

One of the reasons why inhomogeneities need to be given special consideration in the case of III-V semiconductors is the possibility of anisotropic segregation of impurities. This phenomenon has been demonstrated by several investigators[476, 477] in the case of indium antimonide and may be expected to be important in a number of other compounds. It can also occur in elemental semiconductors such as germanium, as was shown by Dikhoff,[478] who observed cross-sectional changes in resistivity of the order of 50% in crystals pulled under certain conditions. Variations of the same magnitude were also found by Ueda.[479] This is large enough to require care to be exercised in the crystal pulling, although it is over an order of magnitude smaller than some of the results found in InSb crystals.[476]

In high-mobility materials, voltages resulting from inhomogeneities may predominate over those due to effects which are characteristic of the material. This situation is illustrated by the directional magneto-resistance measurements of Rupprecht et al.[480] on tellurium-doped indium antimonide. These investigators found that the controlling consideration was not the relation of the current to the crystal axes, but rather the relation of the current to the specific direction, [111], in which the crystal had been pulled. When these directions coincided, the transverse magneto-resistance was much larger. Subsequent measurements by Rupprecht[481] on crystals pulled also in [100] and [113] directions revealed a similar anisotropy, namely, the largest transverse magnetoresistance when the current was in the direction of pull. The magnitude of the effect, which was largest for [111] growth directions became progressively smaller for

475 H. Rupprecht, Z. Naturforsch. 13a, 1094 (1958).
476 J. B. Mullin and K. F. Hulme, J. Phys. Chem. Solids 17, 1 (1960).
477 W. P. Allred and R. T. Bate, J. Electrochem. Soc. 108, 258 (1961).
478 J. A. M. Dikhoff, Solid-State Electronics 1, 202 (1960).
479 H. Ueda, J. Phys. Soc. Japan 16, 61 (1961).
480 H. Rupprecht, R. Weber, and H. Weiss, Z. Naturforsch. 15a, 783 (1960).
481 H. Rupprecht, Z. Naturforsch. 16a, 395 (1961).

the [100] and the [113] directions. Another interesting observation was the influence of the pulling speed on the anisotropy. For a [111] pull, the $\Delta\rho/\rho_0$ dropped from a largest value of 0.7 for a speed of 0.25 mm/min to a largest value of 0.02 for a pulling speed of 4.2 mm/min. Using the stratified model of Herring,[469] Weiss[482] estimates that variations in carrier concentration of the order of 20% would produce a $\Delta\rho/\rho_0$ of 0.3 when the tangent of the Hall angle is 5. Furthermore, by studying crystals with different growth rates so as to be able to obtain an estimate for comparing the inhomogeneity contribution to the measured $\Delta\rho/\rho_0$, he concludes that the true magnetoresistive effect for electrons in InSb is smaller than 1% in 10^4 gauss for $n > 10^{16}$ cm^{-3}.

Some transverse magnetoresistance data are presented by Bate and Beer for specimens of InSb in which a resistivity gradient of 20% per centimeter in the growth direction existed.[471] The results are qualitatively similar to the predictions of the theoretical treatment given in Section 27b(1) above, except that the magnitudes of the observed results are substantially greater. This is attributed to the fact that the variations in carrier concentrations in the measured samples were undoubtedly not exponential and also that it is likely that the mobility was not uniform. Therefore, transverse currents would be present — which could augment the observed magnetoresistance. A few measurements are also available on samples having a sharp change in carrier concentration (illustrative of the step-function model).[472] An interesting observation is the occurrence of negative transverse magnetoresistance at room temperature. The stratified model has also been considered in detail by Bogner and Rupprecht, who examined the effect of the inhomogeneities on magneto-resistence, Hall effect, and planar Hall effect.[482a]

d. Inhomogeneities in Magnetic Field

Spatial variations in the elements of the conductivity tensor can also arise from nonuniform external magnetic fields. The result can be a variation in the Hall field and consequent distortion of the current lines, producing the same contributions to the galvanomagnetic effects as do

[482] H. Weiss, *J. Appl. Phys.* **32**, 2064 (1961).
[482a] G. Bogner and H. Rupprecht, *Z. Naturforsch.* **16a**, 1152 (1961).

material inhomogeneities. Since there is an increasing interest in strong magnetic field measurements, it seems desirable to make some simple calculations to establish a feeling for the order of magnitudes involved. This is readily done by use of the relationships developed in Section 27b(1).

For gradients in the x-direction, we may write

$$\frac{d\sigma_t}{dx} = \frac{\partial\sigma_t}{\partial H}\frac{dH}{dx}, \tag{27.30}$$

so that Eq. (27.13) becomes

$$\frac{\partial^2 V}{\partial x^2} + \frac{\partial^2 V}{\partial y^2} + \frac{1}{\sigma_t}\frac{\partial\sigma_t}{\partial H}\frac{dH}{dx}\frac{\partial V}{\partial x} + \left(\frac{\beta}{\sigma_t}\frac{\partial\sigma_t}{\partial H} + \frac{\partial\beta}{\partial H}\right)\frac{dH}{dx}\frac{\partial V}{\partial y} = 0. \tag{27.31}$$

The σ_t are the diagonal components of the conductivity tensor in the plane normal to the magnetic field, Eq. (27.12), and β is the tangent of the Hall angle. For strong magnetic fields, the above relation reduces to

$$\frac{\partial^2 V}{\partial x^2} + \frac{\partial^2 V}{\partial y^2} + 2K(x)\frac{\partial V}{\partial x} + K(x)\beta(x)\frac{\partial V}{\partial y} = 0, \tag{27.32}$$

$$\beta \gg 1, \qquad \rho(H) \text{ saturates}$$

$$\frac{\partial^2 V}{\partial x^2} + \frac{\partial^2 V}{\partial y^2} + K(x)\frac{\partial V}{\partial x} + K(x)\beta\frac{\partial V}{\partial y} = 0, \qquad \beta \gg 1, \quad \rho(H) \sim H \tag{27.33}$$

where

$$K(x) \equiv -\,[1/H(x)]\,[dH(x)/dx]. \tag{27.34}$$

The above equations are similar to (27.17). If $K(x)$ is a constant, the expression for the current density in the case described by Eq. (27.33) is that given in (27.19). The important point to note is that K is in the exponent and that it is multiplied by the tangent of the Hall angle. Measurements of Hieronymus and Weiss suggest that values of β of 30 are possible in InSb at fields of 60 kgauss.[483] Under such conditions, a

---

[483] H. Hieronymus and H. Weiss (unpublished). See also *Solid-State Electronics* **5**, 71 (1962) in which a value of μ greater than 25,000 cm²/volt-sec at a field of 150 kgauss is estimated; this yields a value of $\beta > 37.5$.

specimen of 1 cm wide in a field gradient such that $H^{-1} \, dH/dx$ is $2\frac{1}{2}\%$ per centimeter will have a ratio of current densities at the two edges of

$$J_x(-w/2)/J_x(w/2) = 2.1. \tag{27.35}$$

It is thus apparent that when large Hall angles are involved, even relatively minor nonhomogeneities can lead to significant distortions of the current lines.

e. Techniques for Reducing Distortion Due to Inhomogeneities

Inasmuch as the large magnitudes of the inhomogeneity contributions arise as a result of perturbations of the Hall voltage, it is of interest to consider measurements in which the Hall field is absent. This was seen to occur, in the case of homogeneous specimens, for the Corbino disk or for the magnetoconductivity plates (see Section 10b, especially Fig. 7). In the former case, the Hall field is absent due to circular symmetry, and in the latter example the transverse field is almost zero throughout the specimen as a result of the proximity of the shorting contacts, because of the large width-to-length ratio geometry. In either case, of course, good low-resistance contacts must be fashioned to the sample.

If the inhomogeneities possess circular symmetry — as might occur in some slices from a pulled crystal or, more likely, in the case of a non-uniform magnetic field — then the reader can readily establish that the potential at radial distance r in the Corbino disk is given by

$$V(r) - V(a) = -\frac{I}{2\pi b} \int_a^r \frac{dr'}{r' \, \sigma_t(r')} \tag{27.36}$$

where b is the thickness of the disk, a is the radius of the center contact, and I is the current. The equation is valid for any variation of σ_t with r — so long as the integral exists — and σ_t may depend explicitly on r or implicitly through $H(r)$. A comparable situation exists for a magneto-conductivity measurement (experimental conditions such that $E_y = 0$, as suggested in Fig. 7b) when the conductivity gradient or magnetic-field gradient is in the direction of the electric field. The expression is

$$V(x) - V(0) = -\frac{I}{wb}\int_0^x \frac{dx'}{\sigma_t(x')} \tag{27.37}$$

where wb is the cross-sectional area of the specimen normal to the x-direction. It is apparent in the two cases above that the equipotentials are not subject to a distortion resulting from the Hall angle.

On the other hand, inhomogeneity gradients in the y-direction would tend to destroy the symmetry in the magnetoconductivity arrangement. In such a case, if β is independent of position, measurements of the ordinary magnetoresistance effect with the current in the x-direction are not subject to increased distortion effects at large Hall angles. Development of the equation for the potential is straightforward, and the result is

$$V(x, y) = -\left[I\bigg/\left\{b\int_{-w/2}^{w/2}\frac{dy}{\rho(y)}\right\}\right][x + \beta y], \qquad \text{grad } \beta = 0 \tag{27.38}$$

where the resistivity $\rho(y)$ is given by $\rho(y) = \{\sigma_t(y)[1 + \beta^2]\}^{-1}$.

The current density is therefore given by

$$J_x = I\bigg/\left[b\rho(y)\int_{-w/2}^{w/2}\frac{dy}{\rho(y)}\right], \qquad \text{grad } \beta = 0. \tag{27.39}$$

Thus it is apparent that there is no distortion of the current lines by the Hall field.

f. Non-Ohmic Effects in Inhomogeneous Specimens

In the preceding divisions of this section, we have assumed the conductivity tensors to be independent of the electric field. This may not be true if nonuniform heating should occur or if minority carrier injection phenomena should become important.

It has been shown by Baranskii and collaborators that an emf — designated "volume-gradient emf" — is produced along resistivity gradients in n- and p-type germanium during passage of current.[483a]

[483a] P. I. Baranskii and E. I. Komukhaev, *J. Tech. Phys. U.S.S.R.* **28**, 1896 (1958) [translation: *Soviet Phys.-Tech. Phys.* **3**, 1744 (1958)].

Apparently a number of phenomena can occur in nonhomogeneous semiconductors as a result of temperature gradients[483b] or nonequilibrium carrier concentration effects. The reversible thermoelectric contributions resulting from temperature gradients brought into existence by current in a solid having a nonuniform resistivity include volume Peltier effects[483c,d] and volume-gradient Thomson effects. [483e] The volume Peltier emf's vary linearly with the current, while the Thomson contributions have an I^3 dependence. Baranskii found that in relatively high-resistivity n-type germanium, an approximately exponential behavior of the volume gradient emf with current existed.[483f] It appears that such behavior results from the injection of minority carriers along the resistivity gradients.[483g] A discussion of the effect of volume-gradient phenomena on the accuracy of the potentiometric probe method of measuring resistivity is given by Baranskii.[483h] Volume gradient effects have also been found to lead to experimental data which appear to violate the Kelvin second relation.[483i]

Investigation of the galvanomagnetic phenomena for cases where nonohmic effects such as those described above exist, would be correspondingly much more difficult, and little such work is reported in the literature. The case where nonuniformities exist as a result of lack of symmetry in surface recombination effects was discussed briefly in Section 9b. The Hall effect in semiconductors containing a number of $p - n$ junctions oriented normal to the Hall field has been studied by

[483b] P. I. Baranskii and N. S. Konoplyasova, *J. Tech. Phys. U.S.S.R.* **28**, 1621 (1958) [translation: *Soviet Phys.-Tech. Phys.* **3**, 1493 (1958)].

[483c] P. I. Baranskii, *J. Tech. Phys. U.S.S.R.* **28**, 225 (1958) [translation: *Soviet Phys.-Tech. Phys.* **3**, 201 (1958)].

[483d] P. I. Baranskii and P. M. Kurilo, *Fiz. Tverdogo Tela* **2**, 458 (1960) [translation: *Soviet Phys.-Solid State* **2**, 424 (1960)].

[483e] P. I. Baranskii, *Fiz. Tverdogo Tela* **2**, 445 (1960) [translation: *Soviet Phys.-Solid State* **2**, 413 (1960)].

[483f] P. I. Baranskii, *Fiz. Tverdogo Tela* **2**, 463 (1960) [translation: *Soviet Phys.-Solid State* **2**, 429 (1960)].

[483g] P. I. Baranskii, G. M. Dzyubenko, and N. S. Konoplyasova, *Fiz. Tverdogo Tela* **3**, 876 (1961) [translation: *Soviet Phys.-Solid State* **3**, 638 (1961)].

[483h] P. I. Baranskii, *Fiz. Tverdogo Tela* **3**, 884 (1961) [translation: *Soviet Phys. Solid State* **3**, 643 (1961)].

[483i] P. I. Baranskii, *Fiz. Tverdogo Tela* **3**, 1616 (1961) [translation: *Soviet Phys. Solid State* **3**, 1172 (1961)].

Madelung.[483j]   A theory of injection of minority carriers during current in a nonhomogeneous semiconductor has been given by Demidenko and Tolpygo.[483k]   A qualitative comparison of the theory is made with Baranskii's experimental data.

28. QUANTUM-MECHANICAL TRANSPORT THEORY, STRONG MAGNETIC FIELD EFFECTS

a. General Discussion

Essentially all of the transport relationships we have discussed thus far were based on the Boltzmann equation. It was pointed out in Section 5 that this representation possessed a number of weaknesses, and literature was cited to indicate various developments which originated from more basic considerations in the statistical mechanics of irreversible processes. Additional literature will be cited here.   Specifically, Cohen[484] has investigated the connection between a number of derivations of the classical Boltzmann equation from the Liouville equation.   Kubo has presented a development based on the use of a response function of the system, which can be defined in a quantum-mechanical way.[485, 486] The conductivity tensor is expressed as a time integral of the response function; the averages in the integrand being taken over the equilibrium ensemble, which is statistically represented by a density matrix. A related treatment was also carried out for the response to thermal disturbances.[487] Discussion of the Kubo formalism is given by Izuyama, who investigates the electric response currents of metals for longitudinal electric fields.[487a] The Boltzmann equation for the case of electric fields only has been re-derived by Greenwood without the necessity for averaging over phases

---

[483j] O. Madelung, *Z. Naturforsch.* **14a**, 951 (1959).

[483k] Z. A. Demidenko and K. B. Tolpygo, *Fiz. Tverdogo Tela* **2**, 2753 (1960) [translation: *Soviet Phys.-Solid State* **2**, 2452 (1961)].

[484] E. G. D. Cohen, *Physica* **27**, 163 (1961).

[485] R. Kubo, *Can. J. Phys.* **34**, 1274 (1956); *J. Phys. Soc. Japan* **12**, 570 (1957).

[486] R. Kubo, H. Hasegawa, and N. Hashitsume, *Phys. Rev. Letters* **1**, 279 (1958); *J. Phys. Soc. Japan* **14**, 56 (1959).

[487] R. Kubo, M. Yokota, and S. Nakajima, *J. Phys. Soc. Japan* **12**, 1203 (1957).

[487a] T. Izuyama, *Progr. Theoret. Phys. (Kyoto)* **25**, 964 (1961).

of different electron states after repeated small time intervals, by using the assumption that the scattering centers are distributed at random in the metal.[488] The condition $\hbar/\tau \ll kT$ is inherent in the derivation. Arguments are advanced, however, to suggest that the weaker condition $\hbar/\tau \ll \zeta$ is sufficient when the scattering of the electrons is elastic. To this end, a general expression is developed for the conductivity, starting from the equation of motion of the density matrix, which is not subject to the restriction to $\hbar/\tau \ll kT$, and which supports an argument due to Landau that conductivity theory is valid provided that $\hbar/\tau \ll \zeta$. Further discussions of this point can be found in the general article by Lewis[489] or the text by Peierls.[490] Several authors have been concerned with general expressions for conductivity such as those developed by Kubo,[485, 486] Kohn and Luttinger,[40] Greenwood,[488] Lukes,[488a] and others, which were not obtained explicitly from a transport equation; e.g., Edwards[491] showed that for the case of a random set of scattering centers, Greenwood's formula could be evaluated to give the usual solution of the Boltzmann equation. A formal theory of conductivity has been presented by Lax,[492] in which only the applied electric field is treated as small, that is, the possibility is allowed that the coupling between electrons and lattice vibrations is too strong for the ordinary transport theory to be valid. His formulation is shown to reduce to the usual transport result when the scattering perturbation is weak, without assuming the existence of a relaxation time. It is further shown that the expression for the conductivity leads to the complex Nyquist theorem. The relation between a many-electron treatment and the one-electron treatment is demonstrated. The approach to equilibrium in quantal systems has also been examined by Sher and Primakoff,[493] who derive the "master" or Boltzmann "gain-loss" equation from the Schrödinger equation and apply the general theory to several magnetic resonance situations. Chester and Thellung[494]

[488] D. A. Greenwood, *Proc. Phys. Soc. (London)* **71**, 585 (1958).

[488a] T. Lukes, *Physica* **27**, 319 (1961).

[489] H. W. Lewis, *Solid State Physics* **7**, 353 (1958).

[490] R. E. Peierls, "The Quantum Theory of Solids," pp. 124, 140. Oxford (Clarendon) Press, Oxford, 1955.

[491] S. F. Edwards, *Phil. Mag.* **3**, 1020 (1958).

[492] M. Lax, *Phys. Rev.* **109**, 1921 (1958).

[493] A. Sher and H. Primakoff, *Phys. Rev.* **119**, 178 (1960).

[494] G. V. Chester and A. Thellung, *Proc. Phys. Soc. (London)* **73**, 745 (1959).

have evaluated the general formula for the conductivity — for example, the expression due to Kubo — using techniques developed by Van Hove.[39] They find that the results of conventional theory can be derived without use of the repeated random phase assumption, and that they are accurate as long as $\hbar/\tau \ll \zeta$. The only really restrictive assumptions are that the electrons are scattered elastically either by static impurities or by lattice vibrations.

The kinetics of the approach to equilibrium have been examined quite generally by Prigogine and Résibois.[494a,b] They find that the form of the kinetic equations depends essentially on the time scale, and that only the long-time behavior of the system in its approach to equilibrium from an arbitrary initial state can be described approximately by Markovian equations — that is, the system can be considered to be devoid of a memory of the initial condition. The considerations of Prigogine and Résibois are employed by Balescu[494c] to provide a link to the general Kubo formalism. In particular, Balescu derives a formula for the evolution in time of the electric current response to a constant electric field switched on at time zero. He finds that the value of the current in the stationary state is determined by a corresponding Boltzmann-like operator alone. That is, transport coefficients can always be calculated exactly by means of a Boltzmann-like equation, even though such equation does not describe the approach to the stationary state. Thus a general justification of the traditional method of calculating transport coefficients is provided. A discussion of irreversible processes has also been given by Adams, who considers a point of view that the problem of irreversibility arises from the existence of not one but two transport equations, each valid under its own conditions.[494d] Use of a many-body technique for developing a theory of impurity resistance in metals was done by Langer.[494e] The work is extended in subsequent publications to include all corrections resulting from electron-electron interactions.[494f] Questions regarding reversible and irreversible systems in connection with the Boltzmann

[494a] I. Prigogine and P. Résibois, *Physica* **27**, 629 (1961).
[494b] See also P. Résibois, *Physica* **27**, 541 (1961).
[494c] R. Balescu, *Physica* **27**, 693 (1961).
[494d] E. N. Adams, *Phys. Rev.* **120**, 675 (1960).
[494e] J. S. Langer, *Phys. Rev.* **120**, 714 (1960).
[494f] J. S. Langer, *Phys. Rev.* **124**, 1003 (1961); **127**, 5 (1962); **128**, 110 (1962).

equation are discussed, for example, by Wu and Rivier[494g] and by MacDonald.[494h, i] The techniques developed by Van Hove for deriving a master equation to general order in the perturbation for the transition probability were applied by Janner to the phase-dependent interference term in the occupational probability density.[494j] The point is made that the special properties of the perturbation responsible for the dissipative behavior of the system are sufficient to derive the quantum mechanical transport equation. No random phase assumption is needed.

Argyres[495] has investigated the effects of inelastic collisions, and he presents a derivation of the Boltzmann equation, for this case, following the general procedure employed by Kohn and Luttinger[40] for the case of elastic collisions. For a general review of the fundamentals of transport phenomena, the reader is referred to the article by Dresden.[496] Particular attention is given to statistical mechanical foundations and to the quantum mechanical aspects. For a discussion of the description of states in quantum mechanics by density matrix and operator techniques, the reader may wish to consult the review article by Fano.[497] Application, in first approximation, of the density matrix method to the interaction of electrons and lattice vibrations was shown by Lang[498] to lead to the usual system of kinetic equations, with the drag effects — namely, phonons by electrons and electrons by phonons — being specifically accounted for. Introduction of the magnetic field into the Boltzmann equation was discussed in Section 5, where a number of references were cited.[35-38a] More recent investigations concerning Bloch electrons in a magnetic field have yielded contributions from Blount,[498a] Roth,[498b] and Wannier and Fredkin.[498c] Interband effects as well as spin-orbit interactions have been considered.

[494g] Ta-You Wu and D. Rivier, *Helv. Phys. Acta* **34**, 661 (1961).
[494h] D. K. C. MacDonald, *Phil. Mag.* **6**, 1407 (1961).
[494i] D. K. C. MacDonald, *Physica* **28**, 409 (1962).
[494j] A. Janner, *Helv. Phys. Acta* **35**, 47 (1962).
[495] P. N. Argyres, *J. Phys. Chem. Solids* **19**, 66 (1961).
[496] M. Dresden, *Revs. Modern Phys.* **33**, 265 (1961).
[497] U. Fano, *Revs. Modern Phys.* **29**, 74 (1957).
[498] I. G. Lang, *Fiz. Tverdogo Tela* **2**, 2330 (1960) [translation: *Soviet Phys.-Solid State* **2**, 2077 (1960)].
[498a] E. I. Blount, *Phys. Rev.* **126**, 1636 (1962).
[498b] L. M. Roth, *J. Phys. Chem. Solids* **23**, 433 (1962).
[498c] G. Wannier and D. Fredkin, *Phys. Rev.* **125**, 1910 (1962).

The strong-magnetic-field region in a conductor is characterized by the fact that the cyclotron frequency is greater than the reciprocal time between collisions, namely, $\omega\tau \gg 1$, so that many cycles of cyclotron motion are completed in a free path. Where classical theory is applicable (i.e., where $kT \gg \hbar\omega$ in semiconductors so that the energy spacing of the Landau levels is not important and the usual Boltzmann treatment is valid[498d, 498e]), we have seen that the strong-field region is characterized by saturation of the magnetoresistance. Quantum effects, on the other hand, become noticeable when the individual quantum levels associated with the electron orbits are fairly distinct, i.e., when $\hbar\omega \gg kT$.

A widely observed manifestation of quantum effects is the oscillatory behavior in magnetic susceptibility and in transport phenomena, resulting basically from the effect of the magnetic field on the density of states. Also affected are Fermi energy[499, 499a] and relaxation time.[500] The oscillatory phenomena are characteristic of the region defined by $\hbar\omega \gg kT$, $\zeta_H \gg kT$, and $\zeta_H > \hbar\omega$, where ζ_H is the Fermi energy in the magnetic field. Therefore charge carrier degeneracy exists. Inasmuch as our concern in this article is principally with nondegenerate semiconductors, we shall refer the reader to literature previously cited, in particular the article by Kahn and Frederikse[357a] in this *Solid State Physics* series, for a discussion of the oscillatory effects. There is also a recent treatment by Hajdu[501] of the magnetoresistance in the oscillatory region. A recent discussion of oscillatory phenomena in indium arsenide and indium antimonide has been given by Shalyt and Éfros.[501a]

[498d] It will be recalled that the usual derivation of the Boltzmann equation is obtained under the condition that $\omega\tau \ll 1$ (see Section 5), but that there are indications that this condition is more restrictive than necessary. That this is indeed the case has been established by Stinchcombe,[498e] who has derived an equation for the distribution function by a weak coupling approach which proceeds from the equation of motion of the quantum mechanical density matrix. It was found that this equation was identical with the usual Boltzmann equation derived by Jones and Zener.[35] At no point is it necessary for Stinchcombe to assume $\omega\tau < 1$; the only limitation being $\hbar\omega, \hbar/\tau \ll \zeta$ and $\hbar\omega < kT$.

[498e] R. B. Stinchcombe, *Proc. Phys. Soc. (London)* **78**, 275 (1961).

[499] J. Appel, *Z. Naturforsch.* **11a**, 689 (1956).

[499a] A. Ansel'm and B. Askerov, *Fiz. Tverdogo Tela* **2**, 2821 (1960) [translation: *Soviet Phys.-Solid State* **2**, 2512 (1961)].

[500] P. N. Argyres, *J. Phys. Chem. Solids* **4**, 19 (1958).

[501] J. Hajdu, *Z. Physik* **160**, 481 (1960); **163**, 108 (1961).

[501a] S. S. Shalyt and A. L. Éfros, *Fiz. Tverdogo Tela* **4**, 1233 (1962) [translation: *Soviet Phys.-Solid State* **4**, 903 (1962)].

At still higher magnetic fields, there exists in addition to $\hbar\omega \gg kT$, the condition that $\hbar\omega > \varepsilon$, where ε is the energy of the carrier which may or may not be degenerate. Now the quantized energy levels of a *free* electron in a magnetic field $(0, 0, H)$ are given by

$$\varepsilon = (n + \tfrac{1}{2})\hbar\omega + \hbar^2 k_z^2/2m, \tag{28.1}$$

so that the behavior of the electron is as though it were free in the z-direction but constrained in the xy-plane with the energy levels of the harmonic oscillator.[499] The effect of a periodic crystal field on the energy levels of an electron in a magnetic field has been examined by Harper,[502] Brailsford,[503] Zil'berman,[504] Kohn,[38a] Yafet,[504a] and others already cited. One may say in general that in the case of closed orbits the consequence of the crystal field is to broaden somewhat the discrete levels in relation (28.1).

It is apparent from Eq. (28.1) that the region for which $\hbar\omega > \varepsilon$ is characterized by most of the electrons being in the lowest quantum state of the transverse motion in the magnetic field. This regime has been called by Adams the "quantum limit,"[505] and it is there where orbital quantization can have a large influence on the galvanomagnetic phenomena. In particular, quantum effects can be responsible for a nonzero longitudinal magnetoresistance in isotropic solids, and can cause failure of the transverse magnetoresistance to saturate.

From simple physical considerations it may be expected that the scattering mechanism will be of great importance in galvanomagnetic effects in the quantum limit, and that substantially different approaches will be necessary in treating the cases of longitudinal and of transverse magnetic fields. For example, in the case of parallel electric and magnetic fields, the collisions are current-limiting mechanisms, while in the case of crossed fields the collisions are perturbations which, in first approximation, are responsible for a current in the direction of the electric field.[357a] If there were no scattering, the cyclotron orbits would not, in first approximation, yield a current in the direction of the electric field.

[502] P. G. Harper, *Proc. Phys. Soc. (London)* **A68**, 874 (1955).

[503] A. D. Brailsford, *Proc. Phys. Soc. (London)* **A70**, 275 (1957).

[504] G. E. Zil'berman, *J. Exptl. Theoret. Phys. U.S.S.R.* **30**, 1092 (1956); **32**, 296 (1957); **33**, 387 (1957); **34**, 515 (1958) [respective translations: *Soviet Phys.-JETP* **3**, 835 (1957); **5**, 208 (1957); **6**, 299 (1958); **7**, 355 (1958)].

[504a] Y. Yafet, *Phys. Rev.* **115**, 1172 (1959).

[505] P. N. Argyres and E. N. Adams, *Phys. Rev.* **104**, 900 (1956).

b. Determination of Transport Coefficients

Initial investigations of conductivity in strong magnetic fields were done by Titeica[506] for a metal where the electrons were degenerate and in which the scattering mechanism was by means of acoustical vibrations of the lattice. Calculations were carried out by Davydov and Pomeranchuk[507] for the case of a semimetal with ellipsoidal energy surfaces, such as bismuth, using a delta function type of scattering potential. A two-band model was also considered by Zil'berman,[508] who in addition to transverse magnetoresistance and Hall effect, considered temperature gradients and the resulting thermoelectric fields.

The case of longitudinal magnetic fields in the quantum limit has been treated by a generalized Boltzmann technique in which account is taken of the distribution of electrons over the quantum states in the magnetic field. Explicit results for the longitudinal magnetoresistance are given by Argyres and Adams for scattering by acoustic phonons and by ionized impurities.[505] The case of acoustic phonon scattering has been considered further by Argyres.[500, 509] The influence of quantum effects on the longitudinal magnetoresistance has also been studied by Appel,[510] by adapting the method employed by Titeica to the case of a nondegenerate semiconductor with scattering by acoustic phonons. Account was taken of quantum states higher than the ground state so that calculations could be carried out for the region between a "weak"-field approximation and the strong-field quantum limit. A related calculation has been done by Barrie[511] in which he determines the relaxation time for acoustic-phonon scattering in the magnetic field. An effect of the higher quantum states is to introduce an oscillatory dependence on the magnetic field into τ — analogous to that in the de Haas-van Alphen effect. Appel estimates that more than 99.9% of all electrons are in the states determined by the relation

$$0 \leqslant n \leqslant (8/\Gamma - 1) \tag{28.2}$$

[506] S. Titeica, *Ann. Physik* **22**, 129 (1935).

[507] B. Davydov and I. Pomeranchuk, *J. Phys. U.S.S.R.* **2**, 147 (1940).

[508] G. E. Zil'berman, *J. Exptl. Theoret. Phys. U.S.S.R.* **29**, 762 (1955) [translation: *Soviet Phys.-JETP* **2**, 650 (1956)].

[509] P. N. Argyres, *Phys. Rev.* **109**, 1115 (1958).

[510] J. Appel, *Z. Naturforsch.* **11a**, 892 (1956).

[511] R. Barrie, *Proc. Phys. Soc. (London)* **B70**, 1008 (1957).

where $\Gamma = \hbar\omega/kT$, and n is the quantum number used in Eq. (28.1).
For $\Gamma = 2$, he takes into account the states $n = 0, 1, 2$, and 3; for a Γ
of 4, the states $n = 0, 1$, and 2; and for a $\Gamma \geqslant 6$, $n = 0$ since he estimates
that for $\Gamma \geqslant 6$, over 99% of the electrons are in the ground state. A plot
of the calculated longitudinal magnetoresistance as a function of Γ
suggests that the quantum limit is approached reasonably closely for
$\Gamma \geqslant 5$. In this region $\Delta\rho/\rho_0 \sim (m_0/m^*)(H/T)$, in accordance with the
findings of Arygres and Adams.[505] A similar dependence was obtained
for the transverse magnetoresistance in the initial calculations by
Arygres.[509] It was, however, subsequently argued by Adams and
Holstein[512] and also by Arygres and Roth[513] that some of the earlier
theoretical developments suffered from an unsatisfactory treatment of
the scattering, in that the effect of the electric field on the relaxation
time had been neglected. Adams and Holstein stress that in the transverse
case the electric current exists "as a result of the effect of the electric
field on the scattering." The consideration is also discussed in the paper
by Arygres and Roth,[513] who consider scattering by inelastic as well as
by elastic lattice vibrations. The matter is also examined in a later paper
by Argyres,[513a] where the case of elastic scattering treated in the Born
approximation is developed. Adams and Holstein[512] present a rather
detailed treatment of the quantum theory of transverse galvanomagnetic
phenomena for cases of elastic scattering. Explicit formulae are developed
for the resistivity in the quantum limit for both longitudinal and transverse
magnetic field, for degenerate and nondegenerate statistics, and for
several different scattering mechanisms. The oscillatory conductivity is
calculated for acoustical and ionized-impurity scattering processes.
A quantum theory of the transverse conductivity in semiconductors in
strong magnetic field for the case of inelastic scattering of the charge
carriers has been developed by Gurevich and Firsov.[514] Their starting

---

[512] E. N. Adams and T. D. Holstein, *J. Phys. Chem. Solids* 10, 254 (1959).

[513] P. N. Argyres and L. M. Roth, *J. Phys. Chem. Solids* 12, 89 (1959).

[513a] P. N. Argyres, *Phys. Rev.* 117, 315 (1960).

[514] V. L. Gurevich and Yu. A. Firsov, *J. Exptl. Theoret. Phys. U.S.S.R.* 40, 199
(1961) [translation: *Soviet Phys.-JETP* 13, 137 (1961)]; Yu. A. Firsov and
V. L. Gurevich, *ibid.* 41, 512 (1961) [translation: *ibid.* 14, 367 (1962)]. See
also, A. L. Éfros, *Fiz. Tverdogo Tela* 3, 2848 (1961) [translation: *Soviet Phys.-
Solid State* 3, 2079 (1962)]. See also V. L. Gurevich, Yu. A. Firsov, and A. L. Éfros,
ibid. 4, 1813 (1962) [translation: *ibid.* 4, 1331 (1963)].

point is Kubo's general formula[486] for the conductivity tensor, and both the classical and quantal regions of the strong-field regime are considered. Scattering by acoustical and by optical phonons is included, and it is found that resonance oscillations in the conductivity, periodic in $1/H$, can exist in the optical scattering region, with maxima occurring when the limiting frequency of the optical phonons is a multiple of the Larmor frequency. A theory of linear irreversible processes in a strong magnetic field has been developed by Klinger for the case of weak scattering of the electrons.[514a] The treatment is applicable to the situation where alternating electric fields are present and also when generalized statistical forces exist, such as gradients of temperature or chemical potential. An expansion is carried out in powers of the interaction parameter between electrons and the scatterers. The case where such an expansion is not possible is considered in a subsequent article.[514b]   A calculation of the transport coefficients for the case of weak magnetic fields and weak interactions appears in an earlier paper.[514c]

Quantization effects at high magnetic fields are also observed in thermomagnetic measurements. Examples are the oscillations in thermoelectric power and thermal conductivity reported by Steele and Babiskin for bismuth,[515, 516] and the variations in thermal conductivity in zinc[517] and tin[518] found by Alers. More recent measurements on zinc have been reported by Bergeron et al.[518a]   A theory of electronic thermomagnetic phenomena in strong magnetic fields has been given by Ansel'm and Askerov.[519] Because of the existence of temperature gradients, the density matrix formulation is avoided. Instead, the authors use a development

514a M. I. Klinger, *Fiz. Tverdogo Tela* **3**, 1342, 2507 (1961) [translation: *Soviet Phys.-Solid State* **3**, 974 (1961), 1824 (1962)].

514b M. I. Klinger, *Fiz. Tverdogo Tela* **3**, 1354 (1961) [translation: *Soviet Phys.-Solid State* **3**, 983 (1961)].

514c M. I. Klinger, *Fiz. Tverdogo Tela* **2**, 3092 (1960) [translation: *Soviet Phys.-Solid State* **2**, 2747 (1961)].

515 M. C. Steele and J. Babiskin, *Phys. Rev.* **94**, 1394 (1954).

516 M. C. Steele and J. Babiskin, *Phys. Rev.* **98**, 359 (1955).

517 P. B. Alers, *Phys. Rev.* **101**, 41 (1956).

518 P. B. Alers, *Phys. Rev.* **107**, 959 (1957).

518a C. Bergeron, C. Grenier, and J. Reynolds, *Phys. Rev.* **119**, 925 (1960); C. Grenier, J. Reynolds, and N. Zebouni, *Phys. Rev.* **129**, 1088 (1963).

519 A. I. Ansel'm and B. M. Askerov, *Fiz. Tverdogo Tela* **2**, 2310 (1960) [translation: *Soviet Phys.-Solid State* **2**, 2060 (1961)]. For the longitudinal effect, see also **4**, 1573 (1962) [translation: **4**, 1154 (1962)].

patterned somewhat after Titeica's[506] early treatment. In a subsequent article these authors point out that their earlier treatment led to a result which, in the quantum limit, did not agree with the Onsager principle.[519a] Their revised formulation is based on a computation of the heat flux transferred by electrons in an electric field, using the density matrix method and the Onsager relations. The dependence of the thermal emf and the Nernst coefficient on magnetic field and temperature is obtained in the quantum limit. It has been found, however, that in the strong-field regime, the augmentation of the phonon-drag contribution (see Section 29) can exceed that from the direct process.[519b] The theory of the effects of phonon drag in a strong magnetic field on thermoelectric power and on electrical conductivity has been studied by Gurevich and collaborators.[519b, c] Experimental data on the magnetothermoelectric power in n-type germanium in the region where quantum effects are significant have been given by Puri and Geballe.[519d] Results are found to be consistent with theoretical predictions.

A recent review article on galvanomagnetic phenomena in very strong magnetic fields by Adams and Keyes has appeared.[519e] Both the classical region and the quantum region of the strong field regime are considered.

c. Data on Strong-Field Magnetoresistance in Semiconductors

A limited quantity of experimental data is available on strong-field magnetoresistance in semiconductors. Particular attention has been paid to indium antimonide,[289, 520–522] although there are recent articles on

---

[519a] A. I. Ansel'm and B. M. Askerov, *ibid.* **3**, 3668 (1961) [translation: *ibid.* **3**, 2665 (1962)].

[519b] L. É. Gurevich and G. M. Nedlin, *Fiz. Tverdogo Tela* **3**, 2779 (1961) [translation: *Soviet Phys.-Solid State* **3**, 2029 (1962)].

[519c] L. É. Gurevich and A. L. Éfros, *J. Exptl. Theoret. Phys. U.S.S.R.* **41**, 1978 (1961) [translation: *Soviet Phys.-JETP* **14**, 1405 (1962)].

[519d] S. M. Puri and T. H. Geballe, *Phys. Rev. Letters* **9**, 378 (1962).

[519e] E. N. Adams and R. W. Keyes, *in* "Progress in Semiconductors" (A. Gibson, ed.), Vol. 6, p. 85. Wiley, New York, 1962.

[520] J. C. Haslett and W. F. Love, *J. Phys. Chem. Solids* **8**, 518 (1959).

[521] Kh. Amirkhanov, R. Bashirov, and Yu. Zakiev, *Doklady Akad. Nauk S.S.S.R.* **132**, 793 (1960) [translation: *Soviet Phys.-Doklady* **5**, 556 (1960)].

[522] R. J. Sladek, *J. Phys. Chem. Solids* **16**, 1 (1960).

n-type germanium.[523, 523a] Analysis of most of the results is clouded by possible presence of complicating effects such as carrier freezeout (Section 28d), nonohmic currents, mixed-scattering mechanisms, and perturbation of the Hall field by contacts or nonuniformities in the specimen or the magnetic field (Section 27). For these reasons it does not appear worthwhile to regard many of the measurements in a quantitative manner. Qualitatively, however, most of the data favor an approximately linear dependence on H, for the longitudinal and transverse strong-field magnetoresistance in indium antimonide. A similar finding holds for the measurements on n-type germanium, which were of the longitudinal resistivity. In analyzing the data on germanium, the theory of Argyres and Adams was modified to take account of the four-ellipsoid nature of the conduction band.[524] In a "many-valley" structure, a strong magnetic field can cause an additional phenomenon, which has been called the "quantum-transfer" effect.[523, 524] In the magnetic field, each valley may have a different zero-point energy, depending on the relative orientation of the valley and the magnetic field, and the variation of effective mass with direction. Therefore, in accordance with the Boltzmann factor, there will be a redistribution of electrons among the valleys, depending on the relative orientation of **H** and resulting separation of the ground states of the ellipsoids. As a consequence, electrons can be shifted into ellipsoids of higher mobility, so that the effect of the quantum transfer is a decrease in resistivity. This behavior is illustrated by the data of Love and Wei.[523] For magnetic fields in the [100] direction, no evidence of quantum transfer is observed — as is expected since **H** makes the same angle with all the [111] type ellipsoids. On the other hand, for **H** in the [110] direction, substantial decreases in $\rho(H)/\rho_0$ are found as the magnetic field increases.

Some information is available from measurements of the Corbino effect. For example, in the case of InSb, it has been found that the Corbino magnetoresistance at 77°K breaks away from an H^2 dependence at strong fields (see Figs. 10 and 19), and it appears likely that quantum effects may in part be responsible for this. This point was made by

[523] W. F. Love and W. F. Wei, *Phys. Rev.* **123**, 67 (1961).

[523a] T. J. Diesel and W. F. Love, *Phys. Rev.* **124**, 666 (1961).

[524] S. C. Miller and M. A. Omar, *Phys. Rev.* **123**, 74 (1961).

Frederikse and Hosler, who observed the slope in a plot of their data to approach a linear dependence on magnetic field at high field strengths.[525]

Although bismuth is a semimetal rather than a semiconductor, it seems desirable to cite representative literature which gives data on galvanomagnetic effects in bismuth at low temperatures in high magnetic fields.[525a−c] Data encompass the oscillatory region and include field strengths such that the quantum limit is approached.

In concluding this section, it may be stated that existing experimental data indicate reasonably persuasively the manifestation of quantum effects. Quantitative reliance on the results requires caution, however, because of the possibility of distortion of the current distribution in the sample by extraneous effects such as inhomogeneities in specimen or magnetic field, by contacting leads, or by surface conduction.[526] Most of these dangers have been discussed in earlier sections of this article. A further complication is that, as we have seen, disagreements exist among the various theoretical developments of quantum transport, due principally to the importance of scattering in transport effects in the high magnetic field region. The point was emphasized by Herring that by equally plausible methods of setting up a quantum transport theory, different authors have arrived at different dependencies of the quantum-limit magnetoresistance on magnetic field.[433] More definitive evidence for the observation of quantum effects exists in the measurements of the magnetothermoelectric power (or magneto-Seebeck coefficient), $\Delta\alpha$, by Puri and Geballe.[519d] The advantage of studying such a quantity rather than $\Delta\rho$, the authors point out, results from the classical behavior of the transverse electric fields set up when α and ρ are measured in a magnetic field. When α is measured, the transverse electric field (Nernst field) associated with the primary heat current classically approaches zero as H increases without limit. In contrast, when ρ is measured, the transverse

---

[525] H. P. R. Frederikse and W. R. Hosler, *in* "Solid State Physics in Electronics and Telecommunications" (M. Désirant and J. Michiels, eds.), Vol. 2, p. 651. Academic Press, New York, 1960.

[525a] P. B. Alers and R. T. Webber, *Phys. Rev.* **91**, 1060 (1953).

[525b] J. Babiskin, *Phys. Rev.* **107**, 981 (1957).

[525c] K. Tanaka, S. Tanuma, and T. Fukuroi, *Sci. Repts. Research Insts. Tôhoku Univ.* **A13**, 67 (1961).

[526] See comment by Herring *et al.*,[468] p. 733.

Hall field associated with the primary electric current goes to infinity with H. Thus, any disturbance of the Nernst field, whether due to contacts, inhomogeneities, or other causes, produces only minor effects. A similar disturbance of the Hall field, on the other hand, can lead to overwhelming effects. In the quantum regime, calculations show that the Nernst field is small, but not zero, and increases with H. However, the ratio of transverse to longitudinal fields $(E_{\text{Nernst}}/E_{\text{Seebeck}} \approx \sigma_{xx}/\sigma_{xy})$ is small compared to unity. The experimental curves of $\Delta\alpha/\alpha_0$ as a function of H exhibit a well-defined plateau corresponding to the classical saturation.[519d] At higher fields $\Delta\alpha/\alpha_0$ begins to rise, in accordance with theoretical predictions, as the quantum effects become important. A similar behavior is seen qualitatively in the data on indium antimonide presented by Amirkhanov and co-workers.[526a]

d. Other Strong-Magnetic-Field Effects — Depopulation Phenomena

In the preceding paragraphs we have considered the influence of strong magnetic fields and resulting orbit quantization phenomena on transport coefficients through the effect of the magnetic field on the density of states and the relaxation time. Another factor which can be important in very high magnetic fields in bands of low effective mass is a change in carrier concentration, resulting from the shifts in energy levels in the field. This was pointed out above in connection with the "quantum-transfer" effect in n-type germanium. Probably the most common manifestations of these phenomena are related to the effects of magnetic field on the ionization of charge carriers from the impurity levels. Analysis of the behavior is somewhat complicated because of the concurrence of a number of effects. These have been categorized by Landsberg[527] as follows. (1) A paramagnetic effect due to the electron magnetic moment, which causes a displacement in energy of both conduction band and impurity states. (2) Diamagnetic effects, in particular the quantization of the orbits of the conduction band electrons. The influence of this effect on the Fermi energy was investigated by Appel.[499]

[526a] Kh. I. Amirkhanov, R. I. Bashirov, and M. M. Gadzhialiev, *Fiz. Tverdogo Tela* **3**, 3743 (1961) [translation: *Soviet Phys.-Solid State* **3**, 2713 (1962)].
[527] P. T. Landsberg, *Proc. Phys. Soc.* (*London*) **71**, 69 (1958).

(3) An increase in the impurity activation energy due to a compression of the electron cloud centered on an impurity atom in a strong magnetic field. This phenomenon was considered by Yafet et al.[528]

Landsberg finds that the paramagnetic effect may result in an increase or a decrease in carrier density in the conduction band, depending on the nature of the donor levels. An important consideration is whether the donor states are localized or nonlocalized. In both cases the effect increases with H and $1/T$. The possibility that these changes in carrier concentration might be responsible for negative magnetoresistance observed in certain cases in InSb at low temperatures[265] is discussed.[527] A difficulty standing in the way of quantitative calculations in the case of InSb is the assessment of the importance of impurity band conduction (see Section 31b).

A theoretical treatment of the energy levels and wave functions for a hydrogen atom in a very strong magnetic field was carried out by Yafet et al.[528] Their results are expressed in terms of a parameter γ defined as the ratio of the zero-point energy of a free carrier in the magnetic field ($\hbar\omega/2$) to the energy of a carrier in the lowest state of the hydrogen atom with no external magnetic field. For hydrogenic impurity states in crystals having a high-frequency dielectric constant of K, the field necessary to achieve a value of γ of unity is given by

$$H^* \cong 2 \times 10^9 \, (m^*/m_0 \, K)^2 \, \text{gauss.} \qquad (28.3)$$

For donors in InSb, the value of H^* is around 1300 gauss. However, a direct quantitative test of the theory on InSb has been precluded by the impossibility of obtaining material of sufficient purity. The point is that the hydrogenic model for impurity states is applicable only if there is negligible overlap of the electronic wave functions centered on different impurity atoms. Now the conditions required for a low H^* in Eq. (28.3), namely, a large dielectric constant and low effective mass, are precisely those responsible for a relatively large Bohr radius, that is, for a substantial spreading of the electronic wave function centered on an impurity atom. The result is that in InSb not many donor atoms can be accommodated in the crystal before noticeable overlap occurs;

[528] Y. Yafet, R. Keyes, and E. Adams, J. Phys. Chem. Solids 1, 137 (1956).

in fact, the measurements of Sladek[529] and also Putley[530] suggest that for concentrations as low as 10^{14} atoms cm^{-3} the donor levels are effectively merged with the conduction band and no carrier freeze-out occurs at low temperatures.   Nevertheless the possibility of a magnetically induced freeze-out exists because of the reduction in spatial extent of the wave functions in directions normal to the magnetic field. Freeze-out effects have been observed experimentally at moderate magnetic field strengths in InSb having donor concentrations in the 10^{14} cm^{-3} range.[529, 531] In analyzing Hall data, Sladek has found impurity band conduction to be significant. A determination was made of the mobility in the impurity band as a function of magnetic field.[529, 532] In an ultrapure specimen of InSb containing around 4×10^{13} extrinsic electrons per cm^3, Putley has measured effective ionization energies of around 2×10^{-4} ev in fields of 4000 gauss.[533] When cooled to $1.5°K$, such a specimen exhibited sensitivity as a photoconductor for electromagnetic radiation having wavelengths of a few millimeters.

Because of the influence of magnetic fields on energy levels in the bands, the effect of strong fields should also show up in interband effects. Inasmuch as most of the studies of transport properties have been made at low temperatures where the semiconductors were extrinsic, there is not much information in the literature on this point.   Some recent measurements of the Hall coefficient in intrinsic InSb show increases with field, which could be accounted for if the band gap were to increase by 1.9×10^{-4} ev/kgauss.[534] Observations made at the Battelle Institute on the effect of a magnetic field of 29 kgauss on the temperature dependence of the saturation current in a reverse-biased InSb diode suggest an increase in band gap of about 2×10^{-4} ev/kgauss in the range $160°K \leqslant T \leqslant 140$.[535]

The effect of a magnetic field on the valence bands of germanium and silicon, has been treated theoretically by Evtuhov.[535a]   His theory does

[529] R. J. Sladek, *J. Phys. Chem. Solids* **5**, 157 (1958).
[530] E. H. Putley, *in* "Solid State Physics in Electronics and Telecommunications" (M. Désirant and J. Michiels, eds.), Vol. 2, p. 751. Academic Press, New York, 1961.
[531] R. W. Keyes and R. J. Sladek, *J. Phys. Chem. Solids* **1**, 143 (1956).
[532] R. J. Sladek, *J. Phys. Chem. Solids* **8**, 515 (1959).
[533] E. H. Putley, *Proc. Phys. Soc.* (*London*) **76**, 802 (1960).
[534] W. F. Love and J. C. Haslett, *Bull. Am. Phys. Soc.* **6**, 129 (1961).
[535] H. C. Gorton and R. T. Bate (unpublished).
[535a] V. Evtuhov, *Phys. Rev.* **125**, 1869 (1962).

not involve the approximation of decoupling of the V_1 and V_2 bands from the V_3 band, thus making the analysis applicable to silicon as well as germanium. Spherical bands are not assumed and the case of $k_H \neq 0$ is considered. Detailed analysis is carried out for the magnetic field in the [001] direction. Numerical calculations of the Landau levels predict an increase in hole effective mass with the magnetic field. A mixing of the Landau levels, even at $k_H = 0$, is indicated — which leads to a prediction of new transitions, some of which are of the "negative-mass" type. These levels of "negative masses" have been discussed in connection with cyclotron resonance in germanium by Dousmanis and co-workers[535b] and by Rosenblum and Duncan.[535c]

The area where the influence of the magnetic fields on the interband transitions has been most conspicuous is that of optical absorption phenomena. The initial experiments on interband optical magneto-absorption effects were done on InSb by Burstein and collaborators[536] and on InSb and InAs by Zwerdling and co-workers.[537] Since then the technique has developed into a powerful tool for studying band structure in solids.[281, 538–542a] Subsequently, the magnetooptical investigations

[535b] G. C. Dousmanis, R. C. Duncan, Jr., J. J. Thomas, and R. C. Williams, in "Proc. Intern. Conf. on Semiconductor Phys., Prague 1960," p. 603. Publishing House Czech. Acad. Sci., Prague, 1961; Phys. Rev. Letters 1, 404 (1958).

[535c] B. Rosenblum and R. C. Duncan, Jr., in "Proc. Intern. Conf. on Semiconductor Phys., Prague 1960," p. 606. Publishing House Czech. Acad. Sci., Prague, 1961; R. C. Duncan, Jr., and B. Rosenblum, Bull. Am. Phys. Soc. 5, 177 (1960); Phys. Rev. 125, 484 (1962).

[536] E. Burstein, G. Picus, H. Gebbie, and F. Blatt, Phys. Rev. 103, 826 (1956).

[537] S. Zwerdling, R. J. Keyes, S. Foner, H. Kolm, and B. Lax, Phys. Rev. 104, 1805 (1956).

[538] S. Zwerdling, B. Lax, and L. Roth, Phys. Rev. 108, 1402 (1957).

[538a] R. J. Elliott, T. P. McLean, and G. G. McFarlane, Proc. Phys. Soc. (London) 72, 553 (1958).

[539] E. Burstein, G. Picus, R. Wallis, and F. Blatt, Phys. Rev. 113, 15 (1959).

[540] L. Roth, B. Lax, and S. Zwerdling, Phys. Rev. 114, 90 (1959).

[541] B. Lax, in "Solid State Physics in Electronics and Telecommunications" (M. Désirant and J. Michiels, eds.), Vol. 3, p. 508. Academic Press, New York, 1960.

[542] S. Zwerdling, in "Solid State Physics in Electronics and Telecommunications" (M. Désirant and J. Michiels, eds.), Vol. 3, p. 526. Academic Press, New York, 1960.

[542a] J. Kolodziejczak, Acta Phys. Polonica 21, 637 (1962).

have been extended to include measurements of magnetoreflectivity.[543, 544] These studies are particularly useful in the case of solids of rather high carrier density where optical absorption measurements are difficult.

An interesting observation in measurements at strong magnetic fields on low-band-gap semiconductors, such as InSb and InAs, is an apparent increase in electron effective mass with magnetic field.[541, 545] This phenomenon is related to the nonparabolic nature of the conduction bands in these materials (Section 24). For example, a fourth-order term in $\varepsilon(k)$ can yield an apparent effective mass which increases linearly with magnetic field.[546, 547] By using for InSb the conduction band model due to Kane,[290] Lax and Mavroides calculate a magnetic field dependence of apparent effective mass in InSb, which fits quite well the experimental findings.[547]

29. ADIABATIC AND ISOTHERMAL PHENOMENA

Most of the equations presented in this monograph were developed under the assumption of isothermal conditions, inasmuch as results are far more tractable for this case. Under actual laboratory measuring conditions, the isothermal state may not always be achieved unless special precautions are taken. The situation was discussed to some extent in Section 9b(4), where some of the principal thermoelectric and thermomagnetic effects contributing to nonisothermal conditions were defined. In this section we shall examine in more detail the effect of materials parameters in causing temperature gradients in the specimen under measurement.

For the isothermal environment, there are, of course, no temperature gradients and the phenomenological transport equations (2.4) and (2.5) reduce to[2]

$$E_k{}^* = \rho_{kl}(\mathbf{H}) J_l,$$

$$\operatorname{grad} T = 0, \quad k = 1, 2, 3. \qquad (29.1)$$

$$q_k = \pi_{kl}(\mathbf{H}) J_l, \qquad (29.2)$$

[543] B. Lax and G. Wright, *Phys. Rev. Letters* **4**, 16 (1960).

[544] G. Wright and B. Lax, *J. Appl. Phys.* **32**, 2113 (1961).

[545] R. Keyes, S. Zwerdling, S. Foner, H. Kolm, and B. Lax, *Phys. Rev.* **104**, 1804 (1956).

[546] R. F. Wallis, *J. Phys. Chem. Solids* **4**, 101 (1958).

[547] B. Lax and J. G. Mavroides, *Solid State Phys.* **11**, 261 (1960), p. 362 ff.

In the strictly adiabatic case, the heat current $\mathbf{q}$ is zero, and the electro-chemical potential gradients and thermal gradients assume values such that

$$E_k{}^* = \rho_{kl}(\mathbf{H})J_l + \alpha_{kl}(\mathbf{H})[\partial T/\partial x_l], \qquad (29.3)$$

$$k = 1, 2, 3.$$

$$q_k = 0 = \pi_{kl}(\mathbf{H})J_l - \kappa_{kl}(\mathbf{H})[\partial T/\partial x_l], \qquad (29.4)$$

It is to be noted that by the designation "strictly adiabatic" we mean that a negligible heat exchange exists between the sample and its surroundings, that is, $\mathbf{q} = 0$. The convention in common use in the literature dealing with thermomagnetic effects is somewhat different. There, the adjective "adiabatic" is used to indicate negligible heat exchange only in directions normal to the primary electric current or heat current,[548] i.e., the condition $q_y = 0$ is assumed. Where only an electric current is involved, the specimen is assumed to be isothermal in the current direction, i.e., $\partial T/\partial x = 0$. One can, of course, approximate this isothermal state in the current direction by the use of large end-contacting blocks of copper or other metal having high thermal conductivity. Nevertheless, to avoid confusion in those cases where attempts are made to maintain strictly adiabatic environments ($q_y = q_x = 0$), we shall refer to the mixed situations involving either primary electric currents or primary heat currents, namely,

$$J_y = q_y = \partial T/\partial x = 0, \qquad J \equiv J_x \qquad (29.5)$$

$$J_y = J_x = q_y = 0, \qquad q = q_x \qquad (29.6)$$

by the use of quotation marks, that is, by the designation "adiabatic." In practice, the difference between isothermal and "adiabatic" conditions (in the transverse direction) occurs as a result of the presence of a magnetic field, which introduces transverse thermomagnetic effects. The strictly adiabatic case allows also for temperature gradients in the current direction resulting from heat transport at the contacts due to the contributions of the Peltier tensor [see Eq. (29.4)].

---

[548] See, for example, refs. 1, 3, 4, 24, 31, and other pertinent literature cited in Chapter II.

Consider now the measurement of resistivity, at zero magnetic field, by the usual potentiometric method, involving current leads attached to the ends of the specimen and potential probes suitably arranged to allow a determination of the ratio E^*/J_x. It is to be noted that both connecting leads are at identical temperatures at the potentiometer and therefore possess the same Fermi energy ζ, so that a potential difference measurement reveals no difference between the electrochemical field $\mathbf{E}^*$ and the electric field $\mathbf{E}$. For illustration here, it is sufficient to assume the material to be isotropic, so that the resistivity tensor is a scalar. With an anisotropic crystal, the only complication is that it is necessary to measure specimens cut along the appropriate principal axes to determine the diagonal elements of the resistivity tensor.

For the isothermal environment, we see from (29.1) that our measurement yields directly the resistivity, namely,

$$(E^*/J)_{T=\text{const}} \equiv \rho^i = \rho. \tag{29.7}$$

For the strictly adiabatic case, with the use of Eqs. (29.3) and (29.4) together with the Onsager relation (2.12), we obtain

$$(E^*/J)_{q=0} \equiv \rho^a = \rho(1 + \alpha^2 \, T/\kappa\rho) \equiv \rho(1 + Z^*). \tag{29.8}$$

The term $\alpha^2 \, T/\kappa\rho$, designated by Z^*, is commonly referred to as the dimensionless thermoelectric figure of merit.[549] This parameter is a measure of the efficiency of the material in a thermoelectric-cooling or power-generation process. As is apparent from Eqs. (29.7) and (29.8), Z^* is given by the relative difference between the strictly adiabatic and the isothermal resistivity measurements, namely,

$$Z^* = (\rho^a - \rho^i)/\rho^i. \tag{29.9}$$

Experimental arrangements for achieving isothermal conditions have been discussed in Section 9b(4), where the use of square-wave currents of alternating polarity obtained through the use of special choppers (motor-driven reversing switches) was suggested. Frequencies of around 20 cps have been computed to be adequate for most measurements.[550]

---

[549] See, for example, p. 39 of the monograph by Ioffe[14]; also F. E. Jaumot, *Proc. I. R. E.* **46**, 538 (1958).

[550] W. C. Myers and R. T. Bate, *Rev. Sci. Instr.* **31**, 464 (1960).

For the strictly adiabatic environment, the sample must be insulated thermally. A possibility is to place it in a vacuum, using small diameter leads to minimize heat conduction.[551–553] It is to be noted that α is the thermoelectric power of the sample relative to that of the current leads and is therefore the difference of the absolute thermoelectric powers of the sample and the metal leads. The thermoelectric power of the metal leads is of course usually quite small compared to that of the semi-conductor.

In metals and other materials having a large charge-carrier degeneracy, Z^* is minute because of the smallness of α. In low-carrier-density semi-conductors, the figure of merit is small because of relatively large values of $\kappa\rho$, due in part to the significance of the thermal transport by the lattice. As a result, it turns out that Z^* is generally negligible compared to unity (the order of a few per cent) for "nonthermoelectric" materials such as silicon, germanium, or gallium antimonide.[554] On the other hand, for the thermoelectric materials the value of the dimensionless figure of merit[554a] has been found to reach between 0.5 and 1 for optimum doping or alloying in semiconductors such as Bi_2Te_3, $PbTe$, $HgTe$, and others.

When a magnetic field is present, the situation is complicated, inasmuch as the off-diagonal elements of the thermoelectric and Peltier tensors are no longer zero even in isotropic solids. As a result there is an intermixing of electrical and thermal effects. These give rise to phenomena such as the Nernst and the Ettingshausen effects. There is also the thermal analog of the Hall effect, which is called the Righi-Leduc effect [Section 9b(4)]. Coefficients of these quantities enter into the relations expressing the difference between isothermal and "adiabatic" coefficients of most of the galvanomagnetic and thermomagnetic effects.

---

[551] T. C. Harman, *J. Appl. Phys.* **29**, 1373 (1958).

[552] T. C. Harman, J. H. Cahn, and M. J. Logan, *J. Appl. Phys.* **30**, 1351 (1959).

[552a] R. Simon, R. T. Bate, and E. H. Lougher, *J. Appl. Phys.* **31**, 2160 (1960).

[553] M. A. Kaganov, I. S. Lisker, and I. G. Mushkin, *Fiz. Tverdogo Tela* **1**, 988 (1959) [translation: *Soviet Phys.-Solid State* **1**, 905 (1959)].

[554] See, for example, the data given by D. A. Wright *in* "Progress in Cryogenics" (K. Mendelssohn, ed.), Vol. I. Academic Press, New York, 1959; also H. J. Goldsmid, "Applications of Thermoelectricity." Methuen, London, 1960.

[554a] For a detailed discussion of the factors influencing the figure of merit consult: R. Simon, *Advanced Energy Conversion.* **1**, 81 (1961); *J. Appl. Phys.* **33**, 1830 (1962).

To discuss thermomagnetic phenomena in detail is beyond the scope of this work. The reader is referred to literature already cited.[93, 375a, 548] Recently there has appeared a monograph, written by Tsidil'kovskii,[554b] which is devoted to thermomagnetic phenomena in semiconductors. Experimental data on a number of common elemental and compound semiconductors are given, as well as theoretical developments. The case of nonparabolic bands (see Section 24) has been considered by Kolodziejczak, and the method of McClure (Section 6b) applied to the solution of the transport equations.[554c] The density of states mass of holes — and its temperature dependences — in indium antimonide resulting from the complex valence-band structure was analyzed by Kolodziejczak and Kowalczyk.[554d] Hole mobility is computed, and incorporation of the temperature-dependent mass yields good agreement between theory and experiment for a scattering by polar optical modes. Specific application of the nonparabolic band theory is made by Kolodziejczak and Sosnowski to the conduction band of indium antimonide.[554e] It is found that the sign of the Nernst[555] effect depends not only on the mechanism of scattering, but also on the shape of the band. Thus, conclusions as to the mechanism of scattering from the sign of the Nernst coefficient alone can be erroneous. Using the band shape proposed by Kane,[290] the authors obtain agreement between theory and experiment for scattering on optical phonons in the case of pure samples, and for a mixed scattering mechanism involving also ionized impurities in the case of doped samples. The observed change in sign of the Nernst effect towards higher electron concentration results from the nonparabolicity of the conduction band. A recent review article on thermomagnetic effects in semiconductors has been written by Zawadzki.[555a] Explicit expressions are given for limiting cases of weak and strong magnetic fields and different degrees of degeneracy. The influence of deviations from a parabolic band structure is discussed for the degenerate case.

[554b] I. M. Tsidil'kovskii, "Thermomagnetic Phenomena in Semiconductors" (in Russian). FIZMATGIZ, Moscow, 1960 (translation: Academic Press, New York, 1962). See also (for III-V materials) Fiz. Tverdogo Tela 4, 2539 (1962).

[554c] J. Kolodziejczak, Acta Phys. Polonica 20, 379 (1961).

[554d] J. Kolodziejczak and R. Kowalczyk, Acta Phys. Polonica 21, 389 (1962).

[554e] J. Kolodziejczak and L. Sosnowski, Acta Phys. Polonica 21, 399 (1962).

[555] The authors use the terminology "Nernst-Ettingshausen." A discussion of this convention was given in Section 9b(4).

[555a] W. Zawadzki, Physica Status Solidi 2, 385 (1962).

Two-band effects have been discussed fairly extensively in the literature, including the *Handbuch* article by Madelung.[555b] A more recent contribution is that of Dannhäuser.[555c] A term which contributes to transport phenomena in multi-band thermal processes is that due to ambipolar transport. Thus when electrons and holes flow down the temperature gradient, the transport of ionization energy as well as kinetic energy occurs, as was pointed out in Section 17a. The equations therefore contain a term involving the energy of separation of the bands. It is possible for this term to dominate those due to each carrier alone.[555d] A term involving the energy of separation of the band edges also contributes to thermal effects when the two charge carriers are of the same sign. An example of such ambi-electronic effects occurs in the case of nonequivalent minima in the conduction bands, as exists in gallium antimonide and gallium arsenide. Models which take this band structure into account are discussed by Rodot,[555e] Ivanov-Omskii,[555f] Carlson *et al.*,[555g] and others. These ambipolar — also called *bipolar* — effects, which result from the fact that the energy transported by a carrier is to be measured with respect to the Fermi level and not the band edge, can also be important in the case of overlapping bands, as occurs in semimetals. This consideration has been discussed by Gallo and collaborators.[555h] The comparison is made that, in the semiconductor case, each pair of carriers transports an energy equal to that of the gap plus the two energies — each measured relative to the respective band edge — characteristic of each of the carriers. In the case of the semimetal, there is no gap but the carriers still transport an energy equal to the sum of the two energies of the pair of carriers measured relative to the Fermi level. Thus the overlap energy can be regarded as a negative gap. Conditions encountered when the gap in a two-band semiconductor is not constant with respect

555b O. Madelung, p. 86 ff. of the 1957 "Handbuch."[132]
555c F. Dannhäuser, *Z. Physik* **166**, 519 (1962).
555d M. Rodot, *Ann. phys.* **5**, 1085 (1960).
555e M. Rodot, *Compt. rend. acad. sci.* (Paris) **252**, 2526 (1961).
555f V. I. Ivanov-Omskii and B. T. Kolomiets, *Fiz. Tverdogo Tela* **3**, 3553 (1961) [translation: *Soviet Phys.-Solid State* **3**, 2581 (1962)].
555g R. O. Carlson, S. J. Silverman, and H. Ehrenreich, *J. Phys. Chem. Solids* **23**, 422 (1962). See also S. J. Silverman, R. O. Carlson, and H. Ehrenreich, *J. Appl. Phys.* **34**, 456 (1963).
555h C. F. Gallo, R. C. Miller, P. H. Sutter, and R. W. Ure, Jr., *J. Appl. Phys.* **33**, 3144 (1962).

to temperature are discussed by Haga[555i] and by Tauc.[3a] Tauc has recently completed a monograph on photo and thermoelectric effects in semiconductors.[555j] This work provides the reader with a basic background in semiconductor physics, as well as devoting specific consideration to more specialized phenomena, such as electron-hole effects, including recombination and nonequilibrium effects, existence of large temperature gradients, inhomogeneities, and other considerations which could be alluded to only briefly here.

It was pointed out in Section 27b that Samoilovich and Korenblit had shown that a nonuniform temperature field in an anisotropic medium could lead to thermoelectric eddy currents.[470a] Now an effective anisotropy can, for many purposes, be created in a structurally isotropic solid by application of a magnetic field. In particular, it has been shown by Stachowiak that the presence of an external magnetic field will lead to the nonvanishing of curl J unless the second spatial derivatives of the temperature are zero.[555k] Thus, in the general case, circulating currents may be expected. The question of circulating currents has also been discussed by Green.[555l]

Thermomagnetic effects can be quite sensitive to the charge-carrier scattering mechanisms, and they therefore provide a means for studying such phenomena as electron-phonon interactions, phonon-drag effects, etc.[61, 468, 556] The sensitivity of thermomagnetic phenomena to scattering processes has been emphasized by Rodot.[555d, 556a] Substantial data on thermomagnetic phenomena are available in the literature on indium antimonide,[556a−c] indium arsenide,[556d, e] and other III–V compounds,

[555i] E. Haga, J. Phys. Soc. Japan 14, 35 (1959).

[555j] J. Tauc, "Photo and Thermoelectric Effects in Semiconductors." Pergamon Press, New York, 1962.

[555k] H. Stachowiak, Acta Phys. Polonica 20, 67 (1961).

[555l] M. Green, Bull. Am. Phys. Soc. 7, 174 (1962).

[556] T. H. Geballe, C. Herring, and J. E. Kunzler, J. Phys. Chem. Solids 8, 347 (1959).

[556a] M. Rodot, in "Solid State Physics in Electronics and Telecommunications" (M. Désirant and J. Michiels, eds.), Vol. 2, p. 680. Academic Press, New York, 1960; J. phys. radium 19, 140 (1958).

[556b] O. V. Emel'yanenko, F. P. Kesamanly, and D. N. Nasledov, Fiz. Tverdogo Tela 4, 546 (1962) [translation: Soviet Phys.-Solid State 4, 397 (1962)].

[556c] I. V. Mochan, Yu. N. Obraztsov, and T. V. Smirnova, Fiz. Tverdogo Tela 4, 1021 (1962) [translation: Soviet Phys.-Solid State 4, 754 (1962)].

[556d] S. S. Shalyt, Fiz. Tverdogo Tela 3, 2887 (1961) [translation: Soviet Phys.-Solid State 3, 2108 (1962)]; also ibid. 4, 1915 (1962) [ibid. 4, 1403 (1963)].

[556e] N. V. Zotova and D. N. Nasledov, Fiz. Tverdogo Tela 4, 681 (1962) [translation: Soviet Phys.-Solid State 4, 496 (1962)].

as well as mercury selenide[556f, g] and telluride,[556g] and lead telluride.[556h] The measurements of Carlson and co-workers on gallium arsenide suggested the necessity for great care, inasmuch as the Nernst coefficient has been found to be very sensitive to surface conditions of the specimen.[555g] The authors point out that a reversal of the sign of the Nernst coefficient in n-type gallium arsenide can arise from the effect of intervalley scattering on polar scattering, and need not be regarded as indicating a dominant acoustic mode lattice scattering mechanism. In the case of germanium the investigations of Geballe, Herring, and co-workers have already been cited. At higher temperatures (300° K to 750° K), measurements have been carried out by Mette *et al.* on both germanium[556i] and silicon.[556j] The data on germanium were analyzed by Paranjape and Levinger.[556k]

Phonon drag, which can produce substantial augmentation of thermoelectric power in a semiconductor at low temperatures, results from charge carriers being pushed from hot to cold by phonon current produced by the temperature gradient. In other words, the thermal gradient introduces an unbalance in the directional distribution of the phonons. The interaction of these phonons with the charge carriers is then responsible for an augmentation of the usual thermoelectric field caused by the tendency of the carriers to diffuse from hot to cold. Hence, the electronic thermoelectric processes become interrelated with the lattice thermal conduction phenomena. Thus a proper description of the transport processes requires that one take account of deviations from equilibrium of both the electron and the phonon distributions. As pointed out by Sondheimer,[59] this must be done in a symmetrical way, and it leads to a pair of coupled equations. In the words of Parrott,[557] one must take into account "phonon drag" on the electrons and "electron drag" on the phonons. Consequences of the departure of the low-frequency phonon system from its normal isotropic equilibrium distribution have been discussed in some detail

[556f] C. R. Whitsett, *J. Appl. Phys.* **32**, 2257 (1961).

[556g] M. Rodot, H. Rodot, and R. Triboulet, *J. Appl. Phys.* **32**, 2254 (1961).

[556h] I. V. Mochan and T. V. Smirnova, *Fiz. Tverdogo Tela* **3**, 2659 (1961) [translation: *Soviet Phys.-Solid State* **3**, 1936 (1962)].

[556i] H. Mette, W. W. Gärtner, and C. Loscoe, *Phys. Rev.* **115**, 537 (1959).

[556j] H. Mette, W. W. Gärtner, and C. Loscoe, *Phys. Rev.* **117**, 1491 (1960).

[556k] B. V. Paranjape and J. S. Levinger, *Phys. Rev.* **120**, 437 (1960).

[557] J. E. Parrott, *in* "Semiconductors and Phosphors" (M. Schön and H. Welker, eds.), p. 495. Interscience, New York,1958, and Vieweg, Braunschweig, 1958.

by Herring.[558] The effect of nonequilibrium of phonons in the thermo-electric power of a metal was first analyzed by Gurevich,[559] and for that reason, phonon drag is often referred to as the Gurevich effect. Measurements by Frederikse[560] and by Geballe[561] on germanium single crystals revealed a substantial increase in thermoelectric power at low temperatures. A theoretical treatment of phonon drag in a semiconductor of rhombohedral symmetry, such as tellurium, was done by Gurevich and Firsov.[561a] Results are obtained as to the order of magnitude of the phonon-drag thermal emf and its temperature dependence for various directions of the temperature gradient relative to the crystal axes. The carrier concentration is assumed to be very small so that the drag of the phonons by the electrons can be neglected.

Literature dealing with the use of the variational principle for obtaining solutions to the coupled Boltzmann equations for phonons and electrons was reviewed in Section 25a. By use of a relaxation-time approximation, Parrott develops explicit expressions for electrical and thermal conductivities and thermoelectric power in semiconductors.[562] A subsequent publication is concerned with the Nernst effect.[563]

It is of interest to know under what conditions one can express the kinetic coefficients, in particular thermoelectric power α, as a sum of two components, a purely electronic contribution and a phonon-drag contribution, thus

$$\alpha = \alpha^{(el)} + \alpha^{(ph)}. \tag{29.10}$$

A similar question may be asked about the electrical conductivity and the electronic component of the thermal conductivity. The point in these cases is somewhat moot however. The influence of phonon drag on electrical conductivity is probably negligible except at low tem-

[558] C. Herring, in "Semiconductors and Phosphors" (M. Schön and H. Welker, eds.), p. 184. Interscience, New York, 1958, and Vieweg, Braunschweig, 1958.
[559] L. Gurevich, J. Phys. U.S.S.R. **9**, 477 (1945); **10**, 67, 174 (1946).
[560] H. P. R. Frederikse, Phys. Rev. **92**, 248 (1953).
[561] T. H. Geballe, Phys. Rev. **92**, 857 (1953).
[561a] V. L. Gurevich and Yu. A. Firsov, Fiz. Tverdogo Tela **4**, 530 (1962) [translation: Soviet Phys.-Solid State **4**, 385 (1962)].
[562] J. E. Parrott, Proc. Phys. Soc. (London) **B70**, 590 (1957).
[563] J. E. Parrott, Proc. Phys. Soc. (London) **71**, 82 (1958).

peratures where it might amount to a few per cent.[562] Its identification at those temperatures would be difficult, however, because of the predominance of other effects, e.g., impurity conduction.[562] In the case of thermal conductivity, the transport by the lattice is most likely to predominate in nondegenerate semiconductors, so that the electronic thermal transport is in itself small, and the influence of phonon drag on this term would be difficult to detect experimentally.

The question regarding the separation indicated in Eq. (29.10) is answered by the general equations developed by Appel.[564] He obtains a self-consistent solution of the coupled Boltzmann equations for the electron and phonon distribution functions for nondegenerate isotropic semiconductors with electrons scattered by longitudinal acoustic phonons and ionized impurities, and longitudinal thermal lattice waves scattered by mutual interaction and by interaction with electrons and crystal boundaries. Appel finds that the simple split shown in Eq. (29.10) cannot be justified for the general case. The additivity is a satisfactory approximation for small charge carrier concentrations at not too low temperatures, where the phonon scattering by the charge carriers is small. Quantitative expressions are developed in terms of a coupling parameter which is related to the relative influence of the phonon-electron interaction upon the deviation of the phonons from equilibrium. In subsequent publications the development is extended to include the presence of a magnetic field, and expressions are presented for the magnetothermoelectric and the Nernst effects.[565, 566] The effects of phonon drag in a strong magnetic field on thermoelectric power and on electrical conductivity have been studied by Gurevich and collaborators.[519b, c] In connection with strong-field effects, it is desirable to mention a low-temperature phenomenon, namely, magnetothermal oscillations, which have been investigated by Kunzler and co-workers.[566a] This oscillatory dependence of temperature on magnetic field results from quantum effects, and the effect can provide a useful tool of high resolution for exploring the band structure of metals or semimetals. Data were taken on bismuth, and the temperature resolution was the order of 10^{-5} degree.

[564] J. Appel, *Z. Naturforsch.* **12a**, 410 (1957).

[565] J. Appel, *Z. Naturforsch.* **13a**, 386 (1958).

[566] J. Appel, *J. Phys. Chem. Solids* **8**, 353 (1959).

[566a] J. E. Kunzler, F. S. L. Hsu, and W. S. Boyle, *Phys. Rev.* **128**, 1084 (1962).

The process of thermal conduction in semiconductors has been treated in a monograph by Drabble and Goldsmid.[566b] A thorough theoretical background is provided, and substantial experimental results are cited. A number of authors have discussed qualitative relations between the lattice thermal conductivity of nonmetallic solids and structural and elastic constants. For details the reader is referred to articles by Keyes[566c] and by Leroux-Hugon and collaborators[566d] and to the literature cited therein. In connection with the *electronic* thermal conductivity, a quantity of basic interest has been the Wiedemann-Franz ratio, κ_e/σ — often written as $\kappa_e/\sigma T$, and referred to as the Lorenz number. The free electron theory of metals yields for the Lorenz number the universal constant[566e] $\frac{1}{3}\pi^2(k/e)^2$. This result has been shown by Chester and Thellung[566f] to hold also under conditions of strong scattering, such that the conventional Boltzmann equation is not valid. The only assumptions required are that (i) the electrons are scattered elastically by impurities or by lattice vibrations and (ii) the electrons do not interact with each other, and they form a degenerate Fermi-Dirac assembly. If the electrons are not degenerate, but obey Boltzmann statistics — as in a typical semiconductor — then the factor $\pi^2/3$ in the Lorenz number may be different, and it will in general depend on the scattering process. When the scattering is inelastic, the factor may be different even if the electrons are degenerate. The case of degenerate charge carriers and polar optical scattering has been treated by Sheard in connection with the analysis of data on impure indium arsenide.[566g]

30. More General Treatments of Scattering

In the developments which have been presented thus far the charge carrier scattering has, for the most part, been dealt with in the simplest possible fashion. There are, however, a number of noteworthy contribu-

[566b] J. R. Drabble and H. J. Goldsmid, "Thermal Conduction in Semiconductors." Pergamon Press, New York, 1961.
[566c] R. W. Keyes, *Phys. Rev.* **115**, 564 (1959).
[566d] P. Leroux-Hugon, M. Rodot, and J. Suchet, *Compt. rend. acad. sci.* (*Paris*) **254**, 1250 (1962).
[566e] See, for example, p. 201 of Wilson's book[9] or p. 178 of Seitz.[209]
[566f] G. V. Chester and A. Thellung, *Proc. Phys. Soc.* (*London*) **77**, 1005 (1961).
[566g] F. W. Sheard, *Phil. Mag.* **5**, 887 (1960).

tions which have recently evolved. Several of these are discussed in this section.

a. Electron-Phonon Interactions in Nonpolar Semiconductors with a Complex Band Structure

The scattering of electrons by thermal lattice vibrations has been discussed briefly in Section 13a, where the concept of a deformation potential was introduced. The earlier work cited there was concerned with cases where the energy minima were located at the center of the Brillouin zone, and the bands were nondegenerate. This simple model does not apply, however, to either of the bands in germanium or silicon.

Certain of the considerations introduced by a many-valley band structure or by degenerate bands have been discussed in literature which has already been quoted, for example, articles by Brooks,[185] Herring,[65] and a number of authors cited in Chapter VIII. The lattice scattering of holes within and between the two valence bands of germanium, degenerate at $k = 0$, was investigated by Ehrenreich and Overhauser.[246, 567] Both the deformable ion and the rigid ion approximations were used. The former hypothesis assumes the atoms to be completely deformable while vibrating; the latter considers the atoms to be totally rigid and displaced as a whole. Since it is not clear from theoretical considerations which approximation is better for crystals such as germanium, Ehrenreich and Overhauser treat both models by incorporating a parameter η into their equations. The limits $\eta = 1$ and 0 correspond, respectively, to the cases named. It is thought that the physical situation might correspond to some intermediate value of η, since the inner cores of the atoms would be likely to be displaced rigidly, while the outer shells would be deformed.[567] Coupled Boltzmann equations are used, describing the distribution of carriers under the influence of electric and phonon fields in the two valence bands of germanium, degenerate at $k = 0$. The electron-lattice interaction Hamiltonian is separable into two parts: the first, associated with acoustical modes, arises from vibrations of the unit cells as a whole, and the other, associated with both acoustical and optical modes, arises from the relative motion of the two atoms in the unit cell.

---

[567] H. Ehrenreich and A. Overhauser, *Phys. Rev.* **104**, 331 (1956).

The matrix elements for scattering are expressed in terms of two constants, C_1 and C_4 associated, respectively, with the two parts of the interaction Hamiltonian. In comparing results with experimental data on mobility, it is found that there exist values of the parameters which provide a good fit if the temperature associated with the fundamental optical frequency is 300°K, but not 500°K. This is true for both the deformable and the rigid ion models.[246] Transport equations for semiconductors possessing degenerate bands of spherical symmetry have been developed by Gorkin and Tolpygo. Expressions for the current density are provided, which are valid for arbitrary values of magnetic field strength in the presence of temperature gradients and carrier-density variations.[567a]

Contributions to the theory of scattering by lattice vibrations in semiconductors such as germanium and silicon have also been made by Dumke,[325, 568] Harrison,[324] Klose,[325a] and others. Most of this work has been referenced in Chapter VIII. The theory of the deformation potential for semiconductors with complex band structure has more recently been investigated by Pikus and Bir.[569-571] These authors describe the method as a successive application of the effective-mass technique to the problem of scattering, inasmuch as the rapidly varying periodic potential is excluded both from the unperturbed Hamiltonian and from terms which describe the interaction between electrons and lattice vibrations.[570] The method possesses a number of advantages. For example, the results obtained with its aid are not connected with any special assumption about the character of changes of the potentials of atoms during the deformation. Also, the constants which determine the scattering cross section also describe the variation of the band during a homogeneous deformation, and, consequently can be determined independently, for example, from elastoresistance measurements. Bir

---

[567a] Yu. Gorkin and K. Tolpygo, *Fiz. Tverdogo Tela* **3**, 2903 (1961) [translation: *Soviet Phys.-Solid State* **3**, 2121 (1962)].

[568] W. P. Dumke, *Phys. Rev.* **101**, 531 (1956).

[569] G. E. Pikus, *J. Tech. Phys. U.S.S.R.* **28**, 2390 (1958) [translation: *Soviet Phys.-Tech. Phys.* **3**, 2194 (1959)].

[570] G. L. Bir and G. E. Pikus, *Fiz. Tverdogo Tela* **2**, 2287 (1960) [translation: *Soviet Phys.-Solid State* **2**, 2039 (1961)].

[571] G. E. Pikus and G. L. Bir, *in* "Proc. Intern. Conf. on Semiconductor Phys., Prague 1960," p. 89 (in Russian). Publishing House Czech. Acad. Sci., Prague, 1961.

and Pikus construct an operator for the interaction between electrons and long-wavelength acoustical and optical phonons for the case of an arbitrarily degenerate band, using the method of Luttinger and Kohn.[572] The matrix describing the interaction between electrons and acoustical vibrations is identical with the matrix which determines the variation in energy of the current carriers during a homogeneous deformation. The treatment of Bir and Pikus leads to somewhat different results from those given in the earlier work which has been referenced. The reasons for this are discussed.

Pikus and Bir have also examined theoretically the effect of deformation on the energy spectrum of the carriers in p-type germanium and silicon.[571, 573, 574] It was pointed out previously that this problem leads to an interaction matrix similar to that between electrons and acoustical phonons. By application of stress, the degeneracy of the valence bands may be removed. The corresponding behavior for n-type germanium and silicon is to render the equivalent valleys nonequivalent.[321, 322, 575–576b] Pikus and Bir point out that such a state of affairs can lead to strongly pronounced effects, which can be useful in elucidating band structure.[573, 574] The technique has been applied experimentally by Feher and collaborators to do cyclotron resonance experiments,[577] and also paramagnetic resonance studies[578] of impurity centers, in p-type silicon. By production of sufficiently large strains the warped degenerate bands become decoupled and ellipsoidal near $k = 0$ with principal axes in the direction of the applied stress (along either [001] or [111] direction). Compressive stresses of order 10^3 kg/cm^2 were used. Several considerations associated with cyclotron resonance studies of degenerate bands by use of strained

[572] J. M. Luttinger and W. Kohn, *Phys. Rev.* **97**, 869 (1955).
[573] G. E. Pikus and G. L. Bir, *Fiz. Tverdogo Tela* **1**, 154 (1959) [translation: *Soviet Phys.-Solid State* **1**, 136 (1959)]; also G. L. Bir and G. E. Pikus, *ibid.* **4**, 2243 (1962) [*ibid.* **4**, 1640 (1963)].
[574] G. E. Pikus and G. L. Bir, *Fiz. Tverdogo Tela* **1**, 1642 (1959) [translation: *Soviet Phys.-Solid State* **1**, 1502 (1960)]; also **4**, 2090 (1962) [**4**, 1530 (1963)].
[575] R. W. Keyes, *Solid State Phys.* **11**, 149 (1960).
[576] J. R. Drabble and R. D. Groves, *Phys. Rev. Letters* **2**, 451 (1959).
[576a] J. R. Drabble, *J. Electronics and Control* **5**, 362 (1958).
[576b] Additional discussion of this point can be found in Section 24b.
[577] J. C. Hensel and G. Feher, *Phys. Rev.* **129**, 1041 (1963).
[578] G. Feher, J. C. Hensel, and E. A. Gere, *Phys. Rev. Letters* **5**, 309 (1960).

crystals are pointed out by Pikus and Bir.[579] For example, in addition
to determining the constants describing the energy surfaces, one can also
obtain the ratio of the deformation potential constants, which are
important in the theory of scattering. The possibility of observing spin
resonance of free carriers in strained crystals of p-type germanium or
silicon is discussed. Finally, the use of strained crystals with an InSb-type
lattice is suggested as a possibility for realizing energy surfaces having
a toroidal shape.

Because of the significant effects of strain on the properties of semiconductors, care must be taken by the experimentalist to avoid the
inadvertent introduction of stresses brought about by temperature
excursions during measurements. If, for example, as in optical absorption
studies, thin specimens should be cemented to substrates for support,
different thermal expansion coefficients could subject the specimen to
strains as it cooled down from room temperature. This situation has
been observed in the case of germanium.[580, 581]

A general treatment of scattering by acoustic modes, which is based
on principles similar to the work of Pikus and Bir, has been formulated
independently by Whitfield.[439, 582] The technique has been described
as a formulation of the interaction of electrons and acoustic phonons in
nonpolar crystals in terms of a new set of basis states, whose wave functions are essentially Bloch functions that deform with the lattice. The
major part of the interaction may then be calculated in terms of the
strain tensor rather than the displacement of the lattice. A result of the
theory is the generalization of the deformation potential theorem. The
theory has subsequently been used by Tiersten[583] to calculate acoustic-
mode scattering of holes in valence band structures such as that of
germanium. An extension to include spin-lattice coupling is carried out.

In a recent article, Bir and co-workers solve the kinetic equations for
the case of two degenerate bands, subject to certain simplifying assump-

[579] G. E. Pikus and G. L. Bir, *Phys. Rev. Letters* **6**, 103 (1961).
[580] G. McFarlane, T. McLean, J. Quarrington, and V. Roberts, *Phys. Rev. Letters*
2, 252 (1959).
[581] W. H. Kleiner and L. M. Roth, *Phys. Rev. Letters* **2**, 334 (1959).
[582] G. D. Whitfield, *in* "Proc. Intern. Conf. on Semiconductor Phys., Prague 1960,"
p. 75. Publishing House Czech. Acad. Sci., Prague, 1961.
[583] M. Tiersten, *IBM J. Research Develop.* **5**, 122 (1961).

tions which permit exact solutions of the equations but retain the main features associated with the zone degeneracy.[583a] The expressions for zero-magnetic-field conductivity (σ_0), Hall conductivity (σ_R), and magnetoconductivity (σ_H) involve relaxation times, τ_{ij}, which are representative of processes in the light- and in the heavy-mass bands, and which also take account of the interband transitions. These cross terms turn out to be quite significant. They lead to a change in the relative contribution of the two kinds of holes to the kinetic coefficients σ_0, σ_R, σ_H. Furthermore, the magnetic-field dependences of the latter are affected. Also, it appears that the more exact scattering theory does not require the inclusion of so large a degree of ionized impurity scattering as did the earlier treatment of Beer and Willardson.[56] Another interesting point is the suggestion that the relaxation times of the light (τ_{11}) and heavy (τ_{22}) masses are unequal $(\tau_{22}/\tau_{11} \sim 1.45$ for the preferred choice for the ratio of deformation constants). Since the equations were solved in the approximation of spherical energy surfaces and warping of the heavy-mass band was not considered, the treatment does not describe the minima which appear in the field-dependence of the Hall coefficient. A treatment of transport phenomena in p-type germanium and silicon, which takes into account the warped band structure was developed by Tauber.[583b] The technique involves the derivation of a variational principle for interband scattering and general energy surfaces, which enables one to obtain the various transport quantities in terms of infinite determinants. The matrix elements are calculated for warped energy surfaces, such as occur in germanium and silicon, using the appropriate transition probabilities derived by Ehrenreich and Overhauser.[567] The general results are applied to the evaluation of the transport quantities for acoustical and optical scattering. In particular, it is found that in that approximation the temperature dependence of the mobility of germanium is given by $T^{-2.5}$, which compares well with the experimental results which lead to a $T^{-2.3}$ dependence, in contrast to the standard theory predicting a temperature dependence of the form $T^{-1.5}$.

[583a] G. L. Bir, E. Normantas, and G. E. Pikus, *Fiz. Tverdogo Tela* 4, 1180 (1962) [translation: *Soviet Phys.-Solid State* 4, 867 (1962)]; E. Normantas and G. E. Pikus, *ibid.* 4, 2692 (1962).

[583b] G. E. Tauber, *J. Phys. Chem. Solids* 23, 7 (1962).

b. Combined Phonon and Impurity Scattering

This process is usually described by means of an "effective" relaxation time obtained as the reciprocal of the sum of the collision frequencies due to phonon scattering acting alone and ionized impurity scattering acting alone [Eq. (13.34)]. It is tacitly recognized that such a representation is valid only when the two scattering processes are independent of each other. In practice, however, a charge carrier may interact with a number of phonons while traversing the field of a single impurity, and therefore the two processes cannot be strictly independent.

Several investigators have dealt with this problem of combined phonon and impurity scattering using a more rigorous approach.[584, 585] The procedure is to treat the action of the impurities as a part of the Hamiltonian of the system. That is, the impurities are regarded as a source of an additional applied electric field with which the electrons are always interacting. The distribution function is thus both velocity and space dependent. The phonon scattering enters through the usual collision term, and the problem of the independence of the two processes does not arise. To illustrate more specifically the distinguishing features of the new approach, we write the classical Boltzmann equation as follows [cf. Eq. (5.5)]:

$$\mathbf{v} \cdot \frac{\partial f}{\partial \mathbf{r}} + \mathbf{a} \cdot \frac{\partial f}{\partial \mathbf{v}} = - \frac{f - f_0}{\tau} \tag{30.1}$$

where $\mathbf{a}$ is the acceleration of the electrons, and the other symbols have their usual meaning. Now in the standard treatment of mixed scattering, $\mathbf{a}$ is assumed to arise only from the effect of the applied electric fields (in the isothermal case) and f is a function of $\mathbf{v}$ only, so that $\partial f / \partial \mathbf{r}$ vanishes. Also, relaxation time τ is taken as an "effective" value obtained under the assumption of independence of the two scattering mechanisms. For the more rigorous approach, τ is the relaxation time describing only the electron-phonon interaction, and the effects of the impurities are manifest by an additional (space dependent) contribution to the acceleration $\mathbf{a}$. Therefore the distribution function f depends on both $\mathbf{v}$ and $\mathbf{r}$.

[584] H. Reiss and A. I. Anderman, *Phys. Rev.* **122**, 1135 (1961).
[585] H. L. Frisch and J. L. Lebowitz, *Phys. Rev.* **123**, 1542 (1961).

In introducing the effect of the impurities into the Hamiltonian and in solving the resulting Boltzmann equation, approximations must be made. In the paper of Reiss and Anderman, a limiting law for the mobility at very small values of the phonon scattering relaxation time is derived. The treatment of Frisch and Lebowitz leads to perturbation expansions in the relative strength of the different scattering mechanisms. A general conclusion is that the addition of impurities always leads to a decrease in the conductivity.

c. Multiphonon Processes

Several investigators have made calculations of the effect of transitions involving two or more phonons.[586-588] Such transitions involving acoustic phonons could account for temperature dependences steeper than the $T^{-1.5}$ variation.   The probability of occurrence of these processes is discussed by Herring,[589] and for most cases it appears to be substantially less than the probability of scattering by a one-phonon collision. Notable exceptions are if the scattering is so strong that $\hbar/\tau \gtrsim \varepsilon_0$, the energy of state $\mathbf{k}_0$, or if one-phonon scattering is essentially impossible. In the former case, the conventional Boltzmann transport equation is not applicable (see next section). An example of the latter case, quoted by Herring, is the scattering of a polaron by optical modes at low temperatures. In connection with silicon, Dumke has presented evidence for two-phonon indirect transitions being responsible for peaks observed in the low-temperature recombination radiation spectrum.[325] Multiphonon processes have recently been considered in connection with tunneling in semiconductors.[589a]

---

[586] Ch. Enz, Helv. Phys. Acta **27**, 199 (1954); Physica **20**, 983 (1954).

[587] S. Koshino, Progr. Theoret. Phys. (Kyoto) **18**, 23 (1957).

[588] A. I. Ansel'm and I. G. Lang, Fiz. Tverdogo Tela **1**, 683 (1959) [translation: Soviet Phys.-Solid State **1**, 621 (1959)]; ibid. **3**, 308 (1961) [translation: ibid. **3**, 223 (1961)]; also I. G. Lang, ibid. **3**, 2573 (1961) [translation: ibid. **3**, 1871 (1962)].

[589] C. Herring in "Proc. Intern. Conf. on Semiconductor Phys., Prague 1960," p. 60. Publishing House Czech. Acad. Sci., Prague, 1961.

[589a] See Section 32a(1). Especially pertinent is the article by Kane.[655] Additional literature is cited therein.

d. Other Investigations of Scattering

A theory of anisotropic scattering of charge carriers in semiconductors with ellipsoidal energy surfaces has also been developed by Samoilovich and collaborators.[589b, c] The method is applied to scattering by ionized impurities as well as to that by acoustic phonons.[589d] A subsequent calculation by Korenblit[589e] shows the anisotropy of the mobility from ionized impurity scattering to be greater for oblate than for prolate spheroids of constant energy, given the same mass anisotropy. Such an energy band structure, consisting of oblate spheroids located at the center of the Brillouin zone, is indicated for $CdAs_2$.[589f, g] The mobility and thermoelectric power for a many-valley semiconductor in which the polar electron-phonon interaction is dominant were calculated variationally by Olechna and Ehrenreich.[589h] Equations applicable to both Fermi and Boltzmann statistics are presented. Numerical results for μ and α for the latter case are given as a function of temperature for varying degrees of ellipticity. It is noted that α is relatively insensitive to changes in ellipticity.

The effect of a large concentration of charge carriers on the phonon spectrum in a semiconductor was considered by Bonch-Bruevich.[589i] The problem was solved for interactions assumed to be isotropic. A linear decrease in the velocity of sound with carrier concentration was found. A subsequent treatment by Khachaturyan included the case of anisotropic electron-phonon interactions.[589j] The Boltzmann equation has been

---

[589b] A. Samoilovich, I. Korenblit, and I. Dakhovskii, *Doklady Akad. Nauk S.S.S.R.* **139** 355 (1961) [translation: *Soviet Phys.-Doklady* **6**, 606 (1962)].

[589c] A. Samoilovich, I. Korenblit, I. Dakhovskii, and V. Iskra, *Fiz. Tverdogo Tela* **3**, 2939 (1961) [translation: *Soviet Phys.-Solid State* **3**, 2148 (1962)].

[589d] A. Samoilovich, I. Korenblit, I. Dakhovskii, and V. Iskra, *ibid.* **3**, 3285 (1961) [translation: *ibid.* **3**, 2385 (1962)].

[589e] I. Korenblit, *Fiz. Tverdogo Tela* **4**, 1667 (1962) [translation: *Soviet Phys.-Solid State* **4**, 1225 (1962)].

[589f] M. J. Stevenson, *Phys. Rev. Letters* **3**, 464 (1959).

[589g] A. S. Fischler, *Phys. Rev.* **122**, 425 (1961).

[589h] D. J. Olechna and H. Ehrenreich, *J. Phys. Chem. Solids* **23**, 1513 (1962).

[589i] V. L. Bonch-Bruevich, *Fiz. Tverdogo Tela* **2**, 1857 (1960) [translation: *Soviet Phys.-Solid State* **2**, 1678 (1961)].

[589j] A. G. Khachaturyan, *Fiz. Tverdogo Tela* **3**, 2540 (1961)]translation: *Soviet Phys.-Solid State* **3**, 1848 (1962)].

solved by Sondheimer for the case of anisotropic metals in which the scattering probability function — the $S(\mathbf{k}, \mathbf{k'})$ in Eq. (25.2) — can be written as a finite sum of products of a function of $\mathbf{k}$ only with a function of $\mathbf{k'}$ only.[589k] The explicit form of the solution, valid for arbitrary energy surfaces, is derived.

Some recent investigations of ionized impurity scattering in isotropic solids involve a consideration of the screening effects.[589 l–o] Also of interest is the application of a variational technique by Csavinszky.[589p] The scattering at charged dislocations has been investigated by Kuznetsova[589q] and that due to composition fluctuations near critical points in alloy systems by Parrott.[589r]

The scattering of charge carriers due to point imperfections having atomic radii different from those of host atoms was calculated for semiconductors by Morimoto and Tani.[589s] From the calculation, using the Born approximation, the interference between the strain scattering associated with the lattice distortion and the Coulomb scattering from charged centers has been found to be quite large, while no interference of scatterings between lattice vibrations and point defects has been deduced. This strain-interference effect is suggested as an explanation of the difference in the electron mobilities between Sb-doped Ge and As-doped Ge.[591f] Dipole scattering from ion pairs can be important in certain compensated semiconductors. This has been considered by Teutsch and Appel[589t] and by Stratton.[589u]

In the case of piezoelectric solids, a plane elastic wave propagating therein may be accompanied by longitudinal electric fields, which provide

[589k] E. H. Sondheimer, *Proc. Roy. Soc. (London)* **A268**, 100 (1962).

[589l] N. Takimoto, *J. Phys. Soc. Japan* **14**, 1142 (1959).

[589m] See also, E. C. McIrvine, *ibid.* **15**, 928 (1960).

[589n] G. L. Hall, *J. Phys. Chem. Solids* **23**, 1147 (1962).

[589o] V. B. Glasko and A. G. Mironov, *Fiz. Tverdogo Tela* **4**, 336 (1962) [translation: *Soviet Phys.-Solid State* **4**, 241 (1962)].

[589p] P. Csavinszky, *Phys. Rev.* **126**, 1436 (1962).

[589q] E. M. Kuznetsova, *Fiz. Tverdogo Tela* **3**, 1987 (1961) [translation: *Soviet Phys.-Solid State* **3**, 1446 (1962)].

[589r] J. E. Parrott, *J. Phys. Chem. Solids* **23**, 1437 (1962).

[589s] T. Morimoto and K. Tani, *J. Phys. Soc. Japan* **17**, 1121 (1962).

[589t] W. B. Teutsch and J. Appel, *Bull. Am. Phys. Soc.* **6**, 137 (1961); J. Appel and W. B. Teutsch, *J. Phys. Chem. Solids* **23**, 1521 (1962).

[589u] R. Stratton, *J. Phys. Chem. Solids* **23**, 1011 (1962).

an additional elastic stiffness. When the crystal is semiconducting, these fields produce currents and space charge, resulting in acoustic dispersion and loss. A linear theory of this effect is developed by Hutson and White, taking into account drift, diffusion, and trapping of carriers for both extrinsic and intrinsic semiconductors.[589v] The absorption of sound in piezoelectric semiconductors, where there exists a rather strong interaction of the sound oscillations with the conduction electrons, has been investigated by Gurevich.[589w] The possibility of polarization due to lattice vibrations in homopolar crystals of the diamond type is discussed by Mashkevich.[589x, y] Such polarization could result from a deformation of the electron shells of the atoms, creating dipole moments, as suggested by Tolpygo.[589z−bb] Expressions are developed for the mobility, taking into account scattering by both acoustical and optical modes. Both the magnitude of the mobility for n-type germanium and its temperature dependence are in good agreement with experiment. In view of this agreement, it is suggested that the polarization process may play a significant role in these crystals.[589x]

The question of inelastic scattering at impurities which are subject to thermal motion is discussed by Taylor.[589cc] An inelastic scattering process which might occur in compensated semiconductors at low temperatures has been investigated by Callaway and Cummings.[589dd] The mechanism is that of a charge carrier exciting a "molecule ion" formed by the sharing of an electron between an un-ionized and an ionized donor.

[589v] A. R. Hutson and D. L. White, *J. Appl. Phys.* **33**, 40 (1962). Also A. R. Hutson, *ibid.* **32**, 2287 (1961).

[589w] V. L. Gurevich, *Fiz. Tverdogo Tela* **4**, 909 (1962) [translation: *Soviet Phys.- Solid State* **4**, 668 (1962)].

[589x] V. S. Mashkevich, *J. Exptl. Theoret. Phys. U.S.S.R.* **36**, 1736 (1959) [translation: *Soviet Phys.-JETP* **9**, 1237 (1959)].

[589y] V. S. Mashkevich, *Fiz. Tverdogo Tela* **2**, 2629 (1960) [translation: *Soviet Phys.- Solid State* **2**, 2345 (1961)]; also K. B. Tolpygo, *ibid.* **4**, 1765 (1962).

[589z] K. B. Tolpygo, *J. Exptl. Theoret. Phys. U.S.S.R.* **20**, 497 (1950).

[589aa] V. S. Mashkevich and K. B. Tolpygo, *J. Exptl. Theoret. Phys. U.S.S.R.* **32**, 520 (1957) [translation: *Soviet Phys.-JETP* **5**, 435 (1957)].

[589bb] V. S. Mashkevich, *J. Exptl. Theoret. Phys. U.S.S.R.* **32**, 866 (1957) [translation: *Soviet Phys.-JETP* **5**, 707 (1957)].

[589cc] P. L. Taylor, *Proc. Phys. Soc. (London)* **80**, 755 (1962).

[589dd] J. Callaway and F. W. Cummings, *Phys. Rev.* **126**, 5 (1962).

31. STRONG INTERACTIONS

a. Discussion of Strong Scattering

We have seen in Section 28a that conventional transport theory is valid if the interaction with the charge carriers is sufficiently weak so that

$$\hbar/\tau \ll \varepsilon_0 \qquad (31.1)$$

where τ is a scattering time and ε_0 is an energy which is important for the charge carriers. For nondegenerate semiconductors $\varepsilon_0 \sim kT$, and the criterion (31.1) may be expressed as a condition on the mobility [cf. Eq. (12.25)], namely,

$$\mu \gg 134\left(\frac{100°}{T}\frac{m^*}{m_0}\right) \qquad [\text{cm}^2/\text{volt-sec}]. \qquad (31.2)$$

In the general area of strong scattering, $\hbar/\tau \gtrsim \varepsilon_0$, there has been little work done. Certain aspects of the problem have been discussed by Herring.[589] Reference is made to the contribution of Kasuya, who presents a treatment of strong impurity scattering.[590] Such scattering is encountered in certain regimes which are encompassed in the general category of impurity conduction. Kasuya points out that, according to the concentration of impurity atoms, it is possible to divide the area of impurity transport into three regions:

(1) Characterized by a high concentration of impurity centers: the impurity levels become very broad and are merged with the conduction band. Thus the transport is by a single band (although of complicated structure[591]), with the impurity atoms providing the principal scattering. Theoretical treatments of the effects of large impurity concentrations on the band structure in semiconductors have recently been given by Klauder,[591a] by Bonch-Bruevich and Mironov,[591b] and by Wolff.[591c] For experimental information through the measurement of optical

---

[590] T. Kasuya, *J. Phys. Soc. Japan* **13**, 1096 (1958).

[591] See, for example, J. I. Pankove, *Phys. Rev. Letters* **4**, 20, 454 (1960).

[591a] J. R. Klauder, *Ann. Phys. (N.Y.)* **14**, 43 (1961).

[591b] V. L. Bonch-Bruevich and A. G. Mironov, *Fiz. Tverdogo Tela* **3**, 3009 (1961) [translation: *Soviet Phys.-Solid State* **3**, 2194 (1962)]; V. L. Bonch-Bruevich, *ibid.* **4**, 2660 (1962).

[591c] P. A. Wolff, *Phys. Rev.* **126**, 405 (1962).

properties of compensated heavily doped germanium, the reader is referred to articles by Cardona and Sommers,[591d] and more recently, by Fowler and co-workers,[591e] and to the literature cited therein. A number of other investigators present information on electrical properties of heavily doped germanium[591f–k] and indium antimonide.[591l,m] Additional literature containing data in this region is cited in Section 31b.

(2) Intermediate impurity concentrations: here the impurity levels are separated from the conduction band, and in the general case it is necessary to consider two-band conduction, i.e., transport in the conduction band in the impurity level.

(3) Low impurity concentration: this region is characterized by the fluctuation of the local potential energy being much larger than the kinetic energy of the electron. Thus one encounters localized states belonging to a particular impurity atom. Transport can occur only through interactions with the electron system, for example by means of interactions of the electrons and phonons. Mobility in this range is treated by a "hopping" model.

Regions (1) and (2) are treated in the first article by Kasuya, while region (3) is considered separately.[592] Inasmuch as considerable literature exists in the areas of impurity band phenomena and hopping processes it seems desirable to give special attention to these phenomena.

[591d] M. Cardona and H. S. Sommers, Jr., *Phys. Rev.* **122**, 1382 (1961).

[591e] A. B. Fowler, W. E. Howard, and G. E. Brock, *Phys. Rev.* **128**, 1664 (1962).

[591f] Y. Furukawa, *J. Phys. Soc. Japan* **16**, 687 (1961); **17**, 630 (1962).

[591g] W. G. Spitzer, F. A. Trumbore, and R. A. Logan, *J. Appl. Phys.* **32**, 1822 (1961).

[591h] H. Roth, W. D. Straub, and R. F. Tramposch, *Bull. Am. Phys. Soc.* **7**, 174 (1962).

[591i] R. G. Zhurkin, V. S. Zemskov, and K. V. Yurkina, *Fiz. Tverdogo Tela* **3**, 3509 (1961) [translation: *Soviet Phys.-Solid State* **3**, 2545 (1962)].

[591j] V. I. Fistul', M. I. Iglitsyn, and É. M. Omel'yanovskii, *Fiz. Tverdogo Tela* **4**, 1065 (1962) [translation: *Soviet Phys.-Solid State* **4**, 784 (1962)].

[591k] V. I. Fistul' and É. M. Omel'yanovskii, *Fiz. Tverdogo Tela* **4**, 1370 (1962) [translation: *Soviet Phys.-Solid State* **4**, 1007 (1962)].

[591l] J. Kolodziejczak, *Acta Phys. Polonica* **20**, 289 (1961).

[591m] K. I. Vinogradova, V. V. Galavanov, and D. N. Nasledov, *Fiz. Tverdogo Tela* **4**, 1673 (1962) [translation: *Soviet Phys.-Solid State* **4**, 1230 (1962)].

[592] T. Kasuya and S. Koide, *J. Phys. Soc. Japan* **13**, 1287 (1958).

b. Impurity Conduction

The possibility of impurity band conduction in germanium at low temperatures was advanced by Hung[593] to explain a flattening of the resistivity and a maximum in the Hall coefficient as the temperature was lowered below 10°K for several specimens.[594] It was found that the two-band model, representative of transport in the principal band and in the impurity band, was capable of explaining the temperature dependence of the measured electrical properties.[593, 595] Besides germanium, impurity conduction has been observed in a number of other semiconductors, including silicon, silicon carbide, cadmium sulfide, and indium antimonide. Much of this work is referenced in the review article on the theory of impurity conduction by Mott and Twose.[596] Additional work which has recently appeared in the literature includes articles on materials such as indium antimonide[596a] and gallium arsenide.[596b-d]

A number of investigators have examined theoretically the problem of electrical conduction by charges in impurity states. In this connection, the theoretical problem of the transition of an array of atoms from the nonmetallic to the metallic state as the interatomic distance is varied is of interest. This problem has been investigated by Mott.[597-599] References to other current literature can be found in his recent article, which discusses in some detail the latest theoretical and experimental findings.[598] In the regions of high impurity concentration, impurity banding may occur, as was mentioned previously. This phenomenon

---

[593] C. S. Hung, *Phys. Rev.* **79**, 727 (1950).

[594] C. S. Hung and J. R. Gliessman, *Phys. Rev.* **79**, 726 (1950).

[595] C. S. Hung and J. R. Gliessman, *Phys. Rev.* **96**, 1226 (1954).

[596] N. F. Mott and W. D. Twose, *Advances in Phys.* **10**, 107 (1961).

[596a] L. Chih Ch'ao and D. N. Nasledov, *Fiz. Tverdogo Tela* **3**, 1185, 1458 (1961) [translation: *Soviet Phys.-Solid State* **3**, 861, 1058 (1961)].

[596b] O. V. Emel'yanenko, T. S. Lagunova, and D. N. Nasledov, *ibid.* **3**, 198 (1961) [translation: *ibid.* **3**, 144 (1961)].

[596c] M. Giterman, L. Krol', V. Medvedev, M. Orlova, and G. Pado, *ibid.* **4**, 1383 (1962) [translation: *ibid.* **4**, 1017 (1962)].

[596d] D. J. Oliver, *Phys. Rev.* **127**, 1045 (1962).

[597] N. F. Mott, *Proc. Phys. Soc.* (*London*) **A62**, 416 (1949); *Progr. Metal Phys.* **3**, 76 (1952); *Can. J. Phys.* **34**, 1356 (1956); *Nuovo cimento* **7** Suppl., 312 (1958).

[598] N. F. Mott, *Phil. Mag.* **6**, 287 (1961).

[599] N. F. Mott and K. W. H. Stevens, *Phil. Mag.* **2**, 1364 (1957).

was discussed in Section 28d in connection with indium antimonide. Theoretical treatments, applying the metallic hydrogen model to semiconductors, have been carried out by Baltensperger[600] and by Stern and Talley.[601] Consequences of replacing the ordered array of impurities by the more realistic case of a random distribution of centers were examined by Aigrain.[602] He found that for certain cases, band reasoning held for much lower densities in the random than in the ordered case. The problem of impurity conduction has been discussed by Conwell,[603] who draws attention, in the case of the less impure samples, to the importance of compensation — i.e., the presence of both donors and acceptors — so that at low temperatures where all charge carriers have dropped back to the impurity levels, there still exist in the major impurity band a number of centers which are without bound electrons. In the case of moderately heavily doped n-type germanium, $N > 10^{17}$ cm^{-3}, Toyozawa suggests that the electron population in excited impurity bands might increase with application of magnetic field. With a larger mobility in these higher bands than in the ground impurity band, a negative magneto-resistance could result.[603a – d]

In reviewing the literature on impurity conduction we shall distinguish between cases of high and low impurity concentrations. In the former case, a collective electron treatment described by modified Bloch type functions is usually applied, while in the latter case one begins to encounter localized states, and the hopping process becomes important.[596, 603] Literature restricted principally to this latter case is reviewed in the next section.

[600] W. Baltensperger, *Phil. Mag.* **44**, 1355 (1953).

[601] F. Stern and R. M. Talley, *Phys. Rev.* **100**, 1638 (1955).

[602] P. Aigrain, *Physica* **20**, 978 (1954).

[603] E. M. Conwell, *Phys. Rev.* **103**, 51 (1956).

[603a] Y. Toyozawa, *in* "Proc. Intern. Conf. on Semiconductor Phys., Prague 1960," p. 215. Publishing House Czech. Acad. Sci., Prague, 1961.

[603b] W. Sasaki, C. Yamanouchi, and G. Hatoyama, *in* "Proc. Intern. Conf. on Semiconductor Phys., Prague 1960," p. 159. Publishing House Czech. Acad. Sci., Prague, 1961.

[603c] In a recent publication, Toyozawa considers the effect of spin ordering in a magnetic field on the electrical resistivity.[603d] Such a model gave results in qualitative agreement with the dependences upon temperature, magnetic field, and impurity concentration found by Sasaki and collaborators.[603b, 609c]

[603d] Y. Toyozawa, *J. Phys. Soc. Japan* **17**, 986 (1962).

For references to most of the experimental work on impurity conduction in semiconductors, we shall refer the reader to the review paper by Mott and Twose[596] or to the literature cited by Fritzsche and Cuevas.[604] Probably the most extensive studies on germanium are those of Fritzsche and collaborators. Although details of most of this work will not be given here, it seems desirable to draw attention to a special procedure which allows a careful control of the impurity content. This technique involved the introduction of impurities into pure germanium by means of transmutations caused by slow-neutron bombardment.[604, 605] It is thus possible to control carefully the concentration of impurities, and specimens were produced which contained major impurities of gallium atoms ranging from 8×10^{14} to 1.8×10^{18} cm^{-3}. Another great advantage of the bombardment method is that the degree of compensation remains constant for all bombardments. This quantity is determined by the abundances and capture cross sections of the various germanium isotopes. The compensation ratio turns out to be about 0.4, the minority impurities being arsenic and selenium. In the case of silicon, deuteron irradiation has been used to introduce controlled amounts of compensation.[606] Another technique, which was used by Ray and Fan in studies of impurity conduction in silicon, involved use of heat treatment to add donors to p-type silicon.[606a] This permitted a determination of the amount of the compensating impurity. In gallium- or aluminum-doped samples, evidence of ion pairing between the acceptor impurity and the compensating impurity was found.

Inasmuch as impurity conduction depends sensitively on the overlap of the wave functions of neighboring impurity sites, it may be expected that the introduction of strains into the crystal would be strongly reflected in the electrical measurements. In particular, shear strains would lift the degeneracy of the conduction band valleys and the corresponding degeneracy of the donor levels.[606b] It was shown by Fritzsche that such

[604] H. Fritzsche and M. Cuevas, *Phys. Rev.* **119**, 1238 (1960).

[605] H. Fritzsche and M. Cuevas, *in* "Proc. Intern. Conf. on Semiconductor Phys., Prague 1960," p. 222. Publishing House Czech. Acad. Sci., Prague, 1961.

[606] T. Longo, R. Ray, and K. Lark-Horovitz, *J. Phys. Chem. Solids* **8**, 259 (1959).

[606a] R. K. Ray and H. Y. Fan, *Phys. Rev.* **121**, 768 (1961).

[606b] This point was also discussed in Sections 24*b* and 30*a*, with additional citation of literature.

experiments could indeed be very useful in studying impurity conduction. Initial researches were carried out on a specimen of germanium containing 1.4×10^{16} antimony atoms/cm³ subjected to uniaxial tensile stresses along a [110] direction.[607] Measurements of resistivity were made between 1.3 and 5°K. Subsequent measurements at 1.9°K on a specimen containing 5.2×10^{15} antimony atoms/cm³ were done for both uniaxial tension and compression.[608] The effect of tensile stress on n-type germanium was also studied by Nakamura and Sasaki for impurity concentrations in the ranges of intermediate and high concentrations.[608a] The stresses were applied along [110] directions, and piezoresistance was measured in the impurity-conduction and in the normal regions. By the use of uniaxial compression along a [111] direction, Fritzsche has investigated as a function of stress the critical impurity separation d_c for the transition from nonmetallic to metallic conduction and impurity conduction in the intermediate concentration range from 7×10^{16} to 3×10^{17} impurities/cm³ in germanium.[608b] Some striking results were obtained. For example, with arsenic or phosphorus doping, the [111] compression increased d_c and decreased the activation energy for impurity conduction. For antimony doping, the exact opposite was observed. At 1.2°K, [111] compression increased the resistivity of antimony-doped germanium by a factor of 10^7; under similar conditions arsenic doping resulted in a decrease by a factor of 5×10^{-4}. Results suggest that the activation energy for impurity conduction depends strongly on the wave function overlap, and that the shear strains change the donor wave functions originating from the individual valleys by an amount which is proportional to the valley-orbit splitting of the donor element.

Valley orbit splitting, i.e., the energy separation between the onefold and threefold 1s-like donor states, was studied for antimony in germanium by measuring the conduction band conductivity in quite pure samples from 4° to 7°K under various amounts of strain.[608c] The temperatures were chosen sufficiently high to render impurity conduction negligible, yet sufficiently low that the conditions $n \ll N_d - N_A$ and

[607] H. Fritzsche, *J. Phys. Chem. Solids* **8**, 257 (1959).

[608] H. Fritzsche, *Phys. Rev.* **119**, 1899 (1960).

[608a] M. Nakamura and W. Sasaki, *J. Phys. Soc. Japan* **17**, 1311 (1962).

[608b] H. Fritzsche, *Phys. Rev.* **125**, 1552, 1560 (1962).

[608c] H. Fritzsche, *Phys. Rev.* **120**, 1120 (1960).

$n \ll N_A$ were satisfied. Determinations of valley-orbit splitting are also possible through measurement of the temperature dependence of the spin-lattice relaxation rate, as was done for shallow donors in silicon by Castner.[608d]

It has been found by Keyes and Sladek that a substantial increase in thermal conductivity can be produced by [111] or [110] tension in antimony-doped germanium in which the scattering of phonons is primarily due to donors.[608e] The theory of scattering of phonons by donors was found to predict the sign and magnitude of the effect. An interesting experiment, which gives information on the redistribution of electron population in the several valleys of the germanium conduction band when the crystal is strained, concerns the propagation of microwave phonons.[609] In the case of heavily doped specimens, only certain types of the elastic waves were propagated.

An investigation of the Hall effect and of the longitudinal and transverse magnetoresistance in n-type germanium has been made by Sladek and Keyes in the impurity conduction range.[609a] The crystalline anisotropy of the impurity conduction magnetoresistance was found to be noticeably different from that of the conduction band. Results are interpreted by the use of a phenomenological model, based on physical arguments and also on theoretical findings in the absence of magnetic field, to account for changes in the donor wave functions which are produced by the magnetic field.[609b] Negative magnetoresistance was found in the impurity conduction region in n-type germanium by Sasaki and De Bruyn Ouboter.[609c] Data were taken at temperatures as low as 0.54°K. Transverse magnetoresistances were measured by Sadasiv in samples of germanium doped with antimony, arsenic, or gallium in the range from 5×10^{16} to 3×10^{17} atoms/cm^3.[609d] Data were taken over the temperature interval from 4.2 to 1.2°K, and a study was made of

608d T. G. Castner, Jr., *Phys. Rev. Letters* **8**, 13 (1962); *Phys. Rev.* **130**, 58 (1963).

608e R. W. Keyes and R. J. Sladek, *Phys. Rev.* **125**, 478 (1962).

609 M. Pomerantz, R. W. Keyes, and P. E. Seiden, *Phys. Rev. Letters* **9**, 312 (1962).

609a R. J. Sladek and R. W. Keyes, *Phys. Rev.* **122**, 437 (1961).

609b A detailed theoretical treatment of these effects has been given by Mikoshiba.[617c]

609c W. Sasaki and R. De Bruyn Ouboter, *Physica* **27**, 877 (1961). A possible explanation of the phenomenon has recently been given by Toyozawa.[603c]

609d G. Sadasiv, *Phys. Rev.* **128**, 1131 (1962).

the magnetoresistance in the region where the impurity conduction is characterized by an activation energy. The magnetic field was found to change the activation energy ε_2 to $\varepsilon_2 + \alpha H^2$, where the value of α depends on the nature and concentration of the impurity.

c. Hopping Processes — "Narrow-Band" Semiconductors

As we have noted before, the transport process described as hopping between localized states occurs in the impurity band when the impurity concentration is not too great. The mechanism may also be important in host conduction in certain low-mobility semiconductors. In particular, the process becomes relatively more predominant as the width of the band decreases, since in the limiting case of extremely narrow bands, the usual conduction described by Bloch theory becomes impossible. To examine these considerations in more detail, we recall from Subsection *a* that the condition for applicability of conventional transport theory required that the mobility of the change carriers be not too small. This restriction has been developed by Ioffe from simple physical considerations.[610] Ioffe points out that (in the neighborhood of room temperature) the mean free path of a charge carrier is related approximately to its mobility by the expression

$$l \sim 10^{-8} \, (m^*/m_0)^{1/2} \, \mu \qquad \text{cm.} \qquad (31.3)$$

Thus, in semiconductors for which the mobility is the order of 1 $\text{cm}^2/\text{volt-sec}$, one would be talking about mean free paths which were smaller than the lattice constant. Obviously, in such cases, the mean free path concept must break down, and the usual band treatment does not apply. Materials in this category are sometimes referred to as "narrow-band" semiconductors inasmuch as large effective masses and low mobilities are associated with a narrow band. For example, if we designate a band width by W, then in the parabolic approximation we may write

$$W = \hbar^2 \, k_B{}^2/2m^* \qquad (31.4)$$

where k_B is determined by the dimensions of the Brillouin zone. It is approximately given by π/a, where a is the distance between nearest-

---
[610] A. F. Ioffe (A. Joffe), *J. Phys. Chem. Solids* 8, 6 (1959).

neighbor ions.[611] The point was made by Fröhlich and Sewell that the usual transport theory breaks down whenever the band width W is less than $k\Theta$ (Θ being the Debye temperature).[612] This is seen from the approximate expression for the maximum velocity in a band, which can be put in the form

$$v_m \simeq c_s W/k\Theta \tag{31.5}$$

where c_s is the velocity of sound. When $v_m < c_s$, i.e., $W < k\Theta$, the absorption or emission of a single acoustic phonon is not possible, and the usual mobility theory breaks down. When $W < kT$, Fröhlich and Sewell show that the uncertainty relation requires that

$$\mu > \frac{ea^2}{\hbar}\left(\frac{W}{kT}\right), \qquad W < kT. \tag{31.6}$$

Of course, as the band becomes extremely narrow, it is no longer meaningful to assign a width to the band.[613] Then, as the interaction with the lattice becomes very strong, the theoretical treatment of the transport is usually based on a Heitler-London approach.[611, 614] The intermediate region between the collective electron of Bloch regime and the localized state or Heitler-London region requires special consideration, as is apparent from the preceding paragraph.[611, 612] In the case of the tight binding situation, the current is associated with a hopping motion of the electron from ion to ion rather than with a translational motion as in a nearly perfect lattice. Thus there is an activation energy associated with self-trapping of the charge carriers. Mobility is extremely low and increases exponentially with temperature. Such behavior is in contrast to transport in the usual band, where mobility decreases with increasing temperature because of lattice scattering.[613] An unresolved question is the Hall effect associated with hopping. In a number of cases, no Hall voltage could be measured. Herring points out that a Hall field

[611] J. Yamashita and T. Kurosawa, *J. Phys. Soc. Japan* **15**, 802 (1960).

[612] H. Fröhlich and G. Sewell, *Proc. Phys. Soc. (London)* **74**, 643 (1959).

[613] F. J. Morin, *Bell. System Tech. J.* **37**, 1047 (1958); also *in* "Semiconductors" (N. B. Hannay, ed.), Chap. 14, p. 600. Reinhold, New York, 1959.

[614] J. Yamashita and T. Kurosawa, *J. Phys. Chem. Solids* **5**, 34 (1958); T. Kurosawa, *J. Phys. Soc. Japan* **15**, 1211 (1960); J. Yamashita, *J. Appl. Phys.* **32**, 2215 (1961); see also, G. L. Sewell, *Phys. Rev.* **129**, 597 (1963).

can arise only from an influence on the probabilities of different jumps which is exerted by some memory of the preceding jump.[589] In the over-the-barrier adiabatic theory, the magnetic field can influence the nuclear motion, because of the electric current associated with it. Herring indicates how in certain cases, the Hall mobility might be larger than the drift mobility.[589] Sewell discusses a jump mechanism involving phonon-activated processes and no tunneling, for which he obtains a zero Hall effect.[614a] The Hall effect in d-band semiconductors also received discussion at the Rochester Conference.[614b] More recently, a theoretical treatment of the Hall effect in impurity conduction where the phonon-induced hopping process prevails has been given by Holstein.[614c] A magnetic-field-dependent contribution to the jump probability between two sites is shown to arise from the interference between the amplitude for a direct transition between the initial and final sites and the amplitude for an indirect second-order transition, involving intermediate occupancy of a third site.

A discussion of certain differences found in published treatments of the mobility in an ideal crystal due to a jump mechanism is given by Nagaev.[614d] The author develops an expression for mobility, starting from a wave function which is propagating along the crystal. He finds that to obtain an activation energy in the mobility expression, he does not require, as did certain other theories, that there be dispersion in the phonon spectrum. In a subsequent article the case of antiferromagnetic materials is considered.[614e] The effect of strong electric fields on the electron states in the narrow bands of a semiconductor has been treated by Yakovlev.[614f] Differences between electron transfer by the "hopping" model, where a thermally assisted transfer over a potential barrier is postulated, and by a tunneling model, where transfer is via a tunneling process through the potential barrier, are discussed by Keller and Rast[614g]

[614a] G. L. Sewell, *Proc. Phys. Soc. (London)* **76**, 985 (1960).

[614b] See discussion for Paper B.2, *J. Phys. Chem. Solids* **8**, 50 (1959).

[614c] T. Holstein, *Phys. Rev.* **124**, 1329 (1961).

[614d] É. L. Nagaev, *Fiz. Tverdogo Tela* **3**, 2567 (1961) [translation: *Soviet Phys.-Solid State* **3**, 1867 (1962)]. See also *ibid.* **4**, 2201 (1962) [*ibid.* **4**, 1611 (1963)].

[614e] É. L. Nagaev, *ibid.* **4**, 413 (1962) [translation: *ibid.* **4**, 300 (1962)].

[614f] V. A. Yakovlev, *Fiz. Tverdogo Tela* **3**, 1983 (1961) [translation: *Soviet Phys.-Solid State* **3**, 1442 (1962)].

[614g] R. A. Keller and H. E. Rast, Jr., *J. Chem. Phys.* **36**, 2640 (1962).

and Tredgold.[614h] Both papers are concerned with the tunneling process, and the authors use an idealized one-dimensional square-wave potential well, which is perturbed by lattice vibrations. Because of different approximations, however, substantial differences in the temperature dependence of the mobility are obtained.

Much of the literature mentioned in the preceding section, especially the review paper of Mott and Twose,[596] includes also the regime where the hopping processes are important. There are, however, a number of articles which have been concerned only with the jump processes. These include the theoretical papers of Miller and Abrahams[615] and those of Mycielski.[616] The model is that of a phonon-induced electron hopping from donor site to donor site, where a fraction of the sites is vacant due to compensation. The latter author considers the possibility that, due to carrier-phonon interaction, the wave functions of the carriers partially lose their coherence. The complex conductivity in n-type silicon containing various kinds of impurities has been measured by Pollak and Geballe at frequencies between 10^2 and 10^5 cps and temperatures between $1°$ and $20°K$.[617] The change in conductivity in the alternating fields is attributed to polarization caused by hopping processes. As the applied frequency is increased above the jumping rate, the magnitude of the polarization decreases since it has less chance to keep up with the field variation. Subsequent experimental results (unpublished) suggest that the real part of the conductivity increases all the way up to 9×10^9 cps. A theory of weak-field magnetoresistance in impurity conduction in n-type germanium was developed by Mikoshiba and Gonda.[617a] The coefficients[617b] b, c, and d were calculated for the phonon-induced hopping region at low temperatures. It was found that the shrinking of each donor wave function by the magnetic field decreased the transition probability of electrons from a donor site to an unoccupied one and gave rise to a magnetoresistive effect. The phase difference produced by the field between two neighboring donor wave functions

---

[614h] R. H. Tredgold, *Proc. Phys. Soc. (London)* **80**, 807 (1962).
[615] A. Miller and E. Abrahams, *Phys. Rev.* **120**, 745 (1960).
[616] J. Mycielski, *Phys. Rev.* **123**, 99 (1961); **125**, 46, 1975 (1962).
[617] M. Pollak and T. H. Geballe, *Phys. Rev.* **122**, 1742 (1961).
[617a] N. Mikoshiba and S. Gonda, *Phys. Rev.* **127**, 1954 (1962).
[617b] For the definition of these coefficients see Eq. (8.30).

contributed to the magnetoresistance by the same order of magnitude as the effect of the shrinking. The results show some characteristic properties of b, c, and d different from those of electrons in the conduction band. The case for strong magnetic fields is discussed by Mikoshiba.[617c] The author finds that in a moderately strong field, the shrinking of a donor wave function and the phase difference produced by the magnetic field between two neighboring donors lead to a formula qualitatively identical with the empirical formula found experimentally by Sladek and Keyes.[609a] The magnetoresistance in an extremely strong magnetic field is also discussed, in which the wave function in the plane perpendicular to the field becomes similar to the free-electron wave function in a magnetic field.

Examples of narrow-band semiconductors, for which considerable information is available, are the oxides of the $3d$ transition metals.[613] Inasmuch as the literature is quite extensive, we are able to refer only to a small number of the pertinent articles. Each of the references does, however, contain many additional citations. Early work in the field involved studies of the conductivities of a number of substituted metal oxides by Verwey and collaborators.[618] Subsequent investigations were done by Heikes and Johnston[619] on lithium-substituted metal oxides. A material which has received considerable emphasis is NiO. In addition to the work due to Mott, which has been referenced in the preceding section, there are articles by Morin,[620] Goodenough[621] and co-workers, Van Houten,[622] and others. Studies on Fe_2O_3 were reported by Morin,[623] on cobalt ferrite by Jonker,[624] and on Ti_2O_3 by Yahia and Frederikse.[625] The effect of pressure on several of the oxides was examined by Young and collaborators.[626] The mobility was found to decrease. The metallic

---

[617c] N. Mikoshiba, *Phys. Rev.* **127**, 1962 (1962).

[618] E. Verwey, P. Haaijman, F. Romeijn, and G. van Oosterhout, *Philips Research Repts.* **5**, 173 (1950).

[619] R. R. Heikes and W. D. Johnston, *J. Chem. Phys.* **26**, 582 (1957).

[620] F. J. Morin, *Phys. Rev.* **93**, 1199 (1954).

[621] J. Goodenough, D. Wickham, and W. J. Croft, *J. Phys. Chem. Solids* **5**, 107 (1958).

[622] S. Van Houten, *J. Phys. Chem. Solids* **17**, 7 (1960).

[623] F. J. Morin, *Phys. Rev.* **93**, 1195 (1954).

[624] G. H. Jonker, *J. Phys. Chem. Solids* **9**, 165 (1959).

[625] J. Yahia and H. P. R. Frederikse, *Phys. Rev.* **123**, 1257 (1961).

[626] A. Young, W. Wilson, and C. Schwartz, *Phys. Rev.* **121**, 77 (1961).

behavior of a number of transition metal oxides has been discussed by Morin in terms of the overlap of the atomic orbitals in the crystal.[627, 628] Miller and collaborators have discussed transport in certain mixed-valency semiconductors which exhibit characteristics attributable to both the band and the localized model.[628a] The behavior appears to be described by a model which, in many respects, can be considered as the localized limit of impurity conduction in the hopping region.

The $3d$ transition metal oxides are noted for their antiferromagnetic behavior. A number of authors have discussed correlations between magnetic and electrical properties. The interaction between the d-shells was examined by Zener.[629] Both electrical conduction and ferromagnetic coupling were considered to arise from an electron spin interaction, called "double exchange."[630] The interactions in transition metal compounds have subsequently been discussed in a number of publications.[631-638]

It appears that narrow-band semiconductors can also be found among certain classes of organic compounds. An example, which has been discussed by Le Blanc in terms of band-approximation schemes, is anthracene.[638a] Calculations, done by means of a tight-binding approximation, suggest that both electron and hole bands are highly anisotropic, with a width of approximately $0.56\,kT$ at room temperature. In anthracene, the mobilities of both holes and electrons are the order of 1 cm^2/volt-sec at room temperature, and vary as T^{-n}, with $1 < n < 2$. In many organic semiconductors, however, the mobility appears to be much lower than in

[627] F. J. Morin, *in* "Proc. Intern. Conf. on Semiconductor Phys., Prague 1960," p. 858. Publishing House Czech. Acad. Sci., Prague, 1961.

[628] F. J. Morin, *Phys. Rev. Letters* **3**, 34 (1959).

[628a] R. Miller, R. Heikes, and R. Mazelsky, *J. Appl. Phys.* **32**, 2202 (1961).

[629] C. Zener, *Phys. Rev.* **81**, 440 (1951).

[630] C. Zener, *Phys. Rev.* **82**, 403 (1951).

[631] P. W. Anderson and H. Hasegawa, *Phys. Rev.* **100**, 675 (1955).

[632] R. R. Heikes, *Phys. Rev.* **99**, 1232 (1955).

[633] J. Yamashita and J. Kondo, *Phys. Rev.* **109**, 730 (1958).

[634] C. Zener, *J. Phys. Chem. Solids* **8**, 26 (1959).

[635] P. W. Anderson, *Phys. Rev.* **115**, 2 (1959).

[636] R. R. Heikes, T. R. McGuire, and R. J. Happel, *Phys. Rev.* **121**, 703 (1961).

[637] J. Goodenough, A. Wold, R. Arnott, and N. Menyuk, *Phys. Rev.* **124**, 373 (1961).

[637a] V. G. Bhide and R. H. Dani, *Physica* **27**, 821 (1961).

[638] M. Asdente and J. Friedel, *Phys. Rev.* **124**, 384 (1961).

[638a] O. H. Le Blanc, *J. Chem. Phys.* **35**, 1275 (1961).

anthracene,[638b] and little can be said, quantitatively, about the conduction mechanisms. For additional information, review articles by Garrett[638c,d] and by Inokuchi and Akamatu[638e] can be consulted. Recently, a measurement of the Hall effect in metal-free phthalocyanine crystals has been reported.[638f] Mobility values were thereby determined to be around 0.1 cm²/volt-sec.

d. Polarons

In the case of ionic crystals, an electron will produce a polarization of the lattice in its neighborhood. Such an interaction affects the energy of the electron. In addition, when the electron moves, the polarization state moves with it. The electron together with the associated distortion of the lattice is commonly referred to as a polaron. The case of weak interactions was alluded to briefly in Section 25b(3), where several references were cited, including the review article of Fröhlich.[411] More recent contributions include articles by Feynman[639] and by Holstein.[640] A review article by Allcock summarizes the work through 1955 on the polaron ground state, with especial attention paid to the results of the various investigators on the rest energy and effective mass.[640a]

A theory, based on the Feynman model, has been presented by Schultz, in which the Boltzmann equation is used with resonance scattering as the fundamental process.[641] The paper includes a review of the various polaron theories, with comments on the ranges of validity. Much informa-

[638b] O. H. LeBlanc, Jr., *J. Chem. Phys.* **37**, 916 (1962).

[638c] C. G. B. Garrett, *in* "Semiconductors" (N. B. Hannay, ed.), Chap. 15, p. 634. Reinhold, New York, 1959.

[638d] C. G. B. Garrett, *in* "Proc. Intern. Conf. on Semiconductor Phys., Prague 1960," p. 844. Publishing House Czech. Acad. Sci., Prague, 1961.

[638e] H. Inokuchi and H. Akamatu, *Solid State Phys.* **12**, 93 (1961).

[638f] G. H. Heilmeier, G. Warfield, and S. E. Harrison, *Phys. Rev. Letters* **8**, 309 (1962).

[639] R. P. Feynman, *Phys. Rev.* **97**, 660 (1955); also R. Feynman, R. Hellwarth, C. Iddings, and P. Platzman, *ibid.* **127**, 1004 (1962).

[640] T. Holstein, *Ann. Phys.* (*N. Y.*) **8**, 325, 343 (1959).

[640a] G. R. Allcock, *Advances in Phys.* **5**, 412 (1956).

[641] T. D. Schultz, *Phys. Rev.* **116**, 526 (1959).

tion appears in the Soviet literature.[641a] Some of the early articles are available in German translation.[642, 643]

By carrying out studies on narrow $p - n$ junctions of various compounds, with conditions such that most of the conduction resulted from tunneling, Hall and collaborators obtained evidence for direct observation of polarons.[644, 645] The measurements permitted a direct experimental determination of the polar electron-phonon coupling constant. A polaron model has been applied by Appel and Kurnick to Ce-S semiconductors.[645a] The experimental data, which include high- and low-frequency dielectric constants and temperature dependences of the mobility and thermoelectric power, appear to support such a picture. Thermoelectric properties of some of the Ce-S compositions have also been investigated by Ryan and co-workers.[645b] Specimens doped with strontium sulfide were included.

32. MISCELLANEOUS

a. Non-ohmic Effects in a Solid

With the exception of Section 27f, where certain non-ohmic effects in inhomogeneous specimens were cited, we have been concerned thus

[641a] For recent work consult; R. Dogonadze and Yu. Chizmadzhev, *Fiz. Tverdogo Tela* **3**, 3712 (1961) [translation: *Soviet Phys.-Solid State* **3**, 2693 (1962)]; R. Dogonadze, A. Chernenko, and Yu. Chizmadzhev, *ibid.* **3**, 3720 (1961) [translation: *ibid.* **3**, 2698 (1962)]; A. Tulub, *J. Exptl. Theoret. Phys. U.S.S.R.* **41**, 1828 (1961) [translation: *Soviet Phys.-JETP* **14**, 1301 (1962)]; Yu. E. Perlin and V. A. Kovarskii, *Fiz. Tverdogo Tela* **3**, 1031 (1961) [translation: *Soviet Phys.-Solid State* **3**, 749 (1961)]; M. I. Klinger, *Doklady Akad. Nauk S.S.S.R.* **142**, 1065 (1962) [translation: *Soviet Phys.-Doklady* **7**, 123 (1962)].

[642] S. I. Pekar, "Untersuchungen über die Elektronentheorie der Kristalle." Akademie-Verlag, Berlin, 1954.

[643] S. V. Tjablikov, *J. Exptl. Theoret. Phys. U.S.S.R.* **22**, 513 (1952); **23**, 381 (1952); **26**, 545 (1954); M. A. Krivoglaz and S. I. Pekar, *Izvest. Akad. Nauk S.S.S.R., Ser. Fiz.* **21**, 3, 16 (1957). These articles appear in German translation in *Fortschr. Physik* Supplement **4**, "Polaronen" (1961).

[644] R. N. Hall, J. H. Racette, and H. Ehrenreich, *Phys. Rev. Letters* **4**, 456 (1960).

[645] R. N. Hall, *in* "Proc. Intern. Conf. on Semiconductor Phys., Prague 1960," p. 193. Publishing House Czech. Acad. Sci., Prague, 1961.

[645a] J. Appel and S. Kurnick, *J. Appl. Phys.* **32**, 2206 (1961).

[645b] F. M. Ryan, I. N. Greenberg, F. L. Carter, and R. C. Miller, *J. Appl. Phys.* **33**, 864 (1962).

far with electrical transport under the conditions of sufficiently weak electric fields such that the conductivity tensor was independent of electric field; that is, the electric current was ohmic, varying linearly with E. There has, however, been substantial work reported on non-ohmic behavior in semiconductors. While it is not possible to present a thorough review of this literature, an attempt will be made to acquaint the reader with the nature of some of the phenomena involved. One may quite broadly distinguish two areas: one involving charge-carrier augmentation, and the other concerned with field-dependent mobilities. Of course both phenomena may be active in a given situation. A third area, namely that of field-dependent recombination rates, is also delineated, although this has received substantially less attention in the literature.

(1) Charge-carrier multiplication. An important mechanism for charge-carrier augmentation in semiconductors is injection of nonequilibrium carriers. This may occur as a result of currents through injecting contacts, $p - n$ junctions, or other external excitations. These phenomena are the basis of transistor action and are discussed in the extensive literature dealing with transistor theory.[646]

The process of charge-carrier augmention in semiconductors is often considered in connection with breakdown in $p - n$ junctions, since large electric fields exist when such junctions are biased in the reverse direction. Two mechanisms of breakdown have been discussed extensively in the literature. These are internal field emission, or Zener breakdown, and avalanche breakdown, or impact ionization.

The Zener breakdown is a direct excitation of electrons from one band to another by the electric field. It is therefore analogous to field emission from metals. The electric field counteracts the barrier tending to keep the electrons in the lower energy band, and they escape to a band of

---

[646] See, for example, the texts by Shockley,[32] Dunlap,[94] or Hannay.[613]   Also: J. N. Shive, "Semiconductor Devices." Van Nostrand, Princeton, New Jersey, 1959. E. Spenke, "Elektronische Halbleiter." Springer-Verlag, Berlin-Göttingen-Heidelberg, 1955 [translated by D. Jenny, H. Kroemer, E. Ramberg, and A. Sommer, "Electronic Semiconductors." McGraw-Hill, New York, 1958]. A. Many and R. Bray, *in* "Progress in Semiconductors" (A. F. Gibson, ed.), Vol. 3, p. 117. Wiley, New York, 1958. R. Bray and A. Many, *in* "Methods of Experimental Physics," Vol. 6B (K. Lark-Horovitz and V. A. Johnson, eds.), p. 78. Academic Press, New York, 1959.

higher energy. The transition probability for the tunneling process in the presence of an external electric field was computed by Zener.[647] Application of Zener's theory to the excitation of electrons directly from the valence band to the conduction band in germanium $p - n$ junctions was done by McAfee and co-workers.[648] The question as to whether the Zener mechanism predominates in various instances of breakdown has not always been capable of a clearcut answer. For example, Chynoweth and McKay present evidence for internal field emission (Zener effect) in narrow $p - n$ junctions of silicon.[649] On the other hand, the data of Pell on germanium $n - p$ junctions in the "soft breakdown" region revealed certain characteristics which, although indicative of a non-multiplicative (i.e., nonavalanching) process, were not entirely satisfactorily interpreted by the usual Zener scheme.[650] A general review of internal field emission effects has been given by Chynoweth.[651] The theory of Zener tunneling has been developed more extensively by Keldysh, who took into account the three-dimensionality of the problem and examined the influence of the electron-phonon interaction.[652, 653] The effects of the phonon processes were also considered by Gosar[654] and Kane.[655]

Investigations into the tunneling phenomena were greatly stimulated by the development of the Esaki diodes or tunnel diodes. These devices, which involve narrow $p - n$ junctions fabricated on heavily doped degenerate semiconductors, exhibit current-voltage characteristics which are attributed to the Zener current across the energy gap at the junc-

[647] C. Zener, *Proc. Roy. Soc.* **A145**, 523 (1934).
[648] K. McAfee, E. Ryder, W. Shockley, and M. Sparks, *Phys. Rev.* **83**, 650 (1951).
[649] A. G. Chynoweth and K. G. McKay, *Phys. Rev.* **106**, 418 (1957).
[650] E. M. Pell, *J. Appl. Phys.* **28**, 459 (1957).
[651] A. G. Chynoweth, *in* "Progress in Semiconductors" (A. F. Gibson, ed.), Vol. 4, p. 97. Wiley, New York, 1960.
[652] L. V. Keldysh, *J. Exptl. Theoret. Phys. U.S.S.R.* **33**, 994 (1957) [translation: *Soviet Phys.-JETP* **6**, 763 (1958)].
[653] L. V. Keldysh, *J. Exptl. Theoret. Phys. U.S.S.R.* **34**, 962 (1958) [translation: *Soviet Phys.-JETP* **7**, 665 (1958)].
[654] P. Gosar, *in* "Proc. Intern. Conf. on Semiconductor Phys., Prague 1960," p. 130. Publishing House Czech. Acad. Sci., Prague, 1961.
[655] E. O. Kane, *in* "Proc. Intern. Conf. on Semiconductor Phys., Prague, 1960," p. 204. Publishing House Czech. Acad. Sci., Prague, 1961.

tion.[656, 657] Theoretical investigations of the current in Esaki junctions have been reported by Kane[658] and by Chynoweth and co-workers.[659] The influence of pressure on tunneling has been studied by Nathan and Paul,[660] the temperature dependence by Shotov and Grishechkina,[660a] and the behavior of the tunnel current in a magnetic field has been investigated by various workers.[661-664] Experiments by Pierce and co-workers suggest that Esaki diodes can be used to show the existence of deep-lying defects.[664a] It was found that a well-defined hump structure in the excess current region of silicon, germanium, and gallium arsenide Esaki diodes was produced by irradiation with 2-Mev electrons.

The other mechanism of breakdown, namely, the avalanche process or impact ionization, is a solid-state analog of the Townsend β avalanche breakdown in gases.[665] In this process, electrons or holes injected into $p - n$ junctions attain sufficient energies in the high electric fields that they interact with valence band electrons, producing new electron-hole pairs. This is a cumulative process and can result in a rigorously defined breakdown inasmuch as both holes and electrons can ionize, providing essentially a positive feedback.[666] In contrast, the Zener internal field emission in junctions does not possess this multiplication feature. Avalanche breakdown in $p - n$ junctions of germanium and silicon has

[656] L. Esaki, *Phys. Rev.* **109**, 603 (1958).
[657] T. Yajima and L. Esaki, *J. Phys. Soc. Japan* **13**, 1281 (1958).
[658] E. O. Kane, *J. Phys. Chem. Solids* **12**, 181 (1959).
[659] A. G. Chynoweth, W. L. Feldmann, and R. A. Logan, *Phys. Rev.* **121**, 684 (1961).
[660] M. I. Nathan and W. Paul, *in* "Proc. Intern. Conf. on Semiconductor Phys., Prague 1960," p. 209. Publishing House Czech. Acad. Sci., Prague, 1961.
[660a] A. P. Shotov and S. P. Grishechkina, *Fiz. Tverdogo Tela* **4**, 1474 (1962) [translation: *Soviet Phys.-Solid State* **4**, 1084 (1962)].
[661] A. Calawa, R. Rediker, B. Lax, and A. McWhorter, *Phys. Rev. Letters* **5**, 55 (1960).
[662] A. G. Chynoweth, R. A. Logan, and P. A. Wolff, *Phys. Rev. Letters* **5**, 548 (1960).
[663] R. R. Haering and P. B. Miller, *Phys. Rev. Letters* **6**, 269 (1961).
[663a] P. N. Butcher, J. A. Hulbert, and K. F. Hulme, *J. Phys. Chem. Solids* **21**, 320 (1961).
[663b] L. Esaki and R. R. Haering, *J. Appl. Phys.* **33**, 2106 (1962).
[664] R. R. Haering and E. N. Adams, *J. Phys. Chem. Solids* **19**, 8 (1961).
[664a] C. B. Pierce, H. H. Sander, and A. D. Kantz, *J. Appl. Phys.* **33**, 3108 (1962).
[665] K. G. McKay and K. B. McAfee, *Phys. Rev.* **91**, 1079 (1953).
[666] K. G. McKay, *Phys. Rev.* **94**, 877 (1954).

been studied by a number of investigators.[650, 665–670] An interesting finding is that in silicon the ionization rate is higher for electron-hole pair production by energetic electrons than by holes, while the opposite is true for germanium. The process of intrinsic impact ionization in semi-conductors has been dealt with by Tauc from another standpoint, namely, the dependence of the quantum yield of the inner photoelectric effect on the energy of the absorbed photon.[671] The photoionization process has also been studied by Vavilov and co-workers.[672] The quantum efficiency in InSb has been studied by Beattie, by consideration of the phonon-less electron collision processes which could create electron-hole pairs.[672a] The analysis includes both the parabolic and the nonparabolic band structures. Discussion of intrinsic impact ionization for a rather general band structure has been given by Dexter.[673] The subject of avalanche multiplication is also included in review papers by Gunn[674] and by Yamashita.[675] Each article includes a listing of pertinent references.

An important charge-carrier multiplication mechanism at low temperatures in semiconductors is impact ionization of impurity centers. This process can be responsible for current augmentation at very small electric fields.[675] Data on germanium have been presented in articles by Sclar and Burstein,[676] Koenig and Gunther-Mohr[677] and in a number of sub-

[667] P. A. Wolff, *Phys. Rev.* **95**, 1415 (1954).

[668] S. L. Miller, *Phys. Rev.* **99**, 1234 (1955); **105**, 1246 (1957).

[669] A. G. Chynoweth and K. G. McKay, *Phys. Rev.* **108**, 29 (1957).

[670] B. M. Vul [Wul] and A. P. Shotov, *in* "Solid State Physics in Electronics and Telecommunications" (M. Désirant and J. Michiels, eds.), Vol. 1, p. 491. Academic Press, New York, 1960.

[671] J. Tauc, *J. Phys. Chem. Solids* **8**, 219 (1959).

[672] See V. S. Vavilov, *J. Phys. Chem. Solids* **8**, 223 (1959) and literature cited therein.

[672a] A. R. Beattie, *J. Phys. Chem. Solids* **23**, 1049 (1962).

[673] D. L. Dexter, *in* "Proc. Intern. Conf. on Semiconductor Phys., Prague 1960," p. 122. Publishing House Czech. Acad. Sci., Prague, 1961.

[674] J. B. Gunn, *in* "Progress in Semiconductors" (A. F. Gibson, ed.), Vol. 2, p. 213. Heywood, London, 1957.

[675] J. Yamashita, *in* "Progress in Semiconductors" (A. F. Gibson, ed.), Vol. 4, p. 65. Wiley, New York, 1960.

[676] N. Sclar and E. Burstein, *J. Phys. Chem. Solids* **2**, 1 (1957).

[677] S. H. Koenig and G. R. Gunther-Mohr, *J. Phys. Chem. Solids* **2**, 268 (1957).

sequent papers.[678–682] In the case of silicon, where the impurity activation energies are larger, there is sufficient carrier freeze-out at liquid hydrogen temperatures for impact ionization to be observed there (20°K) at low electric field strengths.[683–684] In the case of n-type indium antimonide, however, the donor level is merged with the conduction band, except in specimens of the very highest purity (say $N_D < 10^{14}$ cm^{-3}), and electron multiplication effects have been studied with the aid of magnetically induced freeze-out (see Section 28d).[520, 529] A few experiments have, however, been done on ultrapure specimens of n-type InSb, having impurity concentrations in the range 4×10^{12} to 1×10^{14} cm^{-3}. There, Chih-Ch'ao and Nasledov have observed ionization effects at 2.1° and 4.2°K in the absence of external magnetic fields.[685] The increase in conductivity with electric field was attributed to a field-induced activation of the electrons from the impurity band into the conduction band. The mechanism is suggested to be one of Zener tunneling rather than impact ionization. With a low band-gap, high-mobility (permitting larger electric fields for a given amount of Joule heating) semiconductor such as indium antimonide, it has proved possible to observe intrinsic impact ionization in the *bulk material*, i.e., without recourse to $p - n$ junctions.[686–688]

[678] B. M. Vul, *Fiz. Tverdogo Tela* **2**, 2961 (1960) [translation: *Soviet Phys.-Solid State* **2**, 2631 (1961)].

[679] B. M. Vul and E. I. Zavarickaya, *in* "Proc. Intern. Conf. on Semiconductor Phys., Prague 1960," p. 107. Publishing House Czech. Acad. Sci., Prague, 1961.

[680] A. L. McWhorter and R. H. Rediker, *in* "Proc. Intern. Conf. on Semiconductor Phys., Prague 1960," p. 134. Publishing House Czech. Acad. Sci., Prague, 1961.

[681] S. H. Koenig, *in* "Solid State Physics in Electronics and Telecommunications" (M. Désirant and J. Michiels, eds.), Vol. 1, p. 422. Academic Press, New York, 1960.

[681a] E. I. Zavaritskaya, *Fiz. Tverdogo Tela* **3**, 1887 (1961) [translation: *Soviet Phys.-Solid State* **3**, 1374 (1961)].

[681b] L. M. Lambert, *J. Phys. Chem. Solids* **23**, 1481 (1962).

[682] G. Lautz and M. Pilkuhn, *in* "Proc. Intern. Conf. on Semiconductor Phys., Prague 1960," p. 141. Publishing House Czech. Acad. Sci., Prague, 1961.

[683] W. Kaiser and G. H. Wheatley, *Phys. Rev. Letters* **3**, 334 (1959).

[683a] J. Bok, J. Sohm, and A. Zylbersztejn, *in* "Proc. Intern. Conf. on Semiconductor Phys., Prague 1960," p. 138. Publishing House Czech. Acad. Sci., Prague, 1961.

[684] J.-C. Sohm, *J. Phys. Chem. Solids* **18**, 181 (1961).

[685] L. Chih-Ch'ao and D. N. Nasledov, *Fiz. Tverdogo Tela* **2**, 793 (1960) [translation: *Soviet Phys.-Solid State* **2**, 729 (1960)].

[686] M. Glicksman and M. C. Steele, *Phys. Rev.* **110**, 1204 (1958).

[686a] M. C. Steele and M. Glicksman, *J. Phys. Chem. Solids* **8**, 242 (1959).

[687] A. C. Prior, *J. Electronics and Control* **4**, 165 (1958).

[688] Y. Kanai, *J. Phys. Soc. Japan* **14**, 1302 (1959).

Application of longitudinal magnetic fields to InSb specimens in which electron-hole pair creation is taking place has revealed phenomena which are attributed to the occurrence of plasma pinch effects.[689-690] The longitudinal magnetic field was actually used for diagnostic purposes — the criterion for self-pinching being that the energy density of the circumferential magnetic field due to the current in the crystal be equal to that of the carrier energy density.[690] Thus,

$$B_\theta{}^2/8\,\pi = k\,(nT_n + pT_p)$$

where n and p are electron and hole densities, respectively, T_n and T_p are average electron and hole temperatures, respectively, and k is Boltzmann's constant. The result comes out that for pinching to occur, the magnitude of the current must exceed a certain critical value, and the electric field in the crystal must be at least equal to the field necessary for avalanche breakdown.[690] Experiments by Kikuchi and Abe show that oscillations can be produced in high-purity germanium in the absence of a magnetic field.[690a] Conditions for occurrence of the effect involve heavy minority carrier injection, existence of regions of high and low electric fields, high bulk lifetimes, and sufficiently low surface recombination velocities. Theoretical considerations involved in the phenomenon have been discussed by Gold.[690b] Theoretical analyses of impact ionization in germanium and other semiconductors have been given by a number of investigators.[691-694]

[689] M. Glicksman and M. C. Steele, *Phys. Rev. Letters* **2**, 461 (1959).

[689a] M. Glicksman, *Phys. Rev.* **124**, 1655 (1961).

[689b] B. Ancker-Johnson, R. W. Cohen, and M. Glicksman, *Phys. Rev.* **124**, 1745 (1961).

[689c] G. Bemski, *J. Phys. Chem. Solids* **23**, 1433 (1962).

[689d] B. Ancker-Johnson, *Phys. Rev. Letters* **9**, 485 (1962).

[690] A. G. Chynoweth and A. A. Murray, *Phys. Rev.* **123**, 515 (1961).

[690a] M. Kikuchi and Y. Abe, *J. Phys. Soc. Japan* **17**, 1268 (1962).

[690b] L. Gold, *J. Phys. Soc. Japan* **17**, 1193 (1962).

[691] S. H. Koenig, *Phys. Rev.* **110**, 986, 988 (1958).

[692] L. V. Keldysh, *J. Exptl. Theoret. Phys. U.S.S.R.* **37**, 713 (1959) [translation: *Soviet Phys.-JETP* **10**, 509 (1960)].

[693] V. A. Chuenkov, *Fiz. Tverdogo Tela* **2**, 799 (1960) [translation: *Soviet Phys.-Solid State* **2**, 734 (1960)]; V. A. Chuenkov (Čuenkov), *in* "Proc. Intern. Conf. on Semiconductor Phys., Prague 1960," p. 109. Publishing House Czech. Acad. Sci., Prague, 1961.

[693a] V. V. Paranjape, *Proc. Phys. Soc. (London)* **78**, 516 (1961).

[693b] A. Zylbersztejn, *Phys. Rev.* **127**, 744 (1962).

[694] J. Yamashita, *J. Phys. Soc. Japan* **16**, 720 (1961).

(2) *Field-dependent mobilities, "hot electrons."* Non-ohmic currents can occur when the applied electric field is sufficiently large, and the charge carriers absorb so much energy per second that the associated "temperature" of the carriers becomes significantly greater than that of the lattice. The phenomena encountered under such conditions are designated as "warm" or "hot" carrier effects, depending on the magnitude of the field-induced kinetic energy. Early studies of these effects in germanium were reported by Ryder, Shockley, and Conwell.[695-698] In carrying out experiments on the behavior of charge-carrier mobility in large electric fields, heating effects and carrier injection phenomena must be minimized. This usually requires pulsed currents and special sample geometries to permit low current densities at the contacts. A slightly different experimental technique, which possesses certain advantages, is the use of microwave fields, described by Morgan[699] and by Seeger.[700] Another interesting series of experiments involves determination of the complex conductivity at microwave frequencies as a function of an external dc electric field applied to the sample.[701-703] A decrease in microwave absorption occurs when high electric fields are applied, inasmuch as the absorption coefficient is proportional to the differential electron mobility and this decreases at high fields.

The early pulsed-field data on germanium have been extended to specimens of higher purity and to stronger applied fields by a number of investigators.[704-708] It is also possible to produce "hot" carriers through

[695] E. J. Ryder and W. Shockley, *Phys. Rev.* **81**, 139 (1951).
[696] W. Shockley, *Bell System Tech. J.* **30**, 990 (1951).
[697] E. J. Ryder, *Phys. Rev.* **90**, 766 (1953).
[698] E. M. Conwell, *Phys. Rev.* **90**, 769 (1953).
[699] T. N. Morgan, *J. Phys. Chem. Solids* **8**, 245 (1959).
[700] K. Seeger, *Phys. Rev.* **114**, 476 (1959); *Z. Physik* **172**, 68 (1963).
[701] J. Arthur, A. Gibson, and J. Granville, *J. Electronics* **2**, 145 (1956).
[702] A. Gibson, J. Granville, and E. Paige, *in* "Proc. Intern. Conf. on Semiconductor Phys., Prague 1960," p. 112. Publishing House Czech. Acad. Sci., Prague, 1961; *J. Phys. Chem. Solids* **19**, 198 (1961).
[702a] M. A. C. S. Brown, *J. Phys. Chem. Solids* **19**, 218 (1961).
[703] E. M. Conwell and V. J. Fowler, *in* "Proc. Intern. Conf. on Semiconductor Phys., Prague 1960," p. 119. Publishing House Czech. Acad. Sci., Prague, 1961.
[704] J. B. Gunn, *J. Electronics* **2**, 87 (1956).
[705] K. S. Mendelson and R. Bray, *Proc. Phys. Soc. (London)* **B70**, 899 (1957).
[706] E. M. Conwell, *J. Phys. Chem. Solids* **8**, 234 (1959).
[706a] J. Zucker, V. J. Fowler, and E. M. Conwell, *J. Appl. Phys.* **32**, 2606 (1961).
[707] J. B. Gunn, *J. Phys. Chem. Solids* **8**, 239 (1959).
[708] A. C. Prior, *Proc. Phys. Soc. (London)* **76**, 465 (1960).

excitation by radiation.[709] Such experiments, carried out on high-purity germanium, are reported by Rollin and Rowell.[710] Piezoresistance experiments at high electric fields were carried out in n-type germanium by Paige.[710a] By observing the field dependence of drift velocity for a specimen in a strained and unstrained state, the electron temperature could be deduced. Another interesting experiment giving information on electron temperatures is the measurement of noise temperature of hot electrons reported by Erlbach and Gunn.[710b] A discussion of additional literature dealing with experimental and theoretical findings can be found in the review articles of Gunn[674] and Koenig[711] and in the theoretical papers of Stratton,[712] Conwell and co-workers,[706, 713] Yamashita,[714] Dykman and Tomchuk,[715, 716] and in several very recent articles.[716a−d]

Strictly speaking, the spherically symmetric part of the electron distribution in the case of non-ohmic mobilities is not Maxwellian except where electron-electron scattering predominates, and the use of the Maxwellian distribution with an "effective" electron temperature is in general not rigorous.[717] The problem of obtaining the appropriate dis-

[709] A. Honig and R. Levitt, *Phys. Rev. Letters* **5**, 93 (1960).

[710] B. V. Rollin and J. M. Rowell, *Proc. Phys. Soc. (London)* **76**, 1001 (1960).

[710a] E. G. S. Paige, *Proc. Phys. Soc. (London)* **72**, 921 (1958).

[710b] E. Erlbach and J. B. Gunn, *Phys. Rev. Letters* **8**, 280 (1962).

[711] S. H. Koenig, *J. Phys. Chem. Solids* **8**, 227 (1959).

[712] R. Stratton, *Proc. Roy. Soc.* **A242**, 355 (1957); *J. Electronics and Control* **5**, 157 (1958); *Proc. Roy. Soc.* **A246**, 406 (1958); *J. Phys. Soc. Japan* **17**, 590 (1962).

[713] E. M. Conwell and A. L. Brown, *J. Phys. Chem. Solids* **15**, 208 (1960).

[714] J. Yamashita, *Progr. Theoret. Phys.* **24**, 357 (1960).

[715] I. M. Dykman and P. M. Tomchuk, *Fiz. Tverdogo Tela* **2**, 2228 (1960) [translation: *Soviet Phys.-Solid State* **2**, 1988 (1961)]; **3**, 1909 (1961); **4**, 1082 (1962) [respective translations: **3**, 1393 (1962); **4**, 798 (1962)].

[716] P. M. Tomchuk, *Fiz. Tverdogo Tela* **3**, 1019 (1961) [translation: *Soviet Phys.-Solid State* **3**, 740 (1961)].

[716a] A. Hasegawa and J. Yamashita, *J. Phys. Chem. Solids* **23**, 875 (1962).

[716b] I. M. Dykman and E. I. Tolpygo, *Fiz. Tverdogo Tela* **4**, 896 (1962) [translation: *Soviet Phys.-Solid State* **4**, 659 (1962)].

[716c] G. V. Gordeev, *Fiz. Tverdogo Tela* **4**, 317 (1962) [translation: *Soviet Phys.-Solid State* **4**, 228 (1962)].

[716d] Yu. K. Pozhela and V. I. Shilal'nikas, *Fiz. Tverdogo Tela* **4**, 1601 (1962) [translation: *Soviet Phys.-Solid State* **4**, 1173 (1962)].

[717] I. Adawi, *Phys. Rev.* **112**, 1567 (1958).

tribution function has been dealt with by several investigators. For example, Yamashita has employed a technique which, after certain approximations, leads to a second-order differential equation.[718] Morgan, using parameters representative of n-type germanium, obtained solutions of the Boltzmann equation with the aid of a digital computer.[699] A variational treatment has been applied by Adawi, and analytical solutions were obtained for mixed scattering involving acoustical and optical phonons and ionized impurities in nonpolar semiconductors.[320, 401] A variational method was also used by Hattori and Sato in investigating the field dependence of mobility in nonpolar and in polar semiconductors where scattering occurred by means of electron-phonon interactions.[719] The question as to whether an electron gas, subject to specified interactions, can have a current-voltage behavior, when strong electric fields are appl. which is characterized by a negative resistance has been examined by lawi.[720] For a single band and constant electron density, such a behavior is almost certainly ruled out when stability criteria are also taken into account.

Although ohmic conductivity in cubic crystals is isotropic (Section 8a), the conductivity may become anisotropic in the non-ohmic region, as was shown theoretically by Shibuya.[721] T anisotropy was verified from measurements on n- and p-type Ge .44 Further theoretical work on hot electrons in a many-valley semiconductor, or for other nonisotropic energy surfaces, has been done by Gold,[725] Franz,[726] Reik et al.,[726a]

---

[718] J. Yamashita, *Phys. Rev.* **111**, 1529 (1958).

[719] M. Hattori and H. Sato, *J. Phys. Soc. Japan* **15**, 1237 (1960).

[720] I. Adawi, *J. Appl. Phys.* **32**, 1101 (1961).

[721] M. Shibuya, *Phys. Rev.* **99**, 1189 (1955).

[722] W. Sasaki, M. Shibuya, and K. Mizuguchi, *J. Phys. Soc. Japan* **13**, 456 (1958).

[723] W. Sasaki, M. Shibuya, K. Mizuguchi, and G. Hatoyama, *J. Phys. Chem. Solids* **8**, 250 (1959).

[723a] W. E. K. Gibbs, *J. Appl. Phys.* **33**, 3369 (1962).

[724] S. H. Koenig, *Proc. Phys. Soc. (London)* **73**, 959 (1959).

[725] L. Gold, *Phys. Rev.* **104**, 1580 (1956).

[726] W. Franz, *Z. Naturforsch.* **15a**, 366 (1960); *in* "Proc. Intern. Conf. on Semiconductor Phys., Prague 1960," p. 117. Publishing House Czech. Acad. Sci., Prague, 1961.

[726a] H. G. Reik, H. Risken, and G. Finger, *Phys. Rev. Letters* **5**, 423 (1960); H. G. Reik and H. Risken, *Phys. Rev.* **124**, 777 (1961); **126**, 1737 (1962).

Yamashita and Inoue,[727] Paige,[728] Conwell,[729] and Shibuya and Sasaki.[730] The variational treatment developed by Adawi for warm electrons was applied by Klose to the conduction band structure of silicon.[731] The warm-electron data were useful in providing information of value for ascertaining the principal scattering mechanisms operative in the semi-conductor.[325a, 731] Information on scattering in InSb has also been obtained by means of warm-carrier experiments. For example, Sladek has measured conductivity due to warm electrons in InSb at various lattice temperatures in the region $1.27° \leqslant T \leqslant 90°K$.[732] He concludes from his data that at $4.2°K$ piezoelectric scattering is responsible for most of the energy loss of the warm carriers, whereas near $77°K$ polar optical scattering, enhanced by strong electron-electron scattering, was controlling. By application of a strong magnetic field, it was possible to change the sign of the deviation from Ohm's law.

Researches by Kawamura and co-workers indicate that the width of the cyclotron resonance line increases with increase in microwave power absorbed by the crystal, in consequence of the rise of electron temperature and consequent increase in collision frequency.[732a] A theoretical investigation of the frequency-dependent non-ohmic behavior of conduction electrons in a static magnetic field, under the influence of applied microwave fields, was carried out by Hanamura and collaborators.[732b] With increasing microwave power, the absorption line deviates from its Lorentzian shape to one of a more rectangular form, in agreement with experiment. Calculations of the half-widths of the lines as a function of microwave power are in good agreement with experimental findings. In establishing this correspondence, it was found desirable to take into account the effect of neutral impurity scattering.[732c]

(3) *Field-dependent recombination rates.* Another manner in which high electric fields can affect the conductivity in a semiconductor has

[727] J. Yamashita and K. Inoue, *J. Phys. Chem. Solids* 12, 1 (1959).

[728] E. G. S. Paige, *Proc. Phys. Soc. (London)* 75, 174 (1960).

[729] E. M. Conwell, *Phys. Rev.* 123, 454 (1961).

[730] M. Shibuya and W. Sasaki, *J. Phys. Soc. Japan* 15, 207 (1960).

[731] W. Klose, *Ann. Physik* 8, 287 (1961).

[732] R. J. Sladek, *Phys. Rev.* 120, 1589 (1960).

[732a] H. Kawamura, M. Fukai, Y. Hayashi, and T. Hashimura, *J. Phys. Soc. Japan* 16, 1646 (1961).

[732b] E. Hanamura, T. Inui, and Y. Toyozawa, *J. Phys. Soc. Japan* 17, 666 (1962).

[732c] H. Kawamura, M. Fukai, and Y. Hayashi, *J. Phys. Soc. Japan* 17, 970 (1962); M. Fukai, H. Kawamura, I. Imai, and K. Tomishima, *ibid.* 17, 1191 (1962).

been discussed by Conwell.[732d] This arises from changes in recombination rates with the energy of the hot carriers. By this means, a change in carrier concentration from the thermal equilibrium value can occur as a bulk effect at high electric fields. The result can be either an augmentation or an attenuation of the electron-hole concentration product, depending on the dependence of the capture cross section of the traps on carrier speed. Experimental studies of the recombination of excess hot carriers in germanium were done by Zucker and Conwell by measuring changes in photoconductivity caused by excitation with 2.85 kMc microwave power, with fields up to 10^4 volts/cm.[732e] Enhanced recombination was found in the strong field for samples which contained copper impurities and for specimens with high surface recombination. Analysis of the results, making use of the kinetics of recombination in high fields, indicated that the cross section for electron capture by copper centers having a single negative charge decreased with increasing speed of the electrons.[732e, f] Additional studies of the speed-dependence of electronic capture cross sections in germanium, using improved techniques, involved measurements of the variation of excess carrier lifetime with carrier speed by application of the microwave field during the decay of a pulse of injected carriers.[732g] In samples with Cu^- centers, the lifetime decreased with increases in electron speed, as was noted in the earlier experiments. The rate of decrease, however, corresponded to an approximately constant capture cross section. In the case of neutral nickel recombination centers, on the other hand, the lifetime was found to increase with electron speed at a rate corresponding to a rapid decrease in the capture cross section of the centers. The experimental findings are discussed in connection with other evidence reported by Kalashnikov.[732h] Ridley and Watkins[732i] point out that the capture rate for an attractive center should decrease with carrier speed in the hot-electron region, while that for a repulsive center should increase. Since the latter case leads to a decrease in steady-state carrier density, the possibility exists

[732d] E. M. Conwell, *J. Phys. Chem. Solids* **17**, 342 (1961).

[732e] J. Zucker and E. M. Conwell, *J. Phys. Chem. Solids* **22**, 141 (1961).

[732f] E. M. Conwell and J. Zucker, *J. Phys. Chem. Solids* **22**, 149 (1961).

[732g] J. Zucker and E. M. Conwell, *J. Phys. Chem. Solids* **23**, 1549 (1962).

[732h] S. G. Kalashnikov, *in* "Proc. Intern. Conf. on Semiconductor Phys., Prague 1960," p. 241, Publishing House Czech. Acad. Sci., Prague, 1961.

[732i] B. K. Ridley and T. B. Watkins, *J. Phys. Chem. Solids* **22**, 155 (1961).

that a negative resistance could be produced. Requisite conditions for achieving the phenomenon in suitably compensated n-type germauium are discussed. It is pointed out that the long time constants involved preclude the use of short pulse fields. Another possibility for realizing negative resistance considered by the authors involves transfer of hot carriers to sub-bands of lower mobility.[732j]

b. Photon Effects, PEM Phenomena

It is beyond the scope of this work to include photoconductivity. On the other hand, phenomena which may result when a magnetic field as well as radiation is present might properly be discussed. Consider a slab of semiconductor of thickness t along the x-direction, large in the other directions, and illuminated on the yz-face by light of appropriate wavelength directed along the x-axis. The photons release electron-hole pairs, which diffuse in the x-direction. If a magnetic field is directed along the z-axis, the electrons and holes will be oppositely accelerated along the y-direction, and a potential difference will appear along the y-axis in the specimen. The phenomenon is usually referred to as the photoelectromagnetic (PEM) effect, or the photomagnetoelectric (PME) effect. Its discovery is attributed to Kikoin and Noskov, who noted large voltages in a specimen of cuprous oxide.[733] Much of the earlier literature on PEM effects has been covered in several review articles, such as those by Garreta and Grosvalet,[734] Pincherle,[735] and Moss.[736] Another useful reference is the monograph by Tauc.[555j] Subsequent theoretical developments have been carried out by van Roosbroeck[737] and Gärtner.[738] A theoretical analysis, as well as experimental data on InSb, has been

[732j] B. K. Ridley and T. B. Watkins, *Proc. Phys. Soc. (London)* **78**, 293 (1961).

[733] I. K. Kikoin and M. M. Noskov, *Physik. Z. Sowjetunion* **5**, 586 (1934).

[734] O. Garreta and J. Grosvalet, *in* "Progress in Semiconductors" (A. F. Gibson, ed.), Vol. 1, p. 165. Wiley, New York, 1956.

[735] L. Pincherle, *in* "Photoconductivity Conference" (R. Breckenridge, B. Russel, and E. Hahn, eds.), p. 307. Wiley, New York, 1956.

[736] T. S. Moss, "Optical Properties of Semiconductors," p. 63. Academie Press, New York, 1959.

[737] W. van Roosbroeck, *Phys. Rev.* **101**, 1713 (1956).

[738] W. Gärtner, *Phys. Rev.* **105**, 823 (1957).

supplied by Kurnick and Zitter.[739] Large-signal effects have been considered by Beattie and Cunningham.[739a] A number of investigators have carried out measurements on InSb and InAs because of sensitivity as an infrared detector.[739-742] The measurement of PEM voltages or short-circuit currents provides data which can be used to determine carrier lifetimes and surface recombination rates.[734, 739] The technique has been used extensively for materials where the carrier lifetimes are low, say less than 10^{-7} sec, but the carrier mobilities are high. Usually, the photoconductivity response of the specimen is also determined. This information is sometimes used to eliminate the intensity of illumination and surface recombination velocity factors from the equations.[736, 739, 743] When trapping is significant, however, the problem is complicated. Then the lifetimes for electrons and holes may differ appreciably. Furthermore, if a single type carrier is excited from an impurity level, this situation will also cause the steady-state densities of optically generated carriers to be unequal. It has been pointed out by Rose that if the electron and hole lifetimes are not equal, the photoconductive effect measures the larger of the two lifetimes while the PEM and other phenomena that depend on the diffusion of free pairs measure the shorter of the two lifetimes.[744] Furthermore, the short-circuit PEM current is proportional to the square root of the lifetime whereas the photoconductance is proportional to the first power of the lifetime.[745] The effects of traps and recombination centers upon the PEM and photoconductive phenomena have been examined by a number of investigators including Zitter,[746] Amith,[745] Ravich,[746a] and van Roosbroeck.[747]

[739] S. W. Kurnick and R. N. Zitter, *J. Appl. Phys.* **27**, 278 (1956).

[739a] A. R. Beattie and R. W. Cunningham, *Phys. Rev.* **125**, 533 (1962).

[740] S. W. Kurnick and R. N. Zitter, *in* "Photoconductivity Conference" (R. Breckenridge, B. Russel, and E. Hahn, eds.), p. 531. Wiley, New York, 1956.

[740a] V. Zolotarev and D. Nasledov, *Fiz. Tverdogo Tela* **3**, 3306 (1961); **4**, 977 (1962) [respective translations: *Soviet Phys.-Solid State* **3**, 2400 (1962); **4**, 716 (1962)].

[741] C. Hilsum and I. M. Ross, *Nature* **179**, 146 (1957).

[742] C. Hilsum, *Proc. Phys. Soc.* (*London*) **B70**, 1011 (1957).

[743] C. Hilsum, D. Oliver, and G. Rickayzen, *J. Electronics* **1**, 134 (1955).

[744] A. Rose, *in* "Photoconductivity Conference" (R. Breckenridge, B. Russel, and E. Hahn, eds.), p. 17. Wiley, New York, 1956.

[745] A. Amith, *Phys. Rev.* **116**, 793 (1959).

[746] R. N. Zitter, *Phys. Rev.* **112**, 852 (1958).

[746a] Yu. I. Ravich, *Fiz. Tverdogo Tela* **3**, 1601 (1961) [translation: *Soviet Phys.-Solid State* **3**, 1162 (1961)]; **4**, 1928 (1962) [translation: **4**, 1412 (1963)].

[747] W. van Roosbroeck, *Phys. Rev.* **119**, 636 (1960).

Photoconductivity measurements can be carried out in a magnetic field. Such an arrangement leads to various phenomena, including the photo-Hall effect. Studies of such photogalvanomagnetic phenomena have been reported by several investigators.[747a-c] An interesting effect, which has been observed, is that of "negative" photoconductivity.[747b, c] Thermal analogs of photoconductivity and PEM effect exist. These phenomena have been discussed by Gärtner.[748]

ACKNOWLEDGMENTS

The author wishes to express his appreciation to a number of associates at Battelle for comments and discussion. Special thanks are due I. Adawi, E. Baroody, R. Bate, J. Duga, F. Milford, and F. Reid. Early discussions with R. Willardson were helpful, and the encouragement and understanding of Professor Fred Seitz are deeply appreciated. The author is also indebted to Dr. Conyers Herring for a number of comments and suggestions.

[747a] F. van der Maesen, *Philips Research Repts.* **15**, 107 (1960).

[747b] A. A. Grinberg, S. R. Novikov, and S. M. Ryvkin, *Doklady Akad. Nauk S.S.S.R.* **136**, 329 (1961) [translation: *Soviet Phys.-Doklady* **6**, 49 (1961)].

[747c] V. N. Dobrovol'skii, *Fiz. Tverdogo Tela* **4**, 329 (1962) [translation: *Soviet Phys.-Solid State* **4**, 236 (1962)]; **4**, 2806 (1962) [translation: **4**, 2056 (1963)].

[748] W. Gärtner, *Phys. Rev.* **122**, 419 (1961).

Author Index

Numbers in parentheses are reference numbers and indicate that an author's work is referred to although his name is not cited in the text.

A

Abe, Y., 385
Abeles, B., 47, 88, 223, 225, 233, 242, 254
Abrahams, E., 375
Adams, E. N., 20, 21(37), 31, 169(55), 174(55), 193, 195(55), 198(55), 205 (55), 330, 331(37), 333, 334, 335, 337, 341, 382
Adams, E. P., 73
Adawi, I., 219, 282, 283, 285, 287(407), 387, 388
Aigrain, P., 368
Airapetyants, S. V., 56
Akamatu, H., 378
Alekseevskii, N., 304, 306
Alers, P. B., 336, 339
Allcock, G. R., 378
Allgaier, R. S., 238, 239, 240, 241
Allred, W. P., 322
Amirkhanov, Kh., 337, 340
Amith, A., 392
Ancker-Johnson, B., 385
Andermann, A. I., 360
Anderson, O., 62
Anderson, P. W., 377
Anderson, R., 63
Andreatch, P., 62
Ansel'm, A., 332, 336, 337, 361
Appel, J., 130, 146, 147, 159, 205, 280, 282, 302, 332, 333(499), 334, 353, 363, 379
Argyres, P. N., 20, 21(37), 331, 332, 333, 334, 335
Arkhipova, I., 65
Armstrong, J. A., 68, 74(139), 76(139), 129(214), 146(139)
Arndt, D., 132, 143, 145(239)
Arnott, R., 377
Arthur, J., 60, 386
Asdente, M., 377
Askerov, B., 332, 336, 337
Aubrey, J. E., 257

B

Aukerman, L., 272, 273
Averbach, B. L., 56
Azbel', M. Ia., 32, 96, 194, 195, 303

B

Babiskin, J., 336, 339
Bagguley, D., 178, 206
Bailyn, M., 7(21), 281, 299, 300, 302
Baker, W. G., 75
Balescu, R., 330
Baltensperger, W., 368
Banbury, P. C., 61
Baranskii, P. I., 174, 326, 327
Bardeen, J., 61, 108
Bardsley, W., 60
Baroody, E. M., 301
Barrie, R., 157, 158, 269, 271, 334
Barron, T. H. K., 58, 75
Bashirov, R., 337, 340
Bass, F., 195
Bate, R. T., 67, 170, 172(289), 212, 275, 315, 316, 317, 318, 319, 320, 321(472), 322, 323, 337(289), 342, 346, 347
Beattie, A. R., 383, 392
Beer, A. C., 31, 68, 74, 76(139), 90, 93, 103, 104, 105, 129(214), 136(225a), 137, 142, 146, 157, 159(263), 160, 161, 164, 165, 166, 167(263, 283), 168(283), 169(183), 170, 171, 172(283, 289), 173, 196, 199(56), 200(56), 201(56), 202(56), 203, 204, 205(56, 164, 283), 208, 211, 214(56), 315, 316, 317, 318, 319(472), 320(472), 321(472), 323, 337(289), 359
Bell, J. C., 318, 319(472), 320(472), 321(472), 323(472)
Bemski, G., 385
Benedek, G., 97, 234, 252(329)
Bergeron, C., 336
Bethe, H., 19, 108, 109(193), 120, 175, 301
Bhide, V. G., 377
Bidulia, V., 65

395

Bir, G. L., 356, 357, 359
Blakemore, J. S., 155, 161(257)
Blatt, F. J., 9, 23, 26, 27(50), 66, 97(179), 107(186), 109(186), 111, 112(186), 113(186), 121(210), 125 (186), 128, 138(186), 214, 217, 221 (319), 279, 281, 301, 343
Blochinzev, D., 26
Blount, E. I., 255, 303, 331
Blunt, R., 157
Bocciarelli, C. V., 62
Bogner, G., 323
Boiko, I. I., 195
Bok, T., 384
Bonch-Bruevich, V. L., 362, 365
Borovik, E., 304
Boswarva, I. M., 268
Bowers, R., 268
Boyle, W. S., 353
Brailsford, A. D., 257, 333
Braunstein, R., 268, 271
Bray, R., 204, 205, 380, 386
Breckenridge, R., 157
Bresler, M. S., 56
Briggs, H. B., 163
Brock, G. E., 366
Bronstein, M., 26, 66(46)
Brooks, H., 17, 97, 107, 111, 113 (185), 125, 172, 217, 234, 252(329), 267, 276, 355
Broom, R. F., 59, 272
Bross, H., 43, 297
Broudy, R. M., 55, 89, 236, 252, 253, 254
Brown, A. L., 387
Brown, D. M., 204
Brown, M. A. C. S., 386
Bryan, J. M., 58
Budd, H., 194
Bullis, W. M., 84(156), 85, 87, 89, 90, 234(156), 252
Burstein, E., 238, 343, 383
Butcher, P. N., 382
Button, K., 260, 275
Bychkov, Yu., 195

C

Cahn, J. H., 347
Calawa, A. R., 238, 382

Caldwell, R. S., 266
Callaway, J., 163, 272, 307, 364
Callen, H. B., 4, 9, 10, 66(3), 234(3), 345(3, 4), 348(548)
Campbell, L. L., 73
Cardona, M., 267, 366
Carlson, R. O., 349, 351(555g)
Casella, R. E., 195
Carter, F. L., 379
Casimer, H. B. G., 42
Castner, T. G., Jr., 371
Cetlin, B., 257
Chambers, R. G., 21, 29, 32(38), 66, 68, 148, 150, 194, 257, 303, 306, 331(38)
Champness, C. H., 157, 166
Chase, M. N., 93
Chasmar, R. P., 268
Chernenko, A., 379
Chester, G. V., 302, 329, 354
Chih-Ch'ao, L., 367, 384
Chizmadzhev, Yu., 379
Choquard, P. F., 93
Christensen, H., 62
Christian, S. M., 237, 238
Chuenkov, V. A., 385
Chynoweth, A. G., 381, 382, 383, 385
Cohen, E. G. D., 328
Cohen, M. H., 255, 303, 306
Cohen, R., 129
Cohen, R. W., 385
Coldwell-Horsfall, R., 16, 48, 52, 123(31a), 257, 258
Collins, R., 163
Connell, R. A., 48
Conwell, E. M., 54, 108, 111, 112(191), 118, 129(191), 131, 217(192), 278, 368, 386, 387, 389, 390
Corbino, O. M., 72
Cornwell, J. F., 306
Cox, C. D., 60
Croft, W. J., 376
Csavinszky, P., 363
Cuevas, M., 369
Cuff, K., 238
Cummings, F. W., 364
Cunnell, F., 271, 272
Cunningham, R. W., 392
Czaja, W., 154

N

Nabarro, F. R. N., 108
Nagaev, É. L., 374
Nakajima, S., 4, 328
Nakamura, M., 370
Nanney, C., 261
Nasledov, D. N., 268, 350, 366, 367, 384, 392
Nathan, M., 276, 382
Neaves, A., 35
Nedlin, G., 195, 337, 353(519b)
Neuringer, L. J., 254
Nordheim, L., 26
Normantas, E., 359
Noskov, M. M., 391
Novikov, S. R., 393
Novikov, V., 265
Nussbaum, A., 265, 266

O

Obraztsov, Iu., 174, 205(296), 350
Okada, T., 47, 79
Olechna, D. J., 362
Oliver, D.. J., 367, 392
Olson, R., 176
Omar, M. A., 338
Omel'yanovskii, É. M., 366
Orlova, M., 367
Oshinsky, W., 157
Oswald, F., 271
Overhauser, A., 149, 355, 356(246), 359

P

Pado, G., 367
Paige, E., 386, 387, 389
Pankove, J. I., 365
Paranjape, B. V., 351
Paranjape, V. V., 385
Parmenter, R. H., 24, 268(45b)
Parrott, J. E., 351, 352, 353(562), 363
Paul, W., 97(329), 234, 252(329), 267, 276, 382
Pearson, G. L., 45, 54(79), 78, 108, 139, 188, 206(79), 233, 236
Peierls, R. E., 153, 329
Pekar, S. I., 379
Pell, E. M., 381, 383(650)
Pelzer, H., 289, 290(409)
Perlin, Yu. E., 379

Peschanskii, V. G., 195, 303
Peterson, E., 201
Petritz, R. L., 291
Pfann, W., 278
Pfennig, H., 282
Phillips, J., 178
Picus, G., 343
Pierce, C. B., 382
Pikus, G. E., 64, 356, 357, 359
Pilkuhn, M., 384
Pincherle, L., 391
Pines, D., 290
Pippard, A. B., 304, 305
Platzman, P., 378
Pollak, M., 375
Poltinnikov, S. A., 65
Pomeranchuk, I., 334
Pomerantz, M., 371
Pozhela, Yu. K., 387
Price, P. J., 5, 9, 13, 66, 154, 277
Priestley, M. G., 304, 306
Prigogine, I., 330
Primakoff, H., 329
Prior, A. C., 384, 386
Puri, S. M., 337, 339
Putley, E. H., 54, 62, 155, 156(267), 157, 162, 238, 342, 348(93)

Q

Quarrington, J., 358
Quinn, J. J., 306

R

Racette, J. H., 379
Radcliffe, J. M., 269
Rashba, E. I., 195
Rast, H. E., Jr., 374
Rauch, C., 236
Ravich, Yu. I., 392
Ray, R., 369
Read, W. T., 138
Rediker, R. H., 238, 382, 384
Reed, W. A., 307
Reid, F. J., 136(225a), 137, 207, 209, 210, 211, 212
Reik, H. G., 4, 388
Reiss, H., 360
Résibois, P., 330
Reynolds, J., 336

Subject Index

A

Adiabatic phenomena, 66–68, 344–347

Aluminum, 306–307

Aluminum antimonide, 62
Hall effect, 212

Ambipolar (or bipolar) effects, 5, 154, 349–350

Anisotropy factors
conductivity
ellipsoidal surfaces, 214, 221, 239, 242–243, 255–266
ellipsoids (cubic symmetry), 240
spheroids (cubic symmetry), 221, 228, 244–246
warped spheres (Ge & Si), 181–185, 196–200
density of states
ellipsoidal surfaces, 214
warped spheres (Ge & Si), 180
Hall effect
ellipsoidal surfaces, 215, 221
ellipsoids (cubic symmetry), 215, 240
spheroids (cubic symmetry), 216, 222, 228–233, 246–248, 250–251
warped spheres (Ge & Si), 181–185, 196–200
magnetoconductivity
ellipsoidal surfaces, 221, 239, 240–243, 255–266
ellipsoids (cubic symmetry), 240
spheroids (cubic symmetry), 216, 222, 228, 244–246
warped spheres (Ge & Si), 185–188, 196–200
magnetoresistivity
ellipsoids (cubic symmetry), 240–241
spheroids (cubic symmetry), 230–233, 246–250
warped spheres (Ge & Si), 185–188

mass
ellipsoidal surfaces, 240, 263–264
spheroidal surfaces, 215
mass and relaxation time
spheroidal surfaces, 221, 229, 233–237
mobility
ellipsoids (cubic symmetry), 215
spheroids (cubic symmetry), 221, 228

Antimony, 47, 79, 258–261

Avalanche breakdown, 380–385

Averages
Maxwell-Boltzmann, 123, 214
Fermi-Dirac, 94

B

Band effects
indium antimonide series (III–V compounds), 268–277
large impurity concentrations, 365
"magnetic breakdown", 303
many-valley transport, 213–266
multiband conduction, 148–174, 177–212, 272–278
narrow-band semiconductors, 372–378
nonequivalent valleys, 272–278, 357–358
nonparabolic bands, 267–272
nonquadratic energy surfaces, 27–32, 36–49, 175–200
warped bands of germanium and silicon, 177–200
open Fermi surfaces, 32, 303–307
perturbation of equivalent valleys, 277–278, 357–358
quadratic energy surfaces, 24–27, 213–266
sensitivity of thermomagnetic effects, 348, 350–351
spherical energy surfaces, 26, 32–36, 50–54, 93–147, 152–174

406